ADD MATHEMATICS

Pure and Applied

ADDITIONAL MATHEMATICS

Pure and Applied

R P C Forman
T C Basey
J P O Benham
J M Bradley
J P Davis
C H Jones
J C M Rose
N A Routledge
K R Spencer
Department of Mathematics, Eton College

STANLEY THORNES (PUBLISHERS) LTD

First published in 1984 by

Stanley Thornes (Publishers) Ltd
Old Station Drive
Leckhampton
CHELTENHAM GL53 0DN

Reprinted 1987

British Library Cataloguing in Publication Data

Additional Mathematics: pure and applied.
  1. Mathematics—1961–
  I. Forman, R.P.C.
  510   QA39.2

ISBN 0–85950–150–7

Typeset in Times New Roman 10 on 12 point
by Bell and Bain Ltd, Glasgow
Printed and bound in Great Britain by Ebenezer Baylis & Son, Worcester

CONTENTS

PREFACE

This book was originally written, by a team of members of the Mathematics Department at Eton College, in response to the Oxford and Cambridge Board's introduction of a revised Additional Mathematics syllabus in 1980. A draft version of the book has been in use at Eton since September of that year.

Publication of the book has involved substantial expansion and modification of the content, in order to cover the syllabuses of the other major examining boards. In its new form, therefore, the book contains a great deal of material; so students who are aiming no higher than AO-level (or the equivalent) will probably wish to omit certain sections or chapters, while any student who masters the complete book should be capable of tackling the recently proposed Advanced Supplementary examinations and will indeed be well on his or her way towards Advanced Level.

The book should appeal particularly to students aged 15 to 17 who have been making good progress in mathematics and whose ambitions run beyond the average first-level examination. The text is designed to be understood by a student without a teacher's continual intervention, and for this reason there are numerous worked examples embedded in the text. Most sections finish with a more or less brief exercise. In addition, there are twenty quite long supplementary exercises (with answers given to odd-numbered questions), one exercise for each of the twenty chapters of the book. These exercises are designed to give extra practice as required, and cover all the topics discussed in the text.

There is also a collection of over 500 Examination Questions, again arranged in twenty exercises, almost all of which have been taken without modification from past Additional Mathematics AO-level examination papers. So far as possible, the questions in each exercise relate to the material in the corresponding chapter.

Most boards now permit the use of calculators, and expect numerical answers to be given to an appropriate degree of accuracy. In questions on Mechanics, the value of g should be taken as $9.8 \, \text{m/s}^2$ (but $10 \, \text{m/s}^2$ in questions set by the Associated Examining Board), unless the wording of the question suggests otherwise.

Our thanks are due to the following examining boards for permission to use their questions:

O & C   Oxford and Cambridge Schools Examination Board
AEB   Associated Examining Board
JMB   Joint Matriculation Board

UL   University of London
HK   Hong Kong Examinations Authority
SMP   School Mathematics Project (Oxford and Cambridge)
MEI   MEI Schools Project (Oxford and Cambridge)

Our thanks are also due to several generations of Etonians whose comments and reactions assisted in the evolution of the draft, and to the editorial staff of our publishers, whose assistance has been invaluable.

Eton College   R P C Forman
July 1984

1 ALGEBRA I

1.1 QUADRATIC EQUATIONS

You have already met equations of the form $ax+b = 0$ (called linear equations), where a and b are constants, with $a \neq 0$. The usual method of solution is to isolate the term (or terms) involving x on one side of the equation, and the constant term (or terms) on the other:

$$ax+b = 0 \Rightarrow ax = -b$$

$$x = -b/a \quad \text{(a valid step, since } a \neq 0\text{)}$$

Another important type of equation is one of the form $ax^2+bx+c = 0$ (called a quadratic equation), where a, b, and c are constants, with $a \neq 0$. If we try to solve a quadratic equation by using the same kind of method as has been successful with linear equations, we run into immediate difficulties. This is because an equation can have only two sides, but a normal quadratic equation contains terms of three different types (i.e. the term in x^2, the term in x, and the constant term). It is impossible to isolate each of these on a different side of the equation.

EXAMPLE The area of a rectangle is $40\,\text{cm}^2$, and its perimeter is $28\,\text{cm}$. Find the lengths of its sides.

Suppose the rectangle's width to be $x\,\text{cm}$. Then since its semi-perimeter is $14\,\text{cm}$, the height must be $(14-x)\,\text{cm}$.

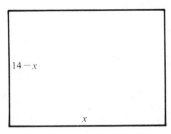

Fig. 1.1

So the area is $x(14-x)\,\text{cm}^2$.

Hence
$$x(14-x) = 40$$
$$14x-x^2 = 40$$
$$x^2-14x+40 = 0$$

1

If we find the value(s) of x satisfying this equation, the problem will be solved.

Various approaches are possible.

(a) The most straightforward approach is *trial and error*—an unsubtle method that sometimes works well. Certainly in this particular case, it should not be too difficult to spot that $x = 4$ and $x = 10$ are both possible, and that either of these values of x leads to a 4 cm by 10 cm rectangle. However, most quadratic equations will not have such simple solutions, and as a general method, trial and error must be considered unsatisfactory. Even if correct solutions are found, we do not know that we have found all those which exist.

(b) *Decimal search* is an improvement on simple trial and error. The solutions can be found to any desired degree of accuracy, and the method can be applied to virtually any type of equation, but does tend to be laborious even with the aid of a calculator. An example of this method in action may be found in section 8.3 (where it is used to solve an equation of the form $a^x = b$).

(c) The equation $x^2 - 14x + 40 = 0$ can be rearranged in various ways into the form $x = f(x)$, suggesting the use of an iterative procedure based on the sequence defined by $u_{n+1} = f(u_n)$. But we have no guarantee that such a rearrangement will lead to a converging sequence of values for u_n, and even if the sequence does converge, the process takes a long time (unless we have a programmable calculator, or can use a computer). Moreover, when there are several solutions, the method tends to find only one.

To illustrate the method, we will rewrite our equation as $x = 14 - 40/x$, and investigate the sequence produced by the rule $u_{n+1} = 14 - 40/u_n$. The starting value must be chosen more or less arbitrarily.

So let us say $\qquad u_1 = 5$

then $\qquad u_2 = 14 - 40/u_1 = 14 - 40/5 = 6$

and $\qquad u_3 = 14 - 40/u_2 = 7.333\,333\,333$

$\qquad\qquad u_4 = 14 - 40/u_3 = 8.545\,454\,545$

$\qquad\qquad u_5 = 14 - 40/u_4 = 9.319\,148\,936$

$\qquad\qquad u_6 = 14 - 40/u_5 = 9.707\,762\,557$

$\qquad\qquad u_7 = 14 - 40/u_6 = 9.879\,586\,077$

$\qquad\qquad u_8 = 14 - 40/u_7 = 9.951\,247\,382$

We are visibly edging nearer and nearer the solution $x = 10$, but very slowly indeed.

1.2 GRAPHICAL METHODS

(d) If we plot the graph of $y = x^2 - 14x + 40$, we get the curve shown in figure 1.2.

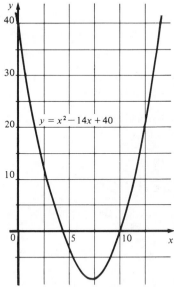

$y = x^2 - 14x + 40$

Fig. 1.2

Since $y = x^2 - 14x + 40$ and $y = 0$ (taken in conjunction) imply that $x^2 - 14x + 40 = 0$, we can solve this equation by finding the points of intersection of the curve and the line $y = 0$ (i.e. the x-axis).

From the graph, we can see that

$$x^2 - 14x + 40 = 0 \Rightarrow x = 4 \text{ or } 10$$

However, this is also a time-consuming method and (usually) will give only very approximate values of the unknown x.

EXERCISE 1A

Plot the graph of $y = x^2 - 2x$ as accurately as you can for $-2 \leqslant x \leqslant +4$. To achieve the desired accuracy, calculate points at least as frequently as every 0.5 along the x-axis. Use a scale of 2 cm for 1 unit along each axis, allowing for a range from -2 to $+8$.

1. Draw the following straight lines on your graph:

(i) $y = 0$,   (ii) $y = -1$,   (iii) $y = 3$.

By seeing where the curve $y = x^2 - 2x$ intersects with each of the lines in turn, solve the equations:

(a) $x^2 - 2x = 0$,   (b) $x^2 - 2x + 1 = 0$,   (c) $x^2 - 2x - 3 = 0$.

Check your solutions mentally.

2. On the same graph plot each of the lines:

(i) $y = 2x$,   (ii) $y = 2x - 4$,   (iii) $y = 2x - 3$.

By seeing where each of these lines cuts the original curve (i.e. $y = x^2 - 2x$), solve the equations:

(a) $x^2 - 4x = 0$,   (b) $x^2 - 4x + 4 = 0$,   (c) $x^2 - 4x + 3 = 0$.

Check your solutions mentally.

3. If you try to find the intersection of $y = x^2 - 2x$ with the line $y = -2$, what happens? What does this tell you about the roots of $x^2 - 2x + 2 = 0$?

4. What straight line would you have to draw on your graph of $y = x^2 - 2x$ in order to solve $x^2 - 6x + 5 = 0$?

1.3 ALGEBRAIC METHODS

(e) We could try to modify the method of isolation used for solving linear equations, as follows.

$$x^2 - 14x + 40 = 0 \qquad\qquad 1$$

$$x^2 - 14x \quad\ \ = -40 \qquad\qquad 2$$

$$x^2 - 14x + 49 = 49 - 40 \qquad\qquad 3$$

$$(x - 7)^2 = 9 \qquad\qquad 4$$

$$x - 7 = \pm 3$$

$$x = 7 \pm 3$$

So $x = 10$ or $x = 4$

This method is known as solution by *completing the square*.

The only difficult step is going from line **2** to line **3**. Once line **4** is reached, with practice the rest of the solution is entirely straightforward. At present, you may not see how to get from line **2** to line **3**, but the technique will be explained later.

(f) We know that if P and Q are algebraic expressions, and if the product $PQ = 0$, then either $P = 0$ or $Q = 0$ (since P and Q both being non-zero would imply that PQ was also non-zero). So if we were able to express $x^2 - 14x + 40$ as a product PQ, we could then say

$$x^2 - 14x + 40 = 0 \Rightarrow PQ = 0 \Rightarrow P = 0 \text{ or } Q = 0$$

The problem would thus reduce to that of investigating the solutions of $P = 0$ and $Q = 0$ separately.

But in fact $x^2 - 14x + 40 = (x - 4)(x - 10)$. Hence

$$x^2 - 14x + 40 = 0 \Rightarrow (x - 4)(x - 10) = 0 \Rightarrow (x - 4) = 0 \text{ or } (x - 10) = 0$$

Now if $(x-4) = 0$ then $x = 4$, and if $(x-10) = 0$ then $x = 10$.

Therefore $x^2 - 14x + 40 = 0 \Rightarrow x = 4$ or $x = 10$.

This method is known as solution by *factorisation*.

Recognising that the factors of $x^2 - 14x + 40$ are $(x-4)$ and $(x-10)$ is the difficult step. The methods of finding factors of quadratic expressions will be considered later.

In practice, you will find that if easy factorisation is possible, (f) is the quickest and simplest method of solution. However, (e) is a more systematic method, which will always work.

1.4 SOLUTION BY COMPLETING THE SQUARE

Now $(x+p)^2 = (x+p)(x+p) = x(x+p) + p(x+p) = x^2 + xp + px + p^2$

Therefore $\underline{(x+p)^2 = x^2 + 2px + p^2}$ (since $xp = px$)

For example, $x^2 + 6x + 9 = (x+3)^2$ with $p = +3$

and $x^2 - 4x + 4 = (x-2)^2$ with $p = -2$

What must be added to $(x^2 + 8x)$ to give a perfect square, i.e. an expression of the form $(x+p)^2$?

Comparing $(x^2 + 2px + p^2)$ underlined above and $(x^2 + 8x)$, we see immediately that $2p$ must equal $+8$, i.e. $p = +4$, and that we must add p^2 , i.e. 16:

thus $(x^2 + 8x) + 16 = (x+4)^2$

Similarly, comparing $(x^2 + 2px + p^2)$ and $(x^2 - 12x)$ shows us that $p = -6$, $p^2 = 36$:

thus $(x^2 - 12x) + 36 = (x-6)^2$

This process is known as completing the square, and can be used to solve any quadratic equation.

First, we restrict ourselves to quadratic equations of the form $x^2 + 2px + q = 0$.

Now $x^2 + 2px + q = 0 \Rightarrow x^2 + 2px = -q$

$$x^2 + 2px + p^2 = p^2 - q$$

$$(x+p)^2 = p^2 - q$$

$$x + p = \pm\sqrt{(p^2 - q)}$$

$$x = -p \pm \sqrt{(p^2 - q)}$$

We can now see that this is exactly the procedure which was followed in method (e) of section 1.3, with $p = -7$ and $q = +40$.

EXAMPLE Solve:

(a) $x^2 - 2x - 3 = 0$
(b) $x^2 + 4x - 12 = 0$
(c) $x^2 - 10x + 16 = 0$
(d) $x^2 + x - 2 = 0$
(e) $2x^2 - 5x + 2 = 0$

(a) $x^2 - 2x - 3 = 0 \Rightarrow x^2 - 2x = +3$

$$x^2 - 2x + 1 = +1 + 3$$
$$(x - 1)^2 = +4$$
$$x - 1 = \pm 2$$
$$x = +1 \pm 2$$

Therefore $x = +3$ or $x = -1$.

(b) $x^2 + 4x - 12 = 0 \Rightarrow x^2 + 4x = +12$

$$x^2 + 4x + 4 = +4 + 12$$
$$(x + 2)^2 = +16$$
$$x + 2 = \pm 4$$
$$x = -2 \pm 4$$

Therefore $x = +2$ or $x = -6$.

(c) $x^2 - 10x + 16 = 0 \Rightarrow x^2 - 10x = -16$

$$x^2 - 10x + 25 = +25 - 16$$
$$(x - 5)^2 = +9$$
$$x - 5 = \pm 3$$
$$x = +5 \pm 3$$

Therefore $x = +8$ or $x = +2$.

(d) Comparing $(x^2 + 2px)$ and $(x^2 + x)$ shows that $p = +\frac{1}{2}$. Hence

$$x^2 + x - 2 = 0 \Rightarrow x^2 + x = +2$$
$$x^2 + x + \tfrac{1}{4} = +\tfrac{1}{4} + 2 \qquad \text{(adding } p^2)$$
$$(x + \tfrac{1}{2})^2 = +\tfrac{9}{4}$$
$$x + \tfrac{1}{2} = \pm \tfrac{3}{2}$$
$$x = -\tfrac{1}{2} \pm \tfrac{3}{2}$$

Therefore $x = +1$ or $x = -2$.

(e) Here we must change the leading term from $2x^2$ to x^2 by dividing throughout by 2, to give $x^2 - \frac{5}{2}x + 1 = 0$. This done, we proceed as before.

$$2x^2 - 5x + 2 = 0 \Rightarrow x^2 - \tfrac{5}{2}x + 1 \quad = 0$$
$$x^2 - \tfrac{5}{2}x \quad = -1$$
$$x^2 - \tfrac{5}{2}x + (-\tfrac{5}{4})^2 = +(-\tfrac{5}{4})^2 - 1$$
$$(x - \tfrac{5}{4})^2 = +\tfrac{25}{16} - 1 = +\tfrac{9}{16}$$
$$x - \tfrac{5}{4} = \pm \tfrac{3}{4}$$
$$x = +\tfrac{5}{4} \pm \tfrac{3}{4}$$

Therefore $x = +2$ or $x = +\frac{1}{2}$.

EXERCISE 1B

1. (a) What must we add to $x^2 - 2x$ to give a perfect square? Of what is the new expression the square?

Use your results to solve:

   (i) $x^2 - 2x = 0$,   (ii) $x^2 - 2x + 1 = 0$,   (iii) $x^2 - 2x - 3 = 0$.

(b) What must we add to $x^2 - 4x$ to give a perfect square? Of what is the new expression the square?

Use your results to solve:

   (i) $x^2 - 4x = 0$,   (ii) $x^2 - 4x + 4 = 0$,   (iii) $x^2 - 4x + 3 = 0$.

(c) What do you find if you try to solve $x^2 - 2x + 2 = 0$?

Compare your results with those obtained in Exercise 1A.

2. Solve the following equations (by completing the square):

(a) $x^2 + 4x + 3 = 0$

(b) $x^2 - 6x + 5 = 0$

(c) $x^2 + 6x + 8 = 0$

(d) $x^2 - 10x + 24 = 0$

(e) $x^2 + 13x + 36 = 0$

(f) $x^2 - x - 110 = 0$

3. The base of a triangle is 4 cm less than its height, and the triangle area is 30 cm². Find the base and height.

4. When a stone is thrown in the air, its height, h m, after t s is given by the formula $h = 5t(4 - t)$. Find the times at which the stone is at a height of 15 m.

5. Solve: (a) $2x^2 - 7x + 5 = 0$,   (b) $3x^2 + 4x + 1 = 0$.

1.5 SOLUTION BY FACTORISATION

Although completing the square will always lead to a full solution, the quickest method of solving many quadratic equations is to factorise them into the form $PQ = 0$, where P and Q are linear factors. To do this efficiently requires some practice.

Check that you agree with the following expansions:

$$(x+1)(x+2) = x^2+3x+2$$
$$(x-1)(x-2) = x^2-3x+2$$
$$(x+1)(x-2) = x^2-x-2$$
$$(x-1)(x+2) = x^2+x-2$$
$$(2x+3)(x-2) = 2x^2-x-6$$
$$(3x-2)(x+3) = 3x^2+7x-6$$

To factorise, we must carry out the reverse process. This is (largely) a matter of informed trial and error (but see section 1.8 for a more systematic approach). Some expressions will not factorise conveniently, and it will then be necessary to return to the method of completing the square. Here are five examples where factorising does work well.

(a) $x^2-2x-3 = 0 \Rightarrow (x-3)(x+1) = 0$

$$(x-3) = 0 \text{ or } (x+1) = 0$$
$$x = +3 \text{ or } x = -1$$

(b) $x^2+4x-12 = 0 \Rightarrow (x+6)(x-2) = 0$

$$(x+6) = 0 \text{ or } (x-2) = 0$$
$$x = -6 \text{ or } x = +2$$

(c) $x^2-10x+16 = 0 \Rightarrow (x-8)(x-2) = 0$

$$(x-8) = 0 \text{ or } (x-2) = 0$$
$$x = +8 \text{ or } x = +2$$

(d) $x^2+x-2 = 0 \Rightarrow (x+2)(x-1) = 0$

$$(x+2) = 0 \text{ or } (x-1) = 0$$
$$x = -2 \text{ or } x = +1$$

(e) $2x^2-5x+2 = 0 \Rightarrow (2x-1)(x-2) = 0$

$$(2x-1) = 0 \text{ or } (x-2) = 0$$
$$x = +\tfrac{1}{2} \text{ or } x = +2$$

Comparing these solutions with those of examples (a) to (e) in section 1.4, you will see that factorisation is very much faster.

The next examples demonstrate a rather more compressed layout.

(f) $x^2+6x+8 = 0 \Rightarrow (x+4)(x+2) = 0 \Rightarrow x = -4$ or -2

(g) $15t^2+35t = 0 \Rightarrow 5t(3t+7) = 0 \Rightarrow t = 0$ or $-7/3$

(h) $y^2-10y+24 = 0 \Rightarrow (y-6)(y-4) = 0 \Rightarrow y = +6$ or $+4$

(i) $x^2+13x+36 = 0 \Rightarrow (x+9)(x+4) = 0 \Rightarrow x = -9$ or -4

(j) $x^2-x-72 = 0 \Rightarrow (x-9)(x+8) = 0 \Rightarrow x = +9$ or -8

(k) $6p^2+5p-6 = 0 \Rightarrow (3p-2)(2p+3) = 0 \Rightarrow p = +\frac{2}{3}$ or $-\frac{3}{2}$

EXERCISE 1C

1. (a) Factorise $x^2+15x+56$, and hence solve the equation $x^2+15x+56 = 0$.
   (b) Factorise $x^2-11x+28$, and hence solve the equation $x^2-11x+28 = 0$.
   (c) Factorise $x^2-4x-32$, and hence solve the equation $x^2-4x-32 = 0$.

2. Solve the following equations by factorisation:
   (a) $x^2+12x+32 = 0$
   (b) $x^2+8x+12 = 0$
   (c) $x^2-18x+77 = 0$
   (d) $x^2+3x-54 = 0$
   (e) $3x^2 = 7x+6$
   (f) $8x^2-2x-21 = 0$

3. Solve the following equations:
   (a) $3-5x+2x^2 = 0$
   (b) $7(x-1)^2 = 252$
   (c) $6x^2-11x = 10$
   (d) $10x(x+2) = 30$
   (e) $3x(4x-3) = 0$
   (f) $(2x-3)(x+2) = (2x-3)(3x-2)$
   (g) $6x^2+5x-4 = 0$

4. Find a positive whole number with the property that twice its square plus the number itself equals 55.

5. The sides of one rectangle are $(x+3)$ cm and $(x-2)$ cm. The sides of another rectangle of equal area are $(x+1)$ cm and $(x-1)$ cm. Find x.

6. Solve simultaneously $(x+y)(x-y) = 0$ and $5x+7y = 12$.

1.6 THE ROOTS OF AN EQUATION

The *roots* of an equation are the elements of its solution set. Thus the roots of the equation $x^2 - 5x + 6 = 0$ are $+2$ and $+3$.

Note that an equation like $x^2 - 4x + 4 = 0$, i.e. $(x-2)^2 = 0$, is said to have *repeated* roots: its roots are $+2$ and $+2$.

Sometimes, instead of trying to solve a given equation, i.e. to find its roots, we know the roots and want to reconstruct the equation itself.

EXAMPLE Find in factor form an equation whose two roots are -7, $+2/3$, and then multiply out the brackets.

$$x = -7 \Leftrightarrow (x+7) = 0 \quad \text{and} \quad x = +2/3 \Leftrightarrow 3x = +2 \Leftrightarrow (3x-2) = 0.$$

Therefore $\qquad x = -7$ or $x = +2/3 \Leftrightarrow (x+7)(3x-2) = 0$

i.e. $\qquad\qquad x(3x-2) + 7(3x-2) = 0$

$$3x^2 - 2x + 21x - 14 = 0$$

Thus the required equation is $3x^2 + 19x - 14 = 0$.

EXAMPLE Find an equation whose two roots are α, β.

$$x = \alpha \Leftrightarrow (x-\alpha) = 0 \quad \text{and} \quad x = \beta \Leftrightarrow (x-\beta) = 0.$$

Therefore $\qquad x = \alpha$ or $x = \beta \Leftrightarrow (x-\alpha)(x-\beta) = 0$

i.e. $\qquad\qquad x(x-\beta) - \alpha(x-\beta) = 0$

$$x^2 - \beta x - \alpha x + \alpha\beta = 0$$

Thus the required equation is $x^2 - (\alpha+\beta)x + \alpha\beta = 0$.

Now suppose that $ax^2 + bx + c = 0$ is another equation whose roots are α, β. Then the coefficients of $x^2 - (\alpha+\beta)x + \alpha\beta = 0$ and $ax^2 + bx + c = 0$ must be proportional, and so we see that $-(\alpha+\beta) = +b/a$ and $\alpha\beta = +c/a$.

Remember this important result:

if α, β are the roots of $ax^2 + bx + c = 0$, then $\alpha+\beta = -b/a$, $\alpha\beta = +c/a$.

EXAMPLE Find the sum and product of the roots of the equation $2x^2 + 8x - 3 = 0$.

Comparing the given equation and $ax^2 + bx + c = 0$, we see that $a = +2$, $b = +8$, $c = -3$.

So the sum of the roots $= -b/a = -8/2 = -4$,
and the product $= +c/a = -3/2 = -1.5$.

Notice that we obtain these results without actually solving the equation.

EXAMPLE If -2 and X are the roots of $4x^2-7x-30 = 0$, find X.

We know that $-2X = +c/a = -30/4 \Rightarrow X = +15/4.$

Alternatively: $-2+X = -b/a = +7/4$, leading to the same result.

EXAMPLE Given that α and β are the roots of $x^2+3x-2 = 0$, find the equations whose roots are:

(a) 2α and 2β,   (b) $\alpha+1$ and $\beta+1$.

Now we know that $\alpha+\beta = -b/a = -3$, and $\alpha\beta = +c/a = -2$.

(a) So $2\alpha+2\beta = 2(\alpha+\beta) = 2\times(-3) = -6$

   and $2\alpha\times2\beta = 4(\alpha\beta) = 4\times(-2) = -8$:

   therefore the required equation is $x^2+6x-8 = 0$.

(b) Now $(\alpha+1)+(\beta+1) = \alpha+\beta+2 = -3+2 = -1$

   and $(\alpha+1)\times(\beta+1) = \alpha\beta+\alpha+\beta+1 = -2+(-3)+1 = -4$:

   therefore the required equation is $x^2+x-4 = 0$.

EXERCISE 1D

1. Find in factor form, and then multiply out, equations whose solutions are:
    (a) $x = -1, -3$
    (b) $x = -3/4, +4/3$
    (c) $x = \pm2$

2. Find the sum and product of the roots of the following equations:
    (a) $x^2+7x-8 = 0$
    (b) $x^2-7x-8 = 0$
    (c) $2x^2-11x+15 = 0$
    (d) $2x^2+x-15 = 0$
    (e) $5x^2+4x-5 = 0$

3. Calculate the value of the following expressions, where in each case α and β are the roots of the equations (a) to (e) given in question 2:
    (a) $\alpha+\beta+\alpha\beta$
    (b) $(\alpha+1)(\beta+1)$
    (c) $1/\alpha+1/\beta$
    (d) $\alpha^2+\beta^2$ by considering $(\alpha+\beta)^2-2\alpha\beta$
    (e) $\alpha^2\beta+\alpha\beta^2$

4. Given that α and β are the roots of $3x^2 - 4x - 5 = 0$, find equations whose roots are:

(a) 3α and 3β

(b) $\alpha - 4$ and $\beta - 4$

(c) $5/\alpha$ and $5/\beta$

(d) α^2 and β^2

(e) α/β and β/α

1.7 THE QUADRATIC FORMULA

By completing the square, let us solve   (a) $x^2 - 6x + 7 = 0$, (b) $3x^2 + 7x + 2 = 0$.

(a) $x^2 - 6x + 7 = 0$

$$x^2 - 6x \qquad = -7$$

$$x^2 - 6x + 9 = +9 - 7$$

$$(x-3)^2 = +2$$

$$x - 3 \quad = \pm\sqrt{2}$$

$$x = +3 \pm \sqrt{2}$$

Therefore $x = +4.41$ or $x = -1.59$ (rounding the solutions to 2 decimal places). Note that here we have an example of a quadratic equation which will not factorise simply, and so the method of completing the square (or the equivalent formula—see below) must be used.

(b) In this case we must first make the coefficient of x^2 equal to 1, by dividing through by 3.

$$3x^2 + 7x + 2 = 0 \Rightarrow x^2 + (7/3)x + (2/3) = 0$$

$$x^2 + (7/3)x + (7/6)^2 = (7/6)^2 - 2/3$$

$$(x + 7/6)^2 = 49/36 - 24/36$$

$$= (49 - 24)/36$$

$$x + \frac{7}{6} = \frac{\pm\sqrt{(49 - 24)}}{6}$$

Therefore $\qquad x = \dfrac{-7 \pm \sqrt{(49 - 24)}}{6}$

$$= (-7 \pm 5)/6$$

$$= -2/6 \quad \text{or} \quad -12/6$$

$$= -1/3 \quad \text{or} \quad -2$$

We started this chapter by solving the general linear equation, i.e. one of the form $ax+b = 0$ (with $a \neq 0$). We are now in a position to solve the general quadratic equation, i.e. one of the form $ax^2+bx+c = 0$ (with $a \neq 0$).

$$ax^2+bx+c = 0 \Rightarrow x^2 + (b/a)x + (c/a) = 0$$

$$x^2 + (b/a)x + (b/2a)^2 = (b/2a)^2 - c/a$$

$$(x + b/2a)^2 = b^2/4a^2 - 4ac/4a^2$$

$$= (b^2 - 4ac)/4a^2$$

$$x + \frac{b}{2a} = \frac{\pm\sqrt{(b^2-4ac)}}{2a}$$

Therefore
$$ax^2+bx+c = 0, a \neq 0 \Leftrightarrow x = \frac{-b\pm\sqrt{(b^2-4ac)}}{2a}$$

So we have arrived at a formula for the solution of the general quadratic equation. Note carefully the close similarity between the algebra used in deriving this formula and the calculations in example (b) above. Hence solving a quadratic by means of the formula and solving it by completing the square are really equivalent. The formula is usually far more convenient, however, as the following examples demonstrate.

EXAMPLE Solve $x^2-6x+7 = 0$.

Comparing the given equation and $ax^2+bx+c = 0$, we see that $a = +1$, $b = -6$, $c = +7$.

So $\quad x = \dfrac{-b\pm\sqrt{(b^2-4ac)}}{2a} = \dfrac{+6\pm\sqrt{(36-28)}}{2}$

$$= (+6\pm\sqrt{8})/2 = +4.41 \quad \text{or} \quad -1.59 \quad \text{(2 d.p.)}$$

EXAMPLE Solve $3x^2+7x+2 = 0$.

Now $a = +3$, $b = +7$, $c = +2$.

So $\quad x = \dfrac{-b\pm\sqrt{(b^2-4ac)}}{2a} = \dfrac{-7\pm\sqrt{(49-24)}}{6}$

$$= (-7\pm\sqrt{25})/6 = -1/3 \quad \text{or} \quad -2$$

As you will have spotted, these two examples are the same as examples (a) and (b) earlier in this section.

Note particularly the significance of the quantity (b^2-4ac), referred to as the *discriminant* of the expression ax^2+bx+c.

In example (a), the discriminant is $+8$; since this is not a perfect square, the two roots are irrational.

In example (b), however, the discriminant is $+25$, which *is* a perfect square. So the roots are rational. This means that we could have solved the equation by factorising:

$$3x^2+7x+2 = 0 \Rightarrow (3x+1)(x+2) = 0 \Rightarrow x = -1/3 \quad \text{or} \quad -2$$

If the discriminant is zero, then of course the equation must have repeated roots: for instance, $x^2+2x+1 = 0$ has the single solution $x = -1$.

EXAMPLE Find the values of m that cause the following equation to have repeated roots: $2x^2-4mx+(m^2+9) = 0$.

We have $a = +2$, $b = -4m$, $c = m^2+9$

so the discriminant $= b^2-4ac = 16m^2-8(m^2+9)$

$$= 16m^2-8m^2-72$$

$$= 8(m^2-9)$$

Therefore the values of m that give repeated roots are $+3$ and -3.

Now suppose that the discriminant proves to be negative. Then solving the equation would involve finding the square root of a negative number, which is impossible in ordinary arithmetic: so in this case the equation can have no roots at all. For example, the equation $x^2+1 = 0$ cannot be solved.

A word of warning! In more advanced work, the system of ordinary numbers (the so-called *real* numbers) is extended in such a way that equations like $x^2+1 = 0$ *can* be solved, by means of what are termed *complex* numbers. Strictly speaking, therefore, we should say that a quadratic equation with negative discriminant has complex roots but no real roots.

EXAMPLE Solve $2x^2+8x-3 = 0$ (rounding to 3 d.p.).

Now $a = +2$, $b = +8$, $c = -3$.

So $\quad x = \dfrac{-b\pm\sqrt{(b^2-4ac)}}{2a} = \dfrac{-8\pm\sqrt{(64+24)}}{4}$

$$= (-8\pm\sqrt{88})/4 = +0.345 \quad \text{or} \quad -4.345$$

These results can be given a rough check quite easily:

$$(+0.345)+(-4.345) = -4 = -b/a \text{ (as expected)},$$
and $\quad (+0.345)\times(-4.345) = -1.499\,025 \approx +c/a$.

The very slight discrepancy is caused by rounding errors.

EXERCISE 1E

In questions 1 to 6 of this exercise, give your answers either in fraction form (and in lowest terms) or in decimal form (and rounded to 3 d.p.), whichever seems appropriate.

1. Solve $2x^2 + 11x + 5 = 0$

2. Solve $6x^2 - 7x + 2 = 0$

3. Solve $4x^2 - 7x + 2 = 0$

4. Solve $3x^2 + 5x - 10 = 0$

5. Solve $2(x+3)(x-2) = 5$

6. Solve $3x^2 = (x-2)(2x+1)$

7. In each case, find the values of m that cause the equation to have repeated roots:

(a) $x^2 + 2mx + 36 = 0$,   (b) $5x^2 - mx + (m+15) = 0$.

8. Discover which of the following two equations has no real roots, and sketch a graph of its left-hand side by way of illustration. Solve the other equation.

(a) $2x^2 + 3x + 4 = 0$,   (b) $2x^2 + 3x - 4 = 0$.

9. A mad brigadier wishes to adjust the numbers in his brigade so that when all the men are formed in a square (n rows of n men) the number of men in the interior of the square is exactly ten times the number on the edge of the square. Can he achieve this?

1.8 FURTHER FACTORISATION

How would you set about factorising $(x^2 - 3x - y^2 + 3y)$? Before an expression with four (or more) terms can be factorised, it must usually be broken down into smaller parts, each of which can be factorised. Some trial and error may be needed to find a useful breakdown. Thus we might try as follows:

$$x^2 - 3x - y^2 + 3y = (x^2 - 3x) - (y^2 - 3y) = x(x-3) - y(y-3)$$

This is perfectly correct, but we cannot go any further. So we try an alternative breakdown, which in fact proves successful:

$$\begin{aligned} x^2 - 3x - y^2 + 3y &= (x^2 - y^2) - (3x - 3y) \\ &= (x+y)(x-y) - 3(x-y) \\ &= (x+y-3)(x-y) \end{aligned}$$

The four-term method forms the basis of the best systematic approach to factorising quadratics. Suppose that we need to factorise the quadratic $ax^2 + bx + c$. We take the following steps:

calculate $d = ac$ (which may be positive or negative)
find two numbers p and q such that $pq = d$ and $p+q = b$
rewrite the quadratic as $ax^2+px+qx+c$
factorise using the four-term method

EXAMPLE Factorise: (a) $3x^2+7x+2$, (b) $8x^2-19x+6$, (c) $6x^2-x-15$.

(a) $a = +3$, $b = +7$, $c = +2$: so $d = ac = +6$. We search for p and q such that $pq = +6$, $p+q = +7$. Since pq is to be positive, p and q must be both positive or both negative; and since $p+q = +7$, they must clearly be positive. It is easy to see that $p = +1$ and $q = +6$ (or, of course, vice versa). So we have

$$3x^2+7x+2 = 3x^2+1x+6x+2$$

$$= (3x^2+1x)+(6x+2)$$

$$= x(3x+1)+2(3x+1) = (x+2)(3x+1)$$

(b) $a = +8$, $b = -19$, $c = +6$: so $d = ac = +48$. Again, p and q must have the same sign, since $pq = +48$, but this time they must both be negative, since $p+q = -19$. Can you see the right values of p, q? If not, make a list of negative factors of $+48$:

$$-1,-48 \quad -2,-24 \quad -3,-16 \quad -4,-12 \quad -6,-8 \quad -8,-6 \quad \text{etc.}$$

and then the right values of p, q are easy to find. So we have

$$8x^2-19x+6 = 8x^2-3x-16x+6$$

$$= (8x^2-3x)-(16x-6)$$

$$= x(8x-3)-2(8x-3) = (x-2)(8x-3)$$

(c) $a = +6$, $b = -1$, $c = -15$: so $d = -90$. Now p and q must have opposite signs; possibilities are

$$+1,-90 \quad +2,-45 \quad +3,-30 \quad +5,-18 \quad +6,-15 \quad +9,-10 \quad +10,-9 \quad \text{etc.}$$

and we choose $+9$, -10 since these add up to -1. So we have

$$6x^2-x-15 = 6x^2+9x-10x-15$$

$$= 3x(2x+3)-5(2x+3) = (3x-5)(2x+3)$$

EXERCISE 1F

1. Factorise the following:
   (a) $a^2+bc+ab+ac$
   (b) $p^2+pq+2q-4$
   (c) $x^2+4xy+4y^2-4z^2$
   (d) x^3+2x^2-4x-8

2. Factorise the following:

(a) $8x^2 - 49x + 6$

(b) $16x^2 - 14x + 3$

(c) $3x^2 + 16x + 16$

(d) $6x^2 - 13x - 15$

(e) $9x^2 + 9x - 10$

(f) $5x^2 + x - 18$

3. Factorise the following:

(a) $4x^2 - 17x - 15$

(b) $4x^2 + 16x + 15$

(c) $25x^2 + 5x - 6$

(d) $25x^2 - 53x + 6$

4. Prove that the following cannot be factorised:

(a) $6x^2 + 14x - 9$

(b) $8x^2 - 33x + 12$

(c) $3x^2 - x - 48$

(d) $5x^2 + 19x + 16$

1.9 QUADRATIC GRAPHS AND INEQUALITIES

Let us consider again the graph of $y = x^2 - 14x + 40$, sketched in figure 1.2.

Since $(x-7)^2 = x^2 - 14x + 49 = (x^2 - 14x + 40) + 9$,
we see that $y = -9 + (x-7)^2$.

Therefore, when $x = 7 + h, \ y = -9 + (+h)^2 = -9 + h^2$

and when $x = 7 - h, \ y = -9 + (-h)^2 = -9 + h^2$

hence the line $x = 7$ is an axis of symmetry of the graph.

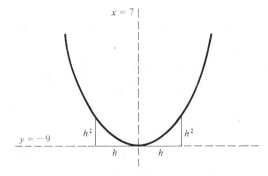

Fig. 1.3

Furthermore, $y = -9$ when $x = 7$

$y > -9$ when $x < 7$

and $y > -9$ when $x > 7$

In other words, $(7, -9)$ is the lowest point on the graph.

EXAMPLE Find the axis of symmetry and the highest point on the graph of $y = 10+6x-x^2$, and sketch the graph.

$$y = 10-(x^2-6x) = 19-(x^2-6x+9) = 19-(x-3)^2$$

so the line $x = 3$ is the axis of symmetry.

Furthermore, $y = 19$ when $x = 3$

and $y < 19$ for all other values of x

therefore $(3, 19)$ is the highest point on the graph.

Now sketch the graph of $y = 10+6x-x^2$ for yourself, marking in its axis of symmetry and highest point, and also the point where it cuts the y-axis.

EXAMPLE For which values of x is $(x+12)(x-2) > 0$?

If the product of $(x+12)$ and $(x-2)$ is to be positive, then
either $(x+12)$ and $(x-2)$ must both be positive, i.e. $x > +2$,
   or $(x+12)$ and $(x-2)$ must both be negative, i.e. $x < -12$.

The table below may serve to make this line of argument rather clearer.

	$x < -12$	$x = -12$	$-12 < x < +2$	$x = +2$	$x > +2$
$(x+12)$	$-$	0	$+$	$+$	$+$
$(x-2)$	$-$	$-$	$-$	0	$+$
$(x+12)(x-2)$	$+$	0	$-$	0	$+$

So $(x+12)(x-2) > 0$ provided that either $x < -12$ or $x > +2$.

EXAMPLE (a) For which values of x is $x^2+10x+32 < 56$?
   (b) Prove that $x^2+10x+32 \geqslant 7$ for all values of x.
   (c) Sketch the graph of $y = x^2+10x+32$.

(a) $x^2+10x+32 < 56 \Leftrightarrow x^2+10x-24 < 0$

i.e. $(x+12)(x-2) < 0$

Now if the product of $(x+12)$ and $(x-2)$ is to be negative, then $(x+12)$ must be positive and $(x-2)$ must be negative (the other way round is impossible—if you do not see why, make a table as in the previous example): i.e. $x > -12$ and $x < +2$.

Therefore $x^2 + 10x + 32 < 56$ provided $-12 < x < +2$.

(b) $x^2 + 10x + 32 \geqslant 7 \Rightarrow x^2 + 10x + 25 \geqslant 0$

$$\text{i.e.} \quad (x+5)(x+5) \geqslant 0$$

Now $(x+5)(x+5)$ equals $(x+5)^2$, which is zero when $x = -5$, but positive for all other values of x.

Therefore $x^2 + 10x + 32 \geqslant 7$ for all values of x.

(c) $y = 32 + (x^2 + 10x) = 7 + (x^2 + 10x + 25) = 7 + (x+5)^2$

so the line $x = -5$ is the axis of symmetry.

Alternatively, we may argue that the axis of symmetry must lie half way between $x = -12$ and $x = +2$, i.e. it must be $x = -5$. Or of course the argument of (b) leads to the same conclusion.

So by one method or another, we can establish that $(-5, 7)$ is the lowest point on the graph. We can easily see that the graph cuts the y-axis at the point $(0, 32)$.

Figure 1.4 shows the facts discovered so far. Copy this diagram and complete it by sketching in the graph.

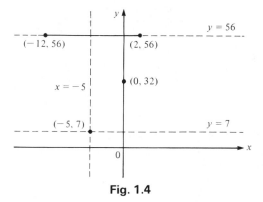

Fig. 1.4

EXERCISE 1G

1. Find the axis of symmetry and the lowest point on the following graphs, and sketch each graph:

   (a) $y = x^2 + 6x + 12$

   (b) $y = x^2 - 18x + 75$

   (c) $y = x^2 + 8x - 1$

   (d) $y = x^2 - 2x - 9$

2. Sketch each of the following graphs, finding (and marking in) any points where the graph cuts the y-axis and x-axis, the axis of symmetry, and the lowest or highest point:

   (a) $y = 10x - x^2$

   (b) $y = 2x^2 + 5x + 2$

   (c) $y = 5 - 4x + x^2$

   (d) $y = 6 - x - x^2$

3. Prove that the following inequalities are true for all values of x:

   (a) $x^2 - 20x + 110 \geqslant 10$

   (b) $x^2 + 3x - 5 \geqslant -7.25$

   (c) $2x - x^2 \leqslant 1$

   (d) $36 - 16x - x^2 \leqslant 100$

2 TRIGONOMETRY I

2.1 RECTANGULAR AND POLAR COORDINATES

If θ is an acute angle, then $\cos\theta$ and $\sin\theta$ are defined as shown in figure 2.1a.

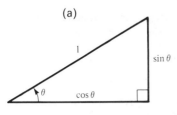

Fig. 2.1

Applying this definition to the graph in figure 2.1b, we see immediately that the point P has coordinates $(r\cos\theta, r\sin\theta)$, i.e. that $x = r\cos\theta$, $y = r\sin\theta$.

The quantities x, y are strictly speaking known as *rectangular* (or Cartesian) coordinates, whereas r, θ are the point's *polar* coordinates.

EXAMPLE Find the rectangular coordinates of the point given by $r = 10$, $\theta = 39.8°$.

We have $x = 10\cos 39.8 = 7.68$

   and $y = 10\sin 39.8 = 6.40$ (3 s.f.)

Alternatively, your calculator may have a polar–rectangular facility, which probably works more or less as follows:

> Enter r, press the P→R key, enter θ, press the $=$ key.
> The value of x now appears on the screen, and the value
> of y can be found by pressing the X↔Y key.

EXERCISE 2A

1. What are the x, y coordinates of the following points? In each case, use the first method of the above example, and then check by means of the alternative method. Round all your answers to 3 significant figures.

(a) A, given by $r = 3$, $\theta = 40°$

(b) B, given by $r = 4$, $\theta = 70°$

(c) C, given by $r = 2.37$, $\theta = 38.4°$

(d) D, given by $r = 3190$, $\theta = 4.8°$

21

2. What are the rectangular coordinates of the points whose polar coordinates are as follows?

(a) 2 and 0°

(b) 4 and 60°

(c) 1 and 54°

(d) 5 and 90°

3. If P is $(x, 0.716)$ and $r = 0.924$, use trigonometry to find θ and then x. Check your value for x by using Pythagoras' theorem.

4. If P is $(3.75, 1.68)$, find r by Pythagoras' theorem, and then θ by trigonometry. Check your value for θ by using a slightly different trigonometrical method.

2.2 ANGLES OF ANY SIZE

If θ is not acute, then the elementary definitions of $\cos \theta$ and $\sin \theta$ given in section 2.1 are of no use, since θ cannot be fitted into a right-angled triangle, as it is in figure 2.1a.

To extend the definitions to cover angles of any size, we use the connection between rectangular and polar coordinates already briefly discussed in section 2.1.

If O is the origin, and OP is one unit long and runs in direction θ (measured from Ox, anti-clockwise counting as positive), then

P has rectangular coordinates ($\cos \theta$, $\sin \theta$).

This is our extended definition of $\cos \theta$ and $\sin \theta$, and it plainly agrees with the earlier, more elementary definition.

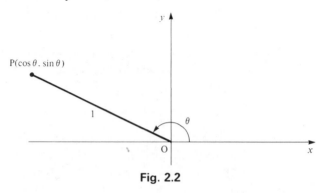

Fig. 2.2

Suppose θ is 155°. A glance at figure 2.2 should convince you that $\cos 155°$ must be negative, and you can confirm on your calculator that this is indeed so (in fact, $\cos 155°$ equals $-0.906\,307\,787$ approximately). Similarly, you can see that $\sin 155°$ must be positive ($\sin 155°$ equals $+0.422\,618\,261$ approximately).

Now look at figure 2.3. Suppose the coordinates of P are (cos 155°, sin 155°). What does the acute angle α equal?

If OA is the reflection of OP in O*y*, what is the length of OA, and what angle does it make with O*x*?

Do you see that cos 155° must equal −cos 25°, and sin 155° must equal +sin 25°? Confirm these facts on your calculator.

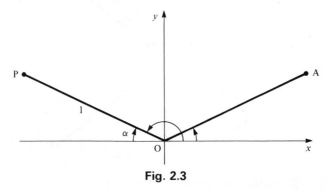

Fig. 2.3

We would get similar results for any other angle, say 126°. Since 126 = 180−54, cos 126° must equal −cos 54°, and sin 126° must equal +sin 54°. More generally, cos(180−α) = −cos α and sin(180−α) = +sin α.

In figure 2.4, the coordinates of P are (cos 214°, sin 214°). What does the acute angle α equal?

This time, OA and OP are equal but in opposite directions. Do you see that cos 214° must equal −cos 34°, and sin 214° must equal −sin 34°?

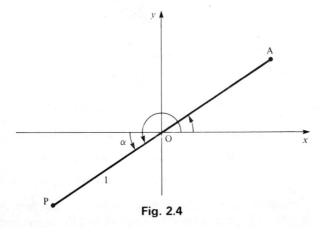

Fig. 2.4

Similarly, since 248 = 180+68, it follows that cos 248° must equal −cos 68°, sin 248° must equal −sin 68°. More generally, cos(180+α) = −cos α and sin(180+α) = −sin α.

In figure 2.5, the coordinates of P are (cos 322°, sin 322°). What does α equal? Do you see that cos 322° must equal +cos 38°, and sin 322° must equal −sin 38°? More generally, cos (360−α) = +cos α and sin (360−α) = −sin α.

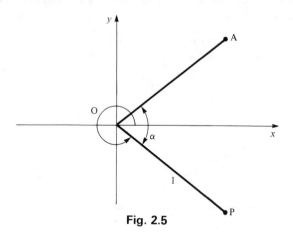

Fig. 2.5

Finally, suppose the coordinates of P in figure 2.6 are (cos 392°, sin 392°). It is obvious that cos 392° = +cos 32° and sin 392° = +sin 32°. More generally, both cosine and sine repeat themselves every 360°: we say these functions have a *period* of 360°.

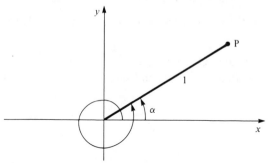

Fig. 2.6

To summarise: cos (180−α) = −cos α   sin (180−α) = +sin α

cos (180+α) = −cos α   sin (180+α) = −sin α

cos (360−α) = +cos α   sin (360−α) = −sin α

cos (360+α) = +cos α   sin (360+α) = +sin α

We have established these eight identities for acute α, but they are in fact true for any α, as may easily be confirmed by inspection of the cosine and sine graphs. All eight are important, but two are especially useful and should be remembered:

$$\underline{\cos (360-\alpha) \;=\; +\cos \alpha \qquad \sin (180-\alpha) \;=\; +\sin \alpha}$$

EXERCISE 2B

1. By drawing diagrams like figure 2.2, state which of the following are positive and which negative, and check on your calculator: $\cos 290°$, $\sin 190°$, $\sin 330°$, $\cos 260°$, $\sin 160°$, $\cos 110°$, $\cos(-70°)$, $\sin(-40°)$, $\cos(-130°)$, $\sin(-170°)$.

2. Express the following in terms of the cosine or sine of an acute angle (e.g. $\cos(-68°) = +\cos 68°$, $\sin 248° = -\sin 68°$): $\sin 314°$, $\cos 253°$, $\sin 178°$, $\cos 138°$, $\cos 338°$, $\sin 236°$.

3. Express the following similarly in terms of an acute angle: $\sin 510°$, $\cos 725°$, $\cos 1100°$, $\cos 36\,200°$, $\cos(-98°)$, $\sin(-25°)$.

4. Write down the values of:
   $\cos(-180°)$, $\cos(-90°)$, $\cos 0°$, $\cos 90°$, $\cos 180°$, $\cos 270°$, $\cos 360°$,
   $\sin(-180°)$, $\sin(-90°)$, $\sin 0°$, $\sin 90°$, $\sin 180°$, $\sin 270°$, $\sin 360°$.

5. Draw a large-scale graph of $\cos\theta$ against θ for values of θ from $0°$ to $360°$ (scales 1 cm to $20°$, 10 cm to 1 unit), plotting values every $20°$. Read off from the graph:

   (a) the values of $\cos 74°$, $\cos 112°$, $\cos 236°$, $\cos 314°$

   (b) two angles whose cosine equals -0.79

   (c) two angles whose cosine equals $+0.56$

6. Draw a graph of $\sin\theta$ against θ as in question 5. From it read off:

   (a) the values of $\sin 24°$, $\sin 152°$, $\sin 261°$, $\sin 302°$

   (b) two angles whose sine equals -0.79

   (c) two angles whose sine equals $+0.56$

2.3 SOLVING EQUATIONS

We saw in questions 5 and 6 of the last exercise that equations involving cosine and sine can have more than a single solution. We now wish to solve such equations without the labour (and inaccuracy) of drawing graphs.

For example, let us solve $\cos\theta = -0.829$. One possible value of θ is found easily from your calculator by using the inverse-function key, labelled INV on most calculators. We enter -0.829, and then press INV COS in that order. In this way, we find $\theta = 146°$ (to the nearest whole number). A second value can be found by using the fact that $\cos(360-\alpha) = +\cos\alpha$ which means that if $\theta = \alpha$ is one solution (found from the calculator) then $\theta = 360-\alpha$ is a second solution. So in our example the second solution is $\theta = 360-146 = 214°$. Inspection of the graph of $\cos\theta$ against θ (see figure 2.7 overleaf) shows that these are the only solutions between $0°$ and $360°$.

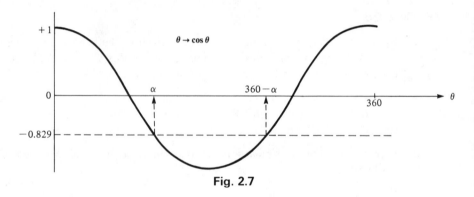

Fig. 2.7

Sometimes a different or wider range of solutions is necessary. In that case, the fact that $\cos(360+\alpha) = +\cos\alpha$ enables us to extend the list as far as we like, by adding on multiples of 360° to any solutions already found. In the above example, for instance, there are further solutions $\theta = 360+146 = 506°$, $\theta = 360+214 = 574°$, $\theta = 720+146 = 866°$, etc.

When you are solving an equation like $\cos\theta = p$, the value of θ which your calculator displays directly is called the principal value. It is written $\arccos(p)$, although some people write $\cos^{-1}p$. So referring back to the previous example, we could write $\arccos(-0.829) = 145.99615°$ (5 d.p.).

As another example, consider $\cos\theta = +0.225$ for $0° \leqslant \theta < 720°$. One possible value of θ is $\arccos(0.225)$, which is 77° (to the nearest integer). So $\theta = 77°$ is one solution, and a second is $\theta = 360-77 = 283°$. Other solutions in the stated range are $\theta = 360+77 = 437°$ and $\theta = 360+283 = 643°$. The final list of solutions is therefore $\theta = 77°, 283°, 437°, 643°$.

EXAMPLE Solve the equations (a) $\cos\theta = +0.7346$ and (b) $\cos\theta = -0.6195$, in each case for $0° \leqslant \theta < 360°$, rounding all your answers to 1 d.p.

(a) Let $\alpha = \arccos(+0.7346) = 42.72657257°$ (8 d.p.).

Now α lies within the range 0° to 360°, and so does $360-\alpha$. But if we try to find other solutions by adding on multiples of 360° to either of these two, the values obtained fall outside the range and can therefore be ignored.

Thus $\theta = \alpha$ or $360-\alpha$ (other values can be ignored)

$= 42.7°$ or $317.3°$ (1 d.p.)

(b) Let $\alpha = \arccos(-0.6195) = 128.2796310°$ (7 d.p.).

Then $\theta = \alpha$ or $360-\alpha$ (other values again ignored)

$= 128.3°$ or $231.7°$ (1 d.p.)

Similar equations involving sine need similar treatment. One possible value of θ is found easily from the calculator. A second value can be found by using the fact that $\sin(180-\alpha) = +\sin\alpha$ which means that if $\theta = \alpha$ is one solution, then $\theta = 180-\alpha$ is a second solution. As with cosine equations, the list of solutions can be extended by adding on multiples of $360°$ to any solutions already found.

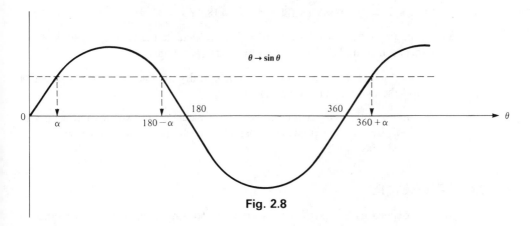

Fig. 2.8

EXAMPLE Solve the equations   (a) $\sin\theta = +0.518$ (b) $\sin\theta = -0.809$, in each case for $0° \leqslant \theta < 360°$, rounding all your answers to 1 d.p.

(a)   Let $\alpha = \arcsin(+0.518) = 31.198\,190\,82°$ (8 d.p.).

Then $\theta = \alpha$ or $180-\alpha$ (other values ignored)

                 $= 31.2°$ or $148.8°$ (1 d.p.)

(b)   Let $\alpha = \arcsin(-0.809) = -53.998\,343\,47°$ (8 d.p.).

Note that this negative α falls outside the stated range, and so is not itself a solution. However, $(180-\alpha)$ and $(360+\alpha)$ both lie between $0°$ and $360°$.

Thus $\theta = 180-\alpha$ or $360+\alpha$ (other values ignored)

             $= 234.0°$ or $306.0°$ (1 d.p.)

EXERCISE 2C

1.   Solve the following equations, in each case for $0° \leqslant \theta < 360°$, rounding all your answers to 1 d.p.:

    (a) $\cos\theta = -0.762$

    (b) $\sin\theta = +0.817$

    (c) $\sin\theta = -0.2429$

    (d) $\cos\theta = +0.6185$

2. Solve the following equations, in each case for the range given, rounding all your answers to 1 d.p.:

    (a) $\sin \theta = -0.964$ $(0° \leqslant \theta < 720°)$

    (b) $\cos \theta = +0.782$ $(0° \leqslant \theta < 720°)$

    (c) $\sin \theta = +0.2006$ $(-180° < \theta \leqslant +180°)$

    (d) $\cos \theta = -0.0038$ $(-180° < \theta \leqslant +180°)$

3. At the point A, $r = 47.3$ and $x = 29.8$. Calculate the two possible values of θ (between 0° and 360°), and the two corresponding values of y.

4. At the point B, $r = 8375$ and $y = 6019$. Calculate the two possible values of θ, and the two corresponding values of x.

5. At the point C, $r = 25$ and $x = -17$. Calculate the two possible values of θ. Find also the two possible values of θ at the point D, given that $r = 25$ and $y = -17$ there.

2.4 TANGENTS

Tan θ is defined as being equal to $\sin \theta / \cos \theta$, so long as $\cos \theta$ is not zero (i.e. so long as θ is not 90°, 270°, 450°, etc.). If $\cos \theta = 0$, then tan θ is not defined.

If you look back to figure 2.1a or 2.2, you will see that the gradient of OP equals $\sin \theta / \cos \theta$, which by our definition equals tan θ. In particular, tan θ is positive when the gradient of OP is positive (i.e. for $0° < \theta < 90°$ and $180° < \theta < 270°$), and otherwise is negative.

Figures 2.3 to 2.6 reveal that

$$\tan(180 - \alpha) = -\tan \alpha$$
$$\tan(180 + \alpha) = +\tan \alpha$$
$$\tan(360 - \alpha) = -\tan \alpha$$
$$\tan(360 + \alpha) = +\tan \alpha$$

The fact that $\tan(180 + \alpha) = +\tan \alpha$ means that the tangent function repeats itself every 180°; it therefore has a period of 180°. This helps us to solve equations. For instance, suppose we need to solve the equation $\tan \theta = 1$. One possible solution is $\theta = \arctan(1) = 45°$ exactly. A second solution is $\theta = 180 + 45 = 225°$, a third is $\theta = 360 + 45 = 405°$, and so on.

EXAMPLE Solve the equations (a) $\tan \theta = 1.477$ and (b) $\tan \theta = -0.404$, in each case for $0° \leqslant \theta < 360°$.

(a) Let $\alpha = \arctan(1.477) = 55.9°$ approximately.

   Then $\theta = \alpha$ or $180 + \alpha$ (other values ignored)

   $\qquad\qquad = 55.9°$ or $235.9°$ (1 d.p.)

(b) Let $\alpha = \arctan(-0.404) = -22.0°$, which we note falls outside the stated range, and so is not itself a solution. However, $(180+\alpha)$ and $(360+\alpha)$ both lie between $0°$ and $360°$.

Thus $\theta = 180+\alpha$ or $360+\alpha$ (other values ignored)

$= 158.0°$ or $338.0°$ (1 d.p.)

EXERCISE 2D

1. Express the following in terms of acute angles: $\tan 153°$, $\tan 208°$, $\tan 299°$, $\tan 380°$, $\tan(-17°)$.

2. Write down the values of $\tan 0°$, $\tan 45°$, $\tan 135°$, $\tan 180°$, $\tan 225°$, $\tan 315°$, $\tan 360°$. What about $\tan 90°$ and $\tan 270°$?

3. Draw a large-scale graph of $\tan \theta$ against θ for values of θ from $-90°$ to $+270°$ (scales 1 cm to $20°$, 2 cm to 1 unit), plotting values every $20°$. Read off from the graph:

   (a) $\tan 34°$, $\tan 74°$, $\tan 114°$, $\tan 214°$, $\tan(-24°)$

   (b) two angles whose tangent equals $+0.73$

   (c) two angles whose tangent equals $+1.42$

   (d) two angles whose tangent equals -0.42

4. Solve the following equations, in each case for the range given, rounding all your answers to 1 d.p.:

   (a) $\tan \theta = +0.3524$ $(0° \leqslant \theta < 360°)$

   (b) $\tan \theta = -2.69$ $(0° \leqslant \theta < 360°)$

   (c) $\tan \theta = -0.06137$ $(0° \leqslant \theta < 720°)$

   (d) $\tan \theta = +11.53$ $(-180° < \theta < +180°)$

2.5 POSITION VECTORS

In sections 2.1 and 2.2 we related the basic ideas of trigonometry to the coordinates of a point in the x–y plane. To specify position, however, we often use position *vectors* instead of coordinates (when dealing with transformation matrices, for instance). Just as there are two types of coordinates, i.e. rectangular and polar, so position vectors (and of course displacement vectors in general) can be given

either   in column form, $\mathbf{r} = \begin{pmatrix} 3 \\ 4 \end{pmatrix}$

or   in polar form, $\mathbf{r} = [5, 53.13°]$

The column form gives the components in the Ox and Oy directions. The polar form gives the magnitude of the displacement, and its direction as an angle measured anti-clockwise from Ox. As we shall see later, displacements are not the only vector quantities that can be given in either of these two forms, and conversion from one form to the other is a common task.

EXAMPLE   Convert   (a) $[10, -40°]$ to column form,

(b) $\begin{pmatrix} -9.3 \\ +4.2 \end{pmatrix}$ to polar form.

(a) We must find P's x and y-coordinates.

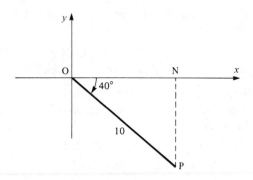

Fig. 2.9

Now $x = 10\cos(-40°) = +10\cos 40° = +7.66$ (to 3 s.f.)

and $y = 10\sin(-40°) = -10\sin 40° = -6.43$ (to 3 s.f.)

So $[10, -40°] = \begin{pmatrix} +7.66 \\ -6.43 \end{pmatrix}$.

(b) We must find r and θ at Q.

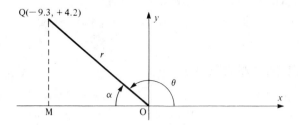

Fig. 2.10

Clearly $\alpha = \arctan(4.2/9.3) = 24.304\,549°$

and so $\theta = 180 - \alpha$ $= 155.695\,451°$

Hence $r = 9.3/\cos\alpha$ $= 10.204\,411$

So $\begin{pmatrix} -9.3 \\ +4.2 \end{pmatrix} = [10.2,\ 155.7°]$ approximately.

Note that in (b) we could have found r as $4.2/\sin\alpha$, but using the larger of OM and MQ will yield a more accurate answer.

EXERCISE 2E

1. Convert to column form: (a) $[5, 30°]$,   (b) $[2, 110°]$,
     (c) $[0.5, 200°]$,   (d) $[20, 300°]$.

2. Convert: (a) $[1742, 151.68°]$,   (b) $[0.06814, 234.56°]$,
     (c) $[9.362, -10.73°]$,   (d) $[4.792, 360°]$.

3. Convert to polar form: (a) $\binom{2}{3}$,   (b) $\binom{+8}{-11}$,   (c) $\binom{-14}{+17}$,   (d) $\binom{-21}{-32}$.

4. Convert: (a) $\binom{2.971}{4.613}$,   (b) $\binom{13.89}{-2.64}$,   (c) $\binom{-1734}{+1473}$,   (d) $\binom{0}{0}$.

2.6 EXACT VALUES FOR SPECIAL ANGLES

We know that $\cos 0°$ equals 1 exactly, and have met other exact values, for example, $\tan 45° = 1$. For the most part, however, the trigonometrical values given by the calculator are not exact.

The triangle in figure 2.11 is isosceles and right-angled.

Fig. 2.11

By Pythagoras' theorem, $OP^2 = 1^2 + 1^2 = 2$, and so $OP = \sqrt{2}$.
Hence $\sqrt{2}\cos 45 = 1$ and $\sqrt{2}\sin 45 = 1$:

so $\cos 45° = \dfrac{1}{\sqrt{2}}$, $\sin 45° = \dfrac{1}{\sqrt{2}}$, $\tan 45° = 1$.

The triangle in figure 2.12 is half an equilateral triangle.

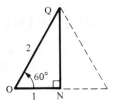

Fig. 2.12

By Pythagoras' theorem again,
$2^2 = 1^2 + QN^2$, and so $QN = \sqrt{3}$:

so $\cos 60° = \dfrac{1}{2}$, $\sin 60° = \dfrac{\sqrt{3}}{2}$, $\tan 60° = \sqrt{3}$.

Note too that angle NQO equals $30°$:

hence $\sin 30° = \dfrac{1}{2}$, $\cos 30° = \dfrac{\sqrt{3}}{2}$, $\tan 30° = \dfrac{1}{\sqrt{3}}$.

These $60°$ and $30°$ results are of course linked by the fact that $\cos(90-\alpha) = \sin\alpha$, $\sin(90-\alpha) = \cos\alpha$, $\tan(90-\alpha) = 1/\tan\alpha$.

In many problems, calculator accuracy is entirely acceptable, and indeed in most problems far less accuracy is quite all right. For instance, in virtually every case we may take $\cos 30°$ to be $0.866\,025\,4$, and very often 0.866 will be sufficiently precise. Every now and again, however, absolute precision is needed, and then it is useful to know the exact values established above, or related results, such as that $\cos 120° = -1/2$.

EXERCISE 2F

1. Write down the exact values of:
   $\sin 120°$, $\tan 120°$, $\cos 135°$, $\sin 135°$, $\tan 135°$, $\cos 150°$, $\sin 150°$, $\tan 150°$.

2. In triangle ABC (figure 2.13), find (without calculator or tables) the exact lengths of (a) AD,   (b) AC,   (c) BC.

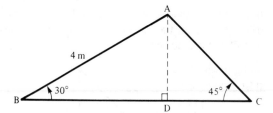

Fig. 2.13

3. A Customs launch leaves Dover harbour on a course of 180°. After going 5 nautical miles, the skipper alters course to 120°, and after 5 miles on that course, he steers 225° for 6 miles. Assuming that the information is exact, find exactly how far south of the harbour the launch's position is now, and whether it is east or west of the harbour.

2.7 FURTHER RATIOS AND IDENTITIES

By definition, $\tan \theta = \sin \theta/\cos \theta$. There are also three other trigonometrical ratios—cotangent, secant, cosecant—which are defined as follows:

$$\cot \theta = \cos \theta/\sin \theta \qquad \sec \theta = 1/\cos \theta \qquad \operatorname{cosec} \theta = 1/\sin \theta$$

EXAMPLE (a) Find $\cot 30°$, $\sec 60°$, and $\operatorname{cosec} 45°$.
   (b) Prove that $\tan \theta/\sec \theta = \sin \theta$.

(a) $\cot 30° = \cos 30°/\sin 30° = (\sqrt{3}/2) / (1/2) = \sqrt{3}$

   $\sec 60° = 1/\cos 60° = 1 / (1/2) = 2$

   $\operatorname{cosec} 45° = 1/\sin 45° = 1 / (1/\sqrt{2}) = \sqrt{2}$

(b) $\tan \theta/\sec \theta = (\sin \theta/\cos \theta) / (1/\cos \theta) = \sin \theta$

The statement proved in example (b) above is true for almost all values of θ. (What are the exceptions?) Statements of this kind are called identities, and they abound in trigonometry. Another very important trigonometrical identity can be obtained from Pythagoras' theorem. If we apply the theorem to the triangle in figure 2.1a, we obtain $(\cos\theta)^2 + (\sin\theta)^2 = 1$, where of course the angle θ is acute. This identity is in fact true for all θ, however, since $\cos\theta$ and $\sin\theta$ equal $\pm\cos\alpha$ and $\pm\sin\alpha$ respectively, for some suitably chosen acute α, as we saw earlier in section 2.2. It is usual to write $(\cos\theta)^2$ as $\cos^2\theta$ and $(\sin\theta)^2$ as $\sin^2\theta$. The identity then assumes its normal form (which you must remember):

$$\cos^2\theta + \sin^2\theta = 1$$

If you check this with a particular value of θ, say $40°$ or $312°$, you may get rounding errors on your calculator: the identity is nevertheless true exactly.

Dividing each term in the identity by $\cos^2\theta$, we obtain $\cos^2\theta/\cos^2\theta + \sin^2\theta/\cos^2\theta = 1/\cos^2\theta$, i.e. $1 + \tan^2\theta = \sec^2\theta$. Dividing through by $\sin^2\theta$ instead, we obtain $\cot^2\theta + 1 = \operatorname{cosec}^2\theta$. Thus we have two alternative forms of the Pythagoras identity:

$$1 + \tan^2\theta = \sec^2\theta \qquad \cot^2\theta + 1 = \operatorname{cosec}^2\theta$$

These three Pythagoras identities can be used to calculate one ratio when another is given.

For instance, if $\sin\theta = 12/13$ and θ is obtuse, we can find $\tan\theta$ exactly, without using calculator or tables.

From the first identity, $\cos^2\theta + (12/13)^2 = 1$

hence $\cos^2\theta = 1 - 144/169 = 25/169 \Rightarrow \cos\theta = \pm 5/13$.

But since θ is obtuse, we must take the negative value.

Thus finally $\tan\theta = \sin\theta/\cos\theta = -12/5 = -2.4$.

Here is another example: find $\cos\theta$ given that θ is acute and $\tan\theta = 2$. Since we know $\tan\theta$, we use the Pythagoras identity involving $\tan\theta$, i.e. $1 + \tan^2\theta = \sec^2\theta$. We can deduce from it that $\sec^2\theta = 5 \Rightarrow \cos^2\theta = 1/5 \Rightarrow \cos\theta = +\sqrt{0.2}$ (choosing the positive root, of course, since θ is acute).

Identities already established can also be used to establish further identities. The best policy is to take either the left- or right-hand side of the target identity, and transform it (by means of known identities) until the other side appears. As an example, we will prove that $(\cos\theta - \sin\theta)(\cos\theta + \sin\theta) = 1 - 2\sin^2\theta$:

$$\begin{aligned}
\text{LHS} = (\cos\theta - \sin\theta)(\cos\theta + \sin\theta) &= \cos^2\theta - \sin^2\theta \\
&= (1 - \sin^2\theta) - \sin^2\theta \\
&= 1 - 2\sin^2\theta = \text{RHS}
\end{aligned}$$

EXAMPLE Prove that $\cot\theta + \tan\theta = \operatorname{cosec}\theta\sec\theta$.

$$\cot\theta + \tan\theta = \frac{\cos\theta}{\sin\theta} + \frac{\sin\theta}{\cos\theta} = \frac{\cos^2\theta + \sin^2\theta}{\sin\theta\cos\theta} = \frac{1}{\sin\theta\cos\theta}$$

$$= \operatorname{cosec}\theta\sec\theta$$

EXERCISE 2G

Do *not* use a calculator or tables.

1. Sketch graphs of $\cot\theta$, $\sec\theta$, $\operatorname{cosec}\theta$ against θ for values of θ between $0°$ and $360°$.

2. If $\sin\theta = 0.6$, find the possible values of $\cos\theta$ exactly.

3. If $\tan\theta = 15/8$ and $180° < \theta < 270°$, find $\sin\theta$ and $\cos\theta$.

4. Demonstrate that $\cos^2\theta + \sin^2\theta = 1$ is true exactly (a) when $\theta = 60°$, (b) when $\theta = 135°$.

5. Prove (a) $\sin\theta\sec\theta\cot\theta = 1$,   (b) $\sin\theta\tan\theta + \cos\theta = \sec\theta$.

6. Prove (a) $1 - 2\sin^2\theta = 2\cos^2\theta - 1$,
   and   (b) $(2\tan^2\theta + 1)/(\tan^2\theta + 2) = (2\sec^2\theta - 1)/(\sec^2\theta + 1)$.

2.8 HARDER EQUATIONS

As our first example of a harder equation, we will consider $\tan^2\theta = 9$ for θ between $0°$ and $360°$. The difficulty here is that $\tan\theta$ can take either of two values, $+3$ or -3, and we must consider them separately. Now $\arctan(3) = 71.6°$ (to   1 d.p.),   so $\theta = 71.6°$ or $251.6°$.   And $\arctan(-3) = -71.6°$, outside our range; so $\theta = 108.4°$ or $288.4°$. The full list of solutions is therefore $\theta = 71.6°$, $108.4°$, $251.6°$, $288.4°$.

Another difficulty arises in an equation such as $\sin 2\theta = 0.5$. If θ lies between $0°$ and $360°$, then 2θ lies between $0°$ and $720°$; so we must find all the possible values of 2θ in this wider range. Now $\arcsin(0.5) = 30°$. Therefore $2\theta = 30°$, $150°$, $390°$, $510°$, and thus $\theta = 15°$, $75°$, $195°$, $255°$.

Equations that involve cot, sec, or cosec cannot be solved directly as a rule, because calculators do not have the appropriate keys. Therefore an equation like $\operatorname{cosec}\theta = 2.5$ must first be transformed into the equivalent equation $\sin\theta = 0.4$ before it can be solved.

Equations involving several difficulties simultaneously can of course be solved, but they lie rather outside our scope.

Many relatively hard equations can be solved by means of trigonometric identities, or sometimes a simple algebraic idea can help.

EXAMPLE Solve $(0° \leqslant \theta < 360°)$:
  (a) $2\sin\theta = 3\cos\theta$
  (b) $6\cos^2\theta - \sin\theta = 5$
  (c) $\cos^2\theta - 3\cos\theta = \sin^2\theta - 3\sin\theta$

(a) $2\sin\theta = 3\cos\theta \implies \sin\theta/\cos\theta = 3/2 \implies \tan\theta = 1.5$

  So $\theta = \arctan(1.5) = 56.3°$, or $\theta = 180 + 56.3 = 236.3°$.

(b) This equation involves both cos and sin, but the approach adopted in (a) will not work. Instead, we use the Pythagoras identity, and substitute $(1-\sin^2\theta)$ for $\cos^2\theta$, thereby producing a quadratic equation in $\sin\theta$.

$$6\cos^2\theta - \sin\theta = 5$$
$$6(1-\sin^2\theta) - \sin\theta - 5 = 0$$
$$6 - 6\sin^2\theta - \sin\theta - 5 = 0$$
$$6\sin^2\theta + \sin\theta - 1 = 0$$
$$(3\sin\theta - 1)(2\sin\theta + 1) = 0$$
$$\sin\theta = 1/3 \text{ or } -1/2$$

First, let $\alpha = \arcsin(1/3) = 19.5°$ (1 d.p.):

then $\qquad\qquad \theta = \alpha \text{ or } 180 - \alpha$ (other values ignored)

$$= 19.5°, 160.5°$$

Next, let $\alpha = \arcsin(-1/2) = -30°$ (outside the range):

then $\qquad\qquad \theta = 180 - \alpha \text{ or } 360 + \alpha$ (other values ignored)

$$= 210°, 330°$$

Therefore the full list is $\theta = 19.5°, 160.5°, 210°, 330°$.

(c) $\qquad\qquad \cos^2\theta - 3\cos\theta = \sin^2\theta - 3\sin\theta$

$$\cos^2\theta - \sin^2\theta = 3\cos\theta - 3\sin\theta$$
$$(\cos\theta + \sin\theta)(\cos\theta - \sin\theta) = 3(\cos\theta - \sin\theta)$$

Therefore *either* $\cos\theta + \sin\theta = 3$ *or* $\cos\theta - \sin\theta = 0$: but in fact $(\cos\theta + \sin\theta)$ cannot possibly equal 3.

So $\cos\theta - \sin\theta = 0 \Rightarrow \cos\theta = \sin\theta \Rightarrow \theta = 45° \text{ or } 225°$.

EXERCISE 2H

Throughout this exercise, use the range $0° \leqslant \theta < 360°$, and where necessary round to 1 d.p.

1. Solve: (a) $\cos^2\theta = 0.49$, (b) $\sin^2\theta = 1$.

2. Solve: (a) $\cos 3\theta = -1$, (b) $\tan 2\theta = 1.6$.

3. Solve: (a) $\sec\theta = 10$, (b) $\cot\theta = 4$.

4. Solve: (a) $\sin\theta + 5\cos\theta = 0$, (b) $\sin\theta = 2\sin\theta\cos\theta$.

5. Solve: (a) $2\sin^2\theta = 1 + \cos\theta$, (b) $4\tan^2\theta + 8\sec\theta = 1$.

2.9 ARCS, SECTORS, AND RADIANS

Fig. 2.14

Consider the sector OAP of the circle centre O, radius r.

Suppose first that the *chord* AP is r units in length (figure 2.14a). Then clearly angle α equals $60°$, since triangle OAP must be equilateral.

But now suppose that the *arc* AP is r units long (figure 2.14b). Since this arc is curved, whereas the chord was straight, the angle α must be slightly less than $60°$. In fact, we can easily calculate its value.

The circumference of the complete circle $= 2\pi r$, and so

$$\alpha = \frac{r}{2\pi r} \times 360° = \frac{1}{2\pi} \times 360° = 57.295\,779\,5°$$

This special angle is of great importance in more advanced work, and is called *one radian*: i.e. $360°/(2\pi) = 1$ radian.

Hence $\underline{360° = 2\pi \text{ radians}}$ or $\underline{180° = \pi \text{ radians}}$

Similarly, $90° = \pi/2$ radians, $60° = \pi/3$ radians, $45° = \pi/4$ radians,   etc.

EXAMPLE Express (a) 72 degrees in radians (as a multiple of π), and (b) $5\pi/4$ radians in degrees.

(a) $72/180 = 2/5$: hence $72° = 2/5 \times \pi$ radians
$= 2\pi/5$ radians
(b) $5\pi/4$ radians $= 5/4 \times 180° = 225°$

The length of an arc and the area of a sector are especially easy to calculate if radians are used.

Thus if α is measured in radians (see figure 2.15):

$$\text{arc AP} = \frac{\alpha}{2\pi} \times 2\pi r = r\alpha$$

and $$\text{area OAP} = \frac{\alpha}{2\pi} \times \pi r^2 = \tfrac{1}{2}r^2\alpha$$

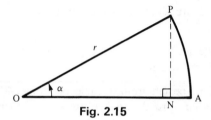

Fig. 2.15

Note, incidentally, that the area of the sector OAP must be greater than the area of the triangle OAP.

So $\frac{1}{2}r^2\alpha > \frac{1}{2}OA \times PN = \frac{1}{2}r \times r \sin\alpha = \frac{1}{2}r^2 \sin\alpha$, i.e. $\alpha > \sin\alpha$.

Test this conclusion with your calculator, for various values of α (remember to switch from **DEG** to **RAD** mode). Is it always true?

EXAMPLE Calculate the areas of triangle OAP and sector OAP, where $r = 5$ units and $\alpha = 0.1$ radians (about 5.7°).

Area of triangle $OAP = \frac{1}{2}r^2 \sin\alpha = 1.2479$ (5 s.f.)

and area of sector $OAP = \frac{1}{2}r^2\alpha$ $= 1.25$ (exactly)

EXAMPLE Solve the equations   (a) $\cos\theta = 0.4$ and   (b) $\sin\theta = 0.5$, in each case for θ between 0 and 2π radians.

(a) Let $\alpha = \arccos(0.4) = 1.159\,279\,48^c$ (8 d.p.)
     (Note the ^{c} symbol used to indicate radians)

    Then $\theta = \alpha$ or $2\pi - \alpha$ (other values lie outside the range)
               $= 1.159, 5.124$ (3 d.p.)

(b) Let $\alpha = \arcsin(0.5) = \pi/6$ exactly.
     (Note that when an angle is expressed in radians as a multiple of π, the unit symbol is usually omitted)

    Then $\theta = \alpha$ or $\pi - \alpha$ (other values ignored)
                 $= \pi/6, 5\pi/6$

EXERCISE 2I

1. Sketch the graphs of the six trigonometrical functions of θ, for values of θ between 0 and 2π.

2. Express the following angles in radians,   (a) as an exact multiple of π, and   (b) as a decimal rounded to 3 places: 20°, 135°, 150°, 270°, 306°.

3. Express the following angles in degrees, either exactly or rounded to 3 places: $\pi/8$, $3\pi/7$, $7\pi/4$, $5\pi/3$, $11\pi/6$.

4. Calculate the arc length and area of a sector whose radius equals 8 m and angle equals 2^c.

5. Calculate the arc length and area of a sector whose radius equals 3 m and angle equals $\pi/3$ radians.

6. A sector is to be cut from a circle of radius 40 cm so that its area equals 2400 cm^2. What must the angle of the sector be (in radians)? Also find the arc length.

7. Solve the following equations, in each case for θ between 0 and 2π radians, giving your answers either as an exact multiple of π or rounded to 3 places:

   (a) $\cos \theta = -0.5$

   (b) $\sin \theta = +0.7$

   (c) $\tan \theta = +1$

   (d) $6 \sin^2\theta - 5 \sin \theta - 1 = 0$

8. By using your calculator, find the values of $(\sin \alpha)/\alpha$ when $\alpha = 0.1, 0.01, 0.001$, etc. Do you think that α can be chosen so that $(\sin \alpha)/\alpha$ equals 1 exactly?

3 COORDINATE GEOMETRY I

3.1 DISPLACEMENTS AND VECTORS

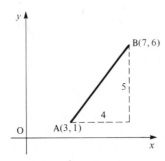

Fig. 3.1

The displacement **AB** from A to B (written by hand as $\overset{\frown}{AB}$) is given by the vector **b**−**a**, where **a** and **b** refer to the position vectors of A and B. Thus

$$\mathbf{AB} = \mathbf{b} - \mathbf{a} = \binom{7}{6} - \binom{3}{1} = \binom{4}{5}$$

The *magnitude* of this vector is the same as the magnitude or length of the displacement **AB**, which by Pythagoras' theorem equals $\sqrt{(4^2+5^2)} = \sqrt{41}$, and the *gradient* of the vector or displacement is 5/4.

In general, the magnitude of a vector $\binom{u}{v}$ equals $\sqrt{(u^2+v^2)}$, and its gradient is v/u (if $u = 0$ then of course the vector has no gradient). Any vector, whatever its gradient, whose magnitude equals exactly 1 is termed a *unit vector*.

EXERCISE 3A

Find the vectors of the displacement from the first point to the second. Find also the magnitude and gradient in each case.

1. B(7, 6)   A(3, 1)

2. O(0, 0)   C(8, 10)

3. J(0, 1)   I(1, 0)

4. D(−1, 0)   E(−3.5, 2)

5. E(−3.5, 2)   F(−4, −7)

6. $P_1(x_1, y_1)$ $P_2(x_2, y_2)$

39

3.2 PARALLEL AND PERPENDICULAR DISPLACEMENTS

As you should have discovered in the last exercise, the displacements **AB** and **OC** have the same gradient—we say they are *parallel*. We would also say that **BA** and **OC** were parallel (although in precisely opposite directions), since they have the same gradient. In terms of vectors, $\begin{pmatrix} 4 \\ 5 \end{pmatrix}$ and $\begin{pmatrix} 8 \\ 10 \end{pmatrix}$ and $\begin{pmatrix} -4 \\ -5 \end{pmatrix}$ and $\begin{pmatrix} -8 \\ -10 \end{pmatrix}$ are all parallel to each other, their common gradient being 1.25 (figure 3.2).

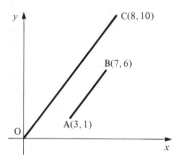

Fig. 3.2

What about *perpendicular* displacements (and vectors)? The matrix of a rotation through $+90°$ about O is $\begin{pmatrix} 0 & -1 \\ 1 & 0 \end{pmatrix}$ —see section 6.3. Under this rotation, $\begin{pmatrix} 4 \\ 5 \end{pmatrix} \rightarrow \begin{pmatrix} 0 & -1 \\ 1 & 0 \end{pmatrix}\begin{pmatrix} 4 \\ 5 \end{pmatrix} = \begin{pmatrix} -5 \\ 4 \end{pmatrix}$. It follows that $\begin{pmatrix} -5 \\ 4 \end{pmatrix}$ is perpendicular to $\begin{pmatrix} 4 \\ 5 \end{pmatrix}$. Similarly, $\begin{pmatrix} 5 \\ -4 \end{pmatrix}$ and $\begin{pmatrix} 4 \\ 5 \end{pmatrix}$ are also perpendicular to each other (figure 3.3).

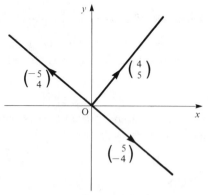

Fig. 3.3

The gradients of these two perpendicular displacements are respectively $-4/5$ and $5/4$. You will observe that each gradient is the negative reciprocal of the other, and therefore their product is -1. This is always true of perpendicular displacements; for example, a displacement with gradient $2/3$ will be perpendicular to one with gradient $-3/2$, and one with gradient 4 will be perpendicular to one with gradient $-1/4$.

EXERCISE 3B

1. Write down *unit* vectors (two in each case) which are parallel to the following vectors:

(a) $\begin{pmatrix} 3 \\ 4 \end{pmatrix}$,   (b) $\begin{pmatrix} -12 \\ 5 \end{pmatrix}$ (c) $\begin{pmatrix} 1 \\ 1 \end{pmatrix}$,   (d) $\begin{pmatrix} 6 \\ -8 \end{pmatrix}$,   (e) $\begin{pmatrix} 9 \\ -40 \end{pmatrix}$,

(f) $\begin{pmatrix} -5 \\ -12 \end{pmatrix}$.

2. Write down unit vectors (two in each case) which are perpendicular to the vectors given in question 1.

3. If m_1 and m_2 are gradients of perpendicular vectors, then $m_1 \times m_2 = -1$. Write down m_2, given that m_1 equals:

(a) 5,   (b) $1\frac{1}{2}$,   (c) -10,   (d) $-3\frac{1}{3}$,   (e) 0.4,   (f) 0.

3.3 STRAIGHT LINES

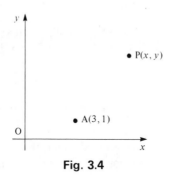

Fig. 3.4

If P lies on the line passing through A whose gradient equals 1.25, then obviously the gradient of **AP** must also equal 1.25.

Since $\mathbf{AP} = \begin{pmatrix} x \\ y \end{pmatrix} - \begin{pmatrix} 3 \\ 1 \end{pmatrix} = \begin{pmatrix} x-3 \\ y-1 \end{pmatrix}$,

the condition is that $\dfrac{y-1}{x-3} = 1.25$, i.e. that $y-1 = 1.25(x-3)$.

This is therefore the equation of the line through $(3, 1)$ with gradient 1.25. The equations can be simplified in various ways, for instance:

$$y-1 = 1.25(x-3) \;\Rightarrow\; y-1 = 1.25x-3.75 \;\Rightarrow\; y = 1.25x-2.75$$

EXAMPLE What is the equation of the straight line through A(3, 1) and C(8, 10)?

Our solution is in two stages: (i) find the gradient, (ii) find the equation.

(i) The line must have the same gradient as **AC**.

$$\text{Now } \mathbf{AC} = \mathbf{c} - \mathbf{a} = \begin{pmatrix} 8 \\ 10 \end{pmatrix} - \begin{pmatrix} 3 \\ 1 \end{pmatrix} = \begin{pmatrix} 5 \\ 9 \end{pmatrix},$$

and so the required gradient is $9/5 = 1.8$.

(ii) Therefore the equation is $\dfrac{y-1}{x-3} = 1.8$.

It is more convenient to write this as $y - 1 = 1.8(x - 3)$,

i.e. $y - 1 = 1.8x - 5.4 \Rightarrow y = 1.8x - 4.4$.

In stage (ii), we might just as well have used C rather than A in our calculation, with just the same result of course: $y - 10 = 1.8(x - 8) \Rightarrow y = 1.8x - 4.4$.

EXAMPLE What is the equation of the line through F(−4, −7) and E(−3.5, 2)?

The line must have the same gradient as **FE**:

$$\text{and since } \mathbf{FE} = \mathbf{e} - \mathbf{f} = \begin{pmatrix} -3.5 \\ 2 \end{pmatrix} - \begin{pmatrix} -4 \\ -7 \end{pmatrix} = \begin{pmatrix} 0.5 \\ 9 \end{pmatrix},$$

the required gradient is $9/0.5 = 18$. Therefore the equation is

$$y - (-7) = 18[x - (-4)] \Rightarrow y + 7 = 18[x + 4] \Rightarrow y = 18x + 65$$

Note that in all the cases considered so far, the equation of the line can eventually be reduced to the standard form $y = mx \pm \text{constant number}$, where *m equals the gradient*.

This is always so, for the equation of the line with gradient *m* through the point (h, k) is

$$\frac{y-k}{x-h} = m \Rightarrow y - k = m(x - h) \Rightarrow y = mx \pm \text{constant}$$

The gradient of a line can therefore be found easily from its equation. For instance, the gradient of $y = 3x + 2$ must be 3 (i.e. $+3$), and the gradient of $y = -3x + 2$ must be -3.

As the next example shows, however, an equation in non-standard form may have to be recast before the gradient can be found.

EXAMPLE Find the gradient of $3x - 2y - 8 = 0$.

We rearrange the equation to read $y = $ something:

$$3x - 2y - 8 = 0 \Rightarrow -2y = -3x + 8 \Rightarrow 2y = 3x - 8 \Rightarrow y = 1\tfrac{1}{2}x - 4$$

We can now see that the gradient equals $+1\tfrac{1}{2}$.

EXERCISE 3C

1. Write down and then simplify—as much as you can—the equations of the following lines:
   (a) through $(4, 11)$ with gradient 4
   (b) through $(-2, -11)$ with gradient -2
   (c) through $(-3, 5)$ with gradient $1/3$
   (d) through $(0, 0)$ with gradient 17
   (e) through $(4, -7)$ with gradient 0
   (f) through $(7, 9)$ with no gradient

2. Write down and then simplify the equations of the following lines:
   (a) through $(2, 3)$ and $(4, 6)$
   (b) through $(-1, 3)$ and $(3, 6)$
   (c) through $(0, 3)$ and $(-3, 0)$
   (d) through $(-1, -3)$ and $(-6, 4)$
   (e) through $(9, 7)$ and $(11, 7)$
   (f) through $(-3, 5)$ and $(-3, 10)$

3. Find (where possible) the gradients of the following lines:
   (a) $y = 5 - 7x$
   (b) $y - 3x + 4 = 0$
   (c) $2x + 3y = 9$
   (d) $x - 5y + 8 = 0$
   (e) $4 + x = 0$
   (f) $y - 2 = 0$

3.4 PARALLEL AND PERPENDICULAR LINES

Are the lines $3x + 4y = 7$ and $3x + 4y - 11 = 0$ parallel to each other? Yes, because when we calculate the gradients, the constant numbers 7 and 11 do not enter into our calculations, and in other respects the two equations agree.

What about $3x+4y = 7$ and $3(x-769)+4(y-985) = 0$? They too must be parallel, because the second one will simplify to $3x+4y = $ constant. Note too that the second of these lines automatically passes through the point $(769, 985)$, since if you substitute 769 for x and 985 for y in the equation, the left-hand side plainly does equal zero.

More generally, $ax+by = c$ and $a(x-h)+b(y-k) = 0$ will be parallel, and the second will pass through (h, k).

EXAMPLE Find the equations of the lines parallel to $5x-2y = 8$ through (a) $(4, 11)$, (b) $(3, -1)$.

(a) The equation is $5(x-4)-2(y-11) = 0$, since this line has the correct gradient, and plainly does pass through $(4, 11)$. Multiplying out the brackets, we obtain

$$5x-20-2y+22=0 \Rightarrow 5x-2y+2 = 0,$$

which is a simplified version of the equation.

(b) The equation is $5(x-3)-2[y-(-1)] = 0$,

i.e. $5(x-3)-2(y+1) = 0 \Rightarrow 5x-2y = 17$.

Now consider the lines $3x+4y = 7$ and $4x-3y = 12$. These are obviously not parallel, since the gradient of the first is $-3/4$, whereas the gradient of the second is $4/3$. But the product of these gradients is -1, and so the two lines are perpendicular.

Similarly, $3x+4y = 7$ and $4(x-769)-3(y-985) = 0$ will be perpendicular, and—as before—the second obviously passes through $(769, 985)$.

More generally, $ax+by = c$ and $b(x-h)-a(y-k) = 0$ will be perpendicular, and the second passes through (h, k).

EXAMPLE Find the line through $(3, -1)$ that is perpendicular to $5x-2y = 8$.

We simply take the equation $5x-2y = 8$ and modify it:

    ignore the constant term (replace 8 by 0)

    interchange the coefficients of x and y (5 and -2)

    change the sign of one of them (replace -2 by $+2$)

    replace x by $(x-3)$ and y by $(y+1)$

Thus we get $2(x-3)+5(y+1) = 0 \Rightarrow 2x+5y = 1$.

EXERCISE 3D

In each case, find the lines through the given point that are (a) parallel and (b) perpendicular to the given line, and simplify both equations.

1. $(1, 5)$ $7x + 9y = 15$
2. $(-4, 2)$ $6x + y = 3$
3. $(12, 10)$ $3x - 4y = -6$
4. $(-3, -8)$ $5y - 8x + 16 = 0$
5. $(0, 0)$ $3x = 5 + y$
6. $(7, 9)$ $x + y = 0$

3.5 DIVIDING A LINE-SEGMENT IN A GIVEN RATIO

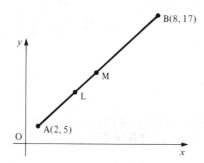

Fig. 3.5

Where is the point M dividing the line-segment AB in the ratio $1:1$, i.e. the mid-point of AB?

$$\mathbf{AB} = \mathbf{b} - \mathbf{a} = \begin{pmatrix} 8 \\ 17 \end{pmatrix} - \begin{pmatrix} 2 \\ 5 \end{pmatrix} = \begin{pmatrix} 6 \\ 12 \end{pmatrix}$$

Thus

$$\mathbf{AM} = \frac{1}{2}\begin{pmatrix} 6 \\ 12 \end{pmatrix} = \begin{pmatrix} 3 \\ 6 \end{pmatrix}$$

and

$$\mathbf{m} = \mathbf{a} + \begin{pmatrix} 3 \\ 6 \end{pmatrix} = \begin{pmatrix} 2 \\ 5 \end{pmatrix} + \begin{pmatrix} 3 \\ 6 \end{pmatrix} = \begin{pmatrix} 5 \\ 11 \end{pmatrix}$$

So M's coordinates are $(5, 11)$.

More generally, $\mathbf{m} = \mathbf{a} + \frac{1}{2}(\mathbf{b} - \mathbf{a}) = \mathbf{a} + \frac{1}{2}\mathbf{b} - \frac{1}{2}\mathbf{a} = \dfrac{\mathbf{a} + \mathbf{b}}{2}$.

Where also is the point L dividing the line-segment in the ratio $1:2$, i.e. one of the two points of trisection (see figure 3.5)?

$$\mathbf{AL} = \frac{1}{3}\begin{pmatrix} 6 \\ 12 \end{pmatrix} = \begin{pmatrix} 2 \\ 4 \end{pmatrix}, \text{ and so } \mathbf{l} = \mathbf{a} + \begin{pmatrix} 2 \\ 4 \end{pmatrix} = \begin{pmatrix} 2 \\ 5 \end{pmatrix} + \begin{pmatrix} 2 \\ 4 \end{pmatrix} = \begin{pmatrix} 4 \\ 9 \end{pmatrix}.$$

Therefore L is at $(4, 9)$.

If N is the other point of trisection,

then $\mathbf{n} = \begin{pmatrix} 2 \\ 5 \end{pmatrix} + \frac{2}{3}\begin{pmatrix} 6 \\ 12 \end{pmatrix} = \begin{pmatrix} 2 \\ 5 \end{pmatrix} + \begin{pmatrix} 4 \\ 8 \end{pmatrix} = \begin{pmatrix} 6 \\ 13 \end{pmatrix}.$

Therefore N is at $(6, 13)$.

EXAMPLE Find the point P dividing the line-segment between C$(-3, 2)$ and D$(13, -6)$ in the ratio $3:5$.

$$\text{P's position vector } \mathbf{p} = \mathbf{c} + \tfrac{3}{8}(\mathbf{d}-\mathbf{c})$$
$$= \mathbf{c} + \tfrac{3}{8}\mathbf{d} - \tfrac{3}{8}\mathbf{c}$$
$$= \frac{5\mathbf{c} + 3\mathbf{d}}{8}$$
$$= \frac{5}{8}\begin{pmatrix} -3 \\ 2 \end{pmatrix} + \frac{3}{8}\begin{pmatrix} 13 \\ -6 \end{pmatrix} = \frac{1}{8}\begin{pmatrix} -15+39 \\ 10-18 \end{pmatrix} = \begin{pmatrix} 3 \\ -1 \end{pmatrix}$$

Therefore P is at $(3, -1)$.

3.6 CIRCUMCENTRE, ORTHOCENTRE, AND CENTROID OF A TRIANGLE

The *circumcentre* of a triangle is the centre of the (only) circle which passes through the vertices. Clearly it is the same distance from all three vertices, and therefore must lie on the three mediators of the sides.

If we are given the coordinates of the vertices, then we can find the circumcentre. For example, let us find the circumcentre C of the triangle P$(-6, 10)$, Q$(8, 12)$, R$(2, -6)$.

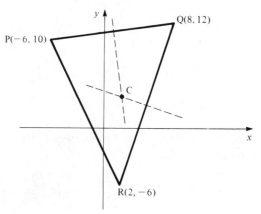

Fig. 3.6

C lies on the mediator (i.e. the perpendicular bisector) of PQ, and so we start by finding the equation of this line.

Now
$$\mathbf{PQ} = \mathbf{q} - \mathbf{p} = \begin{pmatrix} 14 \\ 2 \end{pmatrix}$$

so the gradient of PQ is $2/14 = 1/7$, and the perpendicular gradient is -7. Also the mid-point of PQ is $(1, 11)$. So the required equation is

$$y - 11 = -7(x - 1) \Rightarrow y - 11 = -7x + 7 \Rightarrow y + 7x = 18 \qquad \mathbf{1}$$

Similarly, the mediator of QR has gradient $-1/3$, and passes through $(5, 3)$: so its equation is

$$y - 3 = -\tfrac{1}{3}(x - 5) \Rightarrow 3y - 9 = -x + 5 \Rightarrow 3y + x = 14 \qquad \mathbf{2}$$

By subtracting **2** from $3 \times \mathbf{1}$ we obtain $20x = 40 \Rightarrow x = 2$, and then substitution in **1** gives $y = 4$.

Therefore the circumcentre C is at $(2, 4)$.

The *orthocentre* is where the three altitudes of a triangle meet (an altitude being the perpendicular from a vertex to the opposite side).

For example, let us find the orthocentre H of the same triangle PQR.

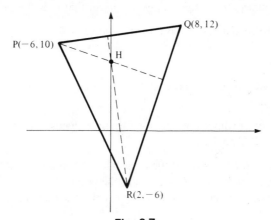

Fig. 3.7

H lies on the altitude through R, which of course is parallel to the mediator of PQ, found above. So the equation of this altitude is

$$y - (-6) = -7(x - 2) \Rightarrow y + 6 = -7x + 14 \Rightarrow y + 7x = 8 \qquad \mathbf{3}$$

Similarly, the equation of the altitude through P is

$$y - 10 = -\tfrac{1}{3}[x - (-6)] \Rightarrow 3y - 30 = -x - 6 \Rightarrow 3y + x = 24 \qquad \mathbf{4}$$

Solving **3** and **4** simultaneously, we find that H is at $(0, 8)$.

Confirm for yourself that QH is perpendicular to RP.

The *centroid* is where the three medians of a triangle meet (a median being the line joining a vertex to the mid-point of the opposite side). The fact that the medians do all pass through a common point, in other words that they are concurrent, is demonstrated in the following exercise.

The centroid has one quite important application in physics. If a triangular object is made of thin uniformly dense material, then the object's centre of mass, and also its centre of gravity, will lie at the centroid of the triangle.

EXERCISE 3E

1. Find the two points of trisection of the line-segment between $P(4, -7)$ and $Q(-1, 13)$.

2. The vertices of a triangle are $A(5, 7)$, $B(-1, 3)$, and $C(2, 8)$. Sketch the figure. Calculate the position of N, the mid-point of AB, and then the position of G, the point dividing CN in the ratio $2:1$.

3. Sketch the triangle DEF, where D, E, F are $(7, 3)$, $(7, 7)$, and $(-11, 3)$ respectively. Find the mediators of DE and DF, and deduce the position of C, the circumcentre of the triangle. Confirm that C is the mid-point of EF.

4. Find the mediators of AB and BC, where A, B, C are $(-12, 22)$, $(24, -2)$, and $(-26, -12)$ respectively. Deduce the coordinates of the circumcentre of the triangle.

5. What are the coordinates of the orthocentre of the triangle DEF defined in question 3?

6. Find the orthocentre of the triangle whose vertices are at $(-1, -4)$, $(-10, -1)$, $(-6, 1)$.

7. Find the equations of all three medians of the triangle ABC, where A is $(1, 3)$, B is $(3, 7)$, and C is $(11, -1)$. Find the point of intersection of two of them, by solving their equations simultaneously. Check that this point satisfies the third equation.

8. **a, b, c** are the position vectors of A, B, C respectively. What are the position vectors of (i) the mid-point L of BC,

   and   (ii) the point dividing AL in the ratio $2:1$?

   Answer the same two questions in respect of the mid-point M of CA, and the mid-point N of AB.

   Deduce that the three medians of any triangle ABC do concur, and that the position vector of G, the triangle's centroid, is given by $\mathbf{g} = \frac{1}{3}(\mathbf{a} + \mathbf{b} + \mathbf{c})$.

9. Using the result of question 8, write down the centroid of the triangle PQR, where P, Q, R are $(1, 2)$, $(4, -1)$, $(-2, 2)$ respectively.

4

CALCULUS I

4.1 GRADIENT OF A CHORD OF A CURVE

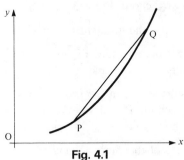

Fig. 4.1

Figure 4.1 shows a chord PQ joining two points P and Q on the graph of $y = f(x)$, where f is some typical function. It is convenient to use small letters for the x-coordinates of points: so that $x = p$ at P, and $x = q$ at Q.

As an example, the curve might be $y = x^2$, and the two points might be P(3, 9) and Q(5, 25). In that case, the gradient of the chord PQ would equal $(25-9)/(5-3) = 16/2 = 8$.

More generally, the gradient of PQ is $\dfrac{f(q)-f(p)}{(q-p)}$.

In practice, as we shall see, $(q-p)$ is very often a factor of $f(q)-f(p)$, and so can be cancelled. In the special case when $f(x) \equiv x^2$, for instance, $f(q)-f(p) = q^2-p^2 = (q-p)(q+p)$, and so the gradient of the chord reduces to $(q+p)$.

EXAMPLE Find the gradient of any chord PQ of $y = x^2+x$.

In this case, we define $f(x) \equiv x^2+x$.
Now at P, $x = p$ and $y = f(p) = p^2+p$,
and at Q, $x = q$ and $y = f(q) = q^2+q$.

So
$$\begin{aligned}
f(q)-f(p) &= (q^2+q)-(p^2+p) \\
&= (q^2-p^2)+(q-p) \\
&= (q-p)(q+p)+(q-p) = (q-p)(q+p+1)
\end{aligned}$$

Therefore the gradient of the chord PQ equals $(q+p+1)$.

49

EXERCISE 4A

1. Write down the gradient of the following chords of $y = x^2$:

(a) the chord joining $(2, 4)$ and $(8, 64)$

(b) the chord joining $(-3, 9)$ and $(3, 9)$

(c) the chord joining $(-5, 25)$ and $(7, 49)$

2. If $f(x) \equiv 3x - 4$, use the method of the example on page 49 to confirm that the gradient of any 'chord' PQ is 3.

3. If $f(x) \equiv 5x^2$, find the gradient of any chord PQ of $y = 5x^2$.

4. Find the gradient of any chord PQ of $y = x^2 + 3x - 4$, and that of the chord joining the points at $x = 2$ and $x = -5$.

5. Comparing results so far, in the text and in questions 2 to 4, write down the gradient of any chord PQ of $y = 5x^2 + 3x - 4$. If you are unable to do so, use the full method again.

6. Find the gradient of the chord joining the points at $x = 4$ and $x = 4.0001$ on the curve $y = x^3$.

4.2 DIFFERENTIATION

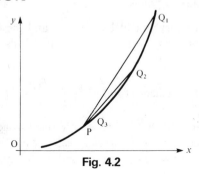

Fig. 4.2

Figure 4.2 shows the graph of $y = x^2$. We found in section 4.1 that the gradient of any chord PQ of this particular curve is $(q + p)$. Suppose now that we allow Q to come closer and closer to P. The figure shows this happening, with Q approaching P via three positions: $Q_1 \rightarrow Q_2 \rightarrow Q_3$. If we take p to be 3, and q successively 3.1, 3.01 and 3.001, then we obtain gradients 6.1, 6.01 and 6.001. The chord PQ_3 is virtually indistinguishable from the curve, and it seems reasonable to guess that the gradient of the curve itself *at* P is 6 precisely.

This conclusion is confirmed by a study of figure 4.3, showing once again the graph of $y = x^2$ and the point $P(3, 9)$. Since Q is to the right of P, $q > 3$ and so the gradient of PQ is greater than 6. Similarly, since R is to the left of P, $r < 3$ and so the gradient of PR is less than 6. Thus every single chord through P has a gradient either greater than 6 or less than 6. What then is the line

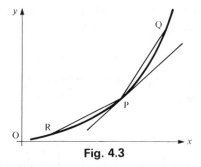

Fig. 4.3

through P with a gradient of 6 precisely? It cannot be a chord, and must therefore be the *tangent* at P. Therefore the gradient of the tangent at P equals 6, and our guess that the gradient of the curve itself at P equalled 6 is confirmed.

More generally, we have the result that the gradient at any point of $y = x^2$ is twice the x-coordinate. Just as the letter y is used to denote the *height* of a point on a curve, so y' (pronounced y dash) is used to denote the *gradient* at that point. If y is given by a formula, so too will y' be. We can now express our result in symbols:

$$y = x^2 \Rightarrow y' = 2x$$

An alternative way of saying the same thing is:

$$f(x) \equiv x^2 \Rightarrow f'(x) \equiv 2x$$

f' is called the derived function of f, and $f'(x)$ the derivative of $f(x)$. The process of finding them is called *differentiation.*

So now we know the derivative of x^2, namely $2x$, and we can apply our knowledge without further ado. For instance, let us find the gradient of $y = x^2$ at $(-10, 100)$.

$y = x^2 \Rightarrow y' = 2x$, and so the gradient at $x = -10$ equals -20.

In question 5 of exercise 4A, we found that the gradient of any chord PQ of $y = 5x^2 + 3x - 4$ equalled $5(q+p) + 3$. When Q is allowed to come closer and closer to P (and q then obviously gets closer and closer to p), the gradient becomes indefinitely close to $5(2p) + 3$. This shows that the gradient of the curve itself at P must equal $10p + 3$. In other words, $y = 5x^2 + 3x - 4$ implies that $y' = 5(2x) + 3$. So if you know the derivative of x^2 (which is $2x$, as we have already discovered) and also know the derivative of $3x - 4$ (which is obviously 3 — see question 2 of exercise 4A), then you can easily find the derivative of $5x^2 + 3x - 4$. The process is as follows:

$$(5x^2 + 3x - 4)' = 5(x^2)' + (3x - 4)' = 5(2x) + 3 = 10x + 3$$

Note very carefully that on differentiating

$$x^2 \text{ becomes } 2x \quad \text{and} \quad mx + c \text{ becomes } m$$

EXAMPLE (a) Differentiate $4x^2 - 2x$, and find the value of the derivative when $x = \frac{1}{4}$.

(b) Find the gradient of $y = 3x^2 - 7x + 4$ at $(-2, 30)$.

(a) $f(x) \equiv 4x^2 - 2x \Rightarrow f'(x) \equiv 4(2x) - 2 = 8x - 2$; so $f'(\frac{1}{4}) = 0$.

(b) $y = 3x^2 - 7x + 4 \Rightarrow y' = 3(2x) - 7 = 6x - 7$.

So the gradient at $x = -2$ equals -19.

EXERCISE 4B

1. Differentiate $f(x)$ in each case, and find the gradient of $y = f(x)$ at the given point:

   (a) $x^2 + 6x - 3$ $(3, 24)$

   (b) $2x^2 + 7x + 5$ $(-1, 0)$

   (c) $8x - 3x^2$ $(2, 4)$

   (d) $10x^2 + 12$ $(1, 22)$

2. In each case, first multiply out the brackets, and then differentiate:

   (a) $(x + 7)(x + 2)$

   (b) $(3x - 4)(2x + 7)$

   (c) $(5 - 4x)(1 - x)$

   (d) $(3x - 1)^2$

3. What are the x-coordinates of the points where the curve $y = (x + 4)(x - 3)$ cuts the x-axis? Now find the gradient of the curve at each of these points, and show that the angle between the curve and the x-axis is the same at both.

4. Find the gradient of $y = 6 + 5x - 3x^2$ at $(1, 8)$. Then find the coordinates of the point on the curve where its direction is perpendicular to its direction at $(1, 8)$.

5. Find where $y = 2x + 3$ meets $y = x^2$. Then find the gradient of $y = x^2$ at these points of intersection.

6. At what point is the gradient of $y = 5x - x^2$ zero? Draw a rough sketch to illustrate this. Does this tell you the greatest value of $5x - x^2$ (if x can take any value)?

4.3 FURTHER DIFFERENTIATION

We have already used the fact that $q^2 - p^2 = (q - p)(q + p)$. By simple multiplication, you can easily verify (and you should do so) that similar results apply when higher powers are involved. For instance

$$q^3 - p^3 = (q - p)(q^2 + qp + p^2)$$
$$q^4 - p^4 = (q - p)(q^3 + q^2 p + qp^2 + p^3)$$

Returning to the method explained in section 4.1, and making use of the facts just established, we see

that if $f(x) \equiv x^3$ then the gradient of PQ is $(q^2 + qp + p^2)$

and if $f(x) \equiv x^4$ then the gradient of PQ is $(q^3 + q^2 p + qp^2 + p^3)$.

If q is now allowed to get closer and closer to p, the first gradient becomes $3p^2$, and the second becomes $4p^3$. In other words,

<u>the derivative of x^3 is $3x^2$</u>   and   <u>the derivative of x^4 is $4x^3$</u>

It is not difficult to guess (correctly) that the derivative of x^5 is $5x^4$, and so on. The general result is that

<u>the derivative of x^n is nx^{n-1}</u>

an exceptionally important fact that should be remembered.

EXAMPLE Differentiate $4x^8 - 11x^3 + 3x + 7$. Hence find the gradient of the curve $y = 4x^8 - 11x^3 + 3x + 7$ at $(1, 3)$, and then the equation of the tangent at this point.

Let $f(x) \equiv 4x^8 - 11x^3 + 3x + 7$

Then $f'(x) \equiv 4(8x^7) - 11(3x^2) + 3 = 32x^7 - 33x^2 + 3$

Therefore the gradient at $(1, 3)$ is $f'(1) = 2$, and so the tangent there is $y - 3 = 2(x - 1)$, i.e. $y = 2x + 1$.

EXAMPLE Differentiate $5/x$. Hence find the equation of the normal to the curve $y = 5/x$ at the point $(5, 1)$.

If we wish to apply the general result stated above, we must first express $1/x$ as a power, i.e. as x^{-1}. We then conclude (taking $n = -1$) that the derivative of $1/x$ is $-1(x^{-2}) = -1/x^2$. Hence the derivative of $5/x$ is $-5/x^2$.

So the gradient of the curve at $(5, 1)$ equals $-5/25 = -1/5$. Therefore the gradient of the normal at this point ('normal' means perpendicular) equals $+5$, and so the equation of the normal is $y - 1 = 5(x - 5)$, i.e. $y = 5x - 24$.

In this example we have simply assumed without proof that the rule for differentiating powers is valid for $n = -1$. Although it is difficult to prove the universal validity of the rule, its validity for $n = -1$ can be established quite easily.

To do so, we return to the fundamental method explained in section 4.1, applying it to a chord PQ of the curve $y = 1/x$.

Let $f(x) \equiv 1/x$.

Then
$$f(q) - f(p) = 1/q - 1/p$$
$$= p/pq - q/pq$$
$$= (p-q)/pq = -(q-p)/pq$$

So the gradient of the chord reduces to $-1/pq$. As q gets closer and closer to p, this becomes $-1/p^2$.

Thus we have proved that $y = 1/x \Rightarrow y' = -1/x^2 = -1x^{-2}$.

Although we are not yet in a position to prove them, it may be sensible to mention here two other results that are well worth remembering:

provided x is measured in radians,

the derivative of $\sin x$ is $+\cos x$, and the derivative of $\cos x$ is $-\sin x$.

EXERCISE 4C

1. Differentiate $f(x)$ in each case, and find the gradient of $y = f(x)$ at the given point:

   (a) x^5 $(2, 32)$

   (b) $3x^3 + 2x - 1$ $(-1, -6)$

   (c) $1 + x + x^2/2 + x^3/6 + x^4/24$ $(6, 115)$

2. Differentiate the following:

   (a) $x(x+7)(x+2)$

   (b) $(x+1)^3$

   (c) $5(x^2 - 1)(x^2 + 8)$

3. What is the gradient of $y = x^2 + 2/x$ at $(2, 5)$, and what is the equation of the tangent there?

4. At what two points is the gradient of $y = x^3$ equal to 12?

5. At what point on $y = 4x^2 + 1/x$ is the gradient zero? What is the equation of the tangent at this point? Sketch the curve for positive values of x.

6. What are the equations of the tangent and the normal to the curve $y = 3x^2 - 4x + 5$ at the point $(1, 4)$?

7. At what three points is the gradient of $y = (x^2 - 1)^2$ equal to zero? Draw a rough sketch of the graph. What is the largest value of $(x^2 - 1)^2$ if $-1 \leqslant x \leqslant +1$?

8. Show that $y = x^3 + x$ and $y = x$ have just one point in common, and that they have the same gradient at that point. What does this tell us about their relationship there?

9. Sketch the graph of $y = \sin x + \cos x$ for values of x between 0 and π, where x is measured in radians. Find the derivative of $\sin x + \cos x$, and show that $y = y' = 1$ when $x = 0$.

4.4 THE CHAIN RULE

The basic method of calculating a derivative involves finding the gradient of a chord (and seeing what happens as one end of the chord is allowed to come closer and closer to the other end). The method therefore relies on the definition:

$$\text{gradient of chord} = \frac{\text{difference in } y}{\text{difference in } x}$$

For this reason, mathematicians also use the expressions

$$\frac{dy}{dx} \quad \text{and} \quad dy/dx \quad \text{(pronounced d } y \text{ by d } x\text{)}$$

to denote the derivative when y is given as a function of x.

Do not be misled by the appearance of these expressions: dy/dx is by no means an ordinary fraction like $2/5$ or ay/bx, since the dy and the dx have no separate meaning, nor would it make sense to cancel the top d and the bottom d. The notation is nevertheless very useful because the two variables are both mentioned explicitly, which can be important (especially in a problem involving several variables).

For instance, the quantity V might be given by two distinct formulae, the first in terms of the variable r, the second in terms of the variable t. Perhaps $V = 4r^3$ and also $V = t^2$. Then we can say that $dV/dr = 12r^2$ and that $dV/dt = 2t$; the first is a formula for the gradient of the graph of V against r, the second for the gradient of the graph of V against t.

EXAMPLE Find dA/du, du/dt, and dA/dt, given that $A = u^2$ and $u = 5t + 3$.

The formula $A = u^2$ tells us that $dA/du = 2u$, while the formula $u = 5t + 3$ tells us that $du/dt = 5$. To find dA/dt, the obvious approach is to use the formula giving A in terms of t, which of course is $A = (5t + 3)^2 = 25t^2 + 30t + 9$. So $dA/dt = 50t + 30$.

You should note that

$$\begin{aligned} dA/dt &= 10(5t + 3) \\ &= 2(5t + 3) \times 5 \\ &= 2u \times 5 \end{aligned}$$

Hence, in this case,
$$\frac{dA}{dt} = \frac{dA}{du} \times \frac{du}{dt}$$

This is an example of the very useful *chain rule*, which runs as follows:

> If one quantity (say v) depends on a second quantity (say u),
> which in turn depends on a third quantity (say t), then
>
> $$\frac{dv}{dt} = \frac{dv}{du} \times \frac{du}{dt}$$

The chain rule is easy to remember and apply, since it *looks* just as if one were simply cancelling tops and bottoms of fractions.

EXAMPLE The length z of the edge of a cube is given by the formula $z = at + b$, where a and b are constants, and t is the time. Find dV/dt, where V is the volume of the cube.

We have $z = at + b \Rightarrow dz/dt = a$, and $V = z^3 \Rightarrow dV/dz = 3z^2$.

So
$$\frac{dV}{dt} = \frac{dV}{dz} \times \frac{dz}{dt}$$

$$= 3z^2 \times a = 3az^2 = 3a(at + b)^2$$

EXAMPLE Differentiate $(2x + 7)^3$.

Let $u = 2x + 7$ and $y = u^3$: then $y = (2x + 7)^3$.

So
$$\frac{dy}{dx} = \frac{dy}{du} \times \frac{du}{dx}$$

$$= 3u^2 \times 2 = 6(2x + 7)^2$$

Therefore the derivative of $(2x + 7)^3$ is $6(2x + 7)^2$. This formula gives the gradient at any point on the graph of $y = (2x + 7)^3$.

EXAMPLE Differentiate $\sin 8\theta$, where θ is measured in radians.

Let $u = 8\theta$, and $y = \sin u = \sin 8\theta$.

Then
$$\frac{dy}{d\theta} = \frac{dy}{du} \times \frac{du}{d\theta}$$

$$= \cos u \times 8 = 8 \cos u = 8 \cos 8\theta$$

Therefore the derivative of $\sin 8\theta$ is $8 \cos 8\theta$.

The chain rule also makes it possible to find dy/dx when y is defined not by means of a formula that gives y explicitly in terms of x, such as $y = x^2$, but by means of an equation such as $x^2 + y^2 = 25$, which is said to give y *implicitly* in terms of x.

EXAMPLE Find dy/dx given that $x^2 + y^2 = 25$. Hence calculate the gradient of the curve $x^2 + y^2 = 25$ at the point $(3, 4)$.

Let $u = y^2$.

Then
$$\frac{du}{dx} = \frac{du}{dy} \times \frac{dy}{dx} = 2y \times y'$$

So $\quad x^2 + y^2 = 25 \Rightarrow d(x^2)/dx + d(y^2)/dx = 0 \Rightarrow 2x + 2yy' = 0$

Therefore $dy/dx = -x/y$.

Thus the gradient at $(3, 4)$ is $-3/4$.

EXERCISE 4D

1. Find dy/dx if   (a) $y = x^6$,   (b) $y = (2x + 3)^2/x$.

2. If $z = t^3$ what is dz/dt? And if $x = y^3$, what is dx/dy?

3. Find dy/dx if $y = x^3 + 3/x$. Show that $dy/dx > 0$ for $x > 1$. Sketch the curve for positive values of x.

4. Find dy/dt given that: (a) $y = u^2, u = 5 + t$ (b) $y = 5 + u, u = t^2$

5. Differentiate the following:
    (a) $(5x - 2)^4$
    (b) $(x^2 + 3x - 4)^2$
    (c) $1/(2x - 3)$

6. Find dy/dx if $y = \cos^2 5x$ and x is measured in radians. (Hint: let $v = 5x$, $u = \cos v$, and $y = u^2$, and use an extended version of the chain rule)

7. Find dy/dx in each case, and calculate the gradient of the curve at the given point:
    (a) $x^2 - y^2 = 8$ $(3, 1)$
    (b) $y^2 = x$ $(4, -2)$
    (c) $x^3 + y^3 = 9$ $(1, 2)$

4.5 SMALL INCREMENTS

Differentiating 'from first principles' involves finding the gradient of a chord whose ends are allowed to become closer and closer together. Once we have acquired a stock of derivatives, this basic principle of calculus can be turned back to front.

If the points P and Q on the graph of $y = f(x)$ are fairly close together (figure 4.4), then the gradient of the chord PQ will be approximately equal to the gradient of the curve itself at P. So we have this useful rule:

$$\frac{f(a+h)-f(a)}{h} \approx f'(a)$$

i.e. $f(a+h) \approx f(a)+hf'(a)$ provided h is fairly small.

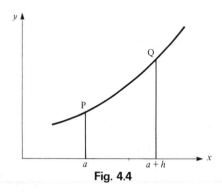

Fig. 4.4

EXAMPLE Find the approximate value of x^2+3x when $x = 2.1$.

Let $f(x) \equiv x^2+3x$: then $f'(x) \equiv 2x+3$.

Then choosing $a = 2$ and $h = 0.1$, we have

$$f(2.1) \approx f(2)+0.1 \times f'(2)$$

$$= 10+0.1 \times 7$$

$$= 10.7 \quad \text{(the exact value is 10.71)}$$

In this calculation, we chose $a = 2$ and $h = 0.1$. We could have given a and h different values, of course, but 2 and 0.1 are the best on this occasion — the crucial thing is to make sure that a has a *convenient* value and that h has a *small* value.

For instance, we could unwisely choose $a = 1$ and $h = 1.1$; then $f(2.1) \approx f(1)+1.1 \times f'(1) = 4+1.1 \times 5 = 9.5$, but this is a very inaccurate result, since 1.1 is far too large.

Now look at figure 4.5. PN and NQ are often denoted by the expressions δx and δy respectively, where δx is taken to mean 'a small increment in x' and δy likewise in y. The rule given above can then be expressed as follows, in a form that is also very easy to remember:

$$\frac{\delta y}{\delta x} \approx \frac{dy}{dx} \quad \text{i.e. } \delta y \approx \delta x \times y' \quad \text{provided } \delta x \text{ is fairly small}$$

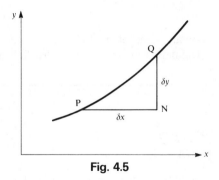

Fig. 4.5

EXAMPLE Find the approximate value of 1.005^{10}.

Let $y = x^{10}$: then $y' = 10x^9$.

Now when $x = 1$, $y = 1$ and $y' = 10$. So taking $\delta x = 0.005$, we have

$$\delta y \approx \delta x \times y'$$

$$= 0.005 \times 10 = 0.05$$

and so $1.005^{10} = y + \delta y \approx 1 + 0.05 = 1.05$.

This approximate result compares quite well with the exact result, which is between 1.0511 and 1.0512.

The δ notation can naturally be used when the variables are letters other than x and y, as the next example illustrates.

EXAMPLE Prove that if the radius of a sphere decreases by 2%, the volume will decrease by about 6%.

The volume of a sphere is given by the formula $V = \frac{4}{3}\pi r^3$, where r is the radius. So $V' = 4\pi r^2$.

In this case, δr is a negative increment, since we are told that r decreases, and in fact $\delta r = -2\% \times r$.

Therefore $\delta V \approx \delta r \times V'$

$$= (-2\% \times r) \times (4\pi r^2)$$

$$= -2\% \times 4\pi r^3$$

$$= -6\% \times V$$

Hence V does indeed decrease by approximately 6%.

EXERCISE 4E

1. Find the approximate value of the following expressions for the given values of x, using the techniques of this section; also find a more exact value using your calculator.

   (a) $3x^2 + 8x + 7$, $x = 10.3$

   (b) $x^4 - 5x$, $x = 3.2$

   (c) x^3, $x = 999$ (choose $a = 1000$, $h = -1$)

   (d) $1/x$, $x = 5.001$

2. Find the approximate increment in the area A of a circle produced by a small increment in the radius r, and justify your result geometrically.

3. A quantity Q is given by the formula $Q = 5t^2$, where t is the time. If measurement of time is subject to an error of up to $p\%$, where p is quite small, show that the calculated value of Q may be in error by up to about $2p\%$.

4.6 INCREASING AND DECREASING FUNCTIONS

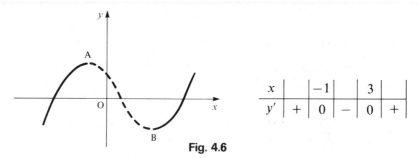

Fig. 4.6

Figure 4.6 shows the graph of $y = f(x)$ for some function f. It might be a cubic function, such as $y = x^3 - 3x^2 - 9x + 3$. On the dashed section AB, the gradient y' is clearly negative, and on the other sections it is positive. At A the gradient is 0, and also at B. If f is the cubic suggested above, then

$$y' = 3x^2 - 6x - 9 = 3(x+1)(x-3)$$

The gradient is therefore zero when $x = -1$ and when $x = 3$, and it changes sign at these values. We can illustrate this by means of a table (see figure 4.6), and can compare this table with the graph. Indeed the table would have enabled us to sketch the graph. We should need additional information about the positioning of A and B, which is easy to obtain using the formula for y: A is $(-1, 8)$ and B is $(3, -24)$. We can now see that the graph in figure 4.6 is not very accurate, but it is none the less useful as a sketch. The function is said to be *increasing* to the left of A and to the right of B (i.e. when $x < -1$ and when $x > 3$), but *decreasing* between A and B (i.e. when $-1 < x < 3$).

EXAMPLE For which positive values of x is $x + 1/x$

(a) decreasing,   (b) increasing?

If $\qquad y = x + 1/x$, then $dy/dx = 1 - 1/x^2 = (x^2 - 1)/x^2$

$$= (x - 1)(x + 1)/x^2$$

Now x^2 and $(x + 1)$ are positive for all $x > 0$, but $(x - 1)$ flips sign from negative to positive as x passes through the value $+1$. Therefore y is decreasing when $x < 1$, increasing when $x > 1$.

EXERCISE 4F

1. If $y = x^3 - 3x$, find y', and complete the table. What are the values of y at the two points where $y' = 0$? Sketch the graph. For what values of x is y decreasing?

x		?		?	
y'	?	0	?	0	?

2. As in the previous question, sketch the following graphs, and say when the functions are increasing or decreasing:

   (a) $y = x^2 + 4$,   (b) $y = x^4 - 2x^2$,   (c) $y = x^2 + 2/x$ $(x > 0)$

3. A projectile's height h m above the ground t s after lift-off is given by $h = 20t - 4.9t^2$. Find dh/dt, and say for what period of time the height is increasing. What is the greatest height achieved?

4. The cost C of a voyage is given by $C = 100v^2 + 200\,000/v$, where v is the ship's speed. Find dC/dv, and say for what values of v the cost C is increasing, and for what values it is decreasing. What is the most economical speed?

4.7 MAXIMA AND MINIMA

The cubic function illustrated in figure 4.6 has two so-called turning points. From left to right, it is increasing up to $A(-1, 8)$, then decreasing from A to $B(3, -24)$, and then increasing again. A and B are called *turning points*, because the graph in a sense turns a corner at them. A is a *maximum*, and 8 a maximum value. B is a *minimum*, and -24 a minimum value.

Notice that a maximum is only a local maximum, and a minimum only a local minimum. The greatest and least values may be something quite different, depending on the domain (the domain is the set of x-values under consideration). Suppose for instance that in the present case we restrict ourselves to the domain $0 \leqslant x \leqslant 4$. Then the least value is indeed -24, but the greatest value is 3, achieved at $x = 0$. To be sure of this, we need to check at the other end of the domain, where $x = 4$ and $y = -17$. If the domain were not restricted, then of course there would be no greatest or least value.

EXAMPLE Find the turning point of the function $x^2 - 6x + 7$, and classify it (i.e. as a maximum or minimum).

Let $f(x) \equiv x^2 - 6x + 7$: then $f'(x) \equiv 2x - 6 = 2(x - 3)$.

So $f'(x)$ flips sign at $x = 3$, which is therefore a turning point. Moreover since the sign changes from negative to positive, the turning point is a minimum, and the minimum value is $f(3) = -2$.

EXAMPLE Find the turning points of the function $x + 1/x$ (discussed in section 4.6), and classify them.

If $y = x + 1/x$, then $dy/dx = (x - 1)(x + 1)/x^2$.

We have already seen that dy/dx flips from negative to positive at $x = +1$, and so there is a minimum at $(1, 2)$. Similarly, dy/dx flips sign at $x = -1$, but now the change is from positive to negative, and so there is a maximum at $(-1, -2)$.

EXAMPLE Two numbers adding up to 100 are to be chosen so that their product is as great as possible. What is the optimum choice?

Let x be the first number: then plainly the second is $(100 - x)$.

If we denote the product by P, then

$$P = x(100 - x) = 100x - x^2 \Rightarrow P' = 100 - 2x = 2(50 - x)$$

We can see immediately that P' changes sign, from positive to negative, at $x = 50$. Moreover, since P is increasing for all $x < 50$ and decreasing for all $x > 50$, it is evident that the maximum value at $x = 50$ is in fact the greatest value. Therefore the first number should be 50, and the second number also 50.

You should sketch the graph of P against x, to confirm the validity of these arguments.

EXAMPLE An open box is to be made by cutting four equal squares from the corners of a large square of cardboard (6 by 6 m), and then bending up the sides (figure 4.7). What is the greatest capacity that can be achieved?

Fig. 4.7

Let x metres be the side of a cut-out square; then the base of the box will measure $(6-2x)$ by $(6-2x)$ m. It is obvious that x must be positive, and fairly obvious that the highest possible value of x is 3: so the domain is $0 \leqslant x \leqslant 3$.

Now the capacity, $C\,\text{m}^3$, of the box will be given by

$$C = x(6-2x)^2 = x(36-24x+4x^2)$$
$$= 36x - 24x^2 + 4x^3$$

Therefore
$$C' = 36 - 48x + 12x^2$$
$$= 12(3-4x+x^2)$$
$$= 12(1-x)(3-x)$$

The gradient is zero when $x = 1$ and when $x = 3$, and it changes sign at these places. Without much difficulty, we can draw a table and a sketch. There is a maximum at $x = 1$, and a minimum at $x = 3$. The domain is $0 \leqslant x \leqslant 3$, and neither $x = 0$ nor $x = 3$ will give a very satisfactory box (try them!). So the greatest capacity comes when $x = 1$, and equals $1 \times 4^2 = 16\,\text{m}^3$.

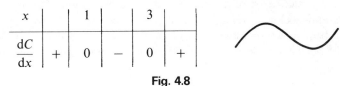

x		1		3	
$\dfrac{dC}{dx}$	+	0	−	0	+

Fig. 4.8

EXERCISE 4G

1. A farmer uses 40 m of fencing to enclose a rectangular area against a long straight wall, as in figure 4.9. Calling the two equal lengths of fencing x m, give the length of the third side of the rectangle, and show that the area $A = 40x - 2x^2\,\text{m}^2$. Find dA/dx, and hence find the greatest possible area of enclosure.

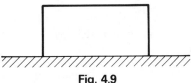

Fig. 4.9

2. Find the turning points of the three functions considered in question 2 of exercise 4F, and discuss their nature.

3. For what value of x will the volume of an open box (like the one considered in the example above) be greatest if the sheet of board measures 2 by 3 m?

4. A cylindrical can of base radius r and height h is open at one end. If it is made to have a surface area of π, show that $r^2 + 2rh = 1$. Express its volume $V = \pi r^2 h$ in terms of r alone. Find dV/dr, and hence the greatest possible volume.

4.8 THE SECOND DERIVATIVE

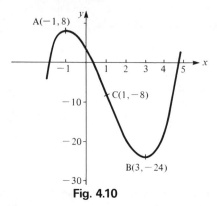

Fig. 4.10

Figure 4.10 gives a rather more accurate version of the graph that was only very roughly sketched in figure 4.6.

Imagine yourself travelling along the graph from west to east. Inspection shows that the western part of the graph is bending clockwise, whereas the eastern part bends anti-clockwise: for instance, at A the bend is clockwise (negative), while at B the bend is anti-clockwise (positive). We see this easily just by looking at the graph; but how could we obtain the same information directly from the equation $y = x^3 - 3x^2 - 9x + 3$?

Well, on the western part of the graph, the gradient of the graph is gradually decreasing: at the westernmost point shown in the figure, the gradient is positive and quite large; the gradient becomes less and less positive as we approach A; at A itself the gradient is zero; and then after A the gradient becomes negative. In other words, the gradient is a decreasing function of x on this western part of the graph, so the gradient of the gradient must be negative. Similarly, on the eastern part of the graph, the gradient is an increasing function of x, so the gradient of the gradient must be positive.

Now the gradient itself is denoted by y', and is given by the formula $y' = 3x^2 - 6x - 9$.

In similar fashion, the gradient of the gradient is denoted by y'', and is given by the formula $y'' = 6x - 6 = 6(x - 1)$.

When $x < 1$, therefore, $y'' < 0$ and the graph bends negatively, but when $x > 1$, $y'' > 0$ and the graph bends positively. We can illustrate this by means of a table; you should compare this table with the graph in figure 4.10 (and with the table in figure 4.6).

x		-1		1		3	
y'	$+$	0	$-$	$-$	$-$	0	$+$
y''	$-$	$-$	$-$	0	$+$	$+$	$+$

Fig. 4.11

In this way, we have discovered that the curvature of this particular graph changes sign at the point where $x = 1$, i.e. C in figure 4.10. Such a point is called a *point of inflection.*

EXAMPLE Find the points of inflection (if any) on the graph of $y = 5 + x + x^3$.

We need to find out where y'', the second derivative, changes sign, either from negative to positive or vice versa.

We have $$y' = 1 + 3x^2$$

and $$y'' = 6x$$

So the second derivative equals $6x$, which changes sign (from negative to positive, in fact) as x passes through the value 0. There is just one point of inflection, therefore, at $(0, 5)$.

You should sketch a graph of the function, marking in its point of inflection.

A *stationary point* on a graph is a point where the gradient is zero. So the graph of $y = 5 + x + x^3$ has no stationary points, since $y' = 1 + 3x^2$ is never zero. Check this fact on your sketch of the graph.

EXAMPLE Find the points of inflection and stationary points (if any) on the graph of
$$y = 8 + 15x + 6x^2 - x^3.$$

We have $$y' = 15 + 12x - 3x^2 = 3(5 + 4x - x^2) = 3(1 + x)(5 - x)$$

and $$y'' = 12 - 6x = 6(2 - x)$$

Thus y'' changes sign (from positive to negative) as x passes through the value 2. Therefore there is one point of inflection, at $(2, 54)$.

Also $y' = 0$ when $x = -1$ or 5, and so there are stationary points at $(-1, 0)$ and $(5, 108)$.

Furthermore, when $x = -1$, $y'' = 12 + 6 > 0$; so at $(-1, 0)$ the graph is bending positively (i.e. anti-clockwise), and therefore this stationary point must be a minimum.

Likewise, when $x = 5$, $y'' = 12 - 30 < 0$: so at $(5, 108)$ the graph is bending negatively (i.e. clockwise), and therefore this stationary point must be a maximum.

This example demonstrates a simple way to test whether a stationary point is a minimum or a maximum:

if $\underline{y'' > 0}$ at a stationary point, then it is a *minimum*

if $\underline{y'' < 0}$ at a stationary point, then it is a *maximum*

Warning If $\underline{y'' = 0}$, then this test does not work, and you must use the method for classifying stationary points explained in section 4.7.

Since the idea of differentiation is central to so many areas of mathematics, it is not surprising that there are numerous ways to denote the first and subsequent derivatives of a function, each of which has its own advantages. If $y = f(x) \equiv x^2 - 3x$, for instance, then the following all denote the (first) derivative:

$$y', \ y_1, \ f'(x), \ (x^2 - 3x)', \ \frac{dy}{dx}, \ \frac{d}{dx}(x^2 - 3x), \ D(x^2 - 3x)$$

There are similarly many ways to express the second derivative:

$$y'', \ y_2, \ f''(x), \ (x^2 - 3x)'', \ \frac{d^2y}{dx^2}, \ \frac{d^2}{dx^2}(x^2 - 3x), \ D^2(x^2 - 3x)$$

Nor are these the only notations in common use among mathematicians! We have already met dy/dx, which is particularly convenient to use when one is typing, and later on we shall meet $\dot{x}$, $\dot{y}$, etc., which are quick ways of writing dx/dt, dy/dt, etc.

EXERCISE 4H

1. If $y = x^3 - 3x^2$, find y' and y'', and construct a table as in figure 4.11. What are the values of y at the points where y' equals zero, and where y'' changes sign? Sketch the graph, marking in any stationary points and points of inflection.

2. Find the stationary points and points of inflection (if any) of the following, and sketch the graphs:

   (a) $y = x^2$,   (b) $y = x^3$,   (c) $y = x^4$.

3. If a cantilever OA is rigidly supported at O and carries a load uniformly distributed along its length L, then obviously it will bend under the load (or break if it is not strong enough). The deflection y at a distance x from O is given by the formula $y = k(x^4 - 4Lx^3 + 6L^2x^2)$, where k is a constant. Find the stationary points and points of inflection (if any), and sketch the graph for $0 \leqslant x \leqslant L$.

4. Find the points of inflection on the graph of $y = \sin x$, where x is measured in radians.

5 MECHANICS I

5.1 INTRODUCTION

Mechanics is the study of the connection between force and movement. The Greeks and the mediaeval scholars believed that nothing would or could move unless a force was pushing it. This view of things was finally discredited by Newton (1642–1727), who in 1687 published one of the most influential books of all time, *Philosophiae Naturalis Principia Mathematica*. In this great work, written in Latin, Newton explained his theories, including his three so-called laws of motion.

Newton's first law states that unless external forces compel it to do otherwise, every object remains at rest or else moves in a straight line at a constant speed (*corpus omne perseverare in statu suo quiescendi vel movendi uniformiter in directum, nisi quatenus a viribus impressis cogitur statum illum mutare*). In other words, a force is needed to produce or modify motion, but not necessarily to sustain it. It turns out, as we shall soon see, that force is closely connected with acceleration.

5.2 VELOCITY AND ACCELERATION

In mechanics we often imagine that some object, a toy train perhaps, is moving along a number line. The velocity–time graph in figure 5.1 shows the motion of such a train during a period of 5 s. The train's velocity differs from its speed only in being a signed quantity, i.e. it can be positive or negative. Thus a velocity of +4 m/s means that the train is moving forwards along the number line with a speed of 4 m/s, whereas a velocity of −4 m/s would mean that it was moving at the same speed of 4 m/s but in the reverse direction. For the moment, we shall confine our attention to cases where the velocities are positive.

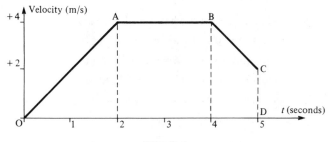

Fig. 5.1

67

An object's acceleration is the rate of change of its velocity. Acceleration is therefore represented by the gradient of the velocity–time graph (and can be positive or negative). For example, consider our train during its first 2 s of motion. Since the velocity increases steadily from 0 to $+4\,$m/s, the rate of change is constant and equals $+2\,$m/s per second, i.e. $+2\,$m/s^2 as we shall say. This is the train's acceleration.

EXAMPLE Find the train's acceleration

 (a) from $t = 2$ to $t = 4$,

 (b) from $t = 4$ to $t = 5$.

(a) The velocity is constant throughout this interval: so the acceleration is zero.

(b) Here the velocity drops by $2\,$m/s over $1\,$s, an acceleration of $-2\,$m/s^2 (which could alternatively be referred to as a deceleration or retardation of $+2\,$m/s^2).

EXAMPLE How far does the train travel during the 5 s?

We must find the average velocity, and thus the distance travelled, during each of the three phases of motion.

Since the graph is made up of straight sections, the average velocities are very easy to determine: they are $2\,$m/s, $4\,$m/s, and $3\,$m/s respectively. Therefore the distance travelled during the first phase is $(2\,\text{m/s}) \times (2\,\text{s}) = 4\,$m. Similarly, we can calculate the distances travelled during the second and third phases: they are $(4\,\text{m/s}) \times (2\,\text{s})$ and $(3\,\text{m/s}) \times (1\,\text{s})$. The total distance is thus $4+8+3 = 15\,$m.

We could also have obtained these results by using the fact that the area under a velocity–time graph represents distance travelled. Check for yourself that the areas of the three parts of the region OABCD do indeed equal 4, 8, and 3 units.

EXERCISE 5A

In this exercise, the four letters t, v, u, and a are used with special meanings. t is the time (in seconds), and v is the velocity (in m/s) at that time. These are both variable quantities, related to each other. u is the value of v when $t = 0$ ($u\,$m/s is the initial velocity), and $a\,$m/s^2 is the supposedly steady (or uniform) acceleration.

 1. If $u = +3$, and $v = +5$ when $t = 4$, find a.

 2. If $u = +1$, and $v = +16$ when $t = 3$, find a.

 3. If $u = +10$, and $v = +2$ when $t = 2$, find a.

 4. If $u = +4$, and $v = +1$ when $t = 6$, find a.

 5. If $u = +3$ and $a = +2$, find v when $t = 4$.

 6. If $u = +10$ and $a = +1/2$, find v when $t = 6$.

 7. If $a = +2$, and $v = +12$ when $t = 4$, find u.

8. If $a = -3$, and $v = +2$ when $t = 4$, find u.

9. If $a = +8$, $u = +3$, and $v = +7$, find t.

10. If $a = -3$, $u = +6$, and $v = 0$, find t.

11. Find a formula connecting t, v, u, and a. Make v the subject.

12. Find a formula giving distance travelled in terms of u, v, and t.

13. A driver travelling along a motorway at $35 \, \text{m/s}$ decelerates at $0.5 \, \text{m/s}^2$ on seeing a danger sign, until he reaches the recommended safe speed of $20 \, \text{m/s}$. He travels at this safe speed for $1 \, \text{km}$, and then accelerates at $1.5 \, \text{m/s}^2$ until he regains his original speed. Draw a velocity–time graph showing all this, and calculate how much time is lost altogether.

5.3 MASS AND NEWTON'S SECOND LAW

If we have a well-oiled trolley and push it, it gathers speed, i.e. it accelerates. If we push harder we get a greater acceleration. Experiments show that for a given object, the force acting on it and its acceleration are proportional to each other, i.e.

$$\text{Force} \propto \text{Acceleration} \qquad \qquad \textbf{1}$$

If we now load up the trolley, we find that a stronger force is needed to produce the same acceleration. Here we become involved with the concept of mass. The *mass* of an object is (roughly speaking) the amount of stuff in it (we all have a vague understanding of what is meant by the terms mass and force, but they are quite hard to define properly: even Newton's definition of mass was circular, and it was not until Einstein that a more satisfactory notion of mass emerged). The greater the mass of an object, the more reluctant that object will be to accelerate. More refined experiments show that for a given acceleration, the force on an object and its mass are proportional to each other, i.e.

$$\text{Force} \propto \text{Mass} \qquad \qquad \textbf{2}$$

1 and **2** taken together lead to the equation

$$\underline{P = kma} \qquad \qquad \textbf{3}$$

where P refers to the force (push or pull), m to the mass, a to the acceleration, and k is a constant.

The standard unit of acceleration is the metre per second per second (m/s^2). The second was defined at a meeting of the General Conference of Weights and Measures in 1967, as 'the duration of 9 192 631 770 periods of the radiation corresponding to the transition between the two hyperfine levels of the ground state of the caesium-133 atom'. At a more recent meeting of the Conference in October 1983, the metre was redefined as 'the length of the path travelled by light in vacuum during a time interval of 1/299 792 458 of a second'.

The standard unit of mass is the kilogram (kg); the mass of an object is fundamentally found by comparing it with a prototype (kept at the International Bureau of Weights and Measures near Paris) whose mass is defined to be 1 kg.

The standard unit of force is the newton (N), defined as follows:

> 1 newton is that force which produces an acceleration of 1 m/s² when applied to a mass of 1 kg

With these units, **3** gives $1 = k \times 1 \times 1$. With the newton, kilogram, and m/s², therefore, we obtain

$$P = ma$$

This equation is *Newton's second law.*

Note   The metre, the second, and the kilogram are three of the base units in the internationally accepted system of units that is generally referred to as SI. The other SI base units are:

the ampere (electric current)
the kelvin (thermodynamic temperature)
the candela (luminous intensity)
the mole (amount of substance)

The radian (and steradian, the unit of solid angle) are SI supplementary units. SI also makes use of many derived units, including the square metre, the cubic metre, the metre per second, the metre per second squared, and of course the newton. You will doubtless have already come across others, in everyday life or in your study of science.

Strictly speaking, the official abbreviation for a unit such as the metre per second is $\mathrm{m\,s}^{-1}$. Similarly, the unit of acceleration should really be abbreviated as $\mathrm{m\,s}^{-2}$, the unit of density as $\mathrm{kg\,m}^{-3}$, and so on. In the earlier chapters of this book, however, we use the simpler abbreviations m/s, m/s², kg/m³, and so on. The less simple but more correct abbreviations are not adopted until chapter 14.

EXERCISE 5B

In this exercise P, m, and a are measured in the standard units.

1. If $m = 4$ and $a = 2$, find P.

2. If $m = 1.78$ and $a = 3.29$, find P.

3. If $a = 4$ and $P = 2$, find m.

4. If $a = 5.27$ and $P = 37.9$, find m.

5. If $m = 0.1$ and $P = 64$, find a.

6. If $m = 0.637$ and $P = 12.4$, find a.

In the remaining questions, you will need to find a as a link between $P = ma$ and the v, u, a, t equation ($v = u + at$).

7. If $m = 0.5$, $u = 2$, and $v = 6$ when $t = 1.5$, find P.

8. A mass of 200 grams has its velocity increased from 1 m/s to 3 m/s over a period of 5 s by a steady force. Find that force.

9. If $P = 5$, $u = 0.5$, and $v = 1.2$ when $t = 7$, find m.

10. A steady force of 2 N acts on a mass for 3 s and increases its velocity from 1.3 m/s to 2.8 m/s. Find the mass.

11. If $m = 0.3$, $P = 4$, $u = -1$, and $v = +2$, find t.

12. A force of 3 N acts on a mass of 200 grams and increases its velocity from -2 m/s to $+2$ m/s. How long does this take?

13. If $m = 0.4$, $P = 10$, $u = 3$, and $t = 5$, find v.

14. A body which has a mass of 1 tonne (i.e. 1000 kg) is moving at 10 m/s. A force of 200 N then acts on the body for 8 s. What is the final speed?

15. Make a the subject of $P = ma$. By substituting for a in $v = u + at$, obtain an equation involving P, m, t, v, u but not a, which begins $Pt = \ldots$

5.4 GRAVITY AND WEIGHT

One of the most important forces is that of gravity: every particle in the universe attracts every other one. The result of the size of the Earth is that every object near the surface of the Earth is pulled downwards by quite a sizeable force, which is called its *weight* (a term often rather loosely used in everyday life to mean mass, but we shall use it strictly).

Galileo (1564–1642) in an important series of experiments (which according to tradition included dropping cannon-balls from the Leaning Tower of Pisa) showed that all freely falling objects (large enough for air resistance to be neglected) fall with the same acceleration, 9.8 m/s², usually denoted by g. Aristotle (384–322 BC) had taught that heavier objects fall much faster: clearly neither he, nor anyone else for almost two thousand years, had bothered to try the experiment. In fact, as more accurate measurements have subsequently shown, g varies slightly from place to place on the Earth: the standard value is defined as 9.806 65 m/s², but the measured value is 9.811 818 6 at Teddington and 9.801 024 0 in Washington. For most practical purposes, however, 9.8 is a satisfactory approximation, and indeed 10 is often quite close enough.

EXAMPLE　Find the weight of a 5 kg mass.

P newtons　　　　　**Fig. 5.2**

Drop the 5 kg mass. Then $a = 9.8$, $m = 5$, and thus $P = ma = 5 \times 9.8 = 49$. Hence the weight (force due to gravity) is 49 N.

The general rule is clearly that an object of mass m kg has a weight of mg N. For this reason, g may be given as 9.8 N/kg instead of 9.8 m/s².

Sometimes we make use of another unit of force, the kilogram-force or kgf. This is defined as 9.80665 N, which is, to a fair degree of accuracy, the weight of 1 kg anywhere on the Earth.

EXERCISE 5C

1.　Find the weight (in newtons) of　(a) 2 kg,　(b) 15 kg,　(c) 0.5 kg, (d) 50 grams,　(e) 1 tonne.

2.　What mass has a weight of　(a) 20 N,　(b) 100 N,　(c) 10^6 N?

3.　I find a box of weights in a laboratory; I hold one in my hand and judge it to have a weight of 1 N (approximately). Which one is it?

4.　There are two standard types of weighing machine:　(a) spring-operated, and (b) a balance with two pans and a box of weights. Would either work in a gravity-free environment? Consider what would happen on the Moon (where gravity is about one-sixth of what it is on Earth): which type would still determine mass correctly?

5.　An astronaut in Venusville is buying potatoes. Is it the mass or the weight that concerns him? What if he has to carry them back to base in a shopping bag?

5.5　MORE THAN ONE FORCE

If two or more forces all act in the same direction, experiments show that their combined effect is found by adding the effects of the individual forces. If two forces act in *opposite* directions, however, then subtraction gives the resultant force.

EXAMPLE　A 2 kg mass hangs on a rope, which I am pulling up and down. What is the tension (pull) in the rope when the mass is accelerating at 3 m/s² (a) upwards,　(b) downwards?

There are two forces on the mass: the tension T N up and the weight $2g = 19.6$ N down (figure 5.3).

19.6   **Fig. 5.3**

(a) For upward acceleration, the resultant force is $(T - 19.6)$.
   Thus $T - 19.6 = 2 \times 3$ (since $P = ma$)
   and so $T = 19.6 + 6 = 25.6$ (N)

(b) For downward acceleration, the resultant force is $(19.6 - T)$.
   Thus $19.6 - T = 2 \times 3$
   and so $T = 19.6 - 6 = 13.6$ (N)

If a book is placed on a table it sits still. Since gravity pulls the book down, there must be a counteracting upward force. This comes about from the fact that when atoms get very close together they repel one another, so that the atoms on the bottom of the book experience a quite powerful upward force caused by the nearby presence of the atoms on the top of the table (the atoms on the top of the table will likewise experience a downward force). A curious property of this contact force is that it can change almost instantaneously: if we put a bottle of ink on top of the book, the upward push on the bottom of the book increases at once, just enough to counteract the extra weight of the ink bottle. The contact force would also change if the table began to accelerate up or down, carrying the book with it.

EXAMPLE A crate of mass 5 kg rests on the floor of a helicopter operating in freak weather conditions. What is the contact force on the crate when the helicopter accelerates at $2 \, \text{m/s}^2$ upwards? What happens if the engine fails and the helicopter falls freely downwards?

Let the contact force be R N. If the helicopter were hovering, its acceleration would be zero, and so the contact force would equal the weight of the crate, i.e. $R = 5g = 49$ (N). If there is an upward acceleration, however, the two forces are *not* equal, since their combined effect $(R - 5g)$ must equal ma, which is no longer zero.

Thus $R - 49 = 5 \times 2 \Rightarrow R = 59$ (N).

Now suppose the helicopter falls freely: the crate has a *downward* acceleration of very nearly g, and so $49 - R = 5 \times g$. So in these conditions R is zero, or nearly zero: in other words, the crate is barely in contact with the floor of the helicopter.

EXAMPLE An astronaut is strapped into the seat of an experimental rocket device which moves on a vertical track. If the weight of the man is 735 N, what other force acts on him when the rocket is made to accelerate upwards at 2g? And what other force acts when the rocket is then decelerated at 2g?

The man's mass $= \dfrac{735}{g} = 75$ kg.

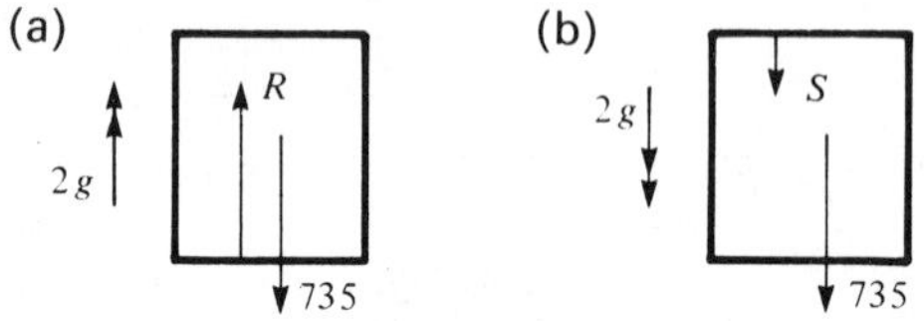

Fig. 5.4

In the first case (figure 5.4a), the other force (apart from his weight) is the contact force R between the man and the seat, and the resultant force is $(R - 735)$.

Thus $R - 735 = 75 \times 2g$

and so $R \quad = 1470 + 735 = 2205$ (N)

In the second case (figure 5.4b), we may assume that R becomes zero, and that the man is held in place by the downward force S of the straps. The resultant force is now $(S + 735)$.

Thus $S + 735 = 75 \times 2g$

and so $S \quad = 1470 - 735 = 735$ (N)

What happens if several forces act on a body, but not all in the same (or opposite) directions? Experiment shows that Newton's second law ($P = ma$) still applies provided that for P we take the vector sum of all the forces: $\mathbf{P} = m\mathbf{a}$. We shall return to this later.

EXERCISE 5D

1. A 3 kg mass hangs on a rope. What is the tension in the rope when the body is:

   (a) at rest,

   (b) accelerating up at 2 m/s^2,

   (c) accelerating down at 2 m/s^2?

2. A 5 kg mass hangs on a rope. Find the acceleration (and say whether it is up or down) when the tension in the rope is:

   (a) 40 N, (b) 50 N, (c) 60 N.

3. A car of mass 1 tonne accelerates from rest to 90 km/h in 10 s against a resisting force of 700 N. Find the acceleration in m/s² (18 km/h = 5 m/s) and the driving force needed.

4. A particle of mass 5 milligrams moves under the action of its own weight (take g to be 10 N/kg) and a magnetic force of 50 μN. Find the resulting acceleration if the two forces act   (a) in the same direction,   (b) in opposite directions.

5. If the astronaut in the example above cannot take a thrust on his shoulders greater than 882 N, what is the greatest acceptable deceleration, as a multiple of g?

6. A balloon of mass 2000 kg is accelerating vertically downwards at 0.98 m/s². Calculate the total upward force exerted on the balloon by the surrounding air. At the moment when the balloon's downward velocity is 24 m/s, ballast of mass 236 kg is dropped out. If the upward force exerted by the air remains unaltered, after how many seconds will the balloon cease to descend? (Take g to be 9.8 m/s².)

6 MATRICES AND TRANSFORMATIONS

6.1 INTRODUCTION

A matrix is a rectangular array of numbers—a simple idea, but one of the very greatest importance in both pure and applied mathematics.

Examples of matrices are:

$$\mathbf{M} = \begin{pmatrix} 3 & 0 \\ 1 & 2 \\ 0 & 5 \end{pmatrix} \quad \mathbf{N} = \begin{pmatrix} 15 & 3 \\ 13 & 2 \end{pmatrix} \quad \mathbf{O} = \begin{pmatrix} 0 & 0 \\ 0 & 0 \end{pmatrix} \quad \mathbf{P} = \begin{pmatrix} 4 \\ 1 \end{pmatrix}$$

$\mathbf{M}$ has three rows and two columns: its shape is 3×2 (not 2×3). $\mathbf{N}$ is a square matrix, 2×2. $\mathbf{O}$ is the 2×2 zero matrix. $\mathbf{P}$ is a column matrix, 2×1.

A matrix can convey information. For example, suppose Alice, Ben, and Charles each take some records to a party. Alice takes 3 albums, Ben takes 1 album and 2 singles, Charles takes 5 singles. The matrix $\mathbf{M}$ could be intended to display this information.

$$\mathbf{M} = \begin{matrix} A \\ B \\ C \end{matrix} \begin{pmatrix} 3 & 0 \\ 1 & 2 \\ 0 & 5 \end{pmatrix}$$

At the party, they agree to swap records. Alice swaps an album for two of Charles' singles, and Ben does the same. The matrix $\mathbf{T}$ shows this transaction.

$$\mathbf{T} = \begin{matrix} A \\ B \\ C \end{matrix} \begin{pmatrix} -1 & +2 \\ -1 & +2 \\ +2 & -4 \end{pmatrix}$$

To find out what each of them now has, we can add these two matrices. The sum gives us the required information.

$$\mathbf{M+T} = \begin{matrix} A \\ B \\ C \end{matrix} \begin{pmatrix} 2 & 2 \\ 0 & 4 \\ 2 & 1 \end{pmatrix}$$

Can matrices always be added? Certainly not: $\mathbf{N+T}$ is an impossible sum, since the shapes of $\mathbf{N}$ and $\mathbf{T}$ are different.

If the price of an album is £4 and the price of a single is £1, what had our three party-goers spent on their records?

$$\text{A's expenditure} = 3 \times £4 + 0 \times £1 = £12$$
$$\text{B's expenditure} = 1 \times £4 + 2 \times £1 = £6$$
$$\text{C's expenditure} = 0 \times £4 + 5 \times £1 = £5$$

So the numbers of our original matrix **M** combined with those of the price matrix **P** produce the expenditure matrix **E**:

$$\mathbf{E} = \mathbf{MP} = \begin{pmatrix} 3 & 0 \\ 1 & 2 \\ 0 & 5 \end{pmatrix} \begin{pmatrix} 4 \\ 1 \end{pmatrix} = \begin{pmatrix} 3 \times 4 + 0 \times 1 \\ 1 \times 4 + 2 \times 1 \\ 0 \times 4 + 5 \times 1 \end{pmatrix} = \begin{pmatrix} 12 \\ 6 \\ 5 \end{pmatrix}$$

This operation is called *matrix multiplication*.

For example, we can work out

$$\begin{pmatrix} 2 & 3 & 1 \\ 1 & 5 & 2 \end{pmatrix} \begin{pmatrix} 3 \\ 6 \\ 5 \end{pmatrix} = \begin{pmatrix} 2 \times 3 + 3 \times 6 + 1 \times 5 \\ 1 \times 3 + 5 \times 6 + 2 \times 5 \end{pmatrix} = \begin{pmatrix} 29 \\ 43 \end{pmatrix}$$

but

$$\begin{pmatrix} 2 & 3 & 1 \\ 1 & 5 & 2 \end{pmatrix} \begin{pmatrix} 3 \\ 6 \end{pmatrix} = \begin{pmatrix} 2 \times 3 + 3 \times 6 + 1 \times ? \\ 1 \times 3 + 5 \times 6 + 2 \times ? \end{pmatrix} \text{ is impossible.}$$

EXAMPLE Calculate **MN**.

$$\mathbf{MN} = \begin{pmatrix} 3 & 0 \\ 1 & 2 \\ 0 & 5 \end{pmatrix} \begin{pmatrix} 15 & 3 \\ 13 & 2 \end{pmatrix} = \begin{pmatrix} 3 \times 15 + 0 \times 13 & 3 \times 3 + 0 \times 2 \\ 1 \times 15 + 2 \times 13 & 1 \times 3 + 2 \times 2 \\ 0 \times 15 + 5 \times 13 & 0 \times 3 + 5 \times 2 \end{pmatrix}$$

$$= \begin{pmatrix} 45 & 9 \\ 41 & 7 \\ 65 & 10 \end{pmatrix}$$

This calculation is possible since each *row* of the left-hand matrix 'fits' each *column* of the right-hand matrix.

EXERCISE 6A

In questions 1 to 9 multiply where possible (and if impossible, say so).

1. $(2 \quad 1 \quad 1) \begin{pmatrix} 5 \\ 4 \\ 3 \end{pmatrix}$ **2.** $(2 \quad 1 \quad 1) \begin{pmatrix} 5 & 3 \\ 4 & -3 \\ 3 & 0 \end{pmatrix}$ **3.** $\begin{pmatrix} 5 \\ 4 \\ 3 \end{pmatrix} (2 \quad 1 \quad 1)$

4. $\begin{pmatrix} 2 & 1 \\ 3 & -1 \end{pmatrix} (1 \quad -2)$ **5.** $\begin{pmatrix} 4 & 2 \\ 2 & 1 \end{pmatrix} \begin{pmatrix} 1 & -2 \\ 3 & -6 \end{pmatrix}$ **6.** $\begin{pmatrix} 1 & -2 \\ 3 & -6 \end{pmatrix} \begin{pmatrix} 4 & 2 \\ 2 & 1 \end{pmatrix}$

7. $\begin{pmatrix} 1 & 0 \\ 0 & -1 \end{pmatrix} \begin{pmatrix} 1 & 0 \\ 0 & -1 \end{pmatrix}$ **8.** $\begin{pmatrix} 1 & 0 \\ 0 & 1 \end{pmatrix} \begin{pmatrix} 2 & -3 \\ 1 & 6 \end{pmatrix}$ **9.** $\begin{pmatrix} 2 & -3 \\ 1 & 6 \end{pmatrix} \begin{pmatrix} 1 & 0 \\ 0 & 1 \end{pmatrix}$

10. Is matrix multiplication commutative? Explain your answer.

11. Choose three matrices, and work out their product in alternative ways to investigate whether matrix multiplication is associative.

12. Is there an identity for matrix multiplication?

6.2 2×2 SQUARE MATRICES

Square matrices are especially important. We shall be concentrating on the 2×2 variety, but our results can more or less easily be extended to square matrices of higher orders.

The last question of exercise 6A asked 'Is there an identity for matrix multiplication?' The answer is 'Yes, there is a 2×2 unit matrix, there is a 3×3 unit matrix, and so on.'

The 2×2 unit matrix is $\begin{pmatrix} 1 & 0 \\ 0 & 1 \end{pmatrix}$, usually referred to as **I**.

It has no effect when other 2×2 matrices are pre-multiplied or post-multiplied by it, i.e.

$$\begin{pmatrix} 1 & 0 \\ 0 & 1 \end{pmatrix} \begin{pmatrix} a & b \\ c & d \end{pmatrix} = \begin{pmatrix} a & b \\ c & d \end{pmatrix} \begin{pmatrix} 1 & 0 \\ 0 & 1 \end{pmatrix} = \begin{pmatrix} a & b \\ c & d \end{pmatrix} \text{ whatever } a, b, c, d \text{ are.}$$

What is the 3×3 identity matrix?

We now go on to ask the question 'Are there inverses in matrix multiplication?' The answer is a qualified 'yes'.

In ordinary arithmetic, the multiplicative inverse of any non-zero number n is the number n^{-1} such that $n^{-1}n = nn^{-1} = 1$. For example, $2^{-1} = 1/2$, $(3/4)^{-1} = 4/3, (-1)^{-1} = -1$, and the only number without an inverse is 0.

We adopt a similar definition for matrices: the multiplicative inverse of a matrix **M** is the matrix $\mathbf{M}^{-1}$ (if there is one) such that $\mathbf{M}^{-1}\mathbf{M} = \mathbf{M}\mathbf{M}^{-1} = \mathbf{I}$.

So $\begin{pmatrix} -1 & -2 \\ 3 & 5 \end{pmatrix}$ is the inverse of $\begin{pmatrix} 5 & 2 \\ -3 & -1 \end{pmatrix}$ and vice versa,

because $\begin{pmatrix} -1 & -2 \\ 3 & 5 \end{pmatrix} \begin{pmatrix} 5 & 2 \\ -3 & -1 \end{pmatrix} = \begin{pmatrix} 5 & 2 \\ -3 & -1 \end{pmatrix} \begin{pmatrix} -1 & -2 \\ 3 & 5 \end{pmatrix} = \begin{pmatrix} 1 & 0 \\ 0 & 1 \end{pmatrix}$

Is there any general method for finding inverses, and are there any matrices (other than the zero matrix) which have no inverse?

Suppose that the inverse of some matrix $\begin{pmatrix} a & b \\ c & d \end{pmatrix}$ is $\begin{pmatrix} A & B \\ C & D \end{pmatrix}$.

Then $$\begin{pmatrix} A & B \\ C & D \end{pmatrix}\begin{pmatrix} a & b \\ c & d \end{pmatrix} = \begin{pmatrix} 1 & 0 \\ 0 & 1 \end{pmatrix} \qquad \textbf{1}$$

and $$\begin{pmatrix} a & b \\ c & d \end{pmatrix}\begin{pmatrix} A & B \\ C & D \end{pmatrix} = \begin{pmatrix} 1 & 0 \\ 0 & 1 \end{pmatrix} \qquad \textbf{2}$$

Focusing our attention upon **1**, we get four simultaneous equations:

$$Aa + Bc = 1 \qquad \textbf{3}$$

$$Ab + Bd = 0 \qquad \textbf{4}$$

$$Ca + Dc = 0 \qquad \textbf{5}$$

$$Cb + Dd = 1 \qquad \textbf{6}$$

We multiply **3** by d to get $Aad + Bcd = d$

and $\qquad$ **4** by c to get $Abc + Bdc = 0$

and now subtraction gives

$$Aad - Abc = d \;\Rightarrow\; A(ad - bc) = d$$

In this way, we solve **3** and **4**:

$$A = \frac{d}{ad - bc} \qquad B = \frac{-b}{ad - bc}$$

and we can also solve **5** and **6**:

$$C = \frac{-c}{ad - bc} \qquad D = \frac{a}{ad - bc}$$

The quantity $(ad - bc)$ which appears as the denominator of the four fractions is called the *determinant* of the matrix, and is often denoted by Δ.

We can soon check that our answers satisfy **2** also.

Therefore the inverse of $\begin{pmatrix} a & b \\ c & d \end{pmatrix}$ is

$$\begin{pmatrix} d & -b \\ -c & a \end{pmatrix} \div \Delta$$

(but can you see a value of Δ that will cause trouble?)

EXAMPLE   Find the inverse of $\mathbf{M} = \begin{pmatrix} 1 & 2 \\ -3 & 4 \end{pmatrix}$.

In this case, $\Delta = 1 \times 4 - 2 \times (-3) = 10$. So $\mathbf{M}^{-1}$ exists since $\Delta \neq 0$, and

$$\mathbf{M}^{-1} = \begin{pmatrix} 4 & -2 \\ 3 & 1 \end{pmatrix} \div 10 = \begin{pmatrix} 0.4 & -0.2 \\ 0.3 & 0.1 \end{pmatrix}$$

EXERCISE 6B

1. Find the determinants of the following matrices:

(a) $\begin{pmatrix} 3 & 2 \\ 5 & 4 \end{pmatrix}$,   (b) $\begin{pmatrix} 4 & 3 \\ 7 & 5 \end{pmatrix}$,   (c) $\begin{pmatrix} 3 & 2 \\ 3 & 2 \end{pmatrix}$,   (d) $\begin{pmatrix} 2 & 3 \\ 4 & 5 \end{pmatrix}$,

(e) $\begin{pmatrix} 4 & -6 \\ 2 & 5 \end{pmatrix}$,   (f) $\begin{pmatrix} 5 & -3 \\ -3 & 2 \end{pmatrix}$.

2. A matrix whose determinant is zero is called *singular*. Find the inverses of the non-singular matrices in question 1.

6.3   MATRICES AND TRANSFORMATIONS

If we take any point in the x–y plane, say $(2, 3)$, and pre-multiply its position vector by the 2×2 matrix

$$\mathbf{M} = \begin{pmatrix} 2 & 0 \\ 1 & 2 \end{pmatrix}, \quad \text{we get} \quad \begin{pmatrix} 2 & 0 \\ 1 & 2 \end{pmatrix} \begin{pmatrix} 2 \\ 3 \end{pmatrix} = \begin{pmatrix} 4 \\ 8 \end{pmatrix}$$

which is the position vector of another point $(4, 8)$. We say that $(4, 8)$ is the image of $(2, 3)$ under the transformation with matrix $\mathbf{M}$.

The transformation applies to the whole plane, of course. Its effect on the unit square—with corners at $(0, 0)$, $(1, 0)$, $(1, 1)$, $(0, 1)$—is shown in figure 6.1. Notice how easy it is to find the images of I and J:

$$\mathbf{Mi} = \begin{pmatrix} 2 \\ 1 \end{pmatrix}, \ \mathbf{M}\text{'s left column,} \quad \text{and} \quad \mathbf{Mj} = \begin{pmatrix} 0 \\ 2 \end{pmatrix}, \ \mathbf{M}\text{'s right column}$$

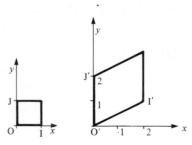

Fig. 6.1

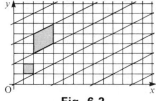

Fig. 6.2

The more general effect is shown in figure 6.2. The grid of small squares is transformed into the grid of larger parallelograms (with the origin remaining invariant): for example, the shaded square becomes the shaded parallelogram.

Any transformation that has an effect of this kind can be represented by a matrix, and vice versa, although in some special cases the parallelograms get squashed up on to a single line. If you know the transformation's effect on I and J, you can immediately write down the matrix. Conversely, if you know the matrix, you can immediately see its effect on I and J, and thus discover the nature of the transformation. Transformations of this type are known as *linear* transformations.

EXERCISE 6C

1. Describe the transformations represented by these matrices:

(a) $\begin{pmatrix} 4 & 0 \\ 0 & 4 \end{pmatrix}$, (b) $\begin{pmatrix} 1 & 1 \\ 0 & 1 \end{pmatrix}$, (c) $\begin{pmatrix} 1 & 0 \\ 2 & 1 \end{pmatrix}$, (d) $\begin{pmatrix} 2 & 0 \\ 0 & 0 \end{pmatrix}$, (e) $\begin{pmatrix} 1 & 0 \\ 0 & -2 \end{pmatrix}$.

2. Make a list of the matrices of these transformations:
   (a) rotations about the origin through $+90, 180, 270, 360°$;
   (b) reflections in Ox, Oy, $y = x$, $x+y = 0$.

3. Suppose $\mathbf{A} = \begin{pmatrix} 1 & 0 \\ 0 & -1 \end{pmatrix}$ and $\mathbf{B} = \begin{pmatrix} 0 & 1 \\ 1 & 0 \end{pmatrix}$.

   (a) Evaluate the product $\mathbf{M} = \mathbf{AB}$, and describe the transformation represented by $\mathbf{M}$.

   (b) Evaluate the product $\mathbf{N} = \mathbf{BA}$, and describe the transformation represented by $\mathbf{N}$.

   (c) Find the inverses of $\mathbf{M}$ and $\mathbf{N}$. Comment on your result.

4. Find the matrix of a transformation that sends both I and J to points on the line $y = x$. Describe your transformation.

5. Prove that the matrix of the rotation about the origin through an angle θ is

$$\begin{pmatrix} \cos \theta & -\sin \theta \\ \sin \theta & \cos \theta \end{pmatrix}$$

By considering the image of $(\cos \phi, \sin \phi)$ under this rotation, show that:

$$\cos (\theta + \phi) = \cos \theta \cos \phi - \sin \theta \sin \phi, \quad \sin (\theta + \phi) = \sin \theta \cos \phi + \cos \theta \sin \phi.$$

6.4 MATRICES AND TRANSFORMATIONS (continued)

The transformation represented by the matrix $\begin{pmatrix} a & b \\ c & d \end{pmatrix}$ maps the unit square into the parallelogram with vertices $(0,0)$, (a,c), $(a+b,c+d)$, (b,d)—see figure 6.3. The area of the rectangle shown is $(a+b)(c+d)$. Moreover

area **1** = area **3** = $\tfrac{1}{2}(a+b)c$, and area **2** = area **4** = $\tfrac{1}{2}(c+d)b$.

Therefore the area of the parallelogram

$$= (a+b)(c+d) - (a+b)c - (c+d)b$$

$$= ac + ad + bc + bd - ac - bc - cb - db$$

$$= ad - bc = \Delta, \text{ the determinant of the matrix.}$$

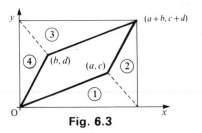

Fig. 6.3

So the unit square's area is multiplied by the determinant when the transformation takes effect, and consideration of figure 6.2 shows that in fact all regions have their areas multiplied by the same amount. Thus transformations of this type (i.e. those that can be represented by a matrix) have an *area scale factor*, which equals the determinant of the matrix. (A really rigorous proof of this result takes into account that the matrix elements may not all be positive, and the determinant itself may not be positive, but we shall not bother ourselves with these complications.)

Some transformations (shears and rotations, for example) keep area invariant: in such a case, the determinant of the matrix is bound to be 1. Other transformations double area (some stretches, for example): in these cases, the determinant will be 2. But what about those cases when the determinant equals -1 or -2 or some other negative number? What then is the significance of the $-$ sign?

Refer back to the matrices given in question 1 of exercise 6B. Which of them has Δ equal to $+2$, and which has Δ equal to -2? Draw two fairly large and accurate diagrams like figure 6.3, one for each matrix. You will find that the two images of the unit square are identical, except that they have opposite orientation. Both transformations double area: but orientation is preserved by one, reversed by the other—which is which? What do you think Δ will equal in the case of a reflection? (Is area preserved by reflection? Is orientation?)

What happens when $\Delta = 0$? Areas are multiplied by zero, and the transformation squashes all regions up on to a single line (or point). Take as an example the matrix $\begin{pmatrix} 1 & 1 \\ 1 & 1 \end{pmatrix}$, whose determinant is obviously 0. The transformation sends both $(1, 0)$ and $(0, 1)$ to $(1, 1)$. It sends $(2, 3)$, $(5, 0)$, $(1, 4)$, $(-1, 6)$, etc., all to $(5, 5)$. It sends every point, in fact, to somewhere on the line $y = x$. Since many points, indeed infinitely many, are sent to each point of $y = x$, it is impossible to unscramble the effects of the transformation. In other words, there can be no inverse transformation—and you will surely remember that when $\Delta = 0$ there is no inverse matrix. This is no accident: for in general, if **M** is the matrix of a transformation **T**, then the inverse matrix $\mathbf{M}^{-1}$ will be the matrix of the inverse transformation $\mathbf{T}^{-1}$, provided the inverses exist.

Similarly, if **L** and **M** are the matrices of two transformations **S** and **T**, then the matrix product $\mathbf{L} \times \mathbf{M}$ will represent the composite transformation **ST** (which means **T** followed by **S**, of course):

$$\begin{pmatrix} x \\ y \end{pmatrix} \xrightarrow{\ \mathbf{T}\ } \mathbf{M}\begin{pmatrix} x \\ y \end{pmatrix} \xrightarrow{\ \mathbf{S}\ } \mathbf{L}\left[\mathbf{M}\begin{pmatrix} x \\ y \end{pmatrix} \right] = \mathbf{LM}\begin{pmatrix} x \\ y \end{pmatrix}$$

Because of this very precise agreement between transformation algebra and matrix algebra, we can often gloss over the distinction between linear transformations and their matrices.

EXAMPLE Find the area of the parallelogram OPQR, where O, P, R are $(0, 0)$, $(7, 3)$, $(4, 6)$ respectively.

We start by drawing a diagram (you should do so—it will be similar to figure 6.3), and then find a matrix **L** that will transform the unit square into the parallelogram.

Since $\mathbf{Li} = \begin{pmatrix} 7 \\ 3 \end{pmatrix}$ and $\mathbf{Lj} = \begin{pmatrix} 4 \\ 6 \end{pmatrix}$, we see immediately that $\mathbf{L} = \begin{pmatrix} 7 & 4 \\ 3 & 6 \end{pmatrix}$.

Now $\Delta = 7 \times 6 - 4 \times 3 = 30$.

So the area of OPQR = (the area of the unit square) $\times 30 = 30$.

We note incidentally that an extension of the idea used in this example allows us to work out the area of any triangle in the x–y plane (and hence—by adding up triangles—the area of any polygon). We take the following steps:

> translate the triangle so that one corner lies at the origin
> complete the parallelogram of which the triangle is half
> find the area of the parallelogram as in the last example
> halve it to give the area of the triangle

EXAMPLE Find a matrix that will map $A(1, -3)$ on to $P(7, 3)$, and $B(2, 4)$ on to $R(4, 6)$.

The required matrix N must transform AB into PR. We achieve this effect in two stages: AB to IJ, IJ to PR.

What matrix will map IJ on to PR?—the matrix L found above. And what matrix will map AB on to IJ?—the inverse of the matrix M that maps IJ on to AB.

Now $M = \begin{pmatrix} 1 & 2 \\ -3 & 4 \end{pmatrix}$, and we showed in section 6.2 that $M^{-1} = \begin{pmatrix} 0.4 & -0.2 \\ 0.3 & 0.1 \end{pmatrix}$.

So $\qquad N = L \times M^{-1} = \begin{pmatrix} 7 & 4 \\ 3 & 6 \end{pmatrix} \begin{pmatrix} 0.4 & -0.2 \\ 0.3 & 0.1 \end{pmatrix} = \begin{pmatrix} 4 & -1 \\ 3 & 0 \end{pmatrix}$

EXERCISE 6D

1. Find the area of the triangle ABC, where A, B, C are $(2, 3)$, $(9, 5)$, $(4, 8)$. Also find the area of ABCD, where D is $(0, 9)$.

2. Find the matrix that maps A and C of question 1 on to $E(8, 0)$ and $F(0, 12)$ respectively.

3. A transformation T is equivalent to the shear which keeps the x-axis invariant and sends $(0, 1)$ to $(2, 1)$, followed by a rotation of $90°$ about O. Find the matrices of the shear and rotation, and then the matrix of T by multiplication. Hence confirm that T preserves area.

7 MECHANICS II

7.1 VECTOR QUANTITIES

At the end of chapter 5, we stated that when several forces act on a body, but not all in the same or opposite directions, then Newton's second law takes the form

$$\mathbf{P} = m\mathbf{a}$$

where $\mathbf{P}$ is the vector sum of the forces,
$\mathbf{a}$ is the acceleration (also a vector quantity),
m is the mass (a scalar quantity).

What is meant by the term *vector quantity*, and how can we justify saying that force and acceleration are both vector quantities? What is meant by saying that mass is a *scalar quantity*?

A well-known physics textbook states that 'Vectors are quantities having magnitude and direction'. This is correct up to a point. But the two essential properties of vector quantities are (roughly speaking) that they can be

(1) added to and subtracted from each other in some way, and
(2) multiplied and divided by ordinary numbers.

Ordinary numbers possess these properties, of course, and can certainly be regarded as having magnitude and direction (-5 has magnitude 5 and direction west, for instance), but they are not usually counted as vectors, being referred to instead as 'scalars'. In general, any quantity like temperature that can be adequately specified by means of one ordinary number is called a scalar quantity (mass and time are other common examples).

In contrast, two or more numbers are needed to specify a vector quantity, and we customarily arrange these numbers in a column, which is itself often referred to as just a 'vector'.

Perhaps the simplest example of a vector quantity is a displacement, such as **AB** in figure 7.1, which obviously has magnitude and direction. Moreover, we can add displacements (by adding their column vectors), we can double them, and so on.

Forces also have magnitude and direction, and so they can be represented graphically by means of displacements. Thus the displacement **AB** might represent a force of 5 N in that direction.

Even more important, experiments show that if **AB** represents one force and **BC** another, then the resultant force can be represented by the vector sum of **AB** and

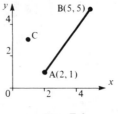

Fig. 7.1

BC, i.e. by the displacement **AC**. It is clear that this vectorial method of adding (and subtracting) forces agrees with the more elementary approach of section 5.5.

7.2 VECTOR SUMS

It is quite easy to add vectors by drawing. You simply represent each vector by a displacement, the various displacements joining on to each other as in follow-my-leader. The vector sum is then represented by the displacement that runs from start to finish: **AC = AB + BC**.

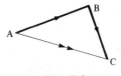

Fig. 7.2

EXAMPLE Find the magnitude and direction of the resultant of two forces, one of 5 N acting due east, the other of 4 N acting north-east.

We first draw a rough sketch showing both forces represented by displacements, which in polar form are $[5, 0°]$ and $[4, 45°]$ (figure 7.3). We then draw it accurately. By measurement, we discover that the magnitude R of the resultant is about 8.3 N, and its direction α about 20°.

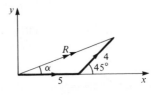

Fig. 7.3

If the accuracy even of a good vector drawing will not do, then you must calculate the sum. When the vectors are given in column form, the calculation is very easy indeed: you just add components. This rule shows that it makes no odds in which order we add two (or more) vectors. Unfortunately there is no simple rule for adding vectors in polar form. You must convert to column form, add, and (if necessary) convert back to polar form.

EXAMPLE Calculate the vector sum of $[10, -40°]$ and $[5, 90°]$.

Here $[10, -40°] = \begin{pmatrix} +7.66 \\ -6.43 \end{pmatrix}$ (see a previous example in section 2.5)

and $[5, 90°] = \begin{pmatrix} 0 \\ 5 \end{pmatrix}$ (obviously)

Their sum $= \begin{pmatrix} +7.66+0 \\ -6.43+5 \end{pmatrix} = \begin{pmatrix} +7.66 \\ -1.43 \end{pmatrix}$ (to 3 s.f.)

EXERCISE 7A

1. By drawing find the polar form of $[5, 0°] + [4, 60°]$. Also add them in reverse order, checking that the sum is the same.

2. By drawing find the polar form of $[3, 90°] + [6, -45°]$.

3. By drawing find the polar form of $[5, 180°] + [4, 70°]$.

4, 5.   Repeat questions 2 and 3 by calculation.

6. Two forces of 8 N and 15 N act east and north. Find the resultant force (magnitude and direction) by drawing.

7. Two forces of 4 N and 7 N act on an object. What are the greatest and least possible magnitudes of the resultant? If in fact its magnitude is 9 N, find (by drawing) the angle between the two forces, and the direction in which the object will accelerate.

8. A body of 0.5 tonne is subject to two forces of 200 N at an angle of 40° to each other. Calculate the acceleration.

9. Three horizontal forces act on a 10 kg mass: 20 N due east, 15 N north-east, 25 N due north. Calculate the magnitude and direction of the acceleration.

7.3 EQUILIBRIUM

If a body is sitting rock steady (is 'in equilibrium'), then its acceleration **a** is zero. Hence by Newton's law, **P** = **0**; that is to say, the vector sum of the forces is zero.

Suppose the body has just three forces **P**, **Q**, **R** acting on it. We find their resultant in the usual way, by drawing a displacement or vector diagram (figure 7.4). The displacement **AD** gives the vector sum: but this must be zero, so that in fact the diagram must be a triangle with D at the same point as A. Such a triangle is known as a *triangle of forces*. Of course, if there are more than three forces in equilibrium, the vector diagram will still close up but not into a triangle.

Fig. 7.4

EXAMPLE   A mass of 5 kg hangs on a rope. A horizontal force on the mass drags the rope to an angle of 30° from the vertical. Find this force and the tension in the rope.

Let the horizontal force be P, and the tension in the rope be T. Since the mass is in equilibrium, the three forces sum to zero and we get a triangle of forces. From the rough vector diagram, we could draw an accurate triangle. Here, more easily, we calculate:

$$P = 49 \times \tan 30° = 28.3 \quad (N)$$

and
$$T = 49 \div \cos 30° = 56.6 \quad (N)$$

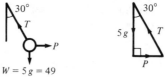

Fig. 7.5

EXAMPLE   The 5 kg object now rests on a smooth plane inclined at 30° to the horizontal (figure 7.6a). It is stopped from sliding down by a rope pulling 'up the line of greatest slope' (i.e. straight up the plane). Find the tension in the rope.

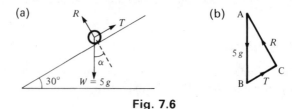

Fig. 7.6

There are three forces once again: the weight, the tension, and the contact force. The directions of the first two are obvious, but what about the third? The plane is said to be 'smooth': this means that the contact force does not help at all in stopping the object from sliding down, and so it must be at right-angles to the plane. We can now find the angles in the vector diagram (figure 7.6b). To find angle BAC we look in the space diagram for directions parallel to AB and AC— these are the direction of W and the direction opposite to R, so that angle BAC equals the one marked α. A little thought tells us this is 30°. Similarly, angle ACB is 90°.

Hence $\qquad\qquad\qquad\qquad R = 49 \cos 30° = 42.4 \quad \text{(N)}$

and $\qquad\qquad\qquad\qquad T = 49 \sin 30° = 24.5 \quad \text{(N)}$

If an object sits on a surface that is *rough* (i.e. not smooth), then the contact force will in general *not* be at right-angles to the surface. It is usual in this case to represent it as the vector sum of two *components*:

a force at right-angles to the surface (known as the normal component, or normal reaction),

a force parallel to the surface (known as the tangential or frictional component, or just as 'the friction').

EXAMPLE A forester is dragging a rock of mass 100 kg across rough horizontal ground, by means of a rope inclined at 20° to the horizontal (figure 7.7a). If the rock is moving at a steady speed, and the tension in the rope is 500 newtons, calculate the normal reaction and the friction.

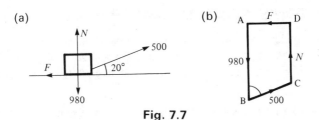

Fig. 7.7

There are four forces: the weight (980 newtons), the tension in the rope (500 newtons), the normal reaction, the friction. Note that although the rock is moving, its acceleration is zero, and so—just as before—the resultant of the forces must be zero also. We can therefore draw the vector diagram, which is a quadrilateral (figure 7.7b). The angles at A and D are obviously 90°, and it is fairly easy to see that angle B is 70°. Hence

$$N = 980 - 500 \cos 70° = 809 \quad \text{(N)}$$

and $\qquad\qquad\qquad F = 500 \sin 70° = 470 \quad \text{(N)}$

EXERCISE 7B

1. A weight of 20 N hangs on a rope of length 50 cm tied to a fixed point. A horizontal force drags the mass a horizontal distance 30 cm sideways. Calculate the angle the string makes with the vertical, and hence the two unknown forces.

2. A mass of 5 kg hangs by two wires of length 10 m and 20 m attached to hooks screwed 25 m apart into a horizontal beam. By drawing a space diagram accurately, find the angle each wire makes with the vertical. Then find the two tensions by drawing an accurate vector diagram.

3. A mass is supported by two strings, which have tensions of 10 N and 20 N and are at an angle of 90°. Calculate the weight and hence the mass.

4. The four forces [6, 0°], [3, 90°], [P, 135°], [Q, 270°] are in equilibrium. Calculate P and Q.

5. The four forces [4, 0°], [7, 60°], [P, 120°], [Q, 270°] are in equilibrium. Find P and Q by accurate drawing.

6. A crate of weight 1 kN is held on a plane sloping at an angle of 37° by a horizontal force of 300 N. Find the normal reaction and the friction by accurate drawing.

7. A 120 kg load is pulled steadily across rough level ground against a constant friction of 200 N. Draw a graph showing how the magnitude of the pull depends on the angle of pull.

7.4 NEWTON'S SECOND LAW: P = *ma*

In the previous section, we considered objects in equilibrium: in each case, the object's acceleration was zero, and so the resultant of the forces acting on it was also zero. We now turn to cases where the acceleration is *not* zero.

EXAMPLE A 5 kg mass is sliding down a rough plane inclined at 40° to the horizontal, with an acceleration of 2 m/s² (figure 7.8a). Find the friction.

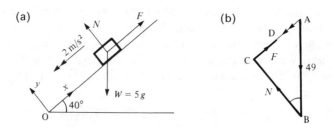

Fig. 7.8

There are three forces: the weight (i.e. $5g = 49$ newtons), the normal reaction N, and the friction F. According to Newton's law, their resultant equals $m\mathbf{a}$. Now the acceleration vector's magnitude is 2, and its direction is directly down the plane: so the resultant's magnitude is 10, and its direction is also directly down the plane. Therefore we can draw a rough version of the vector diagram, as shown in figure 7.8b. Note that ADC is a straight line (make sure you understand why), that AD equals 10, and that angle B equals 40°.

Hence
$$F = 49 \sin 40° - 10 = 21.5 \quad (N)$$

So our answer is that the frictional force equals 21.5 newtons.

A different approach to problems like this is to write all the vector quantities that enter into $\mathbf{P} = m\mathbf{a}$ in column form, i.e. break them down into components in two perpendicular directions, just as we have in fact already been doing with contact forces. We mark the axes Ox and Oy in the figure to show our two chosen directions.

The components of the contact force vector are of course F and N. And since the angle between the weight vector and the x-axis is 50°, its components are $-49\cos 50°$ and $-49\sin 50°$ (make sure you understand why these are both negative). Finally, the components of the acceleration vector are -2 and 0. Thus Newton's law tells us that

$$\begin{pmatrix} F \\ N \end{pmatrix} + \begin{pmatrix} -49\cos 50 \\ -49\sin 50 \end{pmatrix} = 5\begin{pmatrix} -2 \\ 0 \end{pmatrix}$$

Hence $\qquad\qquad\qquad F \;-\; 49\cos 50 \;=\; -10 \qquad\qquad$ **1**

and $\qquad\qquad\qquad N \;-\; 49\sin 50 \;=\; 0 \qquad\qquad$ **2**

and we get the same answer as before.

With some practice one can jump straight from the space diagram to **1** and **2**. This process is known as *resolving*: we resolve 'along the plane' to get **1**, 'normal to the plane' to get **2**. The process of resolving often strikes students as being unnecessarily complicated, but in many problems involving several forces an approach via resolving is much more efficient than the vector diagram approach.

EXAMPLE A train weighs 1 tonne and free-wheels at a steady speed down a slope of 1 in 20. Find the resistance to motion (due to wind, etc.). When it reaches the level ground, what is the deceleration if the resistance remains the same?

In figure 7.9a, $\sin\alpha = 1/20$ (one up for every 20 along the slope, not like an ordinary gradient). There are three forces on the train: the weight W, the resistance R up the slope, and the normal force P from the ground. Since

(a)   (b)

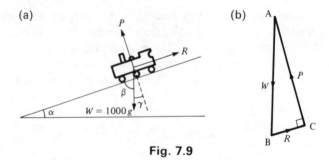

Fig. 7.9

there is no acceleration, these forces sum to zero, and we can draw a rough triangle of forces ABC (figure 7.9b). Clearly angle C = 90°. Now angle A equals the angle marked γ in the space diagram, and therefore equals α, because

$$\gamma = 90 - \beta = 90 - (90 - \alpha) = 90 - 90 + \alpha = \alpha$$

Thus (from the triangle of forces)

$$R = 9800 \sin \alpha = 9800 \times \frac{1}{20} = 490 \quad (N)$$

Figure 7.10a shows the situation when the train reaches the level ground. Note that the train is moving to the left: but since it is *decelerating*, a is shown pointing to the right.

(a)   (b)

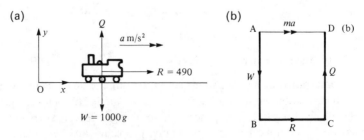

Fig. 7.10

The total force on the train is $\begin{pmatrix} 490 \\ Q - 9800 \end{pmatrix}$, and the acceleration is $\begin{pmatrix} a \\ 0 \end{pmatrix}$.

Hence by Newton's law, $\begin{pmatrix} 490 \\ Q - 9800 \end{pmatrix} = 1000 \begin{pmatrix} a \\ 0 \end{pmatrix}$.

Therefore $490 = 1000\,a$, and so $a = 0.49$.

So the deceleration is $0.49 \, \text{m/s}^2$.

We have not used the vector diagram (figure 7.10b) in our solution, but it does show very plainly the relationship between the various quantities.

Note, by the way, that the normal force Q in figure 7.10a may well be different from P in figure 7.9a, since contact forces may change when circumstances change. In fact, as is easy to find from our work, $P = 9800 \cos \alpha = 9788$ (N), whereas $Q = 9800$ (N).

Note too that in reality the resisting force R would not remain constant as the speed began to fall on the level: so all we can really say is that the *initial* deceleration would be $0.49 \, \text{m/s}^2$.

EXERCISE 7C

1. A 1 tonne mass is moving on a smooth horizontal plane, pulled by a 500 N horizontal force. Use Newton's second law to show (with obvious notation) that $\begin{pmatrix} 500 \\ R-9800 \end{pmatrix} = 1000 \begin{pmatrix} a \\ 0 \end{pmatrix}$, and hence find the acceleration, and the contact force from the ground.

2. Find the acceleration and the contact force in question 1 if the 500 N pull is now at $20°$ to the horizontal.

3. Repeat question 1 if the ground is rough now, and a frictional force of 200 N acts.

4. Repeat question 2 if there is also a frictional force of 200 N.

5. In question 1, the ground is rough and the acceleration is $0.1 \, \text{m/s}^2$. Find the frictional force and the normal force.

6. In question 2, the ground is rough and the acceleration is $0.2 \, \text{m/s}^2$. Find the frictional force.

7. A 10 kg mass sits on a rough plane at $25°$ to the horizontal. Find the frictional force and the normal force. If the roughness can only provide a frictional force of 3 N, find the acceleration of the mass.

8. A 20 kg mass is moving down a slope at $15°$ to the horizontal with an acceleration of $1 \, \text{m/s}^2$. Find the frictional force and the normal force.

9. A 5 kg mass is being dragged up a smooth plane at $35°$ to the horizontal, by means of a force of 40 N which acts at $20°$ to the plane (and so at $55°$ to the horizontal). Find the (normal) contact force and the acceleration.

10. In question 9, if the plane is rough and the acceleration is $0.5 \, \text{m/s}^2$, find the frictional force and the normal force.

11. The resistance to motion of an engine of mass 3 tonnes is 100 N/tonne. What is the total resistance? The engine goes up a slope of 1 in 40 with an acceleration of 0.05 m/s^2. Calculate the driving force. With the same driving force and resistance, what would be the acceleration (a) on the level, and (b) going down the 1 in 40 slope.

12. Repeat question 11 if the engine has mass 2 tonnes, the resistance is 200 N/tonne, the slope is 1 in 50, and the acceleration is 0.08 m/s^2.

13. What is the steepest slope (give the angle to the horizontal) up which an engine of mass 1 tonne can go with a driving force of 500 N (and no resistance)? Note that there would be no acceleration under these conditions.

8 ALGEBRA II

8.1 SURDS

Greek mathematicians based much of their theory of geometry on the assumption that, once a unit of length has been fixed, there corresponds to every line segment a unique number (nowadays referred to as a *real* number) that represents the line segment's length. Given two line segments, it is of course often possible to choose the unit in such a way that both lengths are represented by whole numbers: for example, if the lengths measured in feet were the fractions 2/3 and 3/4, then measured in inches they would become the whole numbers 8 and 9. The Greeks very soon realised, however, that this is not always possible. They proved for instance that the number expressing the ratio between the hypotenuse of an isosceles right-angled triangle and either of the other sides, i.e. $\sqrt{2}$, cannot be expressed in terms of whole numbers. In other words, they proved that the number $\sqrt{2}$ is *irrational*: it cannot be expressed in the form p/q, where p and q are integers. The Greeks thus established the existence of irrational numbers. Later mathematicians have proved that in fact almost all real numbers are irrational, although the task of proving that certain numbers (π is a notorious example) are irrational has turned out to be extremely difficult.

Irrational numbers like $\sqrt{2}$, $\sqrt[3]{5}$, and $\sqrt{(3/4)}$, which are roots of rational numbers but are not themselves rational, are called *surds*. You have already met such numbers in earlier chapters:

e.g. $\tan 60° = \sqrt{3}$, the length of the vector $\begin{pmatrix} 4 \\ 5 \end{pmatrix}$ is $\sqrt{41}$ units.

Before we move on to consider briefly some of the properties of these numbers, it should be noted that $\sqrt{2}$ always means the *positive* number whose square is 2, so that $\sqrt{2} = +1.414\,213\,562$ approximately. The *negative* square root of 2 is written $-\sqrt{2}$. However, because there is no positive number whose cube is -8, we do write $\sqrt[3]{(-8)} = -2$.

Now suppose that a and b are two positive numbers. If we square $\sqrt{(a \times b)}$, we get $a \times b$, and if we square $\sqrt{a} \times \sqrt{b}$, we also get $a \times b$. Since $\sqrt{(a \times b)}$ and $\sqrt{a} \times \sqrt{b}$ are both positive numbers, they must therefore be equal to each other: $\sqrt{(a \times b)} = \sqrt{a} \times \sqrt{b}$. In the same way we can easily establish that $\sqrt{(a \div b)} = \sqrt{a} \div \sqrt{b}$.

Exactly similar rules apply to cube roots, fourth roots, and so on.

EXAMPLE Write $\sqrt{45}$ in terms of the simplest possible surd.

Now $\qquad\qquad\qquad 45 = 9 \times 5 = 3^2 \times 5$

and so $\qquad\qquad\quad \sqrt{45} = \sqrt{(9 \times 5)} = \sqrt{9} \times \sqrt{5} = 3\sqrt{5}$

EXAMPLE Express each of $2\sqrt{3}$ and $5 \div \sqrt{6}$ as square roots.

$$2\sqrt{3} = \sqrt{4} \times \sqrt{3} = \sqrt{(4 \times 3)} = \sqrt{12}$$

and $\qquad\qquad\quad 5 \div \sqrt{6} = \sqrt{25} \div \sqrt{6} = \sqrt{(25/6)}$

EXAMPLE Simplify $\sqrt{3} - \sqrt{27} + \sqrt{48} - \sqrt{12}$.

Now

$$\sqrt{3} - \sqrt{27} + \sqrt{48} - \sqrt{12} = \sqrt{3} - (\sqrt{9} \times \sqrt{3}) + (\sqrt{16} \times \sqrt{3}) - (\sqrt{4} \times \sqrt{3})$$
$$= \sqrt{3} - 3\sqrt{3} + 4\sqrt{3} - 2\sqrt{3}$$
$$= 0$$

EXERCISE 8A

1. Square the following:

(a) $\sqrt{6} \times \sqrt{7}$,   (b) $\sqrt{p} \div \sqrt{3}$,   (c) $1 \div \sqrt{2}$,   (d) $(4\sqrt{a}) \div \sqrt{(3b)}$.

2. Simplify the following:

(a) $\sqrt{12}$,   (b) $\sqrt{40}$,   (c) $\sqrt{32}$,   (d) $\sqrt{60}$,   (e) $\sqrt{24}$,

(f) $\sqrt{63}$,   (g) $\sqrt{98}$,   (h) $\sqrt{512}$,   (i) $\sqrt{810}$.

3. Express each as a single square root:

(a) $2\sqrt{6}$,   (b) $5\sqrt{6}$,   (c) $8\sqrt{8}$,   (d) $\sqrt{3} \div 4$,

(e) $3 \div \sqrt{6}$,   (f) $\sqrt{6} \div 3$.

4. Simplify the following:

(a) $\sqrt{45} - 2\sqrt{20} + \sqrt{125}$

(b) $\sqrt{48} + \sqrt{12} - 2\sqrt{27}$

(c) $\sqrt{490} - \sqrt{250} + 2\sqrt{40}$

(d) $3\sqrt{8} + 2\sqrt{18} - 4\sqrt{50}$

(e) $\sqrt{24} - 5\sqrt{6} + \sqrt{216} + 2\sqrt{294}$

(f) $\sqrt{24} - 3\sqrt{6} - \sqrt{216} + \sqrt{294}$

5. Multiply out, and express in the form $a + b\sqrt{c}$:

   (a) $(\sqrt{5} + 3)^2$ (b) $(1 + \sqrt{2})(3 + 2\sqrt{2})$

   (c) $(\sqrt{3} + 2\sqrt{2})^2$ (d) $(\sqrt{5} - \sqrt{3})(\sqrt{5} + \sqrt{3})$

6. Find out how the Pythagoreans proved that $\sqrt{2}$ is an irrational number, and explain their argument as clearly as you can. Then modify the argument to establish that $\sqrt{3}$ is also an irrational number.

7. Prove that the sum and product of any two rational numbers must also be rational, but show by means of examples that the set of irrational numbers is *not* closed under addition or multiplication.

8.2 THE LAWS OF INDICES

If n is a positive integer, then a^n means $(a \times a \times a \times \ldots \times a)$, where the bracket contains n a's all multiplied together. From this elementary definition, we can immediately deduce the three so-called *index laws*. These three laws state that if m and n are positive integers, then:

(1) $a^m \times a^n = a^{m+n}$

(2) $a^m \div a^n = a^{m-n}$ (for $m > n$)

(3) $(a^m)^n = a^{mn}$

If we now assume that these laws hold for *all* values of m and n, and explore the consequences of that assumption, we can discover how the elementary definition of a^n must be extended to cover three new cases: the case when n is a fraction, the case when n equals 0, and the case when n is negative.

FRACTIONAL INDICES   The first law gives

$$4^{1/2} \times 4^{1/2} = 4^{1/2 + 1/2} = 4^1 = 4$$

This demonstrates that $4^{1/2}$ must be a square root of 4, and we obviously prefer the positive root, i.e. 2.

Similarly $27^{1/3} \times 27^{1/3} = 27^{2/3}$

and so $27^{1/3} \times 27^{1/3} \times 27^{1/3} = 27^{2/3 + 1/3} = 27^1 = 27$

i.e. $(27^{1/3})^3 = 27 \Rightarrow 27^{1/3} = \sqrt[3]{27} = 3$

        More generally, $\underline{a^{1/n} = \sqrt[n]{a}}$.

The third law now suggests that

$$8^{2/3} = (8^{1/3})^2 = (\sqrt[3]{8})^2 = 2^2 = 4$$

or $8^{2/3} = (8^2)^{1/3} = \sqrt[3]{(8^2)} = \sqrt[3]{64} = 4$

        More generally, $\underline{a^{m/n} = (\sqrt[n]{a})^m = \sqrt[n]{(a^m)}}$.

ZERO INDEX   The second law gives

$$2^1 \div 2^1 = 2^{1-1} = 2^0$$

But clearly $2^1 \div 2^1 = 1$, so that 2^0 must equal 1.

Similarly, $10^2 \div 10^2 = 10^0 \Rightarrow 10^0 = 1$.

In general, $\underline{a^0 = 1}$ (provided $a \neq 0$).

NEGATIVE INDICES   The second law gives

$$10^0 \div 10^n = 10^{0-n} = 10^{-n}$$

But $10^0 = 1$, and so $1 \div 10^n = 10^{-n}$,

and in general, $\underline{a^{-n} = 1/a^n}$ (provided $a \neq 0$).

These results are illustrated in the evaluation of $(16/81)^{-3/4}$.

The minus sign shows us that we must turn the fraction upside down (i.e. reciprocate it), the 3 shows that we must cube, and the 4 that we must find the fourth root. We can perform these operations in any order. Thus:

$$(16/81)^{-3/4} = (81/16)^{3/4} = (3/2)^3 = 27/8$$

Alternatively:

$$(16/81)^{-3/4} = (2/3)^{-3} = (8/27)^{-1} = 27/8$$

In chapter 4, we learnt the rule that the derivative of x^n is nx^{n-1}. This rule is in fact valid even when the index n is a fraction or a negative number.

EXAMPLE   Find dy/dx if (a) $y = \sqrt{x}$, (b) $y = 1/x^3$.

(a) If $y = \sqrt{x} = x^{1/2}$ then $dy/dx = \frac{1}{2}x^{-1/2} = \dfrac{1}{2\sqrt{x}}$.

(b) If $y = 1/x^3 = x^{-3}$ then $dy/dx = -3x^{-4} = \dfrac{-3}{x^4}$.

EXERCISE 8B

1. Find the values of:

    (a) $196^{1/2}$ (b) $27^{1/3}$ (c) $125^{2/3}$ (d) $(1\frac{9}{16})^{1/2}$

    (e) $64^{-1/3}$ (f) $9^{3/2}$

2. Find the values of:

    (a) $27^{-2/3}$ (b) $(49/16)^{1/2}$ (c) $(9/25)^{-3/2}$ (d) $1.331^{1/3}$

    (e) $0.16^{-1/2}$ (f) $4^{1/2} \div 8^{-1/3}$

3. Find the values of:

(a) $\dfrac{32^{1/3} \times 2^{1/3}}{8^{1/3}}$ (b) $\dfrac{27^{1/2} \times 243^{1/2}}{27^{2/3}}$

(c) $\dfrac{16^0 \times 8^{5/2}}{128^{3/2}}$ (d) $\dfrac{6^{1/3} \times 24^{1/2}}{54^{1/2} \times 48^{1/3}}$

4. Use your calculator to evaluate $\dfrac{(273)^{-0.4} \times \sqrt[4]{(0.56)}}{(97.8)^{4/3}}$

5. Simplify:

(a) $3^n \times 27^{2n} \div 9^{3n}$,   (b) $16^{n/4} \div 2^{-2n} \times 4^{n+2}$,   (c) $25^{n/2} \div 5^{n+1} \times 125^{-1/3}$

6. Solve: (a) $8^x = 32$,   (b) $243^y = 1/9$.

7. Find dy/dx if   (a) $y = \sqrt[3]{x}$,   (b) $y = \sqrt{(x^3)}$,   (c) $y = 5/x^2$.

8.3 A PROBLEM LEADING TO AN INDEX EQUATION

In a developing country, the school population is growing at a rate of 8% each year. In the immediate past a high priority has been given to providing educational facilities, so that there are now enough places in the existing schools to cope with a 70% increase on present numbers of children. However, the economy is in recession and the new government has said that no more building will take place in the next decade. When will the schools become full?

Each year the school population is multiplied by the scale factor 1.08. So if the schools become full after n years, we have

$$1.08^n = 1.70$$

We can solve this equation by the method of decimal search, which can be continued until n has been found to any required degree of accuracy. The results in the table are obtained by using a calculator.

n	5	9	7	6.8	6.9	6.89	6.895
1.08^n	1.469	1.999	1.714	1.688	1.7007	1.6994	1.70003

So successively we are able to say:

$5 < n < 9$, $5 < n < 7$, $6.8 < n < 7$, $6.8 < n < 6.9$, $6.89 < n < 6.90$,

$6.89 < n < 6.895$.

The final result allows us to say

$$1.08^n = 1.70 \Rightarrow n = 6.89 \quad \text{(to 3 s.f.)}$$

Of course, in this particular problem, $n = 6.89$ represents an absurd degree of accuracy. In other problems, however, this might not be sufficiently precise, and it would be possible to obtain greater accuracy by continuing with the decimal-search process.

EXERCISE 8C

1. Solve the following equations with a calculator, using the decimal-search method, and tabulating your results as in the example above. Your final answers should be accurate to 3 s.f.

(a) $1.1^n = 2$, (b) $1.1^n = 3$, (c) $1.1^n = 4$,

(d) $85^n = 17$, (e) $85^n = 0.2$.

2. On 1 January 1967 the dictator of a country announced that the country's population was to double by 1977. During the five years 1967–1971 the population increased at a rate of 7% per year. Show that if this rate had been maintained during the next five years, the dictator's target would have been very nearly met. Sadly, however, the rate since 1971 has fallen to a mere 3% per year. When in fact will the target be achieved?

8.4 USING INDICES FOR CALCULATION

Until recently, it would not have been possible to solve equations like those in exercise 8C using the decimal-search method without a very great deal of effort. To investigate how such equations would have been solved, we need to know something about logarithms. As a bonus, we shall find that there is an alternative method of solving equations of the form $a^n = b$, which is much quicker than the decimal-search method.

The following table gives powers of 2:

2^1	2^2	2^3	2^4	2^5	2^6	2^7	2^8	2^9	2^{10}	2^{11}	2^{12}
2	4	8	16	32	64	128	256	512	1024	2048	4096

Applying the laws of indices, we can use the table to do certain calculations. For example:

$$32 \times 64 = 2^5 \times 2^6 = 2^{11} = 2048$$

$$512 \div 16 = 2^9 \div 2^4 = 2^5 = 32$$

$$32^2 = (2^5)^2 = 2^{10} = 1024$$

EXERCISE 8D

1. Use the table above to find 16×64, 512×4, 128×32, 256×16.

2. Use the table to find $2048 \div 64$, $4096 \div 8$, $512 \div 16$, $1024 \div 32$.

3. Use the table to find 32^2, 16^3, 4^4, $\sqrt{1024}$, $\sqrt[3]{4096}$.

4. Construct a similar table which gives powers of 4, and use it to find $\sqrt{16\,777\,216}$.

In this work, your attention has been focused on the indices, rather than the original numbers, and the calculations with the indices have been markedly easier than the original problems. In fact, the multiplication of numbers has been reduced to the addition of their indices, division has been reduced to the subtraction of indices, and a number is (say) cubed by multiplying its index by 3. The first man to realise the advantages to be gained by this method was John Napier, Baron of Merchiston. The first public announcement of the discovery was made in his *Mirifici Logarithmorum Canonis Descriptio*, published in 1614, which contained a description of the nature of logarithms. The *Descriptio* was translated into English by Edward Wright (an English mathematician) under the title *A Description of the Admirable Table of Logarithms*, and was published in London in 1616, shortly after Wright's death. There is evidence that Napier had privately communicated a summary of his results to the astronomer Tycho Brahe as early as 1594.

In calculation by logarithms, numbers are multiplied or divided by being first expressed as powers of a single base number, which for practical work is always 10. By the use of fractional and negative indices, any positive number can be so expressed.

We have
$$10^{0.5} = 10^{1/2} = \sqrt{10} = 3.162$$
$$10^{1.5} = 10^1 \times 10^{1/2} = 31.62$$
$$10^{0.25} = 10^{1/4} = \sqrt{(10^{1/2})} = 1.779$$
$$10^{0.75} = 10^{3/4} = \sqrt{(10^{3/2})} = 5.623$$
and
$$10^0 = 1 \quad \text{and} \quad 10^1 = 10$$

By means of these results, a graph can now be constructed which can be used to express any number x between 1 and 10 in the form 10^n. The index n will lie between 0 and 1, and is most conveniently given as a decimal. Further points to assist in drawing the curve may be obtained by using the method outlined above to calculate $10^{1/8}$, $10^{3/8}$, $10^{5/8}$, $10^{7/8}$, and so on. The graph is shown in figure 8.1.

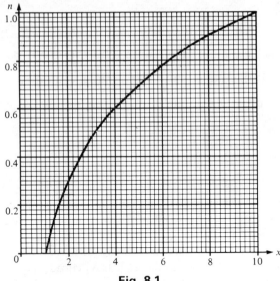

Fig. 8.1

EXERCISE 8E

Use figure 8.1 to answer the following questions.

1. Express as powers of 10:   2, 3, 4, 5, 6, 7, 8, 9, 10.

2. Express as powers of 10:   3.7, 4.6, 6.9, 8.4, 9.6.

3. Express as ordinary numbers: $10^{0.2}$, $10^{0.4}$, $10^{0.6}$, $10^{0.7}$, $10^{0.8}$, $10^{0.9}$, 10^{1}.

4. Express as ordinary numbers: $10^{0.25}$, $10^{0.42}$, $10^{0.57}$, $10^{0.64}$, $10^{0.78}$, $10^{0.95}$.

5. Notice that $2 \times 4 = 10^{0.3} \times 10^{0.6} = 10^{0.9} = 8$. Similarly work out 2×3, 3×3, 2.5×3.

Your readings from the graph will not be absolutely precise, so your results may not be quite correct, but you will see the principle of the methods to be used later.

The graph in figure 8.1 shows values of x between 1 and 10 only, but we do not have to extend the graph in order to express values of x outside this restricted range in the form 10^{n}. For example,

$$20 = 2 \times 10 = 10^{0.3} \times 10^{1} = 10^{1.3}$$

$$200 = 2 \times 100 = 10^{0.3} \times 10^{2} = 10^{2.3}$$

$$2600 = 2.6 \times 1000 = 10^{0.4} \times 10^{3} = 10^{3.4}$$

The first step in this process is equivalent to expressing the number x in standard index form (i.e. scientific notation).

Numbers less than 1 are dealt with in a broadly similar way: i.e. we first express the number x in standard index form, and then refer to the graph. For example,

$$0.2 \quad = 2 \times 10^{-1} = 10^{0.3} \times 10^{-1} = 10^{-0.7}$$

$$0.02 \quad = 2 \times 10^{-2} = 10^{0.3} \times 10^{-2} = 10^{-1.7}$$

$$0.002 = 2 \times 10^{-3} = 10^{0.3} \times 10^{-3} = 10^{-2.7}$$

We can thus express any positive number x, however small, in the form 10^n. But note that we cannot do this for 0 or for any negative number.

We can also express any power of 10 as an ordinary number. For example,

$$10^{-2.4} = 10^{0.6} \times 10^{-3} = 4 \times 10^{-3} = 0.004$$

EXERCISE 8F

Use figure 8.1 to answer the following questions.

1. Express each of the following as a power of 10, i.e. in the form 10^n:
5, 50, 5000, 7.6, 76, 760, 7600.

2. Express as ordinary numbers:
$10^{0.3}$, $10^{1.3}$, $10^{2.3}$, $10^{0.57}$, $10^{1.57}$, $10^{2.57}$, $10^{0.43}$, $10^{2.43}$, $10^{4.43}$, $10^{1.27}$, $10^{2.54}$.

3. Express as powers of 10:
0.3, 0.003, 0.0003, 0.07, 0.0007, 0.7, 0.73, 0.073, 0.0073, 0.023, 0.008 45.

4. Express as ordinary numbers:
$10^{-0.3}$, $10^{-1.3}$, $10^{-3.3}$, $10^{-1.4}$, $10^{-0.4}$, $10^{-2.4}$, $10^{-0.88}$, $10^{-3.88}$, $10^{-1.88}$, $10^{-2.75}$, $10^{-0.75}$, $10^{-1.75}$, $10^{-0.95}$, $10^{-1.95}$, $10^{-4.95}$.

8.5 LOGARITHMS

When a number is expressed as a power of 10, the index is called the *logarithm* (base 10) of the number. For example,

$$10^{0.3010} \quad = 2.00, \quad \text{so} \quad \log_{10} 2.00 = \quad 0.3010$$

$$10^{-0.6021} = 0.25, \quad \text{so} \quad \log_{10} 0.25 = -0.6021$$

Note, in particular, that logarithms are indices, so that we should expect the behaviour of logarithms to be governed by the laws of indices, already discussed in section 8.2.

It is by no means essential that 10 should be the base for logarithms—it is merely the most convenient choice for practical calculations. In fact, referring to our earlier table of powers of 2, we have

$$2^6 = 64, \quad \text{so} \quad \log_2 64 = 6$$

and $$2^3 = 8, \quad \text{so} \quad \log_2 8 = 3$$

A more general definition of logarithms would be:

$$x = a^n \Leftrightarrow n = \log_a x \quad (a > 0)$$

Putting $a = 10$ in this general definition, we obtain:

$$x = 10^n \Leftrightarrow n = \log_{10} x \quad \text{(sometimes written } \lg x)$$

Given x, we can find n by using the log key on a calculator. Conversely, given n, we find x by using the inverse log key.

Note that figure 8.1 shows the graph of $\log_{10} x$ for $1 \leqslant x \leqslant 10$.

EXERCISE 8G

Use your calculator in this exercise.

1. Find the logarithm (base 10) of each of the following numbers:
6.84, 68.4, 6840, 9.082, 908.2, 908.25, 5.2, 52, 0.52, 0.052.

2. Express as ordinary numbers:
$10^{0.671}$, $10^{1.671}$, $10^{2.671}$, $10^{-0.329}$, $10^{-1.329}$, $10^{1.7}$, $10^{0.7}$, $10^{-0.3}$.

3. Find the logarithm (base 2) of each of the following numbers, referring if necessary to the table given in section 8.4:
1, 2, 128, 1024, $\frac{1}{4}$, 0.5, 16 777 216.

4. Estimate the value of the logarithm (base 2) of each of the following numbers:
5, 10, 100, 1000, 1 000 000, $\frac{1}{3}$, 0.1.

8.6 SOME CALCULATIONS USING LOGARITHMS

(a) $7.57 \times 26.04 = 10^{0.8791} \times 10^{1.4156}$ $\quad \begin{bmatrix} \log \ 7.57 = 0.8791 \\ \log 26.04 = 1.4156 \end{bmatrix}$

$\qquad\qquad\qquad = 10^{0.8791 + 1.4156}$

$\qquad\qquad\qquad = 10^{2.2947}$

$\qquad\qquad\qquad = 197 \quad \text{(using } 10^x \text{ key, with } x = 2.2947)$

(b) $191.3 \div 46.7 = 10^{2.2817} \div 10^{1.6693}$

$$= 10^{2.2817 - 1.6693}$$

$$= 10^{0.6124}$$

$$= 4.10$$

(c) $(28.1)^2 = (10^{1.4487})^2 = 10^{1.4487 \times 2}$

$$= 10^{2.8974} = 790$$

(d) $\sqrt[3]{48.3} = \sqrt[3]{(10^{1.6839})} = 10^{1.6839 \div 3}$

$$= 10^{0.5613} = 3.64$$

Note that although the answers in (a) to (d) are given rounded to 3 s.f., it would have been quite easy to obtain further significant figures if we had wished.

Of course, logarithms are no longer used for practical calculations like these, which nowadays can be done so much more efficiently with a calculator, but the examples illustrate how logarithms could be used (and were used until a few years ago).

However, if we return to the solution of the equation $1.08^n = 1.7$, we are now in a position to see how logarithms can help us to solve it with less effort.

EXAMPLE   Solve $1.08^n = 1.70$.

Expressing 1.08 and 1.70 as powers of 10, we have

$$1.08 = 10^{0.0334} \quad \text{and} \quad 1.70 = 10^{0.2304}$$

So $\qquad 1.08^n = 1.70 \quad$ becomes $\quad (10^{0.0334})^n = 10^{0.2304}$

i.e. $\qquad\qquad\qquad\qquad\qquad 10^{0.0334n} = 10^{0.2304}$

Therefore $\qquad 0.0334n = 0.2304 \qquad$ (equating powers of 10)

$$n = \frac{0.2304}{0.0334} \qquad \text{i.e.} \quad \frac{\log_{10} 1.70}{\log_{10} 1.08}$$

$$= 6.89 \quad \text{(to 3 s.f.)}$$

EXAMPLE   Solve $1.5^n = 100$.

Expressing 1.5 and 100 as powers of 10, we have

$$(10^{0.17609})^n = 10^2$$

$$10^{0.17609n} = 10^2$$

$$0.17609n = 2$$

$$n = \frac{2}{0.17609} \qquad \text{i.e.} \quad \frac{\log 100}{\log 1.5}$$

$$= 11.4 \quad \text{(to 3 s.f.)}$$

Suppose now that we need to solve the equation $c^n = k$, where c and k are given constants (1.5 and 100 in the previous example). Expressing c and k as powers of 10, we have

$$(10^{\log c})^n = 10^{\log k}$$

$$10^{\log c \times n} = 10^{\log k}$$

$$n \log c = \log k$$

$$n = \frac{\log k}{\log c}$$

This process is often described as taking the logarithms of both sides of the given equation. The method relies on the fact (discussed more fully in the next section) that $\log(c^n) = n \log c$.

EXAMPLE   Solve $0.95^n = 0.02$.

Taking logarithms of both sides of the equation, we have

$$\log(0.95^n) = \log(0.02)$$

$$n \log 0.95 = \log 0.02$$

$$n = \frac{\log 0.02}{\log 0.95} = \frac{-1.698970004}{-0.022276394} = 76.3 \quad \text{(to 3 s.f.)}$$

Check: $0.95^{76.2} = 0.0200696$ (by calculator)

$0.95^{76.3} = 0.0199669$ and $0.95^{76.25} = 0.0200182$

Therefore $n = 76.3$ *is correct to 3 s.f.*

EXERCISE 8H

1. Solve: (a) $3^n = 7$, (b) $5.8^m = 2.3$, (c) $0.47^x = 159$.

2. The half-life of a radioactive nuclide is 58 minutes. How much time elapses before the activity reduces to (a) 1% and (b) 0.01% of its initial value?

8.7 LAWS OF LOGARITHMS

In section 8.2 we developed the three laws of indices. We now consider the corresponding laws of logarithms.
Let $x = a^m$, $y = a^n$. Then $\log_a x = m$ and $\log_a y = n$. Therefore

$$xy = a^{m+n} \Rightarrow \log_a(xy) = m+n = \log_a x + \log_a y$$
$$x/y = a^{m-n} \Rightarrow \log_a(x/y) = m-n = \log_a x - \log_a y$$
$$x^n = a^{mn} \Rightarrow \log_a(x^n) = m \times n = n\log_a x$$

Thus we have the following three logarithm laws corresponding to the three index laws:

$$a^{m+n} = a^m \times a^n \qquad \log x + \log y = \log xy \qquad \textbf{1}$$
$$a^{m-n} = a^m \div a^n \qquad \log x - \log y = \log x/y \qquad \textbf{2}$$
$$a^{mn} = (a^m)^n \qquad n\log x = \log x^n \qquad \textbf{3}$$

EXAMPLE Find the exact value of $\log_{10}12 + \log_{10}25 - \log_{10}3$.

$$\log_{10}12 + \log_{10}25 - \log_{10}3 = \log_{10}(12 \times 25 \div 3) \qquad \text{using } \textbf{1} \text{ and } \textbf{2}$$
$$= \log_{10}100 = 2$$

EXAMPLE Express $(2\log_{10}a - \log_{10}2c + 2)$ as the logarithm (base 10) of a single number, and express $\log_{10}\sqrt[3]{(a^4b/c^2)}$ in terms of the logarithms of a, b, c.

$$2\log_{10}a - \log_{10}2c + 2 = \log_{10}a^2 - \log_{10}2c + \log_{10}100 \qquad \text{using } \textbf{3}$$
$$= \log_{10}(100a^2/2c) \qquad \text{using } \textbf{1} \text{ and } \textbf{2}$$
$$= \log_{10}(50a^2/c)$$
$$\log_{10}\sqrt[3]{(a^4b/c^2)} = \log_{10}(a^4b/c^2)^{1/3} = \tfrac{1}{3}\log_{10}(a^4b/c^2) \qquad \text{using } \textbf{3}$$
$$= \tfrac{1}{3}[\log_{10}(a^4b) - \log_{10}(c^2)] \qquad \text{using } \textbf{2}$$
$$= \tfrac{1}{3}(4\log_{10}a + \log_{10}b - 2\log_{10}c) \qquad \text{using } \textbf{1} \text{ and } \textbf{3}$$
$$= \tfrac{4}{3}\log_{10}a + \tfrac{1}{3}\log_{10}b - \tfrac{2}{3}\log_{10}c$$

EXAMPLE Simplify $3 \log 2 + 2 \log 3 - 2 \log 6$ and $\log 81 / \log 9$.

Note that the logarithm bases are not specified in this example; this does not matter provided the logs in each calculation are all to the same base.

$$3 \log 2 + 2 \log 3 - 2 \log 6 = \log 2^3 + \log 3^2 - \log 6^2$$
$$= \log(2^3 \times 3^2 \div 6^2) = \log 2$$

$$\frac{\log 81}{\log 9} = \frac{\log 9^2}{\log 9} = \frac{2 \log 9}{\log 9} = 2$$

EXAMPLE Given that $\log_{10} 2 = 0.301\,030$, find without tables or calculator the value (to 5 d.p.) of $\log_{10} 8$, $\log_{10} 160$, $\log_{10} 5$.

$$\log 8 = \log 2^3 = 3 \log 2 = 0.903\,09$$
$$\log 160 = \log(2^4 \times 10) = 4 \log 2 + 1 = 2.204\,12$$
$$\log 5 = \log(10/2) = 1 - \log 2 = 0.698\,97$$

Most calculators have two logarithm keys. Apart from the key labelled 'log' which of course provides logarithms to base 10 and is the one normally used by a pre-A-level student, there may be another, usually labelled ln, which gives logarithms to base e (e is a number of the utmost importance in more advanced work). If you wish to calculate the value of a logarithm to any other base, you must proceed along the lines of the following example.

EXAMPLE Find the value of $\log_3 7$, correct to 2 d.p.

Let $n = \log_3 7$.

Then $\qquad\qquad\qquad 3^n = 7 \qquad$ (converting to an index equation)

$$\log_{10}(3^n) = \log_{10} 7$$
$$n \log_{10} 3 = \log_{10} 7$$

So $\qquad\qquad\qquad n = \dfrac{\log_{10} 7}{\log_{10} 3} \Rightarrow \log_3 7 = 1.77 \quad$ (by calculator)

The previous example illustrates the general method of finding logarithms to any base. Suppose we are given a positive number c, and wish to find its logarithm to base b, where b is also a positive number.

We first of all choose any convenient positive number a to be our working base: in a numerical problem, the best choice is probably $a = 10$, or we can choose $a = e$ if our calculator has the ln key.

Now let $n = \log_b c$.

Then

$$b^n = c$$

$$\log_a(b^n) = \log_a c$$

$$n \log_a b = \log_a c$$

So

$$\log_b c \times \log_a b = \log_a c \Rightarrow \log_b c = \frac{\log_a c}{\log_a b}$$

EXAMPLE Find the value of $\log_2 1000$.

$$\log_2 1000 = \frac{\log_{10} 1000}{\log_{10} 2} \quad \text{(we naturally choose } a = 10\text{)}$$

$$= \frac{3}{0.301\,029\,995} = 9.965\,784\,285 \quad \text{(by calculator)}$$

Or

$$\log_2 1000 = \frac{\ln 1000}{\ln 2} = \frac{6.907\,755\,279}{0.693\,147\,18} = 9.965\,784\,285$$

EXERCISE 8I

1. Express as the logarithm of a single number:

$\log 5 + \log 6, \ \log 6 - \log 5, \ 4 \log 3, \ 5 \log 2, \ \frac{1}{2} \log 81, \ -\log 3$

2. Express in terms of $\log x$ and $\log y$:

$\log xy, \ \log x/y, \ \log x^4, \ \log xy^3, \ \log x/y^2, \ \log \sqrt[3]{x}, \ \log \sqrt{(x/y)}$

3. Without using tables, find x if:

(a) $\log x = \log 3 + \log 4$

(b) $\log x = \log 17 - \log 3.4$

(c) $\log x = 2 \log 6$

(d) $\log x = 0.5 \log 49$

(e) $\log x = 2 \log 2 + \log 5$

(f) $\log x = 2 \log 8 - 1$

4. By expressing the numbers as powers of 2, solve:

(a) $2^x = 16^3$

(b) $2^x = 1/8$

(c) $2^x = 1/\sqrt{2}$

(d) $2^x = \sqrt{128}$

5. By taking logarithms of both sides, solve the following equations, giving your answers to 6 s.f. in each case:

(a) $5^x = 100$

(b) $7^x = \sqrt{1000}$

(c) $8^x = 0.1$

(d) $9^x = 1\frac{1}{9}$

6. Express in terms of $\log a$, $\log b$, $\log c$:

  (a) $\log (ab)$

  (b) $\log \sqrt{(a/b)}$

  (c) $\log \sqrt{(1/b)}$

  (d) $\log (a^{1/3} b^4 / c^3)$

  (e) $\log \sqrt{(a^2 b / c^3)}$

7. Express as single logarithms:

  (a) $\log 24 - \log 6$

  (b) $\log p + \log q$

  (c) $1 + 2 \log a$

  (d) $2 + 3 \log x - 4 \log y$

  (e) $\log a + 2 \log b - 3 \log c$

8. Simplify:

  (a) $\log_{10} 100$

  (b) $\frac{1}{4} \log_2 256$

  (c) $\frac{1}{2} \log 121$

  (d) $4 \log 3 - \log 81$

  (e) $\dfrac{\log 512}{\log 64}$

9. By taking logarithms of both sides, solve the following equations to 6 s.f.:

  (a) $5^{2x+1} = 0.8$ (find $2x+1$ first, then x)

  (b) $2^x \times 2^{x+1} = 100$

  (c) $2^x \times 3^{x+1} = 12$

9 TRIGONOMETRY II

9.1 BASE VECTORS

As you know, we often use the appropriate bold lower-case letter to denote the position vector of a point. If A is the point $(5, 3)$ for example, then **a** means A's position vector, i.e. $\begin{pmatrix} 5 \\ 3 \end{pmatrix}$.

In particular, the position vectors of $I(1, 0)$ and $J(0, 1)$ are called **i** and **j**. These two vectors are said to be *base* vectors, because any position or displacement vector in the x–y plane can be expressed in terms of them. For example

$$\mathbf{a} = \begin{pmatrix} 5 \\ 3 \end{pmatrix} = 5\begin{pmatrix} 1 \\ 0 \end{pmatrix} + 3\begin{pmatrix} 0 \\ 1 \end{pmatrix} = 5\mathbf{i} + 3\mathbf{j}$$

$$\mathbf{PQ} = \begin{pmatrix} 7 \\ -4 \end{pmatrix} = 7\begin{pmatrix} 1 \\ 0 \end{pmatrix} - 4\begin{pmatrix} 0 \\ 1 \end{pmatrix} = 7\mathbf{i} - 4\mathbf{j}$$

Although we usually choose **i** and **j** as our base vectors, any two non-parallel vectors would in fact serve as a base.

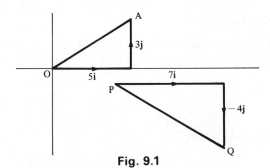

Fig. 9.1

EXAMPLE Express $\mathbf{a} = \begin{pmatrix} 5 \\ 3 \end{pmatrix}$ and $\mathbf{PQ} = \begin{pmatrix} 7 \\ -4 \end{pmatrix}$ in terms of the base vectors $\mathbf{l} = \begin{pmatrix} 2 \\ 1 \end{pmatrix}$ and $\mathbf{m} = \begin{pmatrix} 1 \\ 1 \end{pmatrix}$.

It is fairly easy to see that $\mathbf{a} = 2\mathbf{l} + \mathbf{m}$.

111

Now suppose that $\lambda \begin{pmatrix} 2 \\ 1 \end{pmatrix} + \mu \begin{pmatrix} 1 \\ 1 \end{pmatrix} = \mathbf{PQ}$:

$$\text{then} \qquad 2\lambda + \mu = \quad 7$$
$$\text{and} \qquad \lambda + \mu = -4$$

Solving, we have $\lambda = 11$ and $\mu = -15$; hence $\mathbf{PQ} = \begin{pmatrix} 7 \\ -4 \end{pmatrix} = 11\mathbf{l} - 15\mathbf{m}$

It is obvious that $\mathbf{i}$ and $\mathbf{j}$ are more convenient than $\mathbf{l}$ and $\mathbf{m}$. As we shall see later, $\mathbf{i}$ and $\mathbf{j}$ have two other advantages: they are perpendicular to each other and they are unit vectors.

EXERCISE 9A

1. Express the following in terms of $\mathbf{i}$ and $\mathbf{j}$:

(a) $\begin{pmatrix} 3 \\ 4 \end{pmatrix}$, (b) $\begin{pmatrix} -2 \\ 5 \end{pmatrix}$, (c) $\begin{pmatrix} 7 \\ 0 \end{pmatrix}$, (d) $\begin{pmatrix} 0 \\ -7 \end{pmatrix}$.

2. If $\mathbf{a} = 2\mathbf{i} + \mathbf{j}$ and $\mathbf{b} = 3\mathbf{i} - \mathbf{j}$, express in terms of $\mathbf{i}$ and $\mathbf{j}$: $3\mathbf{a}$, $-2\mathbf{b}$, $\mathbf{a} + \mathbf{b}$, $3\mathbf{a} - 2\mathbf{b}$.

3. Express in terms of $\mathbf{l}$ and $\mathbf{m}$ (as defined above) the position vectors of: $(3, 0)$, $(0, 7)$, $(11, 19)$, $(0, 0)$.

4. Arrange the following vectors in ascending order of magnitude: $4\mathbf{i} - 3\mathbf{j}$, $4\mathbf{l} - 3\mathbf{m}$, $\mathbf{i} + 2\mathbf{j}$, $\mathbf{l} + 2\mathbf{m}$.

5. Why do we need just *two* base vectors in the x–y plane? How many vectors are needed to form a base in one dimension and three dimensions?

9.2 SCALAR PRODUCT

In the expression $5\mathbf{i} + 3\mathbf{j}$, we see the two fundamental vector operations: addition, and multiplication by an ordinary number. We now consider the possibility of multiplying one vector by another. There are in fact several methods of doing this, all of which have their uses in more advanced mathematics, but we shall study only one method.

Since vector multiplication is an entirely new idea, it must be defined with care. If $\mathbf{a}$ and $\mathbf{b}$ are two vectors, of magnitude $|\mathbf{a}|$ and $|\mathbf{b}|$ respectively, and ϕ is the angle between their directions, then their *scalar product* is defined as follows:

$$\mathbf{a} \cdot \mathbf{b} = |\mathbf{a}| \times |\mathbf{b}| \times \cos \phi$$

The right-hand side is the ordinary product of three scalar (i.e. non-vector) quantities, and so **a · b** is a scalar—hence the term 'scalar product'. Note that a dot is invariably used to indicate the scalar product (you should *never* write **ab** or even **a × b**). Since most people read **a · b** as 'a dot b', this method of multiplying vectors is often referred to as dot multiplication.

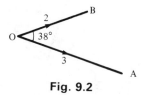

Fig. 9.2

If we know the magnitudes and directions of two vectors, their scalar product is easy to find. For example, in figure 9.2

$$\mathbf{OA} \cdot \mathbf{OB} = 3 \times 2 \times \cos 38°$$

$$= 4.728 \quad (4\,\text{s.f.})$$

In this calculation, we have taken the angle ϕ to be 38°. However, we could equally well have taken ϕ to be $-38°$, or indeed $\pm 322°$, since $\cos(-38) = \cos(\pm 322) = \cos 38$. But 142° (i.e. $180 - 38$) and 218° would not have been correct, since neither of these measures the angle between **OA** and **OB**.

Again, in figure 9.3 (where of course 142° *is* the correct angle)

$$\mathbf{OA} \cdot \mathbf{OC} = 3 \times 2 \times \cos 142°$$

$$= -4.728 \quad (4\,\text{s.f.})$$

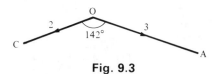

Fig. 9.3

Three important results follow immediately from the definition of the scalar product.

(1) The operation is *commutative* (i.e. **a · b** = **b · a**), since switching **a** and **b** in the definition makes no difference.

(2) The dot product of two perpendicular vectors is zero, since $\cos 90° = 0$. Conversely, if the dot product of two non-zero vectors is zero, then they must be perpendicular.

(3) **a · a** $= |\mathbf{a}| \times |\mathbf{a}| \times \cos 0° = |\mathbf{a}|^2$. Therefore 'squaring' a vector (i.e. dot multiplying it by itself) gives the square of its magnitude.

Here are some more examples of how to calculate the scalar product (or dot product) of two vectors.

EXAMPLE Find $\mathbf{a} \cdot \mathbf{b}$ where $\mathbf{a} = [5, 40°]$ and $\mathbf{b} = [7, 110°]$ (figure 9.4).

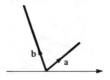

Fig. 9.4

In this case, $\phi = 110 - 40 = 70°$.

So
$$\mathbf{a} \cdot \mathbf{b} = 5 \times 7 \times \cos 70°$$
$$= 11.97 \quad (4 \, \text{s.f.})$$

EXAMPLE Find $\mathbf{c} \cdot \mathbf{d} = [5.16, 68.0°] \cdot [2.37, -72.3°]$ (figure 9.5).

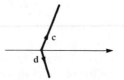

Fig. 9.5

Now $\phi = 68.0 - (-72.3) = 140.3°$.

So
$$\mathbf{c} \cdot \mathbf{d} = 5.16 \times 2.37 \times \cos 140.3°$$
$$= -9.41 \quad (3 \, \text{s.f.})$$

EXAMPLE Calculate $(3\mathbf{i} + 4\mathbf{j}) \cdot 4\mathbf{i}$.

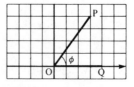

Fig. 9.6

We draw a displacement **OP** equal to $3\mathbf{i} + 4\mathbf{j}$, and a displacement **OQ** equal to $4\mathbf{i}$. We must find out three things: p the magnitude of **OP**, q the magnitude of **OQ**, and ϕ the angle between **OP** and **OQ**. It is easily seen that $p = 5$ and $q = 4$. Is it also fairly obvious that $\cos \phi = 3/5$?

So
$$(3\mathbf{i} + 4\mathbf{j}) \cdot 4\mathbf{i} = pq \cos \phi = 5 \times 4 \times 0.6$$
$$= 12 \text{ exactly}$$

EXAMPLE Calculate $(3\mathbf{i}+4\mathbf{j})\cdot(6\mathbf{i}+6\mathbf{j})$.

We proceed as in the previous example. We already know that $p = 5$, and we can easily see that $q = \sqrt{(6^2+6^2)} = \sqrt{72} = 6\sqrt{2}$.

Now $\phi = \alpha_1-\alpha_2$ (see figure 9.7), where α_1 equals $\arctan(4/3) = 53.130°$ approximately, and α_2 equals $45°$; so $\phi = 53.130-45 = 8.130°$ (3 d.p.).

So
$$(3\mathbf{i}+4\mathbf{j})\cdot(6\mathbf{i}+6\mathbf{j}) = 5\times6\sqrt{2}\times\cos 8.130°$$
$$= 42.00 \quad (4\,\text{s.f.})$$

We shall see later that the answer in fact equals 42 exactly.

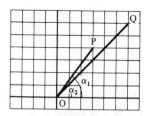

Fig. 9.7

EXAMPLE Find $(-3\mathbf{i}+4\mathbf{j})\cdot(-6\mathbf{i}-6\mathbf{j})$.

Once again $p = 5$ and $q = 6\sqrt{2}$.

But now
$$\phi = \alpha_1+\alpha_2 \quad \text{(see figure 9.8)}$$
$$= 98.130° \quad (3\,\text{d.p.})$$

So
$$(-3\mathbf{i}+4\mathbf{j})\cdot(-6\mathbf{i}-6\mathbf{j}) = 5\times6\sqrt{2}\times\cos 98.130°$$
$$= -6.000 \quad (4\,\text{s.f.})$$

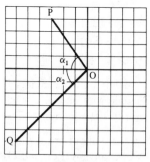

Fig. 9.8

EXAMPLE Find $(-3\mathbf{i}+4\mathbf{j})\cdot(4\mathbf{i}+3\mathbf{j})$.

These vectors are perpendicular (see figure 9.9 overleaf), and so their scalar product equals zero.

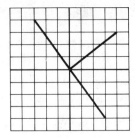

Fig. 9.9

EXAMPLE Find $(-3\mathbf{i}+4\mathbf{j})\cdot(3\mathbf{i}-4\mathbf{j})$.

These vectors point in exactly opposite directions (see figure 9.9), and are both of magnitude 5. So their scalar product equals $5 \times 5 \times \cos 180°$, i.e. -25.

EXERCISE 9B

In questions 1 to 5, the vectors **a** and **b** are given in polar form. In each case, illustrate the two vectors in a freehand sketch, and then calculate $\mathbf{a}\cdot\mathbf{b}$.

 1. $[4, 25°]$ and $[7, 60°]$

 2. $[2.36, 18.7°]$ and $[3.70, 56.3°]$

 3. $[5.61, 154.3°]$ and $[3.05, 37.8°]$

 4. $[6.72, 147.8°]$ and $[2.18, -17.3°]$

 5. $[40.9, 163.1°]$ and $[38.1, -106.9°]$

In questions 6 to 10, the vectors **a** and **b** are given in terms of **i** and **j**. In each case, illustrate the two vectors in a sketch, and then calculate $\mathbf{a}\cdot\mathbf{b}$.

 6. $\mathbf{a}=2\mathbf{i}+3\mathbf{j}, \quad \mathbf{b}=4\mathbf{i}+\mathbf{j}$

 7. $\mathbf{a}=3\mathbf{i}-\mathbf{j}, \quad \mathbf{b}=2\mathbf{i}+\mathbf{j}$

 8. $\mathbf{a}=-4\mathbf{i}+2\mathbf{j}, \quad \mathbf{b}=3\mathbf{i}+\mathbf{j}$

 9. $\mathbf{a}=-2\mathbf{i}+4\mathbf{j}, \quad \mathbf{b}=-2\mathbf{i}-\mathbf{j}$

10. $\mathbf{a}=-3\mathbf{i}+4\mathbf{j}, \quad \mathbf{b}=5\mathbf{i}-12\mathbf{j}$

11. **a**, **b**, and **c** are defined as $[2.36, 18.4°]$, $[3.18, 61.6°]$, and $[4.28, 75.6°]$ respectively. Calculate $\mathbf{a}\cdot\mathbf{b}$ and $\mathbf{a}\cdot\mathbf{c}$, each to 3 s.f. How many solutions do you think there are to the equation $\mathbf{a}\cdot\mathbf{r} = 5.47$?

12. Figure 9.10 shows a cuboid measuring 4 by 3 by 2. By means of an accurate drawing of triangle OPQ, find $\mathbf{OP}\cdot\mathbf{OQ}$.

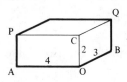

Fig. 9.10

13. Calculate $\mathbf{i} \cdot \mathbf{i}, \mathbf{j} \cdot \mathbf{j}, \mathbf{i} \cdot \mathbf{j}, \mathbf{j} \cdot \mathbf{i}.$

14. Calculate $2\mathbf{i} \cdot 3\mathbf{i}, 4\mathbf{j} \cdot 5\mathbf{j}, 6\mathbf{i} \cdot 7\mathbf{j}, 8\mathbf{j} \cdot 9\mathbf{i}.$

15. Calculate $(3\mathbf{i}+\mathbf{j}) \cdot (3\mathbf{i}-\mathbf{j})$ and $(3\mathbf{i}+\mathbf{j}) \cdot (3\mathbf{j}-\mathbf{i}).$

9.3 PROJECTION

Suppose that in a desert campaign a tank unit's primary objective is to advance in the direction of the vector **OC** (see figure 9.11). One tank moves 8 km from P to Q, the displacement vector **PQ** making an angle of 41° with **OC**. We can see that the tank has been making positive progress, whose magnitude (given by the line segment PM) equals $8 \cos 41° = 6$: so the tank's progress is $+6$ km. In more technical language, we say that the projection of **PQ** on **OC** is $+6$.

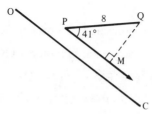

Fig. 9.11

The tank now moves 8 km from Q to R. Its progress is plainly negative, and we say that the projection of **QR** on **OC** is -6 (i.e. $8 \cos 139°$).

Now in figure 9.11, $\mathbf{PQ} \cdot \mathbf{OC} = 8 \times OC \times \cos 41 = 8 \cos 41 \times OC,$
and in figure 9.12, $\mathbf{QR} \cdot \mathbf{OC} = 8 \times OC \times \cos 139 = 8 \cos 139 \times OC.$

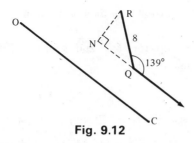

Fig. 9.12

In each case, the scalar product = the projection × OC. This result is quite general:

> if **a** and **c** are any two vectors, then **a** · **c** equals the projection of **a** on **c** multiplied by $|\mathbf{c}|$

This important fact enables us to establish that the scalar product is distributive over addition, i.e. that $(a+b) \cdot c = a \cdot c + b \cdot c$ To prove this, we draw displacements $PQ = a$, $QR = b$, and $OC = c$, as in figure 9.13. The figure shows only the case when the various projections are all positive, but our proof can quickly be adapted to cover every case.

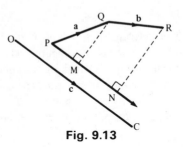

Fig. 9.13

Now $a \cdot c = $ projection of a on $c \times OC = PM \times OC$

          $b \cdot c = $ projection of b on $c \times OC = MN \times OC$

So $a \cdot c + b \cdot c = PM \times OC + MN \times OC$

                    $= (PM + MN) \times OC = PN \times OC$

                    $= $ projection of PR on $OC \times OC$

                    $= PR \cdot OC = (a+b) \cdot c$

We have therefore proved that $(a+b) \cdot c = a \cdot c + b \cdot c$, where a, b, c are any three vectors. Moreover, the fact that the scalar product is commutative means that the distributivity applies the other way too, i.e. that $c \cdot (a+b) = c \cdot a + c \cdot b$. We are therefore entitled to expand the scalar product of brackets just as if we were doing ordinary algebra:

$$(a+b) \cdot (c+d) = a \cdot c + a \cdot d + b \cdot c + b \cdot d$$

EXAMPLE Evaluate $(3i+4j) \cdot (6i+6j)$, and hence find the projection of $3i+4j$ on $6i+6j$ (see figure 9.7).

We have

$$(3i+4j) \cdot (6i+6j) = (3i) \cdot (6i) + (3i) \cdot (6j) + (4j) \cdot (6i) + (4j) \cdot (6j)$$

$$= 18i \cdot i + 18i \cdot j + 24j \cdot i + 24j \cdot j$$

$$= 18 \times 1 + 18 \times 0 + 24 \times 0 + 24 \times 1$$

$$= 42 \text{ exactly}$$

Therefore the required projection multiplied by $|6i+6j|$ equals 42, and hence the projection $= 42 \div \sqrt{72} = 4.95$ (3 s.f.).

EXAMPLE A convoy is steaming south-east across the Atlantic at a speed of 15 knots. An escorting submarine zig-zags 17 nautical miles due east and then 8 due south at her operational speed of 25 knots. Is the submarine keeping up with the convoy?

The displacement vector **a** = 17**i**−8**j** describes the submarine's movements (which occupy one hour, we note), and the vector **c** = **i**−**j** gives the direction of the convoy's track.

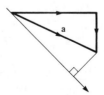

Fig. 9.14

Now $\qquad\qquad\qquad$ **a** · **c** = $(17\mathbf{i}-8\mathbf{j})\cdot(\mathbf{i}-\mathbf{j})$

$$= 17+8 = 25$$

Therefore the projection of **a** on **c** $= 25 \div |\mathbf{c}| = 25 \div \sqrt{2} = 17.7$

i.e. the effective speed of the submarine is 17.7 knots, and so she is more than keeping up with the convoy.

EXERCISE 9C

1. A is $(3,2)$, B is $(5,7)$, C is $(1,1)$, D is $(1,9)$. Draw a rough sketch, and find the projection of **AB** on **CD**.

2. A is $(0,-3)$, B $(0,8)$, and D $(4,-2)$. Find by means of an accurate drawing (on graph paper) the projection of **AB** on **AD**, and the projection of **BD** on **AD**.

3. Calculate the scalar product **a** · **c**, where **a** = $[392, 78.5°]$, **c** = $[10, 18.5°]$. Hence find the projection of **a** on **c**.

4. Evaluate $(3\mathbf{i}-4\mathbf{j})\cdot(7\mathbf{i}+24\mathbf{j})$, and hence find
    (a) the projection of $3\mathbf{i}-4\mathbf{j}$ on $7\mathbf{i}+24\mathbf{j}$,
    (b) the projection of $7\mathbf{i}+24\mathbf{j}$ on $3\mathbf{i}-4\mathbf{j}$.
    Illustrate both your answers in a sketch.

5. A is at $(12, 11\frac{1}{2})$ and C at $(15, 8)$. Calculate **OA** · **OC**, and hence find the projection of **OA** on **OC**. Then use Pythagoras' theorem to find the distance of A from the line OC.

6. The proof given in the text that the scalar product is distributive over addition applies only to the case when the various projections are positive. By drawing figures like figure 9.13, establish that the result is valid in all cases.

9.4 SCALAR PRODUCTS IN ACTION

The definition given in section 9.2 states that if the magnitudes of vectors **a** and **b** are $|\mathbf{a}|$ and $|\mathbf{b}|$, and the angle between them is ϕ, then $\mathbf{a} \cdot \mathbf{b} = |\mathbf{a}| \times |\mathbf{b}| \times \cos \phi$.

This equation provides the fundamental method of calculating a scalar product. In section 9.3, however, we developed an alternative method. The equivalence of the two methods provides the mathematician with a powerful weapon.

If $\qquad \mathbf{a} = \begin{pmatrix} a_1 \\ a_2 \end{pmatrix} = a_1\mathbf{i} + a_2\mathbf{j} \qquad$ and $\qquad \mathbf{b} = \begin{pmatrix} b_1 \\ b_2 \end{pmatrix} = b_1\mathbf{i} + b_2\mathbf{j}$

then
$$\begin{aligned}
\mathbf{a} \cdot \mathbf{b} &= (a_1\mathbf{i} + a_2\mathbf{j}) \cdot (b_1\mathbf{i} + b_2\mathbf{j}) \\
&= (a_1 b_1 \times 1) + (a_1 b_2 \times 0) + (a_2 b_1 \times 0) + (a_2 b_2 \times 1) \\
&= a_1 b_1 + a_2 b_2
\end{aligned}$$

EXAMPLE Find the angle between $2\mathbf{i} + 3\mathbf{j}$ and $\mathbf{i} + 4\mathbf{j}$.

Suppose the angle is ϕ. We calculate the scalar product of the two vectors by each method and equate the results:

$$\begin{aligned}
(2\mathbf{i} + 3\mathbf{j}) \cdot (\mathbf{i} + 4\mathbf{j}) &= |2\mathbf{i} + 3\mathbf{j}| \times |\mathbf{i} + 4\mathbf{j}| \times \cos \phi \\
&= \sqrt{13} \times \sqrt{17} \times \cos \phi
\end{aligned}$$

and $\qquad (2\mathbf{i} + 3\mathbf{j}) \cdot (\mathbf{i} + 4\mathbf{j}) = 2 \times 1 + 3 \times 4 = 14$

So $\qquad \cos \phi = 14 \div (\sqrt{13} \times \sqrt{17}) \Rightarrow \phi = 19.65°$ (2 d.p.)

Note There are other possible values of ϕ (such as -19.65, 340.35, etc.), but we usually choose the principal value, i.e. the value between 0 and 180°.

EXAMPLE Find the angle between $2\mathbf{i} - 3\mathbf{j}$ and $\mathbf{i} + 4\mathbf{j}$.

Suppose the angle is ϕ.

Then $\qquad \sqrt{13} \times \sqrt{17} \times \cos \phi = 2 \times 1 - 3 \times 4 = -10$

So $\qquad \cos \phi = -10 \div (\sqrt{13} \times \sqrt{17}) \Rightarrow \phi = 132.27°$

EXAMPLE Find the angle between the lines $y = 7x$ and $2y = x$.

We find vectors parallel to each line. $(0, 0)$ and $(1, 7)$ are points on the first line; so a parallel vector is $\mathbf{i} + 7\mathbf{j}$. Similarly, a vector parallel to the second line is $2\mathbf{i} + \mathbf{j}$.

Now suppose the required angle is ϕ. Then

$$\sqrt{50} \times \sqrt{5} \times \cos \phi = 1 \times 2 + 7 \times 1 = 9$$

So $\qquad \cos \phi = 9 \div (\sqrt{50} \times \sqrt{5}) \Rightarrow \phi = 55.30°$

EXAMPLE How do you test whether the two non-zero vectors $\mathbf{a} = a_1\mathbf{i}+a_2\mathbf{j}$ and $\mathbf{b} = b_1\mathbf{i}+b_2\mathbf{j}$ are perpendicular?

$\mathbf{a}$ is perpendicular to $\mathbf{b} \Leftrightarrow \mathbf{a} \cdot \mathbf{b} = 0 \Leftrightarrow a_1b_1+a_2b_2 = 0$.

All these ideas can be extended to three dimensions, where of course we need *three* base vectors: $\mathbf{i}$, $\mathbf{j}$, $\mathbf{k}$. The definition of scalar product is unchanged. Distributivity can be established very much as it can for two dimensions. And since $\mathbf{i}$, $\mathbf{j}$, $\mathbf{k}$ are perpendicular to each other and are unit vectors, their scalar products with each other are again very simple:

$$\mathbf{i} \cdot \mathbf{i} = \mathbf{j} \cdot \mathbf{j} = \mathbf{k} \cdot \mathbf{k} = 1$$
$$\mathbf{i} \cdot \mathbf{j} = \mathbf{j} \cdot \mathbf{i} = \mathbf{j} \cdot \mathbf{k} = \mathbf{k} \cdot \mathbf{j} = \mathbf{k} \cdot \mathbf{i} = \mathbf{i} \cdot \mathbf{k} = 0$$

EXAMPLE Calculate $(\mathbf{i}+2\mathbf{j}-3\mathbf{k}) \cdot (-2\mathbf{i}+3\mathbf{j}+2\mathbf{k})$.

The scalar product $= (1 \times -2)+(2 \times 3)+(-3 \times 2)$
$$= -2+6-6 = -2$$

EXAMPLE Find the angle ϕ between the diagonals AQ and BP of the cuboid in question 12 of exercise 9B.

We set up axes along OA, OB, OC: then

$$\mathbf{AQ} = -4\mathbf{i}+3\mathbf{j}+2\mathbf{k}$$

and $$\mathbf{BP} = +4\mathbf{i}-3\mathbf{j}+2\mathbf{k}$$

So $\mathbf{AQ} \cdot \mathbf{BP} = \sqrt{(4^2+3^2+2^2)} \times \sqrt{(4^2+3^2+2^2)} \times \cos \phi = 29 \cos \phi$

and $\mathbf{AQ} \cdot \mathbf{BP} = (-4 \times 4)+(3 \times -3)+(2 \times 2) = -21$

So $\cos \phi = -21/29 \Rightarrow \phi = 136.40°$ (2 d.p.)

In this case, an alternative answer is obviously $43.60°$.

EXERCISE 9D

1. Calculate:
    (a) $(3\mathbf{i}+4\mathbf{j}) \cdot (\mathbf{i}-2\mathbf{j})$
    (b) $(2\mathbf{i}-\mathbf{j}) \cdot (\mathbf{i}-4\mathbf{j})$
    (c) $(6\mathbf{i}+8\mathbf{j}) \cdot (4\mathbf{i}-3\mathbf{j})$

2. Find the angle between each pair of vectors in question 1, and illustrate graphically.

3. OACB is a parallelogram, and $\mathbf{OA} = \mathbf{a}$, $\mathbf{OB} = \mathbf{b}$. Express $\mathbf{OC}$ and $\mathbf{AB}$ in terms of $\mathbf{a}$ and $\mathbf{b}$, and thus calculate and simplify $\mathbf{OC} \cdot \mathbf{AB}$. Hence prove that OACB is a rhombus if and only if OC and AB are perpendicular.

4. AB is a diameter of a circle, centre O. If $\mathbf{OA} = \mathbf{a}$, what is $\mathbf{OB}$? If C is any other point on the circle and $\mathbf{OC} = \mathbf{c}$, express $\mathbf{AC}$ and $\mathbf{BC}$ in terms of $\mathbf{a}$ and $\mathbf{c}$. Remembering that $|\mathbf{a}|$ equals $|\mathbf{c}|$, calculate and simplify $\mathbf{AC} \cdot \mathbf{BC}$. Hence prove that angle ACB equals $90°$.

5. OPQ is a right-angled triangle, PQ being the hypotenuse. If $\mathbf{OP} = \mathbf{p}$ and $\mathbf{OQ} = \mathbf{q}$, express $\mathbf{PQ}$ in terms of $\mathbf{p}$ and $\mathbf{q}$. By considering $\mathbf{PQ} \cdot \mathbf{PQ}$, prove that $PQ^2 = OQ^2 + OP^2$.

6. $\mathbf{OA}$ and $\mathbf{OB}$ are unit vectors in directions α and β respectively. By considering $\mathbf{OA} \cdot \mathbf{OB}$, show that $\cos(\alpha - \beta) = \cos\alpha\cos\beta + \sin\alpha\sin\beta$.

7. If $\mathbf{l} = 2\mathbf{i} - \mathbf{j} + 3\mathbf{k}$ and $\mathbf{m} = \mathbf{i} - 3\mathbf{j} - \mathbf{k}$, work out $\mathbf{l} \cdot \mathbf{m}$, and hence calculate the angle between $\mathbf{l}$ and $\mathbf{m}$.

8. What is the condition for the non-zero vectors $(a_1\mathbf{i} + a_2\mathbf{j} + a_3\mathbf{k})$ and $(b_1\mathbf{i} + b_2\mathbf{j} + b_3\mathbf{k})$ to be perpendicular?

9.5 COSINE RULE

In question 5 of the last exercise, you proved by use of the scalar product that $PQ^2 = OQ^2 + OP^2$ where angle POQ equals $90°$. We now consider the more general case shown in figure 9.15, where angle POQ equals ϕ, not necessarily $90°$.

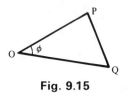

Fig. 9.15

$$PQ^2 = \mathbf{PQ} \cdot \mathbf{PQ}$$

$$= (\mathbf{q} - \mathbf{p}) \cdot (\mathbf{q} - \mathbf{p}) \quad \text{(where } \mathbf{OP} = \mathbf{p} \text{ and } \mathbf{OQ} = \mathbf{q}\text{)}$$

$$= \mathbf{q} \cdot \mathbf{q} - \mathbf{q} \cdot \mathbf{p} - \mathbf{p} \cdot \mathbf{q} + \mathbf{p} \cdot \mathbf{p}$$

$$= \mathbf{q} \cdot \mathbf{q} + \mathbf{p} \cdot \mathbf{p} - 2\mathbf{q} \cdot \mathbf{p} \quad \text{(rearranging the terms)}$$

So $\qquad PQ^2 = OQ^2 + OP^2 - 2 \times OQ \times OP \times \cos\phi$

This important result is usually known as *the cosine rule*. It applies to any triangle (note that if ϕ has the special value of $90°$ we have Pythagoras' theorem). We shall now apply the cosine rule to various triangle problems.

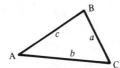

Fig. 9.16

We must first clarify the notation to be used. We shall refer to the angles of any triangle, such as ABC in figure 9.16, by single *capital* letters (thus *B* denotes angle ABC), and to the lengths of the sides of the triangle by single *lower-case* letters (corresponding to the opposite vertices—thus *b* denotes the length AC). We shall refer to the area of the triangle by the single symbol $\triangle$.

With this notation, the cosine rule applied successively to the three sides of triangle ABC in figure 9.16 gives

$$a^2 = b^2 + c^2 - 2bc \cos A$$

$$b^2 = c^2 + a^2 - 2ca \cos B$$

$$c^2 = a^2 + b^2 - 2ab \cos C$$

These formulae can be used to calculate:

(1) the third side of a triangle when we know two sides and also the angle contained between them, and

(2) any angle of a triangle when we know all three sides.

EXAMPLE Find *c* if $a = 7.4$, $b = 5.7$, and $C = 42°$.

$$c^2 = 7.4^2 + 5.7^2 - 2 \times 7.4 \times 5.7 \times \cos 42°$$
$$= 24.558\,303 \quad \text{(calculator)}$$

So $c = 4.955\,633\,4$

Since the data is given to 2 s.f. only, our answer is $c = 5.0$.

EXAMPLE Find *A* if $a = 7.4$, $b = 5.7$, and $c = 5.0$.

$$7.4^2 = 5.7^2 + 5.0^2 - 2 \times 5.7 \times 5.0 \times \cos A$$

So $2 \times 5.7 \times 5.0 \times \cos A = 5.7^2 + 5.0^2 - 7.4^2$

i.e. $\cos A = \dfrac{5.7^2 + 5.0^2 - 7.4^2}{2 \times 5.7 \times 5.0} \Rightarrow A = 87°$ approximately.

EXAMPLE Find *b* if $a = 391$, $c = 476$, and $B = 151.2°$.

$$b^2 = 391^2 + 476^2 - 2 \times 391 \times 476 \times \cos 151.2°$$
$$= 705\,646.39$$

So $b = 840.027\,61 = 840$ (3 s.f.)

EXAMPLE Find B if $a = 391$, $b = 840$, and $c = 476$.

$$\cos B = \frac{391^2 + 476^2 - 840^2}{2 \times 391 \times 476} \qquad \text{i.e.} \quad \frac{a^2 + c^2 - b^2}{2ac}$$

So $B = 151.185\,18° = 151.2°$ (1 d.p.)

Note that in these last two examples the angle involved has been obtuse, but we have not had to make any adjustment to the formulae: they apply whether the angle is acute, obtuse, or a right-angle.

EXERCISE 9E

1. Calculate (to 3 s.f.) the third side in each of the following triangles:
    (a) $b = 3.18$, $c = 1.27$, $A = 54.8°$
    (b) $c = 42.1$, $a = 37.8$, $B = 106.9°$
    (c) $a = 8.47$, $b = 11.4$, $C = 73.1°$

2. Calculate (to nearest 0.1°) the named angle in each of the following triangles, and explain any odd results:
    (a) $a = 7.34$, $b = 3.61$, $c = 6.12$; B
    (b) $a = 7.34$, $b = 3.61$, $c = 5.24$; A
    (c) $a = 7.34$, $b = 3.61$, $c = 3.47$; C

3. If $a = 8$, $b = 5$, and $C = 60°$, use the fact that $\cos 60° = 0.5$ exactly to calculate c exactly.

4. If $a = 3$, $b = 5$, and $c = 7$, all exactly, calculate C exactly.

5. If $a = 3.76$, $b = 6.27$, and $c = 2.51$, calculate A and B by the cosine rule. Explain your results.

6. Sketch the cuboid defined in question 12 of exercise 9B. Use Pythagoras' theorem three times to find OP, OQ, and PQ, and then use the cosine rule to find angle POQ.

9.6 SINE RULE

In figure 9.17, the line m is the mediator of the line-segment AC, and B is to the left of m. It is evident that $c < a$ and $C < A$, whereas if B had been to the right of m, then $a < c$ and $A < C$. This demonstrates that in any triangle the greatest side is opposite the greatest angle, etc. For example,

$$c < a < b \Leftrightarrow C < A < B$$

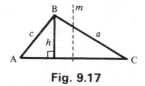

Fig. 9.17

More specifically, if we know that $C = 30°$ and $A = 60°$ say, then we can be sure that $c<a$ (since $30<60$). In such a case, beginners are apt to think that because C is half of A, c will also be half of a, but this is a mistaken idea. The correct relationship between the sides and angles of a triangle is not quite so simple.

Looking again at figure 9.17, we see that the height h of the triangle equals $c \times \sin A$ (and that this would be so even if A or C were obtuse). Alternatively, the height equals $a \times \sin C$. So these two expressions for h can be equated:

$$c \times \sin A = a \times \sin C, \quad \text{i.e.} \quad (\sin A) \div a = (\sin C) \div c$$

We can similarly establish that $(\sin A) \div a = (\sin B) \div b$.

Hence we have the following two forms of *the sine rule*:

$$\frac{\sin A}{a} = \frac{\sin B}{b} = \frac{\sin C}{c}$$

$$\frac{a}{\sin A} = \frac{b}{\sin B} = \frac{c}{\sin C} \quad \text{(reciprocating each fraction)}$$

These formulae are useful when we can find the value of one of the fractions involved and also know one other angle or side.

You will notice that the sine rule can be used in precisely those circumstances when the cosine rule would be of no use. So the two rules complement each other very conveniently.

EXAMPLE Find A if $b = 43$, $c = 63$, and $C = 51°$.

We can find the value of $(\sin C)/c$, and so can use the sine rule:

$$\frac{\sin A}{a} = \frac{\sin B}{43} = \frac{\sin 51}{63}$$

Since we know b but not a, we must calculate B to begin with:

$$\sin B = \frac{\sin 51}{63} \times 43 \Rightarrow B = 32° \text{ or } 148°$$

Now $b<c$, and so $B<C$: therefore $B = 32°$ (not $148°$).

So finally we deduce that $A = 180 - B - C = 97°$.

EXAMPLE Find B if $a = 8.27$, $b = 11.3$, $A = 37.2°$, given also that B is an acute angle.

The sine rule tells us that $\dfrac{\sin 37.2}{8.27} = \dfrac{\sin B}{11.3}$

So $\qquad \sin B = \dfrac{\sin 37.2}{8.27} \times 11.3 \Rightarrow B = 55.7°$ (not 124.3°)

Note that if we had not been given the extra information that B was an acute angle, then we should not have been able to decide between the two alternative values, 55.7° and 124.3°. We do know that B must be greater than A, since b is greater than a: but both the calculated values of B *are* greater than A. Inspection of figure 9.18 reveals that there are in fact two quite different triangles which both satisfy the numerical information given.

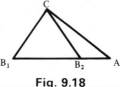

Fig. 9.18

EXAMPLE Find a and c if $b = 11.3$, $A = 37.2°$, $B = 124.3°$.

First, we can say that $C = 180 - 37.2 - 124.3 = 18.5°$.

The sine rule (in its second form) then tells us that

$$\frac{a}{\sin 37.2} = \frac{11.3}{\sin 124.3} = \frac{c}{\sin 18.5}$$

So $\qquad a = \dfrac{11.3}{\sin 124.3} \times \sin 37.2 = 8.27$ (3 s.f.)

and $\qquad c = \dfrac{11.3}{\sin 124.3} \times \sin 18.5 = 4.34$ (3 s.f.)

In such a pair of calculations, the value of the fraction, i.e. $11.3 \div \sin 124.3°$ in this case, should either be stored in your calculator's memory or be set as a constant multiplier.

We found earlier in this section that the height of the triangle ABC equals $c \times \sin A$ (see figure 9.17). Therefore the area of the triangle is given by the formula

$$\triangle = \tfrac{1}{2} \times \text{base} \times \text{height}$$

$$= \tfrac{1}{2} \times b \times (c \times \sin A)$$

$$= \tfrac{1}{2}bc \sin A$$

Similarly, $\qquad \triangle = \tfrac{1}{2}ca \sin B = \tfrac{1}{2}ab \sin C$

EXAMPLE Find $\triangle$ if $a = 3.76 \times 10^3$, $b = 7.19 \times 10^4$, and $C = 12.26°$.

We have
$$\triangle = \tfrac{1}{2}ab \sin C$$
$$= \tfrac{1}{2} \times 3.76 \times 10^3 \times 7.19 \times 10^4 \times \sin 12.26°$$
$$= 2.87 \times 10^7 \quad (3\,\text{s.f.})$$

EXERCISE 9F

1. Calculate (to nearest 0.1°) the named angles in each of the following triangles:

   (a) $a = 7.23$, $b = 6.18$, $A = 107.3°$; B, then C

   (b) $a = 46.3$, $c = 28.4$, $A = 67.4°$; C, then B

   (c) $b = 0.174$, $c = 0.216$, $B = 44.2°$; C (acute), then A

   (d) $a = 5.79$, $c = 4.18$, $C = 33.6°$; A (obtuse), then B

2. Calculate (to 3 s.f.) the named sides in each of the following triangles:

   (a) $a = 7.27$, $A = 64.7°$, $B = 38.7°$; b

   (b) $c = 68.3$, $A = 37.4°$, $C = 108.7°$; a

   (c) $b = 0.892$, $A = 85.5°$, $B = 73.9°$; c

   (d) $a = 143$, $B = 17.8°$, $C = 76.9°$; b and c

3. Calculate to an appropriate degree of accuracy the areas of the following triangles:

   (a) $b = 76$, $c = 49$, $A = 65.4°$

   (b) $a = 139$, $b = 225$, $C = 17.8°$

   (c) $b = 5.718$, $c = 9.405$, $A = 93.4°$

   (d) $c = 0.007\,19$, $a = 0.0136$, $B = 147.9°$

4. Calculate the value of $\sin A$ given by the sine rule if $a = 7$, $b = 4$, and $B = 60°$. Explain why the value is impossible. By trying to construct the triangle, show what is wrong with the information.

5. Use the cosine rule to calculate a if $b = 73$, $c = 24$, and $A = 37.8°$. Then use the sine rule to calculate B and C, and check your results by evaluating $A+B+C$.

6. Construct as accurately as you can the triangle ABC given that $b = 7.3$ inches, $c = 2.4$ inches, and $A = 37.8°$. Measure B and C.

7. The sides of the triangular base of a pyramid measure 12 m, 17 m, and 25 m. Use the cosine formula to find the largest angle of the triangle, and hence its area. Then calculate the volume of the pyramid, given that its height is 19 m.

8. Given that $a = 34$, $b = 47$, and $C = 130°$, all this information being correct to 2 figures only, calculate the maximum and minimum possible values of both c and $\triangle$.

9. A circle is drawn through the three vertices of a triangle ABC, and BD is a diameter of this circle. It can be proved that the angle BCD must equal 90°, and that angle BDC equals either A or $(180° - A)$. Show that in either case $a \div (\sin A) = 2R$ where R is the radius of the circle.

10 COORDINATE GEOMETRY II

10.1 LINES AND VECTORS

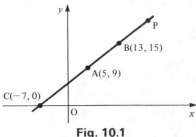

Fig. 10.1

What is the position vector of a point such as P on the line AB in figure 10.1? The displacement vectors **AP** and **AB** are parallel, but differ in magnitude. Therefore **AP** must be some multiple of **AB**. And to judge from the figure, **AP** is about twice **AB**: so

$$\mathbf{OP} = \mathbf{OA} + \mathbf{AP} = \mathbf{OA} + 2\mathbf{AB}$$

$$= \binom{5}{9} + 2\binom{8}{6} = \binom{21}{21}$$

In fact, whichever point P on the line is selected, its position vector **r** will equal $\binom{5}{9} + t\binom{8}{6}$ for some suitable value of t. For example, setting $t = 0.8$, we find

$$\mathbf{r} = \binom{5}{9} + 0.8\binom{8}{6} = \binom{5}{9} + \binom{6.4}{4.8} = \binom{11.4}{13.8}$$

and so the point $(11.4, 13.8)$ lies on the line.

Where is P when $t = 1$? $\quad \mathbf{r} = \binom{5}{9} + 1\binom{8}{6} = \binom{13}{15}$, i.e. P is B.

Where is P when $t = 0$? $\quad \mathbf{r} = \binom{5}{9} + 0\binom{8}{6} = \binom{5}{9}$, i.e. P is A.

What value of t sends P to C$(-7, 0)$?

At C, $\quad \mathbf{r} = \binom{-7}{0} = \binom{5}{9} - \binom{12}{9} = \binom{5}{9} - 1.5\binom{8}{6}$: $\quad$ so $t = -1.5$.

129

It is evident that every value of t corresponds to a point on the line, and vice versa. We say that $\mathbf{r} = \begin{pmatrix} 5 \\ 9 \end{pmatrix} + t \begin{pmatrix} 8 \\ 6 \end{pmatrix}$ is a *vector equation* of the line AB.

More generally (see figure 10.2), suppose that A is a point on a line, $\mathbf{a}$ being its position vector, and suppose that $\mathbf{m}$ is a vector parallel to the line. Now if P is any point on the line, then $\mathbf{AP} = t\mathbf{m}$, where t is an ordinary number, either positive (as in the figure) or negative (if P were the other side of A) or zero (if P coincided with A). So the position vector of P is given by the formula $\mathbf{r} = \mathbf{a} + t\mathbf{m}$, the vector equation of the line.

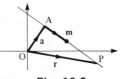

Fig. 10.2

How far is it from A to P (in figure 10.2)? That depends on the magnitude of $\mathbf{m}$ and the value of t.

For example, suppose that $\mathbf{a} = \begin{pmatrix} 6 \\ 14 \end{pmatrix}$ and $\mathbf{m} = \begin{pmatrix} 12 \\ -5 \end{pmatrix}$.

Then $|\mathbf{m}| = \sqrt{(12^2 + 5^2)} = \sqrt{(144 + 25)} = \sqrt{169} = 13$. So if $t = +3.5$, the distance AP $= 3.5 \times 13 = 45.5$. The distance is still 45.5 if $t = -3.5$, but P is now the other side of A.

Conversely, if the distance is 39, then $t = \pm 39 \div 13 = \pm 3$,

and so $\mathbf{r} = \begin{pmatrix} 6 \\ 14 \end{pmatrix} \pm 3 \begin{pmatrix} 12 \\ -5 \end{pmatrix} = \begin{pmatrix} 6 \\ 14 \end{pmatrix} \pm \begin{pmatrix} 36 \\ -15 \end{pmatrix} = \begin{pmatrix} 42 \\ -1 \end{pmatrix}$ or $\begin{pmatrix} -30 \\ 29 \end{pmatrix}$.

EXAMPLE Find a vector equation of the line through $(3, 7)$ and $(5, 9)$. Find the two points on the line which are $\sqrt{72}$ units from $(3, 7)$.

We choose $\mathbf{a} = \begin{pmatrix} 3 \\ 7 \end{pmatrix}$. Then $\mathbf{m} = \begin{pmatrix} 5 \\ 9 \end{pmatrix} - \begin{pmatrix} 3 \\ 7 \end{pmatrix} = \begin{pmatrix} 2 \\ 2 \end{pmatrix}$.

So the vector equation is $\mathbf{r} = \begin{pmatrix} 3 \\ 7 \end{pmatrix} + t \begin{pmatrix} 2 \\ 2 \end{pmatrix}$.

Now $|\mathbf{m}| = \sqrt{(2^2 + 2^2)} = \sqrt{8}$, and the required distance is $\sqrt{72}$.

Thus $t = \pm\sqrt{72} \div \sqrt{8} = \pm 3$, and $\mathbf{r} = \begin{pmatrix} 3 \\ 7 \end{pmatrix} \pm 3 \begin{pmatrix} 2 \\ 2 \end{pmatrix} = \begin{pmatrix} 9 \\ 13 \end{pmatrix}$ or $\begin{pmatrix} -3 \\ 1 \end{pmatrix}$.

Therefore the two points are $(9, 13)$ and $(-3, 1)$.

EXERCISE 10A

In questions 1 to 6, find (a) the coordinates of P, and (b) a vector equation (i.e. in the form $\mathbf{r} = \mathbf{a} + t\mathbf{m}$) of the line AB.

1. A is $(5, 9)$, B is $(13, 15)$, and $\mathbf{AP} = 3\mathbf{AB}$.

2. A is $(1, 3)$, B is $(2, 7)$, and $\mathbf{AP} = 4\mathbf{AB}$.

3. A is $(-1, 4)$, B is $(1, 6)$, and $\mathbf{AP} = 2\mathbf{AB}$.

4. A is $(-5, -2)$, B is $(-3, 2)$, and $\mathbf{AP} = 1.5\mathbf{AB}$.

5. A is $(4, 2)$, B is $(-2, 6)$, and $\mathbf{AP} = \frac{1}{2}\mathbf{AB}$.

6. A is $(-3, 5)$, B is $(1, 1)$, and $\mathbf{AP} = \frac{1}{4}\mathbf{AB}$.

7. If R is $(-1, 4)$ and S is $(2, 8)$, find the coordinates of the point Q between R and S such that $RQ = 2$, and the point T on QR produced such that $QT = 10$.

8. If F is $(1, 3)$ and G is $(3, 2)$, find the two points on FG which are $\sqrt{20}$ units from F, and the two points on FG which are $2\sqrt{20}$ units from G.

9. Given $\mathbf{r} = \begin{pmatrix} 1 \\ 4 \end{pmatrix} + t\begin{pmatrix} 3 \\ 4 \end{pmatrix}$ is the equation of a line, find how far it is along the line from the point $(1, 4)$ to the point where $t = -3$. Find also the two points on the line which are 15 units from $(1, 4)$.

10. Given $\mathbf{r} = \begin{pmatrix} -2 \\ 36 \end{pmatrix} + t\begin{pmatrix} -7 \\ 24 \end{pmatrix}$ is the equation of a line, find how far it is along the line from the point $(-2, 36)$ to the point where $t = 6$. Find also the two points on the line which are 50 units from the point $(-2, 36)$.

10.2 DISTANCE FROM A POINT TO A LINE

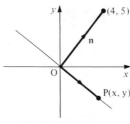

Fig. 10.3

The line OP in figure 10.3 has equation $4x + 5y = 0$. This can be rewritten in the form $\begin{pmatrix} 4 \\ 5 \end{pmatrix} \cdot \begin{pmatrix} x \\ y \end{pmatrix} = 0$, which tells us that the vectors $\begin{pmatrix} 4 \\ 5 \end{pmatrix}$ and $\begin{pmatrix} x \\ y \end{pmatrix}$ are perpendicular, i.e. that $\mathbf{n}$ and $\mathbf{OP}$ are perpendicular. In other words, $\begin{pmatrix} 4 \\ 5 \end{pmatrix}$ is normal to the line $4x+5y = 0$. Similarly, $\begin{pmatrix} 2 \\ -5 \end{pmatrix}$ is normal to $2x-5y = 0$, and

in general $\begin{pmatrix} a \\ b \end{pmatrix}$ is normal to $ax+by = 0$. This result can easily be extended to all

straight lines: for example, the line $4x+5y = 7$ is parallel to $4x+5y = 0$ and so

$\begin{pmatrix} 4 \\ 5 \end{pmatrix}$ is normal to both of them, $\begin{pmatrix} 2 \\ -5 \end{pmatrix}$ is normal to $2x-5y+3 = 0$, and so on.

The distance from a point to a line is measured perpendicular to that line. So the first step in calculating the distance is to find a vector normal to the line. The technique is best illustrated by means of a numerical example.

EXAMPLE Find the perpendicular distance from the point $A(3, 7)$ to the line $3y = 4x+59$.

Now $3y = 4x+59$ can be written as $-4x+3y = 59$ and so $\begin{pmatrix} -4 \\ +3 \end{pmatrix}$ is a normal

vector. The vector equation of the line ABF (see figure 10.4) is thus

$\mathbf{r} = \begin{pmatrix} 3 \\ 7 \end{pmatrix} + t \begin{pmatrix} -4 \\ +3 \end{pmatrix}$. So at F, $x = 3-4t$ and $y = 7+3t$ for some suitable t; and

the value of t can be found by noting that F lies on $3y = 4x+59$ and that therefore $3(7+3t) = 4(3-4t)+59$. Hence

$$21+9t = 12-16t+59 \Rightarrow 25t = 50 \Rightarrow t = 2.$$

Thus the vector **AF** is $2\begin{pmatrix} -4 \\ +3 \end{pmatrix}$, i.e. $\begin{pmatrix} -8 \\ +6 \end{pmatrix}$, and the distance from A to the line

equals the magnitude of this vector, i.e. 10 units.

This numerical example can be generalised to provide a formula for the distance AF from any point $A(h, k)$ to any line $ax+by+c = 0$.

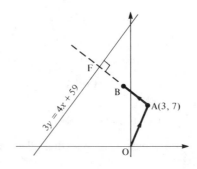

Fig. 10.4

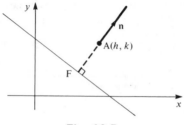

Fig. 10.5

In figure 10.5, the vector $\mathbf{n} = \begin{pmatrix} a \\ b \end{pmatrix}$ is normal to the line: thus a vector equation

of the line AF is $\mathbf{r} = \begin{pmatrix} h \\ k \end{pmatrix} - t\begin{pmatrix} a \\ b \end{pmatrix}$. So at F, $x = h - at$ and $y = k - bt$ for some

suitable t. But since F lies on the line $ax + by + c = 0$, we see that
$a(h - at) + b(k - bt) + c = 0$.

Hence $\qquad ah - a^2t + bk - b^2t + c = 0 \Rightarrow t = \dfrac{(ah + bk + c)}{(a^2 + b^2)}$

So $\qquad AF = \left| t\begin{pmatrix} a \\ b \end{pmatrix} \right| = \dfrac{ah + bk + c}{(a^2 + b^2)} \times \sqrt{(a^2 + b^2)} = \dfrac{ah + bk + c}{\sqrt{(a^2 + b^2)}}$

This formula may produce the right answer or minus the right answer (since $ah + bk + c$ can be positive or negative): it all depends on the values of a, b, c you happen to use.

EXAMPLE   Find the distance from $(3, 7)$ to $3y = 4x + 59$.

If we rearrange the equation as $4x - 3y + 59 = 0$, we obtain the answer

$$\frac{4 \times 3 - 3 \times 7 + 59}{\sqrt{(4^2 + 3^2)}} = \frac{12 - 21 + 59}{5} = +10$$

But if we rearrange the equation as $-4x + 3y - 59 = 0$, we get

$$\frac{-4 \times 3 + 3 \times 7 - 59}{5} = -10$$

In either case, we find the distance to be 10 units.

EXERCISE 10B

1. Write down vectors normal to: $2x + y = 0$, $3x + 4y = 0$, $3x - 5y = 0$, $7x - 9y = 0$, $4y + x = 0$, $7y - 2x = 0$.

2. Write down vectors normal to: $3x + 4y = 5$, $9x + 7y = 11$, $11x - 15y + 9 = 0$, $14x - 9y + 3 = 0$, $y = 3x - 7$, $2y = x + 2$.

3. Find a vector equation of the perpendicular from $A(-6, 9)$ to $y = x+3$, and hence find the distance from the point to the line.

4. Find the distance from $L(16, 11)$ to the line joining $M(6, -7)$ and $N(0, 14)$.

5. Find the distance from $A(3, 7)$ to the line joining $B(-2, 5)$ and $C(4, 11)$. Deduce the area of triangle ABC.

6. Find the distance from $(-3, 5)$ to $3x - 2y = 5$, using the formula given above.

10.3 EQUATIONS OF CIRCLES

Fig. 10.6

If a point $P(x, y)$ moves so that its distance from a fixed point remains fixed, then it traces out a circle.

Let the fixed point be $C(h, k)$ and the constant distance be r: then

$$CP^2 = r^2, \quad \text{i.e.} \quad (x-h)^2 + (y-k)^2 = r^2$$

This is therefore the equation of a circle with centre at (h, k) and radius equal to r.

So, for instance, $(x-2)^2 + (y+5)^2 = 625$ is the equation of a circle with centre $(2, -5)$ and radius 25.

EXAMPLE Show that $x^2 + y^2 + 4x - 6y - 3 = 0$ is the equation of a circle, and find the centre and radius.

First, we rearrange the equation as follows:

$$x^2 + 4x \quad + y^2 - 6y \quad = 3$$

Then we complete the squares by adding the same two numbers to both sides of the equation:

$$(x^2 + 4x + 4) + (y^2 - 6y + 9) = 3 + 4 + 9$$

And finally we factorise the left-hand side:

$$(x+2)^2 \quad + (y-3)^2 \quad = 16 = 4^2$$

So the equation does indeed represent a circle, and we see that the centre is $(-2, 3)$ and the radius is 4.

EXERCISE 10C

1. Find the equations of the circles with centre and radius as given, expanding the brackets and simplifying in each case:

   (a) $(3, 4)$ 2   (b) $(-2, 3)$ 10
   (c) $(-3, 4)$ $\sqrt{3}$ (d) $(0, 9)$ 9
   (e) $(-4, -3)$ 5   (f) $(0, 0)$ 20

2. Find the centre and radius of the following circles:

   (a) $x^2 + y^2 = 36$
   (b) $x^2 + 2x + y^2 = 24$
   (c) $x^2 + y^2 - 4x - 6y - 156 = 0$
   (d) $x^2 + y^2 + 8x - 12y = 48$
   (e) $x^2 + y^2 + 3x - 4y = 0$
   (f) $x^2 + y^2 - 16x - y = 7.75$

3. Find the centre and radius of the following circles:

   (a) $4x^2 + 4y^2 + 8x + 16y = 5$ (divide through by 4)
   (b) $x^2 + y^2 + 2gx + 2fy = 0$
   (c) $x^2 + y^2 + 2gx + 2fy + c = 0$

10.4 TANGENTS TO CIRCLES

Methods for finding the tangent to a given circle at a given point on its circumference, or the tangents with a given gradient, are best explained by means of numerical examples.

EXAMPLE   Find the tangent at $F(10, 13)$ to the circle $(x-4)^2 + (y-5)^2 = 100$.

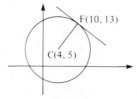

Fig. 10.7

The centre of the circle is at $C(4, 5)$.

Now $\mathbf{CF} = \begin{pmatrix} 6 \\ 8 \end{pmatrix}$ is normal to the tangent, and so the equation of the tangent must be $3x + 4y = c$, for some suitably chosen c. But $(10, 13)$ lies on the tangent, and so $3 \times 10 + 4 \times 13 = c \Rightarrow c = 82$. Thus the equation of the tangent is $3x + 4y = 82$.

Alternatively, we may argue that since the gradient of **CF** is 4/3, the gradient of the tangent must be $-3/4$. Therefore by the method of section 3.3, the equation of the tangent must be

$$\frac{y-13}{x-10} = \frac{-3}{4} \quad \text{i.e.} \quad 3x+4y = 82$$

EXAMPLE Find the equations of the tangents to the circle $(x-4)^2+(y-5)^2 = 100$ with gradient $= -3/4$.

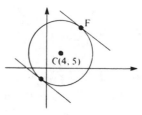

Fig. 10.8

Since the tangents have a gradient of $-3/4$, their equations must be of the form $3x+4y = c$, where c is a constant. For such a line to be a tangent to the circle, the distance from the centre of the circle to the line must equal the radius,

i.e.
$$\frac{3 \times 4+4 \times 5-c}{\sqrt{(9+16)}} = \pm 10$$

and therefore $c = 32 \pm 50$.

Thus we have the equations $3x+4y = 82$ and $3x+4y = -18$; inspection of figure 10.8 shows us which tangent is which.

Alternatively, we can start by finding the coordinates of the two points of contact. If F is such a point, then the magnitude of the displacement vector **CF** must be 10 (i.e. the radius of the circle), and the gradient of **CF** must be $+4/3$ (since the gradient of the required tangents is $-3/4$): so

$$\mathbf{CF} = \pm 10 \times \binom{3}{4} \div \sqrt{(3^2+4^2)} = \pm \binom{6}{8}$$

Thus the two points of contact are $(4, 5) \pm (6, 8)$, i.e. $(10, 13)$ and $(-2, -3)$. It is now an easy matter to write down the equations of the lines through these points with the required gradient of $-3/4$. This is left as an exercise for the reader.

EXERCISE 10D

1. Using both methods discussed in the text, find the equation of the tangent at $F(1.2, 14.6)$ to the circle $(x-4)^2+(y-5)^2 = 100$.

2. Using either method discussed in the text, find the tangents to the circles given in question 2 of exercise 10C at the following points:
   (a) $(0, 6)$ and $(-6, 0)$
   (b) $(-4, 4)$ and $(2, 4)$
   (c) $(7, 15)$ and $(7, -9)$
   (d) $(-12, 0)$ and $(2, 14)$
   (e) $(0, 4)$ and $(0.5, 3.5)$
   (f) $(14, 6.5)$

3. Using both methods discussed in the text, find the equations of the tangents to the circle $(x-4)^2+(y-5)^2 = 100$ with gradient $= +7/24$.

4. Using either method discussed in the text, find the equations of the tangents to the following circles, in each case with the given gradient:
   (a) $x^2+y^2 = 25$; $+3/4$
   (b) $x^2+y^2 = 100$; $-4/3$
   (c) $x^2+y^2+2x+6y = 15$; $+4/3$
   (d) $x^2+y^2-4x-8y = 5$; $-3/4$
   (e) $x^2+y^2+2x-4y = 164$; $+5/12$
   (f) $x^2+y^2+4x-2y = 164$; $+12/5$
   (g) $x^2+y^2+2x+14y+1 = 0$; ∞
   (h) $2x^2+2y^2-6x+2y = 3$; 0

5. Using the first method, find the equations of the tangents to the following circles with the given gradient:
   (a) $x^2+y^2+14x+2y+1 = 0$; $+1/3$
   (b) $x^2+y^2+4x+6y-3 = 0$; $+4$
   (c) $x^2+y^2+8x-6y = 75$; $+2$
   (d) $x^2+y^2+6x-10y+9 = 0$; $+3$

6. Find the coordinates of the centre C of the circle whose equation is $x^2+y^2-6x+4y-12 = 0$, and verify that the point $F(7, 1)$ lies on the circumference of this circle. Find the equation of the tangent at F.

7. The three sides of the triangle PQR are all tangents to the circle defined in question 6. PQ touches the circle at F, QR runs parallel to the x-axis, and RP runs parallel to the y-axis. Calculate the coordinates of P, Q, and R, and hence calculate the area of the triangle.

10.5 EQUATIONS OF LOCI

A locus is a set of points that all satisfy certain conditions. In many cases the locus is a curve (or straight line) with an x–y equation. The techniques involved in finding the equation of a locus are illustrated once again by means of examples.

EXAMPLE The point $P(x, y)$ remains a fixed distance of 5 units from a fixed point $(3, 4)$.

Obviously, the locus is a circle with centre $(3, 4)$ and radius 5. Its equation is

$$\sqrt{(x-3)^2 + (y-4)^2} = 5, \quad \text{i.e.} \quad (x-3)^2 + (y-4)^2 = 25$$

EXAMPLE The point $P(x, y)$ remains equidistant from the points $A(1, 2)$ and $B(4, 5)$.

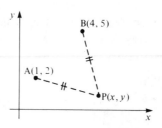

Fig. 10.9

In this case, the locus is the perpendicular bisector (the mediator) of the line segment AB. One way to find its equation was described in section 3.6 (we find the gradient of AB, then the perpendicular gradient, then the mid-point of AB, and finally the equation: refer back to section 3.6 if you are in doubt).

Alternatively, we may argue as follows:

$$\mathbf{AP} = \begin{pmatrix} x-1 \\ y-2 \end{pmatrix}, \text{ and so the distance } AP = \sqrt{(x-1)^2 + (y-2)^2}$$

and similarly

$$BP = \sqrt{(x-4)^2 + (y-5)^2}$$

Thus

$$(x-1)^2 + (y-2)^2 = (x-4)^2 + (y-5)^2$$

i.e.

$$x^2 - 2x + 1 + y^2 - 4y + 4 = x^2 - 8x + 16 + y^2 - 10y + 25$$

i.e.

$$6x + 6y - 36 = 0$$

Therefore the equation of the locus is $x + y = 6$.

EXAMPLE   The point $P(x, y)$ remains equidistant from the point $A(1, 2)$ and the line $4x + 3y = 0$.

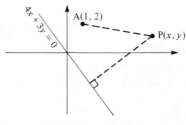

Fig. 10.10

P's distance from A equals $\sqrt{(x-1)^2 + (y-2)^2}$, as in the example above. Its distance from the line is $(4x + 3y) \div \sqrt{(16 + 9)}$. Equating the squares of these two distances, we have

$$(x-1)^2 \quad + \quad (y-2)^2 \quad = \quad (4x + 3y)^2 \div 25$$

i.e. $\qquad 25(x^2 - 2x + 1 + y^2 - 4y + 4) = 16x^2 + 24xy + 9y^2$

So the equation is

$$9x^2 - 24xy + 16y^2 - 50x - 100y + 125 = 0$$

EXAMPLE   The point $P(x, y)$ moves so that its distance from $A(1, 2)$ is twice its distance from $B(4, 5)$, i.e. $AP = 2BP$.

Squaring each side of the equation $AP = 2BP$, we obtain the equivalent condition $AP^2 = 4BP^2$.

Now $\qquad\qquad AP^2 = (x-1)^2 + (y-2)^2$

$$= x^2 - 2x + 1 + y^2 - 4y + 4$$

$$= x^2 + y^2 - 2x - 4y + 5$$

and $\qquad\qquad 4BP^2 = 4[(x-4)^2 + (y-5)^2]$

$$= 4[x^2 - 8x + 16 + y^2 - 10y + 25]$$

$$= 4x^2 - 32x + 64 + 4y^2 - 40y + 100$$

$$= 4x^2 + 4y^2 - 32x - 40y + 164$$

So $\qquad x^2 + y^2 - 2x - 4y + 5 = 4x^2 + 4y^2 - 32x - 40y + 164$

i.e. $\qquad\qquad 0 = 3x^2 + 3y^2 - 30x - 36y + 159$

So the equation is $\qquad x^2 + y^2 - 10x - 12y + 53 = 0$

In this example, you probably did not know what kind of curve the locus was, but since the equation can be rewritten as $(x-5)^2+(y-6)^2 = 8$, we can now see that the locus is a circle with centre $(5,6)$ and radius $2\sqrt{2}$.

EXERCISE 10E

The conditions to be satisfied by $P(x, y)$ are as stated in each question. Find the equation of the locus, and state whether the locus is a straight line, a circle (in which case give its centre and radius), or some other curve.

1. A is $(2,0)$, B is $(4,6)$; $AP = BP$.

2. A is $(-3,5)$, B is $(-1, -7)$; $AP = BP$.

3. A is $(1,3)$, B is $(3,6)$; $AP = 2BP$.

4. A is $(1,3)$, B is $(3,6)$;   P is twice as far from B as it is from A.

5. A is $(-3,4)$, B is $(-5, -4)$;   P is three times as far from A as from B.

6. A is $(5,2)$, B is $(12,2)$;   P is six times as far from A as from B.

7. A is $(3,5)$, l is the line $y = 2x+1$;   the distance AP equals the distance from P to l.

8. A is $(1,2)$, l is the line $3x+2y = 5$;   the distance AP equals the distance from P to l.

9. P is equidistant from the lines $4y = 3x+4$ and $4x+3y = 3$.

10. P is equidistant from the lines $y = 2x+1$ and $x+3y = 0$.

11. A is $(7,3)$, B is $(1,3)$;   the area of APB is 9 units.

10.6 VECTOR EQUATIONS

As we saw in section 10.1, the vector equation $\mathbf{r} = \mathbf{a}+t\mathbf{m}$ represents a straight line (the unique line passing through the point with position vector $\mathbf{a}$, and running parallel to the vector $\mathbf{m}$).

For   instance,   if $\mathbf{a} = 5\mathbf{i}+9\mathbf{j}$ and $\mathbf{m} = 8\mathbf{i}+6\mathbf{j}$,   the   equation   is $\mathbf{r} = (5\mathbf{i}+9\mathbf{j})+t(8\mathbf{i}+6\mathbf{j})$, i.e. $\mathbf{r} = (5+8t)\mathbf{i}+(9+6t)\mathbf{j}$.

At any point on the line, $x = 5+8t$ and $y = 9+6t$ for some suitable value of t. We refer to t as a *parameter*.

EXAMPLE   Find the ordinary x–y equation of the above line.

We must eliminate t from the formulae for x and y:

we have $8t = x-5$ and $6t = y-9$

and so $6(x-5) = 48t = 8(y-9)$

Thus the equation is $6x-30 = 8y-72$, i.e. $4y-3x = 21$.

EXAMPLE Express the line $y = 3x-2$ in vector form, using t as the parameter.

The line has gradient 3: so $\mathbf{i}+3\mathbf{j}$ is a vector parallel to it. We need a point on the line: $(2,4)$ will do.

Hence $\mathbf{r} = (2\mathbf{i}+4\mathbf{j})+t(\mathbf{i}+3\mathbf{j})$ is a vector equation.

It should be obvious that we could have made different choices for $\mathbf{a}$ and $\mathbf{m}$, leading to different but equivalent results.

A vector equation does not necessarily represent a straight line. For instance, if $\mathbf{r} = t\mathbf{i}+(5-t^2)\mathbf{j}$, we have the formulae $x = t$ and $y = 5-t^2$. So the x–y equation is $y = 5-x^2$, which is a parabolic curve with apex at $(0,5)$.

The task of finding where two lines or curves cut is particularly simple if one equation is in vector form while the other is in x–y form.

EXAMPLE Where does the line $\mathbf{r} = (2+t)\mathbf{i}+(3+t)\mathbf{j}$ cut the circle $x^2+y^2 = 25$?

On the line, $x = 2+t$ and $y = 3+t$; on the circle, $x^2+y^2 = 25$.

So they intersect where $(2+t)^2+(3+t)^2 = 25$,

i.e.
$$4+4t+t^2+9+6t+t^2 = 25$$
$$2t^2+10t-12 = 0$$
$$(t+6)(t-1) = 0$$

Thus $t = -6$ or 1, and the points of intersection are $(2-6, 3-6)$ and $(2+1, 3+1)$, i.e. $(-4, -3)$ and $(3, 4)$.

EXAMPLE Where do the lines $\mathbf{r} = (3\mathbf{i}+4\mathbf{j})+s(-\mathbf{i}+2\mathbf{j})$ and $\mathbf{r} = (2\mathbf{i}+4\mathbf{j})+t(\mathbf{i}+3\mathbf{j})$ cut each other?

We would prefer one of the equations to be in x–y form, and we know from an earlier example that the x–y equation of the second line is $y = 3x-2$.

On the first line, $x = 3-s$ and $y = 4+2s$; on the second, $y = 3x-2$.

So they intersect where $4+2s = 3(3-s)-2$

i.e. $5s = 3$

Thus $s = 0.6$, and so at the point of intersection
$$x = 3-s = 3-0.6 = 2.4, \quad \text{and} \quad y = 4+2s = 4+1.2 = 5.2$$

The two lines therefore cut each other at $(2.4, 5.2)$.

We can confirm this result by considering the second vector equation, which tells us that $x = 2+t$ and $y = 4+3t$ at every point on the second line. Therefore $2+t = 2.4$ and $4+3t = 5.2$ should be true simultaneously, and we can easily check that $t = 0.4$ does indeed satisfy them both.

EXERCISE 10F

1. For each of the following vector equations, mark on graph paper the seven points given by $t = 3, 2, 1, 0, -1, -2, -3$:
   (a) $\mathbf{r} = (1+3t)\mathbf{i}+(2+t)\mathbf{j}$
   (b) $\mathbf{r} = (-4\mathbf{i}+3\mathbf{j})+t(-\mathbf{i}+2\mathbf{j})$
   (c) $\mathbf{r} = 2t\mathbf{i}+t^2\mathbf{j}$
   (d) $\mathbf{r} = (\cos 60\,t°)\mathbf{i}+(\sin 60\,t°)\mathbf{j}$

2. Express the following lines in x–y form:
   (a) $\mathbf{r} = (4\mathbf{i}+2\mathbf{j})+t(\mathbf{i}+3\mathbf{j})$
   (b) $\mathbf{r} = (-\mathbf{i}+3\mathbf{j})+t(\mathbf{i}-2\mathbf{j})$
   (c) $\mathbf{r} = (2+4t)\mathbf{i}+t\mathbf{j}$
   (d) $\mathbf{r} = (5+3t)\mathbf{i}-(2+t)\mathbf{j}$

3. Express the following lines in vector form:
   (a) $y = 2x+3$
   (b) $y = -3x+4$
   (c) $2y+3x = 1$
   (d) $3y+4x+5 = 0$

4. Where does the line $\mathbf{r} = (2\mathbf{i}+6\mathbf{j})+t(\mathbf{i}+2\mathbf{j})$ cut the circle $x^2+y^2 = 169$?

5. Where does the line $\mathbf{r} = (2+t)\mathbf{i}-(1+2t)\mathbf{j}$ cut $y = x^2$?

6. Find where the following pairs of lines meet:
   (a) $\mathbf{r} = (1+3s)\mathbf{i}+(2+4s)\mathbf{j}$ and $\mathbf{r} = (3+2t)\mathbf{i}+(4+3t)\mathbf{j}$
   (b) $\mathbf{r} = (2+s)\mathbf{i}+(3+2s)\mathbf{j}$ and $\mathbf{r} = (3t-1)\mathbf{i}+(t+4)\mathbf{j}$

CALCULUS II

11.1 RATES OF CHANGE

If a quantity depends on time, i.e. it is a function of time and can be expressed in the form $F(t)$, then the derivative of the function, $F'(t)$, is called the *rate of change* of the quantity.

If a point is moving, for instance, then its position varies with time, and the rate of change of position is the velocity, while the rate of change of the point's velocity is its acceleration. Or if a bath is being filled with water, the rate of change of the volume of water in the bath will be the rate at which water is flowing through the taps (unless the bath is leaking).

EXAMPLE A stone is dropped down a mine shaft. The distance fallen is found by experiment to be $4.9t^2$ m, where t is the time in seconds. What is the stone's velocity at time t? What is its acceleration? How fast will the stone be travelling after 10 s?

Now
$$F(t) \equiv 4.9t^2 \;\Rightarrow\; F'(t) \equiv 9.8t$$

and
$$f(t) \equiv 9.8t \;\Rightarrow\; f'(t) \equiv 9.8$$

Hence the velocity of the stone at time t equals $9.8t$ m/s, and in particular the velocity when $t = 10$ will be $F'(10) = 98$ m/s.

The acceleration $f'(t)$ equals 9.8 m/s^2, a constant we note.

EXAMPLE A balloon, initially of radius 1 cm, is being inflated in such a way that its radius at time t seconds equals $1 + 2t$ cm. What is the rate of increase of its volume when $t = 2$?

Let V cm^3 be the volume of the balloon at time t.

Then
$$V = \tfrac{4}{3}\pi r^3, \quad \text{where} \quad r = 1 + 2t$$

So
$$\frac{dV}{dt} = \frac{dV}{dr} \times \frac{dr}{dt} \quad \text{(by the chain rule)}$$

$$= 4\pi r^2 \times 2$$

$$= 8\pi(1 + 2t)^2$$

143

Alternatively, if you prefer not to use the chain rule, you may argue as follows:

$$V = \tfrac{4}{3}\pi r^3$$
$$= \tfrac{4}{3}\pi(1+2t)^3$$
$$= \tfrac{4}{3}\pi(1+2t)(1+4t+4t^2)$$
$$= \tfrac{4}{3}\pi(1+6t+12t^2+8t^3)$$

so $\qquad dV/dt = \tfrac{4}{3}\pi(6+24t+24t^2)$
$$= 8\pi(1+4t+4t^2)$$

In either case,

the rate of increase after $2\,\mathrm{s}$ = the value of dV/dt when $t=2$
$$= 8\pi \times 25 = 200\pi\,\mathrm{cm^3/s}$$

Note that in our solution to this problem we avoid specifying any particular decimal approximation for π (such as 3.14 or 3.141 592 654), preferring to present the answer in terms of π. This is very often the best policy.

EXAMPLE The volume of water in a reservoir, $V\,\mathrm{m^3}$, is given by the formula $V = 1000z^2$, where $z\,\mathrm{m}$ is the depth of water. If water is being drawn from the reservoir at the steady rate of $50\,\mathrm{m^3/s}$, find the rate at which the level is falling when the depth is $25\,\mathrm{m}$.

Since $V = 1000z^2$, $dV/dz = 2000z$.

So we have $\qquad\qquad \dfrac{dV}{dt} = \dfrac{dV}{dz} \times \dfrac{dz}{dt}$

i.e. $\qquad\qquad -50 = 2000z \times dz/dt$

So when $z = 25$, $\qquad -50 = 50\,000 \times dz/dt \;\Rightarrow\; dz/dt = -0.001$

Therefore the level is falling at a rate of $1\,\mathrm{mm/s}$.

EXERCISE 11A

1. A point moves along a straight line in such a way that at time $t\,\mathrm{s}$ its position in relation to a fixed point O is given by $x = F(t)\,\mathrm{m}$, where $F(t)$ is defined as

(a) $8t-t^2$

(b) t^3+3t

(c) $(10-t)^3$

(d) $100t-5t^2$

In each case, find the velocity $v = f(t)$ at time t, and the velocity after $8\,\mathrm{s}$.

2. A point is moving along a straight line in such a way that its velocity at time t s is given by $v = G(t)$ m/s, where $G(t)$ is defined as

(a) $4t$,   (b) $(t-3)^2$,   (c) t^2+4t,   (d) $100-6t$.

In each case, find the acceleration $a = g(t)$ at time t, and the acceleration after 4 s.

3. An open cubical tank, measuring $4 \times 4 \times 4$ m, is being filled with water in such a way that after t h (where $0 \leqslant t \leqslant 2$) the depth of water is t^2 m. Find an expression for the volume of water in the tank after t h, and hence an expression for the rate at which it is being filled at that time. What is the fastest rate of filling?

4. A circular puddle is evaporating in such a way that its radius after t minutes is $100-20\sqrt{t}$ cm, where t lies between 1 and 25. What is the area of the puddle at time t, and what is the rate of change of its area? Find the rate of change when $t = 1$ and when $t = 25$. (*Note* Throughout this question, express your answers in terms of π)

5. The length z m of a bar made from Y-alloy is given by the formula $z = 1+\alpha\theta$, where $\alpha = 2.2 \times 10^{-5}$ and θ is the bar's temperature in °C. Choosing suitable scales, draw a graph of z against θ.

If θ is given by the formula $\theta = 60+0.1t$ (t being the time in seconds), show that the rate of change of the bar's length with respect to time is 2.2×10^{-6} m/s.

6. The dimensions x, y, z of a rectangular region of space obey the following rules, where t ($0 \leqslant t \leqslant 20$) denotes the time: $x = y = 20-t$ and $z = 2t$. Prove that the volume V of the region is given by the formula $V = 800t-80t^2+2t^3$, and thus find a formula for dV/dt, the rate of change of volume. Show that both V and dV/dt equal 0 when $t = 20$, and find their values when $t = 0$ and when $t = 10$. Use your results to make a freehand sketch of the graph of V against t.

7. Normal biological processes cause a circular patch of mould to grow in area at a constant rate of 6 cm^2/s. Taking π to be 3, find the instantaneous rate at which the radius is growing when it equals 5 cm.

11.2 INVERSE PROBLEM

Suppose that instead of having to find the rate of increase $F'(t)$ of a function $F(t)$, we are given $F'(t)$ and have to find $F(t)$. For example, a point travels along the number line with velocity $v = 2t+3$. How far has it gone after t s?

The straight line graph of v against t is shown in figure 11.1. P is a typical point on the graph:

$$\text{OM} = t, \quad \text{MP} = 2t+3, \quad \text{and of course OU} = 3$$

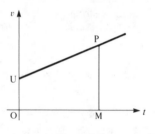

Fig. 11.1

We know that the distance travelled, or more precisely the change in position, is the area under the velocity–time graph, which in this case is a trapezium [area $= \frac{1}{2}(a+b) \times h$].

Therefore

$$\text{distance travelled} = \text{area of OMPU} = \tfrac{1}{2}[3+(2t+3)] \times t = t^2+3t$$

Of course, the actual position on the number line (normally denoted by x) and the *change* in position will be identical if and only if the point starts at the origin.

If so, i.e. if $x = 0$ when $t = 0$, then at any later time t

$$x = t^2+3t$$

If the point had started at 5 (i.e. at $x = 5$), however, then

$$x = 5+\text{change in position} = t^2+3t+5$$

We could have solved this problem without reference to a graph.

If $F(t)$ represents the position after t s, then

$$v = F'(t) \equiv 2t+3$$

What function when differentiated gives $2t+3$?

It is clear that $F(t) \equiv t^2+3t$ is one possibility, but it is equally clear that another is $F(t) \equiv t^2+3t+5$, since the derivative of 5 is zero. Indeed there is a whole family of answers of the form

$$F(t) \equiv t^2+3t+c$$

where c is a numerical constant (such as 0, 5, -2), which we need more information to find. In our example, c represents the starting position on the number line.

A process similar to that used above is useful whenever we are trying to find a quantity $F(t)$, and our information is that the rate of change function F' equals some given function f. We can determine the constant c if we also know the quantity's initial value, i.e. $F(0)$, or perhaps its value at some other time.

EXAMPLE If a point moves along the number line in such a way that t s after it leaves O its velocity is $(3t^2+4t+5)$ m/s, how far does it travel during the first 2 s?

Now $$v = 3t^2+4t+5 \Rightarrow x = t^3+2t^2+5t+c$$

Moreover $c = 0$, since the point started at O, and so x is given by the formula $x = t^3+2t^2+5t$.

Therefore when $t = 2$, $x = 8+8+10$, i.e. it travels 26 m in the first 2 s.

EXAMPLE A tank is filled with water at a rate that starts at $12\,\text{m}^3/\text{h}$ and decreases uniformly to zero within 2 h. If the tank contained $10\,\text{m}^3$ of water to start with, how much does it contain after these 2 h?

The rate of increase after t h is $(12-6t)\,\text{m}^3/\text{h}$.

Now $F'(t) \equiv (12-6t) \Rightarrow F(t) \equiv (12t-3t^2)+c.$

In this problem, $F(0) = 10$, and so $c = 10$.

Therefore, the volume of water in the tank after 2 h is

$$F(2) = (12 \times 2 - 3 \times 2^2)+10 = 22\,\text{m}^3$$

EXERCISE 11B

1. A point moves along the number line in such a way that its velocity $v = F'(t)$ at time t s and its starting position c are as given. What is its position $x = F(t)$ after the stated number of seconds?
   (a) $v = 6t+7$, $c = 3$; after 4 s
   (b) $v = 4t^3+1$, $c = -5$; after 2 s
   (c) $v = t^3+t$, $c = 0$; after 4 s

2. If a point moves along the number line in such a way that its acceleration $a = G'(t)$ at time t s and its starting velocity u are as given, what is its velocity $v = G(t)$ after the stated number of seconds?
   (a) $a = 4t-3$, $u = 5$; after 2 s
   (b) $a = 3t^2+2t$, $u = 0$; after 3 s
   (c) $a = t^4/200$, $u = -100$; after 10 s

3. For 6 h a tank is filled with water, the rate after t h being $36-t^2\,\text{m}^3/\text{h}$. How much water is there eventually in the tank (assuming that it was empty to start with)?

4. The volume of a balloon increases for 10 s, the rate after t s $(0 \leqslant t \leqslant 10)$ being $50-5t\,\text{cm}^3/\text{s}$. Its final volume is $400\,\text{cm}^3$. What was its initial volume?

11.3 AREA UNDER A GRAPH

We saw, at the start of section 11.2, that the inverse problem of finding $F(t)$ when we know $F'(t)$ is related to finding an area under a graph.

Figure 11.2 represents the graph of $v = f(t)$. How can we find an area like ABED, where $OA = a$ and $OB = b$?

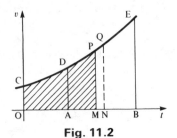

Fig. 11.2

Let us approach this problem by considering the area of the shaded region OMPC, where $OM = t$. OC is a fixed (left-hand) boundary of this region, whereas we imagine MP to be a movable (right-hand) boundary. So the area of OMPC depends on t, and we refer to this area as $F(t)$.

Now since area ABED = area OBEC − area OADC = $F(b) - F(a)$, we shall have solved our problem if we can find the function F.

The crucial relation between $F(t)$ and $f(t)$ is that $F'(t)$, i.e. the rate of change of the area, equals $f(t)$.

To see why this is so, let us suppose that t is increased by a very small amount, which we shall call δt (meaning a small increment in t—refer back to section 4.5). Obviously the area also increases by a very small amount, which we shall call δF. Looking at figure 11.2, we see that $\delta t = $ MN and $\delta F = $ MNQP. Now since MN is meant to be so very small, the region MNQP is very nearly a rectangle of area MP $\times$ MN, i.e. δF very nearly equals $f(t) \times \delta t$. In other words, $\delta F \div \delta t$ very nearly equals $f(t)$, and the discrepancy becomes indefinitely small as MN is made indefinitely small. This argument demonstrates that $F'(t)$, the rate of change of the area, does exactly equal $f(t)$.

So the area OMPC = $F(t)$ where F is a function which when differentiated gives f. You will remember that there is a whole family of such functions, all of the form $F(t) = $ something$+c$, where c is a numerical constant. But luckily it does not matter which member of the family we choose when evaluating area ABED as $F(b) - F(a)$, because the constant automatically cancels out.

Let us now consider an actual example. Suppose $f(x) \equiv 50 - 3x^2$. Its graph is sketched in figure 11.3. What is the area of the region under the graph between the two boundaries $x = 1$ and $x = 4$?

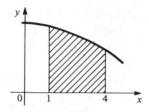

Fig. 11.3

First of all, we must find a function $F(x)$ which when differentiated gives $50-3x^2$. This is not at all difficult: plainly $F(x) \equiv 50x-x^3$ will do.

Therefore the area between $x = 1$ and $x = 4$ equals $F(4)-F(1)$, i.e. the required area $= (200-64)-(50-1) = 136-49 = 87$.

Note what would happen if we had chosen $F(x) \equiv 50x-x^3+c$. Then $F(4)-F(1) = (200-64+c)-(50-1+c) = 87$, as before.

When calculus was being developed, mathematicians treated the area of a region such as ABED in figure 11.4 rather differently. They regarded the region as being made up of very many narrow vertical strips like MNQP. If P is the point $(x, f(x))$, then the area of the shaded strip equals $f(x)\, \delta x$ very nearly. So the area ABED was regarded as the sum from $x = a$ to $x = b$ of lots of small bits like $f(x)\, \delta x$. The notation we use nowadays is based on this idea: we write $\int_a^b f(x)\, dx$, the $\int$ sign being an old-fashioned S (for 'sum').

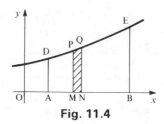

Fig. 11.4

Earlier in this section, we established that

$$\text{area ABED} = F(b)-F(a)$$

where F is any function such that $F' = f$. Such a function $F(x)$ is called an *indefinite integral* of $f(x)$.

One further piece of notation is worth learning at this stage: we use $\left[F(x) \right]_a^b$ to mean $F(b)-F(a)$.

Thus $\qquad \text{area ABED} = \int_a^b f(x)\, dx = \left[F(x) \right]_a^b = F(b)-F(a)$

EXAMPLE In figure 11.5, the curve is $y = 3x^2 - 12x + 20$. Find the area of the shaded region between $x = 1$ and $x = 4$.

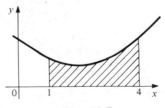

Fig. 11.5

Here $f(x) \equiv 3x^2 - 12x + 20$,   and   a   convenient   indefinite   integral   is $F(x) \equiv x^3 - 6x^2 + 20x$.

So

$$\text{area} = \int_1^4 (3x^2 - 12x + 20) \, dx$$

$$= \left[x^3 - 6x^2 + 20x \right]_1^4$$

$$= (64 - 96 + 80) - (1 - 6 + 20)$$

$$= 48 - 15$$

$$= 33$$

In this example, the result of our calculation, i.e. 33, is called the *definite integral* of $(3x^2 - 12x + 20)$ between the *limits* $x = 1$ and $x = 4$ (*lower* and *upper* limits respectively).

Note These various technical terms (indefinite integral, definite integral, lower and upper limit) are not essential for an understanding of this part of mathematics, but they are widely used and you should remember them if possible.

EXAMPLE Find the area between the curve $y = 9 - x^2$ and the x-axis.

Figure 11.6 shows a rough sketch of the graph. The required area is shaded. We can see that the limits are $x = -3$ and $x = +3$.

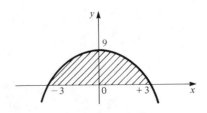

Fig. 11.6

So   the area $= \displaystyle\int_{-3}^{+3} (9-x^2)\,dx$

$$= \left[9x - x^3/3 \right]_{-3}^{+3}$$

$$= (27.-9) - (-27+9)$$

$$= (18) - (-18)$$

$$= 36$$

Note that evaluation of the square bracket calls for careful handling of the signs.

EXERCISE 11C

1. Find the areas underneath the following graphs between the given limits:
   (a) $y = 2x$; $x = 1$ to $x = 3$
   (b) $y = 4x^3$; $x = 1$ to $x = 3$
   (c) $y = 4 - x^2$; $x = 0$ to $x = 2$
   (d) $y = x^4$; $x = -2$ to $x = +2$

2. Evaluate the following definite integrals, and sketch in each case the region whose area has been found:

   (a) $\displaystyle\int_1^5 3x^2\,dx$ (b) $\displaystyle\int_0^1 x^3\,dx$

   (c) $\displaystyle\int_2^7 \pi\,dx$ (d) $\displaystyle\int_1^5 1/x^2\,dx$

3. Sketch the curve $y = 4x - x^2$ for values of x between -1 and 5. Find the area enclosed between the curve and the x-axis.

4. Sketch the curve $y = 16 - x^2$ for values of x between -5 and $+5$. Find the area enclosed in the positive quadrant between the curve and the two axes.

5. Find $\displaystyle\int_{-4}^{+4} x^1\,dx, \quad \int_{-4}^{+4} x^2\,dx, \quad \text{and} \quad \int_{-4}^{+4} x^3\,dx.$

   Comment on your answers with the aid of three sketches.

6. Sketch the curve $y = 1/x$ for values of x between 1 and 5. What difficulty arises when you attempt to find (by means of a definite integral) the area enclosed between the curve, the lines $x = 1$ and $x = 5$, and the x-axis?

11.4 INTEGRATION

The process discussed in this chapter, i.e. the reverse of differentiation, is called *integration*. The notation and terms developed in section 11.3 can be used in any problem where integration is appropriate, and are not confined to area problems.

EXAMPLE Find the distance travelled by a stone falling with velocity $9.8t$ m/s over a period $t = 0$ to 5 s.

Here $v = f(t) = 9.8t$. If x gives the position of the stone, then $dx/dt = v$: so integration is an appropriate technique.

If we wanted a formula for x in terms of t, we would write

$$x = \int 9.8t \, dt = 4.9t^2 + c \quad (c \text{ being a constant})$$

An integral sign used as here without limits always indicates that an indefinite integral is intended. It is essential to include the constant c in your answer. Further information is needed to find the value of c. In this case, if we defined x in such a way that $x = 0$ coincided with the stone's starting position, then plainly c would equal zero, and we would have the formula $x = 4.9t^2$.

However, the question as set calls for a definite integral:

$$\text{distance travelled} = \int_0^5 9.8t \, dt = \left[4.9t^2 \right]_0^5$$

$$= (4.9 \times 5^2) - 0 = 122.5 \, \text{m}$$

EXAMPLE Solve the equation $dy/dx = x/5$ (i.e. find y).

The problem here is to find a function $f(x)$ whose derivative equals $x/5$, in other words an indefinite integral. We write

$$y = \int x/5 \, dx = x^2/10 + c \quad (c \text{ being a constant})$$

Since c may take any value, we obtain a family of functions. Figure 11.7 shows a sketch of $y = x^2/10 + c$ for three typical values of c ($c > 0$, $c = 0$, $c < 0$). Because they all obey the equation $dy/dx = x/5$, these curves have the same gradient at points such as P, Q, R. A translation up or down in the y-direction maps one curve on to another. The constant c tells us the position of a particular curve by giving us the intercept on the y-axis (as with the straight line $y = mx + c$). Or given any point on the curve, we can determine c: if $(3,5)$ is to lie on the curve, for example, then c must equal 4.1.

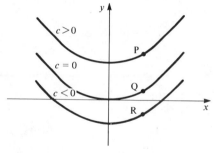

Fig. 11.7

EXAMPLE Find the equation of the curve for which $dy/dx = x^3$, given that $(2, 7)$ lies on the curve.

We have $y = \int x^3 \, dx = x^4/4 + c$. Now the point $(2, 7)$ lies on the curve, so $7 = 2^4/4 + c \Rightarrow c = 3$. So the solution is $y = x^4/4 + 3$.

EXAMPLE Integrate $x^4 - 4x^3 + 4x^2$.

We have $\int (x^4 - 4x^3 + 4x^2) \, dx = x^5/5 - 4x^4/4 + 4x^3/3 + c = x^5/5 - x^4 + 4x^3/3 + c$.

Note that just as the power drops one in differentiation, so in integration the power rises one. Note too that just as when we differentiate we have to incorporate a multiplier (x^3 becomes $3x^2$, for instance), so when we integrate we have to incorporate a divisor (x^3 becomes $x^4/4$).

The general rule of integration is that x^n becomes $\dfrac{x^{n+1}}{n+1}$.

EXAMPLE Integrate (a) $1/x^2$, (b) $1/(\sqrt[3]{x})$, (c) $\sqrt{x^3}$.

(a) $1/x^2 = x^{-2}$. We raise the power from -2 to -1, and then divide by -1.

Thus
$$\int 1/x^2 \, dx = \frac{x^{-1}}{-1} + c = -1/x + c$$

(b) $1/(\sqrt[3]{x}) = x^{-1/3}$. We raise the power from $-1/3$ to $2/3$, and divide by $2/3$.

Thus
$$\int 1/(\sqrt[3]{x}) \, dx = \frac{x^{2/3}}{2/3} + c = \frac{3\sqrt[3]{x^2}}{2} + c$$

(c)
$$\int \sqrt{x^3} \, dx = \int x^{3/2} \, dx = \frac{x^{5/2}}{5/2} + c = \frac{2\sqrt{x^5}}{5} + c$$

EXERCISE 11D

1. Find y, given that dy/dx equals

(a) $5x^4$

(b) $7-x^3$

(c) $(3x+2)^2$

(d) $(x+1/x)^2$

2. Find equations for the following curves, where dy/dx is as given, and the given point lies on the curve:

(a) $dy/dx = 2x$; $(0,7)$

(b) $dy/dx = x^2$; $(3,2)$

(c) $dy/dx = 1.5\sqrt{x}$; $(4,8)$

(d) $dy/dx = 1/x^2$; $(1,1)$

3. Write down the results of the following integrations, not forgetting the constant:

(a) $\displaystyle\int (x^6+3)\,dx$

(b) $\displaystyle\int (x-3)^2\,dx$

(c) $\displaystyle\int 4x^7\,dx$

(d) $\displaystyle\int \frac{x^3+1}{x^3}\,dx$

4. Integrate the following functions:

(a) $(x+1)^3$ (b) x^{-9} (c) $x^3\sqrt{x}$ (d) $\dfrac{5}{\sqrt{x}}$

12   MECHANICS III

12.1 CONSTANT ACCELERATION

In this and the following sections, the four letters t, v, u, a carry the same special meanings as in chapter 5 (refer back if you have forgotten). We now introduce a fifth letter:

s will mean the change in position since $t = 0$.

Suppose that an object is moving along a straight line with constant acceleration $3\,\text{m/s}^2$. If its initial velocity is $2\,\text{m/s}$, what is its velocity when $t = 4$? Here $u = 2$, $a = 3$, $t = 4$; hence $v = 2 + 3 \times 4 = 14$. Our calculation is based on the formula

$$v = u + at \qquad\qquad\qquad 1$$

We can now calculate the value of s by using the basic principle that change in position equals the area under the velocity–time graph.

Since in our example the acceleration is constant, the v–t graph is a straight line, as shown in figure 12.1. The area involved is therefore a trapezium, and we can see that $s = \frac{1}{2}(2 + 14) \times 4 = 32$.

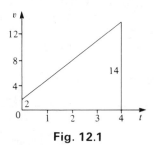

Fig. 12.1

This calculation demonstrates a second formula:

$$s = \tfrac{1}{2}(u + v)t \qquad\qquad\qquad 2$$

Formulae **1** and **2** lead to three other useful formulae.

For $\mathbf{1} \Rightarrow v - u = at$ and $\mathbf{2} \Rightarrow v + u = 2s/t$, and now multiplication gives $(v - u)(v + u) = at \times 2s/t = 2as$.

Therefore

$$v^2 = u^2 + 2as \qquad\qquad\qquad 3$$

155

But **1** and **2** also imply $s = \frac{1}{2}[u+(u+at)]t = \frac{1}{2}[(v-at)+v]t$.

Therefore
$$s = ut + \frac{1}{2}at^2 \qquad\qquad\qquad \textbf{4}$$

$$s = vt - \frac{1}{2}at^2 \qquad\qquad\qquad \textbf{5}$$

You will notice that each of the formulae involves four of the five quantities t, v, u, a, s. For example, **1** involves all the quantities except s: it is thus called the s-free formula. Similarly, **2** is the a-free formula, **3** is the t-free formula, **4** is the v-free formula, and **5** is the u-free formula.

Clearly, given any *three* of t, v, u, a, s, we can determine either of the remaining two by use of the correct formula.

EXAMPLE $u = 2$, $v = 3$, $a = 0.5$; find s.

Here t is not involved, and so we use the t-free formula: $v^2 = u^2 + 2as \Rightarrow 2as = v^2 - u^2$. Thus $s = 3^2 - 2^2 = 5$.

If we are asked to find both the missing quantities, we have a choice of which formulae to use. The rule of thumb is 'always use the simplest available', which usually means the one with the lowest number, i.e. we prefer **1** to **2**, **2** to **3**, and so on.

EXAMPLE $v = 2.5$, $a = -0.2$, $s = 4$; find u and t.

We must start by using either the t-free formula (i.e. **3**) to find u, or the u-free formula (i.e. **5**) to find t. The former is plainly very much easier: $v^2 = u^2 + 2as \Rightarrow u^2 = v^2 - 2as$.

Thus $\qquad u^2 = 2.5^2 - 2 \times (-0.2) \times 4 = 7.85 \Rightarrow u = \pm 2.801\,785\,145$

Hence (if we assume forward motion) $u = 2.8$ (2 s.f.).

Now to find t: we have four formulae available (all except the t-free one). We naturally use **1**: $v = u + at \Rightarrow at = v - u$.

So $\qquad -0.2t = 2.5 - u = -0.301\,785\,145 \Rightarrow t = 1.5$ (2 s.f.)

In fact there are no fewer than twenty different types of problem of the form 'Given v, a, and s, find t'. Our rule of thumb will see us safely through any of these. Note, however, that when required to find t, you are often best advised to find u or v first, and only then to find t. For instance, even if we had not been asked to find u in the above example, it would none the less have been good policy to do so: this is because trying to find t direct from the u-free formula (and the same applies to the v-free formula) would involve us in an awkward quadratic.

EXERCISE 12A

(Assume forward motion throughout)

1. $s = 12, u = 3, v = 6$;   find a.

2. $s = 3, u = 4, v = 1$;   find t.

3. $s = 8, u = 1.5, a = 0.1$;   find v.

4. $s = 6, u = 2, a = -0.2$;   find t.

5. $s = 20, u = 1, t = 4$;   find v.

6. $s = 10, u = 2.5, t = 3$;   find a.

7. $s = 5, v = 0.5, a = -0.3$;   find u.

8. $s = 4, v = 1.5, a = 0.25$;   find t.

9. $s = 2, v = 1, t = 3$;   find u.

10. $s = 3.5, v = 4, t = 0.5$;   find a.

11. $s = 0.5, a = 0.01, t = 2$;   find u.

12. $s = 100, a = 5, t = 4$;   find v.

13. $u = 2.2, v = 3.5, a = 0.1$;   find s.

14. $u = 1.34, v = 3.62, a = 0.684$;   find t.

15. $u = 3.81, v = 0.78, t = 8.92$;   find s.

16. $u = 5.36, v = 2.43, t = 18.2$;   find a.

17. $u = 2.65, a = -0.32, t = 4.69$;   find s.

18. $u = 0.27, a = -0.045, t = 0.79$;   find v.

19. $v = 3.86, a = -0.263, t = 1.68$;   find s.

20. $v = 26.5, a = 0.673, t = 14.6$;   find u.

21. Express s in terms of t and draw the graph if $u = 2$, $a = 3$.

12.2 NEGATIVE VALUES

The previous section dealt only with forward motion, although we allowed accelerations to be negative. By using integration, however, we can show that the five famous formulae of section 12.1 do in fact apply (for constant acceleration) even for backward movement, or motion that is partly forwards and partly backwards.

EXAMPLE I am standing over a well and throw a cricket ball up at 3 m/s. Find its velocity and position t s later.

Imagine an x-axis pointing straight up, with the origin O at the point where I release the ball (figure 12.2). Then $x = 0$ when $t = 0$.

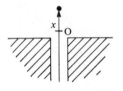

Fig. 12.2

The ball's acceleration $= -9.8\,\text{m/s}^2$

$$\text{i.e. } \frac{dv}{dt} = -9.8$$

Hence by integration $v = -9.8t + 3$ ($v = +3$ when $t = 0$)

Thus $dx/dt = 3 - 9.8t$; hence by further integration

$$x = 3t - 4.9t^2 \quad (\text{ constant } = 0 \text{ since } x = 0 \text{ initially})$$

It is instructive to draw the graphs of v and x (figure 12.3). Note that $v = 0$ when $t \approx 0.3$, so that x has a stationary value about then, and that $x = 0$ when $t \approx 0.6$. We can see that eventually both v and x are negative: the ball is dropping down the well.

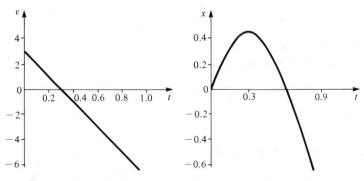

Fig. 12.3

We can generalise this problem by taking a starting velocity of $u\,\text{m/s}$ and a constant acceleration of $a\,\text{m/s}^2$ (either of which may be negative). If we now integrate in a precisely similar way, we get

$$v = u + at \quad (\text{since } a \text{ is a constant}) \qquad \text{and} \qquad x = ut + \tfrac{1}{2}at^2$$

Hence $x = ut + \tfrac{1}{2}at \times t = ut + \tfrac{1}{2}(v - u)t = \tfrac{1}{2}(u + v)t$

Thus formulae **1**, **2**, **4** still hold (even if some or all of t, v, u, a, x are negative) and since formulae **3** and **5** follow from **1** and **2**, they must also be true.

EXAMPLE If the well in the previous example is 20 m deep, how long is it before the ball hits the bottom?

Here $u = +3$, $a = -9.8$, and we want to find t when $x = -20$.

The best policy is to find v first, by using $v^2 = u^2 + 2ax$:

$$v^2 = 3^2 + 2 \times (-9.8) \times (-20) = 401 \Rightarrow v = \pm 20.024\,984\,39$$

Now v is clearly negative: so $v = -20$ (2 s.f.).

Next we must find t. For this purpose we choose formula **1**, using (as we did in section 12.1) the modified version $at = v - u$.

Thus $-9.8t = v - 3 = -23.024\,984\,39 \Rightarrow t = 2.349\,488\,203$

and so the ball takes between 2.3 and 2.4 s to reach the bottom.

It is worthwhile repeating this question with the x-axis pointing *down* from the point of projection.

Then $u = -3$, $a = +9.8$, $x = +20$: and so

$$v^2 = u^2 + 2ax \Rightarrow v^2 = 9 + 392 \Rightarrow v = \pm 20.025 \text{ as before}$$

But now v is clearly positive, so $v = +20$ (2 s.f.).

Hence $at = v - u \Rightarrow 9.8t = 20.025 + 3 \Rightarrow t = 2.35$

and we obtain the same value of t as before.

EXERCISE 12B

Remember to say in each case whether your axis points up or down.

1. I drop (i.e. $u = 0$) a pebble down a well. It takes 1.5 s to reach the bottom. How deep is the well?

2. I throw a pebble down a well 20 m deep. It takes 1.2 s to reach the bottom. What speed did I throw it at?

3. I throw a pebble upwards at 2 m/s from a window. How long is it before the pebble hits the ground 15 m below?

4. I fire a gun vertically upwards at 14.7 m/s. How high does the bullet rise (you must ignore air resistance), and when does it hit the ground?

5. Find the velocities of the bullet in question 4 when it is at roof level (5 m up). Hence find for how long it is above roof level.

6. I fling a pebble up and catch it 3 s later. How fast did I fling it? How high does it rise?

7. A bird drops a stone, which hits the ground at 15 m/s. How high was the bird?

8. I drop a stone down a well. How far does it travel during the first, second, and third seconds?

9. On another planet I fling a stone up at $12\,\text{m/s}$. After $4\,\text{s}$ I see it descending at $4\,\text{m/s}$. How high is it now, and what is g on that planet?

10. I fling a stone up at $u\,\text{m/s}$. Find formulae (in terms of u and g) for its maximum height, its velocity on returning to the point of projection, and its overall time of flight.

12.3 MORE ELABORATE PROBLEMS

EXAMPLE I catapult a stone up at $14.7\,\text{m/s}$ followed $1\,\text{s}$ later by another at the same speed. Where do they collide?

We let the x-axis point up. Now at the moment of collision, the two stones are in the same position, i.e. $x_1 = x_2$; we start by finding out *when* this happens.

If $t = 0$ when the first stone is fired, then $t = 1$ when the second is fired. So using formula **5**, we have

$$x_1 = 14.7t - 4.9t^2 \qquad \text{and} \qquad x_2 = 14.7(t-1) - 4.9(t-1)^2$$

On collision, $x_1 = x_2$: therefore

$$14.7t - 4.9t^2 = 14.7t - 14.7 - 4.9t^2 + 9.8t - 4.9$$

So $19.6 = 9.8t \Rightarrow t = 2$, and $x = 14.7 \times 2 - 4.9 \times 4 = 9.8\ (\text{m})$.

EXAMPLE A train passes through station A at $54\,\text{km/h}$ and heads east towards station B ($1350\,\text{m}$ away) accelerating at $0.5\,\text{m/s}^2$. Five seconds later, another train travelling west at a steady $36\,\text{km/h}$ passes through B. Where do they meet? (Remember $18\,\text{km/h} = 5\,\text{m/s}$)

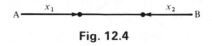

Fig. 12.4

Working in metres and seconds, we define:

$$x_1 = \text{position of train 1 east of A}$$
$$x_2 = \text{position of train 2 west of B}$$
$$t = \text{time (zero when train 1 is at A)}$$

Now $x_1 = 15t + 0.25t^2$ ($u = 15$, $a = 0.5$)

and $x_2 = 10(t-5)$ ($u = 10$, $a = 0$).

When they meet, $x_1 + x_2 = 1350$: therefore

$$15t + 0.25t^2 + 10t - 50 = 1350 \Rightarrow 0.25t^2 + 25t - 1400 = 0$$

So by the quadratic formula (we need the positive root)

$$t = (-25 + \sqrt{625 + 1400}) \div 0.5 = (-25 + 45) \div 0.5 = 40$$

Hence $x_1 = 15 \times 40 + 0.25 \times 1600 = 1000$: they meet 1 km from A.

EXERCISE 12C

1. I throw up a stone at $8 \, \text{m/s}$, and $0.5 \, \text{s}$ later another at $6 \, \text{m/s}$. When and where do they collide?

2. A train passes through station A at $72 \, \text{km/h}$, and heads east towards station B ($500 \, \text{m}$ away) decelerating at $0.25 \, \text{m/s}^2$. Six seconds later, another train travelling west at a steady $27 \, \text{km/h}$ passes through B. Where do they meet (explain why we need the smaller of the two values of t)?

3. A metal ball is dropped from a height of $2 \, \text{m}$ to the floor. How high will it bounce if its speed on impact is halved?

4. A lift accelerates from rest at $1.2 \, \text{m/s}^2$ for $1.5 \, \text{s}$, travels at a steady speed for $5 \, \text{s}$, then comes to a stop decelerating at $0.5 \, \text{m/s}^2$. How far does it go in all?

12.4 VARIABLE ACCELERATION

In section 12.2 we used integration to treat constant acceleration. It can also be used to deal with variable acceleration.

EXAMPLE A body moves along the x-axis with acceleration given by $dv/dt = 4 - 0.6t$. When $t = 0$, $x = 0$ and $v = +7.5$. Find when (if ever) the body begins to move backwards, and how far it then is from O.

Integrating the formula for dv/dt, we have

$$dx/dt = v = 4t - 0.3t^2 + 7.5 \qquad (v = +7.5 \text{ when } t = 0)$$

and

$$x = 2t^2 - 0.1t^3 + 7.5t + 0 \qquad (x = 0 \text{ when } t = 0)$$

Now $v > 0$ initially: so the body keeps moving forward until $v = 0$,

i.e.   until $3t^2 - 40t - 75 = 0 \Rightarrow (3t + 5)(t - 15) = 0$

So $v = 0$ when $t = 15$ (we are not interested in negative t). Will the body now move backwards? When $t = 15$, $v = 0$ and $a = -5$: the negative acceleration means that it will indeed go backwards. This happens when $x = 225$, i.e. 225 units from the origin.

Another way to deal with variable acceleration is to use the principle that change in velocity equals the area under the acceleration–time graph (corresponding to the principle mentioned in section 12.1 that change in position equals the area under the velocity–time graph).

EXAMPLE My acceleration rises steadily over 2 s from $2 \, \text{m/s}^2$ to $3 \, \text{m/s}^2$, and then drops steadily over the next 2 s to zero. If my original velocity was $1 \, \text{m/s}$, what is my final velocity?

Sketch the a–t graph (figure 12.5).

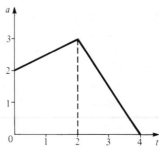

Fig. 12.5

The area under the graph $= \text{trapezium} + \text{triangle}$

$$= \tfrac{1}{2} \times (2+3) \times 2 + \tfrac{1}{2} \times 3 \times 2$$

$$= 5 + 3 = 8$$

So my gain in velocity is $8 \, \text{m/s}$, and my final velocity $= 1 + 8 = 9 \, \text{m/s}$.

EXERCISE 12D

1. Find v and x (if $v = u$ and $x = 0$ initially) given that:

(a) $a = 4 + 6t$, $u = -2$ (b) $a = 40 - 5t$, $u = 30$

(c) $a = (t+1)(t+2)$, $u = 0$ (d) $a = 1 - 12t^2$, $u = 2$

2. During a period of time my acceleration falls steadily from 6 to $2 \, \text{m/s}^2$, while my speed rises from 3 to $15 \, \text{m/s}$. How long is the period, and how far do I travel during it?

3. My acceleration rises steadily from 0 to $5 \, \text{m/s}^2$ over 6 s, then falls steadily to $2 \, \text{m/s}^2$ over 4 s. If my final speed is $37 \, \text{m/s}$, what was my initial speed?

12.5 VELOCITY AND ACCELERATION IN TWO DIMENSIONS

If a spider is scuttling about on a piece of graph paper, then it is clear what we mean by its velocity vector at any moment: a vector of magnitude equal to its speed, and pointing in the direction of motion. There is, fortunately, a simple rule for calculating this vector if we know the x and y coordinates of the spider in terms of the time t:

$$\mathbf{v} = \begin{pmatrix} dx/dt \\ dy/dt \end{pmatrix}, \text{ or } \begin{pmatrix} \dot{x} \\ \dot{y} \end{pmatrix} \text{ to use Newton's alternative notation.}$$

Thus if $x = t$ and $y = t^2$, then $\mathbf{v} = \begin{pmatrix} 1 \\ 2t \end{pmatrix} = \mathbf{i} + 2t\mathbf{j}$.

EXAMPLE If $\mathbf{r} = 2t\mathbf{i} + (6t - t^2)\mathbf{j}$ is a bug's position vector, find:

(a) its positions when $t = 1$ and $t = 2$,
(b) the vector joining these positions,
(c) the bug's velocity when $t = 3$,
(d) its speed when $t = 5$,
(e) the bug's greatest height (i.e. y-value),
(f) when and where the bug hits the x-axis,
(g) the angle at which it hits the x-axis.

In the bug's case $x = 2t$, $y = 6t - t^2$, so $\mathbf{v} = 2\mathbf{i} + (6 - 2t)\mathbf{j}$.

(a) When $t = 1$, $x = 2$ and $y = 5$: so the bug is at $(2, 5)$.
     Similarly, when $t = 2$ it is at $(4, 8)$.
(b) The vector is $(4\mathbf{i} + 8\mathbf{j}) - (2\mathbf{i} + 5\mathbf{j}) = 2\mathbf{i} + 3\mathbf{j}$.
(c) When $t = 3$, $\mathbf{v} = 2\mathbf{i} + 0\mathbf{j} = 2\mathbf{i}$: it is moving horizontally.
(d) When $t = 5$, $\mathbf{v} = 2\mathbf{i} - 4\mathbf{j}$. So the speed $= \sqrt{(4 + 16)} = \sqrt{20}$.
(e) The bug's height $y = 6t - t^2$. This has a quadratic graph, increasing to a local maximum and then decreasing: so the greatest y-value occurs when $\dot{y} = 0$, i.e. when $6 - 2t = 0$. Thus $t = 3$, and the greatest height equals $6 \times 3 - 3^2 = 9$.
(f) On the x-axis, $y = 0$, i.e. $6t = t^2$. Thus $t = 6$ (or 0). So $x = 2t = 12$.
(g) When $t = 6$, $\mathbf{v} = 2\mathbf{i} - 6\mathbf{j}$. This vector makes an angle $\arctan(6/2) = 71.6°$ (1 d.p.) with the horizontal.

Conversely, if we know formulae for the components of the velocity vector, we can use integration to find the position vector, as in the next example.

EXAMPLE Find **r** given that $\mathbf{v} = 5\mathbf{i} + (8 - 2t)\mathbf{j}$, and that $\mathbf{r} = \mathbf{0}$ when $t = 0$. Find also the distance from the origin and the direction of motion when $t = 10$.

By the basic rule, $\dot{x} = 5$ and $\dot{y} = 8 - 2t$. Integrating,

$$x = 5t + c \quad \text{and} \quad y = 8t - t^2 + d \quad (c \text{ and } d \text{ constants})$$

But when $t = 0$, $x = 0$ and $y = 0$; hence $c = d = 0$.

Therefore $\qquad\qquad\qquad\qquad\qquad \mathbf{r} = 5t\mathbf{i} + (8t - t^2)\mathbf{j}$

Now when $t = 10$, $\mathbf{r} = 50\mathbf{i} - 20\mathbf{j}$ and $\mathbf{v} = 5\mathbf{i} - 12\mathbf{j}$. Therefore the distance from the origin is $\sqrt{(50^2 + 20^2)} = \sqrt{2900} \approx 53.9$. And the direction of motion ψ is given by $\cos\psi = 5/13$, $\sin\psi = -12/13$: so ψ lies in the fourth quadrant, and equals about $-67.4°$.

We define an acceleration vector by analogy with the basic rule for velocity:

$$\text{if } \mathbf{v} = \begin{pmatrix} u \\ w \end{pmatrix} \text{ then } \mathbf{a} = \begin{pmatrix} du/dt \\ dw/dt \end{pmatrix}, \text{ or } \begin{pmatrix} \dot{u} \\ \dot{w} \end{pmatrix}$$

Since $\mathbf{v} = \begin{pmatrix} \dot{x} \\ \dot{y} \end{pmatrix}$, we can also say $\mathbf{a} = \begin{pmatrix} \ddot{x} \\ \ddot{y} \end{pmatrix}$.

This definition has the surprising property that **a** is not necessarily in the direction of motion. For instance, if $x = t$ and $y = t^2$, then $\mathbf{v} = \mathbf{i} + 2t\mathbf{j}$, and $\mathbf{a} = 2\mathbf{j}$. Thus the acceleration is always in the direction of the y-axis, but the motion is not.

The definition has one supreme virtue: Newton's second law, that $\mathbf{P} = m\mathbf{a}$, remains true for two-dimensional motion.

EXAMPLE A mass of $2\,\text{kg}$ has a position vector given by $\mathbf{r} = (t + 2t^2)\mathbf{i} + 3t^2\mathbf{j}$. Find **v** and **a** at time t. If the motion is caused by a single force **P**, find the magnitude and direction of this force. (Assume all quantities are in standard units)

Here $\mathbf{v} = (1 + 4t)\mathbf{i} + 6t\mathbf{j}$, differentiating x and y.

Also $\mathbf{a} = 4\mathbf{i} + 6\mathbf{j}$, differentiating the components of **v**.

By Newton's law $\qquad\quad \mathbf{P} = m\mathbf{a} = 2(4\mathbf{i} + 6\mathbf{j}) = 8\mathbf{i} + 12\mathbf{j}$

Thus the force is constant in magnitude and direction. Its magnitude P equals $\sqrt{(8^2 + 12^2)} = \sqrt{208} \approx 14.4\,\text{N}$. And its direction is given by the angle α where $\cos\alpha = 8/P$, $\sin\alpha = 12/P$; so α is acute and equals $\arctan(12/8) \approx +56.3°$.

EXERCISE 12E

1. If $\mathbf{r} = (t+1)\mathbf{i} + (t^2-1)\mathbf{j}$, find $\mathbf{v}$.

2. If $\mathbf{r} = t\mathbf{i} + 5\mathbf{j}$, find $\mathbf{v}$.

3. If $\mathbf{r} = t^2\mathbf{i} + \mathbf{j}$, find $\mathbf{v}$.

4. If $\mathbf{v} = t^2\mathbf{i} + t^3\mathbf{j}$, find $\mathbf{a}$.

5. If $\mathbf{v} = t(t+1)\mathbf{i} - t(t-1)\mathbf{j}$, find $\mathbf{a}$.

6. If $\mathbf{v} = 2(t^3\mathbf{i} - t^4\mathbf{j})$, find $\mathbf{a}$.

7. to 9. Determine $\mathbf{a}$ also in questions 1, 2, and 3.

10. If $\mathbf{v} = 3t^2\mathbf{i} + 4\mathbf{j}$, determine $\mathbf{r}$ if $\mathbf{r}_0$ (the value of $\mathbf{r}$ when $t = 0$) is $2\mathbf{i} + 3\mathbf{j}$.

11. If $\mathbf{v} = 4(\mathbf{i} - t^3\mathbf{j})$, determine $\mathbf{r}$ if $\mathbf{r} = \mathbf{0}$ when $t = 1$.

12. If $\mathbf{v} = (t+1)(\mathbf{i} + t\mathbf{j})$, determine $\mathbf{r}$ if $\mathbf{r}_0 = \mathbf{i} + \mathbf{j}$.

13. A varying force acting on a $0.5\,\mathrm{kg}$ mass produces a velocity $\mathbf{v} = 3t\mathbf{i} + 2t^2\mathbf{j}$. Find the acceleration and hence the force at time t. What are the magnitude and direction of the force when $t = 1$?

14. A varying force acting on a $2\,\mathrm{kg}$ mass causes its position vector $\mathbf{r}$ to equal $(4t^2+t)\mathbf{i} + (t^3+1)\mathbf{j}$. Find the velocity, the acceleration, and hence the force. Give the magnitude and direction of the force when $t = 0$ and when $t = 1$.

12.6 PROJECTILES

The most important application of the ideas in the previous section is to the study of projectiles (stones, bullets, etc., projected at an angle to the horizontal).

If such complications as aerodynamic forces and the rotation of the Earth are ignored, then the path of a projectile can be assumed to lie in a vertical plane. To describe the projectile's position during its flight, therefore, just two axes are sufficient. It is customary to choose O at the point of projection, with Ox lying horizontally underneath the flight path, and Oy pointing vertically upwards.

EXAMPLE I fire a bullet from O with velocity $20\mathbf{i} + 30\mathbf{j}$ (we use the standard units). Find the greatest height attained. Find also the time of flight and the horizontal range (i.e. when and where it hits the x-axis again).

We know that $\mathbf{a} = -g\mathbf{j}$, i.e. that $\ddot{x} = 0$ and $\ddot{y} = -g$.

Integrating twice, we obtain:

$$\dot{x} = 20 \qquad \text{and} \qquad \dot{y} = -gt + 30 \quad (\dot{x} = 20 \text{ and } \dot{y} = 30 \text{ when } t = 0)$$

$$x = 20t \qquad \text{and} \qquad y = -\tfrac{1}{2}gt^2 + 30t \quad (x = y = 0 \text{ when } t = 0)$$

Now y reaches its greatest value when $\dot{y} = 0$, i.e. when $-gt + 30 = 0 \Rightarrow t = 30/g$.

Thus the greatest height is

$$y = -\tfrac{1}{2}g(30/g)^2 + 30(30/g)$$

$$= -450/g + 900/g$$

$$= 450/g \approx 46 \text{ (m), taking } g = 9.8$$

On the x-axis, $y = 0$, i.e. $\tfrac{1}{2}gt^2 = 30t$. Thus $t = 60/g$ (or 0), and at that time $x = 20t = 1200/g$. Hence (to 2 s.f.) the time of flight is 6.1 s and the range is 120 m, again taking $g = 9.8$.

Note that in this example we have not used the value 9.8 for g until the very end of each stage. We adopted a rather similar policy with π, you may remember, in an earlier example in section 11.1.

EXAMPLE A projectile is fired at an angle α to the horizontal with an initial speed of V. Prove that the equation of the flight path (with the usual axes) is

$$y = x \tan \alpha - \frac{\tfrac{1}{2}x^2 \sec^2\alpha}{(V^2/g)}$$

Hence show that the horizontal range is given by the formula

$$R = 2(V^2/g)\sin \alpha \cos \alpha$$

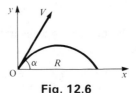

Fig. 12.6

The initial conditions are as follows:

$\dot{x} = V \cos \alpha$, $\dot{y} = V \sin \alpha$, and $x = y = 0$.

Hence $\ddot{x} = 0 \Rightarrow \dot{x} = V \cos \alpha \Rightarrow x = Vt \cos \alpha \Rightarrow t = x/(V \cos \alpha)$

and $\ddot{y} = -g \Rightarrow \dot{y} = -gt + V \sin \alpha \Rightarrow y = -\tfrac{1}{2}gt^2 + Vt \sin \alpha$

Substituting $x/(V \cos \alpha)$ for t in the equation for y, we obtain

$$y = -\tfrac{1}{2}g\left(\frac{x}{V \cos \alpha}\right)^2 + V\left(\frac{x}{V \cos \alpha}\right)\sin \alpha$$

$$= x \tan \alpha - \frac{\tfrac{1}{2}x^2 \sec^2\alpha}{(V^2/g)} \quad \text{(simplifying and inter-changing the two terms)}$$

When the projectile returns to the x-axis, we have $y = 0$, and so

$$\frac{\frac{1}{2}x^2 \sec^2\alpha}{(V^2/g)} = x\tan\alpha \;\Rightarrow\; x = \frac{2(V^2/g)\tan\alpha}{\sec^2\alpha} \quad (\text{or } x = 0)$$

Hence $R = 2(V^2/g)\sin\alpha\cos\alpha$.

This formula for R can be rewritten as $R = (V^2/g)\sin 2\alpha$ (since $2\sin\alpha\cos\alpha = \sin 2\alpha$, as we shall discover later on, in chapter 16). This shows that the maximum range equals V^2/g, and that this is achieved when $2\alpha = 90°$, i.e. when the angle of projection is $45°$.

Note that the equation giving y in terms of x is a quadratic, and so the flight path is a symmetric curve of the type studied in chapter 1 (such curves are technically known as parabolas). Note also that if $g = 0$ then the equation reduces to $y = x\tan\alpha$: this represents a straight line at an angle of α to the horizontal, which is what one would expect.

EXAMPLE A crusader fires his cross-bow at a castle turret 400 m away. If he wants the bolt to pass through an opening 50 m above the point of projection, show that there are two possible angles of projection, assuming that the maximum range of the weapon is 500 m.

Let V be the speed of projection, and α the angle. Then $V^2/g = $ maximum range $= 500$.

Now the equation of the trajectory of the bolt is

$$y = x\tan\alpha - \tfrac{1}{2}x^2\sec^2\alpha/(V^2/g)$$

where the axes are chosen as in the last example. And the point $(400, 50)$ has to lie on the trajectory. Therefore

$$50 = 400\tan\alpha - 80\,000\sec^2\alpha/500 \;\Rightarrow\; 5 = 40\tan\alpha - 16\sec^2\alpha$$

and so $5 = 40t - 16(1+t^2)$ where $t = \tan\alpha$,

i.e. $16t^2 - 40t + 21 = 0 \;\Rightarrow\; (4t-3)(4t-7) = 0$

Therefore t can take either of the two values $3/4$ or $7/4$, and each of these yields a value for α (about $37°$ and $60°$).

EXERCISE 12F

Assume standard axes and units throughout.

1. Calculate the greatest height, time of flight, and range for projectiles whose initial velocities are:

(a) $10\mathbf{i} + 20\mathbf{j}$,   (b) $20\mathbf{i} + 10\mathbf{j}$,   (c) $5\mathbf{i} + 30\mathbf{j}$.

2. Calculate the greatest height, time of flight, and range for projectiles with initial velocities of 24.5 m/s at the following angles to the horizontal:

(a) 30°,   (b) 45°,   (c) 60°,   (d) 90°.

3. A projectile is fired horizontally from O in the x-direction at a speed of 400 m/s. Find t and y when $x = 400$. Find when it reaches the level $y = -14.4$, and give the value of x and the direction of the velocity at that time.

4. A projectile is fired from O on horizontal ground, and 3 s later hits the ground 58.8 m from O. Find the velocity of projection. Find t and y when $x = 19.6$, and the direction of the velocity then.

5. A Roman soldier at the siege of Carthage (146 BC) decided to hurl a stone ball weighing about 40 kg (the regulation size) at an enemy position 400 m away. If the maximum range of his ballista was 500 m, find the possible angles of projection. Assume that the ground was level.

12.7 MOTION IN A CIRCLE

Suppose a particle P is moving anti-clockwise at a steady speed of v round a circle with centre $(0, 0)$ and radius r. Suppose also that when $t = 0$ the particle is at A on the x-axis (see figure 12.7).

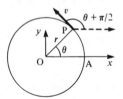

Fig. 12.7

At time t, let us suppose that OP makes an angle θ with Ox (θ is measured in radians, naturally).

Then $\qquad r\theta = \text{arc AP} = vt \Rightarrow \theta = vt/r \Rightarrow d\theta/dt = v/r$

and of course $\qquad x = r\cos\theta, \quad y = r\sin\theta$

Now the velocity vector is of magnitude v and pointing in the direction of motion at any instant, i.e. along the tangent at P, which makes an angle $(\theta + \pi/2)$ with Ox.

So $\qquad dx/dt = v\cos(\theta + \pi/2), \quad dy/dt = v\sin(\theta + \pi/2)$

This fact incidentally provides us with an informal demonstration that the derivatives of $\sin\theta$ and $\cos\theta$ really are $+\cos\theta$ and $-\sin\theta$ respectively, as stated in section 4.3. To simplify matters, we will temporarily make the assumption that $r = 1$.

Then $d\theta/dt = v$, $y = \sin\theta$, and $dy/dt = v\sin(\theta + \pi/2)$.

Now by the chain rule,
$$\frac{dy}{d\theta} \times \frac{d\theta}{dt} = \frac{dy}{dt}$$

i.e.
$$\frac{dy}{d\theta} \times v = v\sin(\theta + \pi/2)$$

i.e.
$$\frac{d(\sin\theta)}{d\theta} = \sin(\theta + \pi/2) = +\cos\theta$$

This argument establishes one of our results, that the derivative of $\sin\theta$ is $+\cos\theta$. By considering x rather than y, we can likewise establish that the derivative of $\cos\theta$ is $\cos(\theta + \pi/2) = -\sin\theta$.

[The proof that $\sin(\theta + \pi/2) = +\cos\theta$ and $\cos(\theta + \pi/2) = -\sin\theta$ is a simple exercise in trigonometry, which is left to you]

Dropping the assumption that $r = 1$, we now consider the following question: what is the acceleration of the particle as it moves with steady speed v round the circle of radius r?

The components of the acceleration vector are $\ddot{x}$ and $\ddot{y}$, where

$$\ddot{x} = \frac{d(\dot{x})}{dt} = \frac{d(-v\sin\theta)}{dt}$$

$$= -v \times \frac{d(\sin\theta)}{d\theta} \times \frac{d\theta}{dt} \quad \text{(by the chain rule)}$$

$$= -v \times \cos\theta \times v/r$$

$$= (v^2/r) \times -\cos\theta$$

$$= (v^2/r)\cos(\theta + \pi)$$

and
$$\ddot{y} = \frac{d(\dot{y})}{dt} = (v^2/r)\sin(\theta + \pi) \quad \text{by a similar argument}$$

Therefore the acceleration vector is of magnitude (v^2/r) and makes an angle $(\theta + \pi)$ with Ox, i.e. it points directly towards the centre of the circle (see figure 12.8).

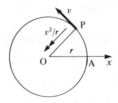

Fig. 12.8

We can see, therefore, that if an object is moving in a circle there must be a force directed towards the centre of the circle of a magnitude sufficient to produce this so-called radial acceleration.

EXAMPLE A boy ties a stone of mass 0.2 kg to a string, and swings it round and round in a horizontal circle of radius 0.6 m. If the stone's speed is 9 m/s, find the tension in the string (assuming it to be horizontal).

The radial acceleration $\qquad\qquad = v^2/r$ inwards

$$= 81/0.6 \, \text{m/s}^2$$

So the necessary inward force $\qquad = ma$

$$= 0.2 \times 81/0.6$$

$$= 27 \, \text{N}$$

and so the tension in the string equals 27 N.

If the string were to break, then the tension would suddenly vanish, and the stone would no longer be able to travel round in a circle, but would fly off at a tangent.

EXAMPLE A small object of mass m kg is attached by a string of length 7.5 m to a fixed point A, and is set rotating at a steady speed in a horizontal circle whose centre O lies 7.2 m vertically beneath A. Find the radius r of the circle and the speed v of the object.

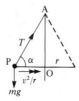

Fig. 12.9

Figure 12.9 gives a side-on view of the system at some moment of time. There are two forces acting on the object: its weight mg, and the tension T in the string. Because the object is moving in a circle of radius r at a steady speed v, its acceleration is directed towards the centre O of the circle, and is of magnitude v^2/r.

Now r can be found easily: AP $= 7.5$ m and AO $= 7.2$ m,

and so $\qquad\qquad r = $ OP $= \sqrt{(7.5^2 - 7.2^2)} = 2.1$ m

Hence $\cos \alpha = 21/75$ and $\sin \alpha = 72/75$.

Now the horizontal and vertical components of acceleration are v^2/r and 0 respectively. So we have:

$$T \cos \alpha = mv^2/r \quad \text{(resolving horizontally)}$$

and
$$T \sin \alpha - mg = 0 \quad \text{(resolving vertically)}$$

Combining these two equations, we obtain:

$$mv^2 = T \times r \cos \alpha = \frac{mg}{\sin \alpha} \times r \cos \alpha$$

and so
$$v^2 = \frac{9.8}{72/75} \times 2.1 \times \frac{21}{75} = 6.0025 \Rightarrow v = 2.45$$

Hence the speed of the object is 2.45 m/s.

EXERCISE 12G

1. At a fair-ground, a cylindrical 'room' of radius 5 m rotates about its vertical axis so that a man standing inside the cylinder with his back to the wall is moving at 14 m/s. Find the man's inward radial acceleration as a multiple of g.

2. A toad of mass 60 grams crouches on a horizontal turntable rotating at a steady 45 r.p.m., 15 cm away from the spindle. Find (a) the toad's speed, (b) his inward acceleration, and (c) the horizontal force acting on him.

3. At what steady speed can the driver of a BMW 320i (of mass 1350 kg) safely take a bend of radius 50 m, without danger of skidding, if the road is horizontal and the greatest possible sideways frictional force between it and the tyres of the car is 9600 N?

4. A particle of mass m kg is attached by a wire of length 60 cm to a fixed point A, and is set rotating at a steady speed of 3 m/s in a horizontal circle whose centre O lies directly beneath A. If the wire makes a constant angle α to the horizontal, show that $2 \cos^2 \alpha = 3 \sin \alpha$, and then solve this equation to show that $\alpha = 30°$. (Take g to be 10 m/s²)

12.8 OBSERVED VELOCITY

If we look out of a moving train, a cow in a field will appear to have a backward velocity, even if we can see that it is walking forwards. Thus the observed velocity of an object may be different from its true velocity. There is, however, a simple connection between (a) the true velocity, (b) the observed velocity, and (c) the velocity of the observer.

EXAMPLE A train is at $25t\mathbf{i}+40t\mathbf{j}$ and a cow is at $2t\mathbf{i}+3t\mathbf{j}$. Find the velocities of the train and the cow, and the velocity of the cow as observed by a mathematician in the train.

Differentiating, we find that the train and cow have velocities $25\mathbf{i}+40\mathbf{j}$ and $2\mathbf{i}+3\mathbf{j}$. Now the mathematician thinks the cow has coordinates $x = 2t-25t = -23t$ and $y = 3t-40t = -37t$; so (differentiating) he reckons the cow's velocity is $-23\mathbf{i}-37\mathbf{j}$.

Note that $(\mathbf{i}+3\mathbf{j}) = (-23\mathbf{i}-37\mathbf{j})+(25\mathbf{i}+40\mathbf{j})$.

This illustrates the general rule:

true velocity = observed velocity plus observer's velocity

EXAMPLE I am bicycling at 5 m/s due north. The wind appears to be blowing at 8 m/s from the east. What is the true wind direction and speed?

We draw a rough vector diagram to show observed velocity plus observer's velocity (figure 12.10). The answers can now be obtained by accurate construction and measurement, or (more easily in this case) by calculation.

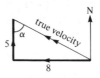

Fig. 12.10

The wind blows from α east of south, where $\alpha = \arctan(8/5) = 58°$ approximately, and the wind speed $= 8/\sin\alpha \approx 9.4$ m/s.

EXAMPLE A submarine wishes to go straight across a channel 48 km wide down which a tide of 7 km/h is running. What course must she steer, and how long will the crossing take, if her speed (through the water) is 25 km/h?

In this case, there is no real observer: but we may imagine an observant fish floating motionless in the sea (swept along by the tide just like the submarine), and the same principles will apply. Let us suppose the tide runs due south (figure 12.11). The true velocity of the submarine is due east, the observed velocity is 25 km/h but of course *not* due east, and the observer's velocity is 7 km/h due south. The figure shows that the submarine must steer $\arcsin(7/25) \approx 16°$ north of east, i.e. on a course of 074°. We see too that her true speed equals $\sqrt{(25^2-7^2)} = 24$ km/h, and so the crossing will take 2 h.

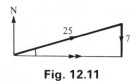

Fig. 12.11

EXAMPLE At the moment when my boat, the *Centaurus*, passes through C(1, 2) with steady velocity $3\mathbf{i}+4\mathbf{j}$, the *Pristis* passes through P(15, 30) at $\mathbf{i}+\mathbf{j}$, and the *Scylla* through S(11, −6) at $-2\mathbf{i}+8\mathbf{j}$. Show that one of them collides with me, and find out when.

Figure 12.12 shows the positions of the three boats at the moment referred to in the question. I regard myself (in *Centaurus*) as the observer.

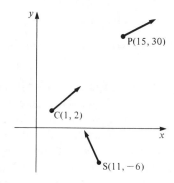

Fig. 12.12

Let us consider *Pristis* first:

　　observed velocity + observer's velocity = true velocity

⇒ observed velocity = true velocity − observer's velocity

$$= (\mathbf{i}+\mathbf{j})-(3\mathbf{i}+4\mathbf{j}) = -2\mathbf{i}-3\mathbf{j}$$

Now if she and I are to collide, her observed velocity must point straight towards me, i.e. along

$$\mathbf{PC} = (1\mathbf{i}+2\mathbf{j})-(15\mathbf{i}+30\mathbf{j}) = -14\mathbf{i}-28\mathbf{j}$$

But these two vectors have different gradients (1.5 and 2), and so there is no collision between *Pristis* and *Centaurus*.

We consider *Scylla* in a similar manner:

$$\text{observed velocity} = (-2\mathbf{i}+8\mathbf{j})-(3\mathbf{i}+4\mathbf{j}) = -5\mathbf{i}+4\mathbf{j}$$

and　　　　$$\mathbf{SC} = (1\mathbf{i}+2\mathbf{j})-(11\mathbf{i}-6\mathbf{j}) = -10\mathbf{i}+8\mathbf{j} = 2(-5\mathbf{i}+4\mathbf{j})$$

These vectors have the same directions, and so *Scylla* and I do collide. Since the relative position vector is twice the relative velocity vector, the collision takes place after 2 units of time.

EXAMPLE I am at $P(1, 2)$ travelling with constant velocity $3\mathbf{i} + 4\mathbf{j}$. An interceptor is at $Q(19, -7)$ and can travel at a speed of 10. In which direction should he move in order to intercept me rapidly, and how long will this take?

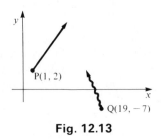

Fig. 12.13

We regard the interceptor as the observer.

Now $\mathbf{PQ} = 18\mathbf{i} - 9\mathbf{j} = 9(2\mathbf{i} - \mathbf{j})$, and he wants to see me approaching in this direction.

So we have a vector diagram (figure 12.14): AB represents my observed velocity, in the same direction as $9(2\mathbf{i} - \mathbf{j})$, BC represents the observer's velocity, of magnitude 10, and AC represents my true velocity, $3\mathbf{i} + 4\mathbf{j}$. Since we know the directions of two sides of this triangle (AB and AC) and the lengths of two (BC and AC), it can be drawn to scale. We can then measure the direction of BC, which gives the interceptor's course (326°), and the length of AB (9.6), which combined with the distance PQ ($9\sqrt{5}$) gives the time required (about 126 minutes, assuming standard units).

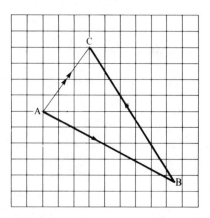

Fig. 12.14

EXERCISE 12H

1. I am bicycling at 15 km/h due west. The wind appears to be coming at 8 km/h from the north. Calculate the true speed and direction of the wind.

2. I am bicycling at 20 km/h due south, and the wind appears to be at 10 km/h from the south-west. By accurate drawing, find the true speed and direction of the wind. How will the wind seem if I speed up to 24 km/h?

3. Caspar leaves C(−2, 5) with steady velocity $3\mathbf{i} - 4\mathbf{j}$ as Fergus leaves F(10, −12) with steady velocity $-2\mathbf{i} + 3.5\mathbf{j}$. Find whether they collide, and if so when.

4. Repeat question 3 if Fergus starts at (8, −10).

5. A stream is flowing at 4 m/s. In still water I can swim at 5 m/s. I want to swim straight across the stream, a distance of 40 m. In which direction should I point, and how long will I take?

6. London to Paris is 350 km on a bearing of 150°. A plane can fly at 500 km/h in still air. When a gale blows from the east at 100 km/h, find by drawing how long it will take to fly there and back.

7. I am at (2, 3) travelling with velocity $5\mathbf{i} + 12\mathbf{j}$. An interceptor is at (15, 0). If he can travel with a speed of 13 units, find, by drawing, in which direction he should move to intercept me, and how long he will take.

8. Answer question 7 by calculation.

13 PROBABILITY

13.1 MEASURING PROBABILITY

Suppose that a microcomputer has been programmed to select a set of digits from 1 to 9 inclusive, and then to print one of these digits whenever a particular key is pressed. The operator does not know which digits have been selected, nor can he in any way predict which digit will appear when he presses the key.

Now suppose that this program is the basis for a game, in which the appearance or non-appearance of the digit 9 is critical. A boy playing the game might well need to know the probability of getting a 9, i.e. $\Pr(9)$: how can he find out? It is not much use conducting a single trial, i.e. pressing the key once and noting the outcome. What he must do is to conduct a series of N trials, technically known as an *experiment*, and note the frequency f with which the digit 9 appears (he might for instance decide to have $N = 10$, and find that $f = 4$). Then the *relative frequency* f/N (in this case 0.4) provides him with a measurement of Pr(9).

If the boy conducted experiment after experiment, choosing $N = 10$ each time, then obviously he would not always get the same value for f/N. Figure 13.1 shows the results of 100 actual such experiments. In 4 cases, the relative frequency lay between 0 and 0.1, in 18 cases between 0.1 and 0.2, and so on. You can see that if the boy chooses $N = 10$, he cannot tell with any precision what the probability is. The reason for this is that an experiment with only 10 trials is too short. If the value of N is increased to 50, the graph (figure 13.2) gives a much more precise impression, because the relative frequencies are not so vaguely spread out over the range 0 to 1. Even better results can be obtained if N is made 100 (figure 13.3). $N = 500$ is better still (figure 13.4): the relative frequencies now all lie between 0.2 and 0.3, and we need figure 13.5 to show the data in greater detail. It is evident that if the boy conducts an experiment with $N = 500$, the value of the relative frequency that he obtains gives him quite a reliable estimate

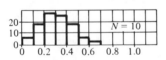

Fig. 13.1

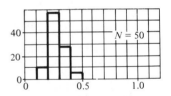

Fig. 13.2

of the probability. If he found that $f = 127$, for instance, and calculated $f/N = 0.254$, he could conclude with some confidence that $\Pr(9)$ was about 0.254. He could of course also conclude that the probability of *not* getting a 9 was about 0.746.

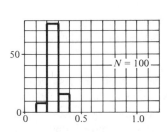

Fig. 13.3

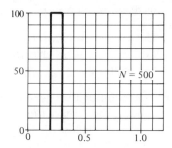

Fig. 13.4

Fig. 13.5

EXERCISE 13A

1. Get a drawing pin and let it fall from a height of about 12 inches on to a carpet. Conduct an experiment by doing this ten times (or by letting ten pins fall simultaneously) and note how many times the pin lands point down. Repeat this experiment 100 times, and draw a graph as in figure 13.1.

2. Regarding your activities in question 1 as a single series of 1000 trials, estimate the probability that a drawing pin will land point down. What then is the probability that it will land point up?

3. Draw a 4×4 cm grid on a piece of graph paper. Let a 50 p piece fall repeatedly in random fashion on to the grid, counting it a success if the coin lands wholly within one of the squares of the grid. Hence measure the probability of success. Now attempt to estimate the probability of success if you were to use a 1 p piece instead, and then check your estimate by conducting a suitable experiment.

4. Measure as reliably as you can the probabilities that a word in the English language contains:

   (a) an A,   (b) an E,   (c) an I,   (d) an O.

13.2 CALCULATING PROBABILITIES

In the previous section, we saw that if you want to measure a probability, you must conduct an experiment, i.e. a series of trials, and calculate the relative frequency of the outcome in question. To achieve greater precision, you must increase the number of trials in the experiment.

However, if you have helpful information, or are prepared to make assumptions, then you may be able to find out probabilities by calculation rather than by measurement.

For instance, if we assume in the example discussed in the last section that $Pr(9)$ is 0.254, then without further experiment we can calculate that $Pr(not\ 9)$ is 0.746. Similarly, suppose that by asking the programmer we discover that the digits selected are invariably 6, 7, 8, or 9. Then once we have found by measurement that $Pr(9) = 0.254$, $Pr(8) = 0.265$, and $Pr(7) = 0.232$, we can calculate that $Pr(6) = 1 - (0.254 + 0.265 + 0.232) = 0.249$, and we can deduce too that $Pr(1) = Pr(2) = Pr(3) = Pr(4) = Pr(5) = 0$.

Suppose now that the programmer reveals in addition that the program shows no preference towards any of 6, 7, 8, or 9: the computer prints them indiscriminately (*at random*). In this case, it is plain that $Pr(6) = Pr(7) = Pr(8) = Pr(9)$, and since the sum of these four probabilities is 1, each must equal 0.25. In this situation, we would have to admit that our measurements had not been as precise as we had thought.

The line of reasoning used in the last paragraph is quite common. It enables us to say that when we toss a normal coin, $Pr(heads) = Pr(tails)$ and so each must equal $\frac{1}{2}$. It enables us to say that when we throw a single unbiased die, the probability of each of the six numbers 1 to 6 falling uppermost must be $\frac{1}{6}$.

13.3 EVENTS

Returning once again to the example of section 13.1, we can imagine a game where both 8 and 9 were critical numbers: perhaps your opponent pays you £5 if 8 or 9 appears. When outcomes are taken together like this, the result is called an *event*.

In this case, we can see that $Pr(8\ or\ 9) = Pr(8) + Pr(9)$.

For another example of events, we will consider the act of throwing two dice, one red and one green, and recording the two numbers that fall uppermost. There are now 36 separate possible outcomes, illustrated in figure 13.6.

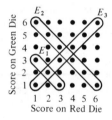

Fig. 13.6

We scarcely need an experiment to accept that unless the dice are somehow biased, these 36 outcomes are equally probable: so the probability of each equals $\frac{1}{36}$.

The events illustrated in the figure are

E_1: the total score is 4

E_2: the total score is 7

E_3: a double is thrown

A glance at the figure shows that

$$\Pr(E_1) = 3/36 = 1/12, \quad \Pr(E_2) = \Pr(E_3) = 6/36 = 1/6$$

Just as we may combine outcomes to form events, so we may combine events to form further events. For instance, the event (E_1 or E_2) involves a total score of 4 or 7, i.e. it involves getting one or other of the nine outcomes $(1,3)$, $(2,2)$, $(3,1)$, $(1,6)$, $(2,5)$, $(3,4)$, $(4,3)$, $(5,2)$, $(6,1)$. Thus $\Pr(E_1 \text{ or } E_2) = 9/36 = 1/4$.

Note that in this case $\Pr(E_1 \text{ or } E_2) = \Pr(E_1) + \Pr(E_2)$.

This simple result holds because E_1 and E_2 do not overlap, i.e. they are mutually exclusive. When two events do overlap, like E_1 and E_3, things are slightly more complicated.

The trouble with (E_1 or E_3), i.e. a total of 4 or a double, is that $(2,2)$ occurs on both counts. There are only eight distinct outcomes involved now—$(1,3)$, $(2,2)$, $(3,1)$, $(1,1)$, $(3,3)$, $(4,4)$, $(5,5)$, $(6,6)$—as you can soon confirm by consulting figure 13.6. Therefore $\Pr(E_1 \text{ or } E_3) = 8/36 = 2/9$. If we simply add $\Pr(E_1)$ and $\Pr(E_3)$ when finding $\Pr(E_1 \text{ or } E_3)$, we shall in effect be counting $(2,2)$ twice; to compensate for this, we must subtract the probability of $(2,2)$, i.e. $\frac{1}{36}$.

So $$\Pr(E_1 \text{ or } E_3) = 3/36 + 6/36 - 1/36 = 8/36$$

More generally, if E and F are any two events, then to find $\Pr(E \text{ or } F)$ we may need first of all to find the probability of the overlap event, usually denoted by (E and F). Of course, if E and F are mutually exclusive, then they do not overlap and so $\Pr(E \text{ and } F) = 0$: in this special case, therefore, it is true that $\Pr(E \text{ or } F) = \Pr(E) + \Pr(F)$. However, the general rule is that

$$\Pr(E \text{ or } F) = \Pr(E) + \Pr(F) - \Pr(E \text{ and } F)$$

EXAMPLE A card is drawn at random from an ordinary 52-card pack. What is the probability that the card is either a spade or else a court card (king, queen, or jack)?

We define two events, as follows:

$$E = \text{the card is any spade}$$
$$F = \text{the card is a court card}$$

Since the card is drawn at random, and since the pack contains 4 suits, each containing an equal number of cards, we see immediately that $\Pr(E) = 1/4$. Moreover, there are 3 court cards in each suit, and so 12 in all: therefore $\Pr(F) = 12/52 = 3/13$.

Now event E and event F clearly overlap, since there are 3 court cards in the spade suit. Thus $\Pr(E \text{ and } F) = 3/52$.

So finally
$$\begin{aligned}
\Pr(E \text{ or } F) &= \Pr(E) + \Pr(F) - \Pr(E \text{ and } F) \\
&= 1/4 + 3/13 - 3/52 \\
&= (13 + 12 - 3)/52 \\
&= 22/52, \quad \text{i.e. about } 42\%
\end{aligned}$$

Note Many mathematicians use P rather than Pr to indicate probability: thus they would write $P(E)$ rather than $\Pr(E)$.

And many write $(E \vee F)$ or $(E \cup F)$ rather than $(E \text{ or } F)$, and $(E \wedge F)$ or $(E \cap F)$ rather than $(E \text{ and } F)$.

In this book, however, we stick to the notation that seems easiest to understand.

EXERCISE 13B

1. Random numbers are generated from the set of integers 1, 2, 3, ... , 60. What is the probability of the event E, that the number is prime? What is the probability of F, that the number is divisible by 7? List the elements of the events $(E \text{ and } F)$ and $(E \text{ or } F)$. What are the probabilities of these two events? What is the probability that the number is neither prime nor divisible by 7?

2. An unbiased die is thrown. If E means getting a score of 4, and F means getting an even score, what are $\Pr(E)$, $\Pr(F)$, $\Pr(E \text{ and } F)$, and $\Pr(E \text{ or } F)$?

3. Two coins are tossed. Let E be getting 2 heads, F be getting 2 tails. Are E and F mutually exclusive events? Evaluate $\Pr(E)$, $\Pr(F)$, $\Pr(E \text{ and } F)$, and $\Pr(E \text{ or } F)$.

4. Two ordinary unbiased dice are thrown. Find the probabilities that the total score is

(a) even,   (b) 4 or less,   (c) 13,   (d) more than 9.

5. Two unbiased dodecahedral dice are thrown. Draw a figure like figure 13.6, and show the following events:

(a) the total showing is 11,

(b) the difference between the numbers showing is 2,

(c) the product of the numbers showing is 12,

(d) the product of the numbers showing is 11.

Calculate the probabilities of these events.

6. In the latest family game, an electronic device produces a random two-digit number (00 to 99). In order to start, you have to get a number divisible by 3 or a number with a 3 in it. What is the probability that you succeed in this?

13.4 SUCCESSIVE EVENTS

EXAMPLE A die is thrown twice. What is the probability of getting an odd number followed by a square number?

There are two ways of looking at this problem: (1) in terms of a single event, or (2) in terms of two successive events.

(1) We think of the double throw of the die as a single act, with outcomes such as $(1, 1)$, $(1, 2)$, etc. The situation is as in figure 13.6. The relevant outcomes are $(1, 1)$, $(1, 4)$, $(3, 1)$, $(3, 4)$, $(5, 1)$, $(5, 4)$, six in all. Therefore the required probability is $6/36 = \frac{1}{6}$.

(2) We consider two successive events, E and F, where E is 'being odd' and F is 'being square'. We then find out $\Pr(E \text{ and } F)$. Now $\Pr(E) = \frac{1}{2}$ and $\Pr(F) = \frac{1}{3}$. So we see that in this case $\Pr(E \text{ and } F) = \Pr(E) \times \Pr(F) = \frac{1}{6}$.

Note, incidentally, that the first throw in no way affects the probabilities associated with the second throw. Many people are confused on this matter. They think, for instance, that if I toss a coin and it comes up heads, then $\Pr(\text{heads})$ will no longer be $\frac{1}{2}$ when I next toss the coin. This misconception is especially strong when a coin has turned up heads several times running: people will then tend to say that 'by the law of averages' it is now more likely to turn up tails. But coins do not seem to behave like this. On the contrary, all the evidence suggests that the result of one throw does not affect the probabilities for the next throw. We express this fact in technical language by saying that the throws or the events are *statistically independent*.

Thus E and F in the above example are independent. Now we discovered in that example that $\Pr(E \text{ and } F)$ equalled $\Pr(E) \times \Pr(F)$. This is an instance of a very useful general rule: $\Pr(E_1 \text{ and } E_2) = \Pr(E_1) \times \Pr(E_2)$, where E_1 and E_2 are two statistically independent events. This rule can be generalised:

$$\Pr(E_1 \text{ and } E_2 \text{ and } E_3 \text{ and} \ldots) = \Pr(E_1) \times \Pr(E_2) \times \ldots$$

where E_1, $E_2, \ldots$ are statistically independent events.

EXAMPLE What is the probability that the captain of a football team wins the toss in nine successive league matches?

We define nine events: $E_1 =$ he wins the toss in match 1, and so on. Now it should be obvious that these events are statistically independent (at any rate if the coin in use is an unbiased one). The value of $\Pr(E_9)$, for instance, is entirely unaffected by the captain's luck in the first eight matches. Therefore

$$\Pr(E_1 \text{ and } E_2 \text{ and} \ldots \text{and } E_9) = \Pr(E_1) \times \ldots \times \Pr(E_9)$$

which equals $\qquad 0.5 \times \ldots \times 0.5 = 0.5^9 \approx 0.2\%$

This is the answer if the coin is unbiased. But what if it is not?

Suppose that the bias is such that $\Pr(\text{heads})$ equals 0.7 rather than 0.5. If the captain calls heads and tails indiscriminately, then the answer is still 0.2%. But if for some reason he habitually calls heads, then the answer becomes $0.7^9 \approx 4\%$.

EXAMPLE In a large consignment of oranges, 7% are bad. If I choose 4 at random, what is the probability that none of these 4 is bad?

We consider four events: $E_1 =$ the first orange is good

$E_2 =$ the second orange is good, etc.

Then assuming the batch is so large that the events are in effect statistically independent, we have

$$\Pr(E_1) = \Pr(E_2) = \Pr(E_3) = \Pr(E_4) = 1-0.07 = 0.93$$

So

$$\begin{aligned} \Pr(\text{all oranges are good}) &= \Pr(E_1 \text{ and } E_2 \text{ and } E_3 \text{ and } E_4) \\ &= \Pr(E_1) \times \Pr(E_2) \times \Pr(E_3) \times \Pr(E_4) \\ &= 0.93 \times 0.93 \times 0.93 \times 0.93 \end{aligned}$$

Therefore the required probability is $0.93^4 \approx 75\%$.

In many cases, of course, events are *not* independent. Let us return to the football captain considered earlier. Suppose that his policy is to call heads for match 1, but thereafter to call heads or tails depending on the fall of the coin in the previous match. Now the question whether or not the events E_1, etc., are independent hinges on whether or not the coin is unbiased.

EXAMPLE A conjuror draws 2 cards in succession from an ordinary pack and tears them up before the eyes of his audience. What are the probabilities that he has drawn: (a) 2 cards from the same suit,   (b) 2 aces?

(a) It does not matter to which suit the first card belongs: we simply work out the probability that the second card matches. When the second card is drawn, there are 51 cards in the pack, of which 12 are right. So the required probability equals $12/51 = 4/17$.

(b) We consider the two events: $E_1 =$ the first card is an ace, and $E_2 =$ the second card is an ace. It should be evident that these events are not independent. If the first card is an ace, then $\Pr(E_2) = 3/51$, whereas if the first card is not an ace, then $\Pr(E_2) = 4/51$. Now our calculation must obviously be based throughout on the hypothesis that the first card is indeed an ace. So we need the former of these two probabilities, i.e. we need the probability of E_2 given the occurrence of E_1, usually abbreviated to $\Pr(E_2 \mid E_1)$. Therefore

$$\begin{aligned} \Pr(\text{both cards are aces}) &= \Pr(E_1 \text{ and } E_2) \\ &= \Pr(E_1) \times \Pr(E_2 \mid E_1) \\ &= 4/52 \times 3/51 \\ &= 1/221 \end{aligned}$$

Thus we have the following quite general rule, which applies to any two events E and F, whether statistically independent or not:

$$\Pr(E \text{ and } F) = \Pr(E) \times \Pr(F \mid E)$$

Of course, if E and F happen to be statistically independent, then $\Pr(F \mid E) = \Pr(F)$. In this special case, therefore, the general rule reduces to the form $\Pr(E \text{ and } F) = \Pr(E) \times \Pr(F)$, which we considered earlier in this section.

Note that since the event $(F \text{ and } E)$ is exactly the same as the event $(E \text{ and } F)$, and since $\Pr(F \text{ and } E) = \Pr(F) \times \Pr(E \mid F)$, we may rephrase our general rule in the following alternative form, which is often rather more convenient:

$$\Pr(E \text{ and } F) = \Pr(E \mid F) \times \Pr(F)$$

EXAMPLE When I spend a weekend in Paris, the probability of my enjoying the weekend is 80% if the weather is fine, but only 30% if the weather is foul. Assuming that the probabilities of the weather in Paris being fine and foul during a weekend are 40% and 60% respectively, find the probability that I enjoy my weekend in Paris.

We define three events: $E =$ I enjoy the weekend

$$F_1 = \text{the weather is fine}$$
$$F_2 = \text{the weather is foul}$$

Now $\Pr(E|F_1) = 80\%$ and $\Pr(E|F_2) = 30\%$. And since F_1 and F_2 between them cover all possible weather conditions, and are mutually exclusive, we see that

$$\begin{aligned} \Pr(E) &= \Pr(E \text{ and } F_1) + \Pr(E \text{ and } F_2) \\ &= \Pr(E|F_1) \times \Pr(F_1) + \Pr(E|F_2) \times \Pr(F_2) \\ &= 80\% \times 40\% + 30\% \times 60\% \\ &= 50\% \end{aligned}$$

Suppose now that when I return from Paris I tell my friends that the weekend was enjoyable. What then is the probability that the weather was in fact fine?

We need to calculate $\Pr(F_1|E)$.

Now $\quad \Pr(E \text{ and } F_1) = \Pr(E) \times \Pr(F_1|E) = \Pr(E|F_1) \times \Pr(F_1)$

So $\qquad \Pr(F_1|E) = \dfrac{\Pr(E|F_1) \times \Pr(F_1)}{\Pr(E)}$

$$= \dfrac{80\% \times 40\%}{50\%}$$

$$= 64\%$$

Problems of this type are often more easily solved by means of tree diagrams.

EXAMPLE Bag A contains 5 red and 4 green disks, while a similar bag B contains 6 red and 3 green. One bag is chosen at random and 2 disks are drawn from it.

(a) Find the probability that the disks have different colours.

(b) If the 2 disks are both red, find the probability that bag A was the one chosen.

We solve both these problems by drawing a tree diagram (figure 13.7).

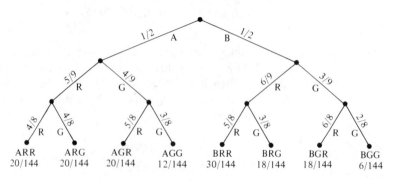

Fig. 13.7

Remember to multiply as you work your way down a tree diagram, and then if necessary to add across at the foot.

Thus the probability that the disks are both green equals

$$1/2 \times 4/9 \times 3/8 + 1/2 \times 3/9 \times 2/8 = (12+6)/144 = 18/144 = 1/8$$

Looking at the tree diagram, you will notice that the probabilities of the events leading from each growth point add up to 1, and of course $(20+20+20+12+30+18+18+6)/144$, i.e. the total probability, also equals 1.

(a) One sequence of events that yields disks of different colours is (A and then R and then G). If we follow this sequence down the tree, multiplying probabilities as we go (according to the usual rule), we obtain

$$\Pr(ARG) = 1/2 \times 5/9 \times 4/8 = 20/144 \text{ (see figure 13.7)}$$

The full list of sequences that yield different colours is (ARG), (AGR), (BRG), and (BGR).

Therefore the required probability is

$$\Pr(ARG) + \Pr(AGR) + \Pr(BRG) + \Pr(BGR)$$
$$= (20+20+18+18)/144 = 76/144 = 19/36$$

(b) If the disks are known to be both red, there are only two possible sequences, (ARR) and (BRR), with probabilities in the ratio $20:30$, i.e. $2:3$. Therefore the probability that bag A was the one chosen is $2/(2+3) = 2/5 = 40\%$.

EXERCISE 13C

1. Three transistors in a batch of 10 are faulty. Two are chosen at random for testing. What are the probabilities
   (a) that both are defective,
   (b) that neither is defective?

2. Repeat question 1 if the numbers are:
   (a) 30 faulty in a batch of 100,
   (b) 300 faulty in a batch of 1000,
   (c) 30% faulty in a large batch.

3. A card is drawn from a pack and then returned. This process is repeated. What are the probabilities that the cards are (a) the same card, (b) black cards, (c) of the same suit, (d) both hearts, (e) of different suits, (f) a club and a heart or vice versa, (g) an ace and a king or vice versa?

4. Repeat question 3 if the first card is not replaced.

5. A bag contains 3 white, 5 black, and 7 yellow marbles. Three marbles are drawn in succession, each being replaced before the next is drawn. What is

the probability that the first is white, the second black, and the third yellow? What is the probability that one of each colour is drawn?

6. Repeat question 5 if the marbles are not replaced.

7. A student takes three examinations. In the first examination, the probabilities of his getting a distinction, a pass, and a fail are 0.1, 0.6, 0.3 respectively. The corresponding probabilities in the second and third examinations are 0.2, 0.7, 0.1, and 0.05, 0.55, 0.4. Draw a tree diagram, and use it to answer the following questions.

   (a) A prize is awarded for three distinctions. What is the probability of the student winning this prize?

   (b) The three grades earn him 2, 1, 0 points, and he needs at least 3 points overall to gain a certificate. What is the probability of this?

   (c) Given that the student got the same grade in all three examinations, what are the probabilities that the grades were all Ds, all Ps, all Fs?

8. A playing-card is found in a house where there are known to be 6 packs of cards: 5 ordinary 52-card packs, and one bezique pack (like an ordinary pack except that all cards with face value 2 to 6 have been removed). Find the probability that the card came from the bezique pack if its face value is   (a) 4,   (b) 9.

9. 60% of the pupils in a school are boys, the rest girls. 70% of the boys and 80% of the girls have bought a ticket for a concert. What is the probability that a stray ticket belongs to a girl?

10. 50% of the members of a town council are Conservatives, 30% are Labour, and 20% Alliance. A committee of 3 is chosen by lot. What is the probability that the 3 parties are all represented on this committee? What is the probability that one party has a majority?

13.5 PERMUTATIONS AND COMBINATIONS

Let us consider again that large consignment of oranges, 7% of which were bad. Suppose we choose 9 oranges at random. What is the probability that 5 are bad and the rest good?

We could try drawing a tree diagram to help us answer this question, but it would be excessively cumbersome. The tree we used in section 13.4 to solve the disk problem had branches at only 3 levels, and so had $2^3 = 8$ points across the foot: whereas our orange tree will have branches at 9 levels and $2^9 = 512$ points across the foot. However, the tree is really quite unnecessary, once we realise that every sequence of precisely 5 Bs and 4 Gs has the same probability of $(0.07)^5 \times (0.93)^4$: the problem then reduces to finding how many such sequences there are. We shall now address ourselves to this and similar questions.

Suppose we have the 5 bad oranges, and 5 little boxes, in which we plan to place the oranges. One possible arrangement is

$$\boxed{|B_4|B_2|B_1|B_5|B_3|}$$ (i.e. the first orange in the third box, and so on)

The mathematical name for such an arrangement is a *permutation*.

How many permutations are there in all? We can place the first orange in any of the 5 boxes, then the second orange in any of the other 4 boxes, the third in any of the other 3, and so on.

So the number of permutations is $5 \times 4 \times 3 \times 2 \times 1 = 120$.

Now suppose we have the 5 oranges again but 9 boxes (5 to be filled, 4 to be left empty). How many permutations will there be?

In this case, we have $9 \times 8 \times 7 \times 6 \times 5 = 15\,120$ permutations.

Mathematicians use products like $5 \times 4 \times 3 \times 2 \times 1$ and $9 \times 8 \times 7 \times 6 \times 5$ repeatedly, and there is a standard shorthand:

$$5 \times 4 \times 3 \times 2 \times 1 = 5!\ (\text{pronounced '5 factorial' or '5 shriek'})$$

So $4! = 4 \times 3 \times 2 \times 1$, and $9 \times 8 \times 7 \times 6 \times 5 = 9! \div 4!$. Such calculations are so common that many calculators have a special factorial key.

When we arrange r bad oranges in n boxes, or perform any similar operation involving r and n, the number of permutations is denoted by ^nP_r. Thus $^5P_5 = 120$, and $^9P_5 = 15\,120$.

In the bad orange problem, we have assumed that the oranges can be told apart. For example, the 15 120 permutations include both

$$| \quad |B_3| \quad |B_1|B_4| \quad |B_5|B_2| \quad |$$

and

$$| \quad |B_2| \quad |B_4|B_1| \quad |B_5|B_3| \quad |$$

Indeed every one of the 5! permutations of the Bs among themselves in these particular boxes is included. If therefore we cannot or need not distinguish between the oranges, the number of arrangements is not 15 120 but $15\,120 \div 5!$, i.e. 126. When we do not bother to distinguish between the objects being arranged, the mathematical name for the arrangement is a *combination*. So we can say there are 126 combinations of 5 oranges in 9 boxes, and this number of combinations is denoted by $^9C_5$.

We are now in a position to solve the question at the start of this section about the probability of finding 5 bad oranges in a sample of 9. A typical sequence of events (as we choose the 9 oranges, including 5 bad ones) is $G\ B\ G\ B\ B\ G\ B\ B\ G$. Each such sequence is a combination of 5 Bs (and the rest Gs) in 9 'boxes', and we worked out in the last paragraph that $^9C_5$, the number of such combinations, was 126. Therefore the probability of finding that 5 of the 9 are bad equals

$$126 \times (0.07)^5 \times (0.93)^4 = 0.00016 \quad (2 \text{ s.f.})$$

EXAMPLE A microcomputer produces random digits (0 to 9) in groups of 5. What is the probability that a group contains just 3 zeros.

A typical group might be 05009: since we are interested only in whether a digit is zero or not, we shall symbolise this group by $ZNZZN$. It is easy to see that $\Pr(Z) = 0.1$ and $\Pr(N) = 0.9$. We must discover two things: (a) what is the probability of a typical sequence containing 3 zeros, and (b) how many such sequences there are.

(a) $ZNZZN$ is a sequence containing 3 zeros, and

$$\Pr(ZNZZN) = 0.1 \times 0.9 \times 0.1 \times 0.1 \times 0.9$$
$$= (0.1)^3 \times (0.9)^2 = 8.1 \times 10^{-4}$$

(b) The required number is $^5C_3$.

Now $^5P_3 = 5 \times 4 \times 3 = 60$, and so $^5C_3 = 60 \div 3! = 10$.

Thus   the probability $= 10 \times (8.1 \times 10^{-4}) = 8.1 \times 10^{-3}$

EXAMPLE There are 14 players available for a soccer XI. How many possible teams may be chosen? And how many if the squad includes 2 goal-keepers, one or other of whom (but not both) must be chosen?

If there are no restraints on team selection, the answer is $^{14}C_{11}$. However $^{14}C_3$ is far easier to calculate than $^{14}C_{11}$, and of course they are equivalent (the number of ways of choosing the substitutes must equal the number of ways of choosing the team); so we have

$$^{14}C_3 = (14 \times 13 \times 12) \div 3! = 364$$

With the restraint involving the goal-keepers, we must choose 1 of the 2 goal-keepers and 2 of the remaining 12 as substitutes. Therefore the answer is

$$2 \times {}^{12}C_2 = 2 \times (12 \times 11) \div 2! = 132$$

EXAMPLE How many anagrams are there of the word ERROR?

Note In a question like this, we do not worry whether the anagrams are proper words, or even pronounceable.

If we were to distinguish between the three Rs, there would be 5! anagrams. But the Rs are indistinguishable, and so the correct answer is $5! \div 3! = 20$.

EXERCISE 13D

1. A menu has 8 different starters, 11 different main courses, and 3 different puddings. How many different three-course meals are possible?

2. I have room on a shelf for 5 books. In how many ways can 5 different books be arranged on the shelf? How many arrangements are there if I have 7 books and put 5 of them on the shelf?

3. I have 7 books and intend to take 5 of them with me on holiday. How many different selections can I make?

4. How many numbers greater than 6000 can be formed using the digits 3, 5, 7, 8, 9, if no digit is repeated?

5. A pupil studying English has to read 5 novels and 4 plays. In how many ways can he plan his reading if he is to start with a novel, and then read plays and novels alternately?

6. Calculate the following: $^5P_5$, $^5P_4$, $^5P_3$, $^5P_2$, $^5P_1$. Can you find a meaning for $^5P_0$?

7. How many anagrams are there of the word NIECE?

8. How many anagrams are there of the word MATHEMATICIAN?

9. Calculate the following: $^5C_5$, $^5C_4$, $^5C_3$, $^5C_2$, $^5C_1$. Can you find a meaning for $^5C_0$? What does 0! mean?

10. Solve: (a) $^nC_2 = 45$,   (b) $^nC_6 = {}^nC_9$.

11. In how many ways can a committee of 5 be chosen from 12 people? Once the committee has been formed, in how many ways can a sub-committee of 2 be formed?

12. 24 boys are to be divided into two teams of 11, with 2 to act as judges. In how many ways can this be done?

13. An electronics factory manufactures microchips. 2% of these are faulty. If they are sold in packs of 6, find the probability that in a pack   (a) none are faulty,   (b) all are faulty,   (c) just 2 are faulty.

14. In an examination, the probability that I get a grade 6 or better, i.e. that I pass, in any particular subject is 90%. I take 8 subjects and to pass overall must pass in at least 5 of them. What is the probability that I pass in   (a) all 8 subjects,   (b) just 7 subjects,   (c) just 6,   (d) just 5? What is the probability that I pass overall?

15. A girl decides to buy a box of 20 chocolates every Monday during term-time, and consume the lot by nightfall. There is a small but finite probability of 0.01 that any particular chocolate contains poison, but it would take 2 poisoned chocolates eaten within 24 hours to dispatch the girl. Calculate the probability that she survives her first box. Calculate too (assuming 34 Mondays per school year) the probability that she survives a full year.

13.6 RANDOM VARIABLES

In probability theory, a *population* is a set of elements each of which bears a number (denoted by x or y or whatever). The elements may be real things, like human beings, or more abstract, like throws of a die or a coin. They may bear their numbers naturally, like a human being and his height in mm, or the throw of a die and the number on top. Or the connection may be more artificial: for instance, when we toss a coin, we may say $x = 1$ if the coin comes up heads, $x = 0$ if it comes up tails.

If every value of x has a probability, then we talk of a *probability distribution*, and x is termed a *random variable*.

EXAMPLE The elements are the throws of an unbiased die, and the random variable x equals 1 if the number on top is a six, otherwise 0. Find the probability distribution.

Clearly $\Pr(x = 1) = \frac{1}{6}$ and $\Pr(x = 0) = \frac{5}{6}$.

EXAMPLE A microcomputer produces random digits in groups of five. The random variable z is defined to be the number of zeros in a group. What is the probability distribution?

It is clear that z can take any of six values: 0, 1, 2, 3, 4, 5.

We considered the case when $z = 3$ in the previous section, and calculated that

$$\Pr(z = 3) = {}^{5}C_{3} \times (0.1)^{3} \times (0.9)^{2} = 0.0081$$

Similarly, we calculate that

$$\Pr(z = 0) = {}^{5}C_{0} \times (0.1)^{0} \times (0.9)^{5} = 0.59049$$

$$\Pr(z = 1) = {}^{5}C_{1} \times (0.1)^{1} \times (0.9)^{4} = 0.32805$$

$$\Pr(z = 2) = {}^{5}C_{2} \times (0.1)^{2} \times (0.9)^{3} = 0.0729$$

$$\Pr(z = 4) = {}^{5}C_{4} \times (0.1)^{4} \times (0.9)^{1} = 0.00045$$

$$\Pr(z = 5) = {}^{5}C_{5} \times (0.1)^{5} \times (0.9)^{0} = 0.00001$$

If we have a probability distribution, then the random variable x will usually have several different possible values, and we may ask what is its average or *expected value*, written as $E(x)$. We work this out by multiplying each possible value by its own probability, and adding all the results together.

EXAMPLE What is E(z) in the previous example?

$$E(z) = 0 \times 0.590\,49 + 1 \times 0.328\,05 + 2 \times 0.0729$$

$$+ \, 3 \times 0.0081 + 4 \times 0.000\,45 + 5 \times 0.000\,01$$

$$= 0.5$$

Note that the expected value of a random variable may (as in the example about the microcomputer) not in fact be a possible value of the variable at all. The word 'expected' in this context is not really appropriate, therefore: we certainly do not expect the variable z in our last example ever to have the value 0.5! Nevertheless, the E(variable) notation is very widely accepted, and we do use it in this book.

EXAMPLE The probability of an event is p. Calculate $E(x)$, where x is a random variable associated with the event, and defined as follows:

$$x = 1 \text{ if the event happens}$$
$$x = 0 \text{ otherwise}$$

Now $Pr(x = 1) = p$ and $Pr(x = 0) = 1 - p$.

So
$$E(x) = 1 \times Pr(x = 1) + 0 \times Pr(x = 0)$$

$$= p$$

So if a random variable x is defined in terms of an event in this special way, then $E(x)$ equals the probability of the event.

EXAMPLE In a large consignment of oranges, 7% are bad. If z is defined to be the number of bad oranges in a sample of nine oranges, find $E(z)$.

We define nine variables x_1 to x_9, as follows:

$$x_1 = 1 \text{ if the first orange is bad}$$
$$0 \text{ otherwise}$$

and so on.

Then $E(x_1) = Pr(\text{first orange is bad}) = 0.07$, and so on.

Now
$$z = x_1 + x_2 + \ldots + x_9$$

and so
$$E(z) = E(x_1) + E(x_2) + \ldots + E(x_9)$$

$$= 0.07 + 0.07 + \ldots + 0.07$$

$$= 9 \times 0.07$$

$$= 0.63$$

In our solution to this problem, we have made use of a fairly obvious principle, that if z equals the sum of x_1, x_2, etc., then

$$E(z) = E(x_1) + E(x_2) + \ldots$$

Less obvious is the principle that if z equals the products of x_1, x_2, etc., *and if the x variables are independent* (i.e. if their probability distributions are independent of each other), then

$$E(z) = E(x_1) \times E(x_2) \times \ldots$$

We use these principles in the next example.

EXAMPLE   A game in a fair-ground works like this. A customer pays 25 p to throw two dice. Each die scores the number that falls uppermost, except that one and two count as zero, and six counts as twelve. The stall-holder then pays out a prize of n pence, where n equals the sum of the two scores plus their product. Is this game fair?

We define x, y, z as follows:

$$x = \text{the score for the first die}$$

$$y = \text{the score for the second die}$$

$$z = \text{the product of } x \text{ and } y$$

Now
$$
\begin{aligned}
E(x) &= 0 \times \tfrac{1}{6} + 0 \times \tfrac{1}{6} + 3 \times \tfrac{1}{6} + 4 \times \tfrac{1}{6} + 5 \times \tfrac{1}{6} + 12 \times \tfrac{1}{6} \\
&= (0 + 0 + 3 + 4 + 5 + 12) \times \tfrac{1}{6} \\
&= 24 \times \tfrac{1}{6} = 4
\end{aligned}
$$

and similarly, $E(y) = 4$.

Since $z = xy$, therefore, and since x and y are independent, we have

$$E(z) = E(x) \times E(y) = 4 \times 4 = 16$$

So
$$E(n) = E(x+y+z) = E(x) + E(y) + E(z) = 4 + 4 + 16 = 24$$

Thus we see that the average prize money is only 24 p, whereas the customer has to pay 25 p for each turn. The stall-keeper therefore makes 1 p on average every time a customer has a go, and so the game is not fair.

EXERCISE 13E

1. Three unbiased coins are thrown, and the random variable z equals the number of heads obtained. Find the probability distribution, and illustrate it by means of a block graph.

2. A word in this sentence is randomly chosen and the random variable equals the number of letters in the word. Find the probability distribution, and illustrate it.

3. The random variable x takes the values 1 to 5 each with probability 20%, while the independent variable y takes the values 6 to 10 with probabilities 10%, 20%, 40%, 20%, and 10% respectively. Calculate $E(x)$, $E(y)$, $E(x+y)$, and $E(xy)$.

4. In a two-person betting game, one of the players pays the other a stake in order to throw 2 dice. If he throws a double he receives £5, if he throws a single six or deuce–ace he receives £2. What is the fair stake in this game?

5. There are two alternative drugs that are given to patients suffering from a certain disease, drug 1 and drug 2. Each produces one of four degrees of recovery: $0 =$ no recovery, $1 =$ some recovery, $2 =$ fair recovery, $3 =$ full recovery. In the case of drug 1, the associated probabilities are 20%, 35%, 25%, and 20%, while in the case of drug 2, the figures are 40%, 15%, 10%, and 35%. If x stands for the drug administered, and z for the degree of recovery, calculate $E(z \mid x = 1)$ and $E(z \mid x = 2)$. Which is the better drug, in your opinion?

14 MECHANICS IV

14.1 ACTION AND REACTION

Newton's third law states that whenever a body A exerts a force directly on another body B, then B must exert an exactly equal force on A, along the same line of action but in the reverse direction. This law is usually remembered in the more succinct form

Action and Reaction are Equal and Opposite

Suppose, for example, that a crate is sitting on the floor of a lift.

Figure 14.1 shows the forces on the crate. They are: the crate's own weight mg vertically downwards, and the contact force exerted by the floor R_1 vertically upwards.

Fig. 14.1

Figure 14.2 shows the forces on the lift. These are: its own weight Mg vertically downwards, the pull of the lift rope T vertically upwards, and the contact force exerted by the crate R_2 downwards. The figure omits frictional forces (though these might be quite large).

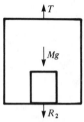

Fig. 14.2

Newton's third law tells us that $R_1 = R_2$. This will be so whether or not the lift and crate are in equilibrium, and whether they are stationary or in motion. Forces (like R_1 and R_2) that are bound to be equal are usually not given distinct names, so in this case we might use the letter R, without subscripts, to denote each of these contact forces.

194

The most obvious application of the law is to contact forces, but it can apply to other types of force. For instance, your weight is the gravitational pull of the Earth on yourself; Newton's third law tells us that you must exert an exactly equal pull on the Earth (although since the Earth is so massive this force on it is too small to affect its motion to any significant extent).

Figure 14.3 shows two boys having a tug-of-war. If the rope connecting them is light (i.e. has negligible mass), then they are in effect pulling directly on each other, and so by Newton's law $T_1 = T_2$. Note incidentally how the diagram portrays a rope in tension: boy A is being pulled to the right, boy B to the left. Figure 14.4, by contrast, portrays a rigid bar in thrust: the two boys are pushing, not pulling.

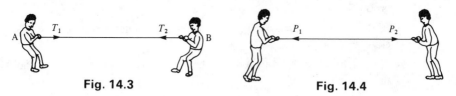

Fig. 14.3   Fig. 14.4

14.2 MOTION OF CONNECTED BODIES

When considering the motion of bodies which are connected, we can always apply Newton's second law, $\mathbf{P} = m\mathbf{a}$, to each of the individual bodies, or we may be able to think of the various bodies as forming one single body and apply $\mathbf{P} = m\mathbf{a}$ to that.

For example, let us return to the crate in the lift. Suppose first that the system is in equilibrium (either motionless, or moving up or down at uniform speed). Then we may consider

either	the crate	$R = mg$
or	the lift	$T = R + Mg$
or	the whole system	$T = mg + Mg$

Note that although we can form three equations, we have only two pieces of independent information: any one of the three equations can obviously be deduced from the other two.

Now suppose that the system is not in equilibrium, but that crate and lift share an upward acceleration of $a\,\mathrm{m\,s^{-2}}$. Then we may analyse the situation by applying $\mathbf{P} = m\mathbf{a}$ to

either	the crate	$R - mg = ma$
or	the lift	$T - R - Mg = Ma$
or	the whole system	$T - (m + M)g = (m + M)a$

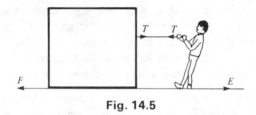

Fig. 14.5

Figure 14.5 shows another situation: a crate is being pulled horizontally by a man with a rope. We need concern ourselves for the moment only with the horizontal forces acting on the man and on the crate. These are:

(1) E, the frictional force on the man, caused by contact between his feet and the ground;

(2) F, the frictional force on the crate, caused by contact between the base of the crate and the ground;

(3) T, the tension in the rope, pulling the crate to the right but pulling the man to the left.

If we consider the man and crate as a single body, then it is easily seen that the tension in the rope cancels out, and so the only two effective horizontal forces are E and F. If $E > F$, then the man and the crate will accelerate to the right. We reach the same conclusion if we consider the two bodies separately, but now the tension T enters our calculations.

What *actually* happens depends, of course, on various practical considerations, such as the relative weights of man and crate, the strength of the man, the type of shoes he is wearing, the breaking strain of the rope, and so on.

In order to illustrate these ideas, we now consider four numerical examples.

EXAMPLE   A car of mass 900 kg tows a caravan of mass 700 kg along a horizontal road by means of a rigid tow-bar. If the driving force from the engine is 960 N, and frictional and other resisting forces can be neglected, find   (a) the acceleration of the car, and   (b) the tension in the tow-bar.

Suppose the car's acceleration is $a\,\mathrm{m\,s^{-2}}$. Since the tow-bar is rigid, the caravan will have the same acceleration. Figure 14.6 shows the various horizontal forces.

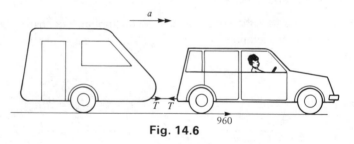

Fig. 14.6

The equation of motion of the whole system is

$$960 = (900+700)a \Rightarrow 960 = 1600a \Rightarrow a = 0.6 \ (\text{m s}^{-2})$$

To find T, the tension, we need the equation of motion of the caravan alone, which is

$$T = 700a \Rightarrow T = 700 \times 0.6 = 420 \ (\text{N})$$

Note We could instead have used the equation of motion of the car alone: $960 - T = 900a \Rightarrow T = 960 - 540 = 420$.

EXAMPLE The car and caravan in the example above are in fact found to accelerate at only $0.45 \, \text{m s}^{-2}$. What must the resisting forces be in total, and if they are divided between car and caravan in the ratio $1:2$, what is the true tension in the tow-bar?

Suppose the total resistance equals $3R \, \text{N}$ (i.e. R on the car and $2R$ on the caravan). Draw a diagram like figure 14.6 showing all the relevant forces.

The equation of motion of the whole system is

$$960 - 3R = 1600 \times 0.45 \Rightarrow 3R = 960 - 720 = 240 \ (\text{N})$$

To find the tension, which we will call T again, we can use the equation of motion of either body. We choose the caravan, since it is slightly easier, and we obtain

$$T - 2R = 700 \times 0.45 \Rightarrow T = 315 + 160 = 475 \ (\text{N})$$

EXAMPLE A 91 kg man is descending in a lift of mass 500 kg with a downward acceleration of $1.4 \, \text{m s}^{-2}$. Find the contact force between the man and the floor of the lift, and hence find how much he would appear to weigh if he weighed himself at that moment. Find also the tension in the cable.

Figure 14.7 shows the vertical forces acting on the man and on the lift.

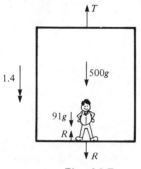

Fig. 14.7

The man's equation of motion is

$$91g - R = 91 \times 1.4$$

i.e. $R = 91(9.8 - 1.4) = 764.4 \ (\text{N})$

If he appeared to weigh M kg, then $Mg = 764.4$, i.e. $M = 78 \,(\text{kg})$.

The lift's equation of motion is

$$500g + R - T = 500 \times 1.4$$

i.e. $T = 4900 + 764.4 - 700 = 4964.4 \ (\text{N})$

Since we have used 9.8 as the value of g, and in any case the data does not look very precise, we should round all our answers to at most 2 s.f.

EXAMPLE Two masses of 9 kg and 5 kg are connected by a light, inextensible string which passes over a smooth beam. Find the acceleration of the two masses, and the tension in the string.

Since the beam is smooth and the string is light, the tension in the string is the same all the way along. And since the string is inextensible, the two masses move with equal accelerations, although naturally in opposite directions. See figure 14.8.

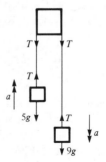

Fig. 14.8

The equations of motion of the 9 kg and 5 kg masses are respectively

$$9g - T = 9a$$

and $T - 5g = 5a$

Adding these, we get

$$4g = 14a$$

i.e. $a = 2g/7 = 2.8 \ (\text{m s}^{-2})$

and so $T = 5a + 5g = 63 \ (\text{N})$

Note that in this problem, we cannot conveniently think of the two bodies as forming one single body, because they are moving and accelerating in different directions.

EXERCISE 14A

Throughout this exercise (and indeed whenever solving a problem that involves forces), remember to draw clear diagrams, showing all the relevant forces and accelerations.

1. A car of mass 1000 kg tows a caravan of mass 600 kg along a horizontal road. If the driving force of the engine is 480 N, and resisting forces are negligible, find the acceleration of the car, and the tension in the tow-bar.

2. When the car in question 1 is braked, the deceleration of car and caravan is $0.35\,\mathrm{m\,s^{-2}}$. Find the braking force, and the thrust in the tow-bar.

3. An engine of mass 4×10^4 kg pulls a single coach of mass 3×10^4 kg along a stretch of horizontal track. Supposing that there is a resisting force of 1 N per 100 kg acting on both engine and coach, and that the driving force is 3500 N, find   (a) the acceleration of the train, and   (b) the tension in the coupling.

4. A 50 kg boy goes up in a lift. What force does he exert on the floor of the lift when the system has   (a) an upward acceleration of $0.6\,\mathrm{m\,s^{-2}}$, and   (b) a downward acceleration of $0.8\,\mathrm{m\,s^{-2}}$?

5. An 80 kg man is descending in a lift of mass 500 kg with a downward acceleration of $1.5\,\mathrm{m\,s^{-2}}$. Draw diagrams showing the forces acting on   (a) the man, and   (b) the lift. Find the tension in the lift cable, and the reaction between the man and the floor.

6. A man of 80 kg is standing in a lift. When the lift accelerates at $f\,\mathrm{m\,s^{-2}}$, the reaction between the floor and the man is R newtons. Express R in terms of f, and hence draw a graph showing the relation between R and f.

7. An object of mass 7 kg lies on a horizontal table. It is connected by means of a light string passing over the edge of the table to another mass of 7 kg hanging freely. What will be the acceleration of the system, and the tension in the string, if all surfaces are smooth?

8. A monkey climbs up a light rope at a uniform speed, and it is found that the tension in the rope is 100 N: what is the weight of the monkey? Taking g to be 10, find the tension in the rope when the monkey then slides down   (a) at constant speed,   (b) with an acceleration of $3\,\mathrm{m\,s^{-2}}$,   (c) with a deceleration of $2\,\mathrm{m\,s^{-2}}$.

14.3 LIMITING FRICTION

Suppose the crate in figure 14.5 is at rest. If the man now pulls more and more strongly, the tension in the rope will increase, but the crate will not move, since F will increase so as to counterbalance T. As T gradually gets greater and greater, however, there will finally come a moment when the magnitude of the frictional force needed to maintain equilibrium reaches a certain limiting value; as soon as

T exceeds this value, equilibrium becomes impossible and the crate will suddenly begin sliding to the right.

We are all familiar with phenomena of this kind. Whenever two surfaces are in contact, and some force is tending to cause the surfaces to slide across one another, then a frictional force will act in such a way as to oppose sliding, but it has a limiting value. Laboratory experiments have shown that provided the surfaces are reasonably dry, the limiting value of the frictional force (*limiting friction*) is proportional to the normal contact force between the surfaces: i.e. $F \leqslant \mu N$, where μ is a constant known as the *coefficient of friction*. The value of the constant μ depends on the nature of the surfaces involved (but not significantly on the area of surface in contact): very slippery surfaces would have a coefficient of friction quite near 0, whereas if the surfaces were very rough the value might be 0.5 or even higher. We may note in passing that if the surfaces are wet or lubricated (as in the case of a skate sliding over ice, for instance) then the frictional force will follow a quite different rule.

To recapitulate: if the man gradually increases T, F will increase too until it reaches limiting friction. The crate will then be on the verge of sliding. If the man now pulls slightly harder, T will increase but F will not, and so the crate will slide. Similar considerations apply of course to E, the other frictional force: if that were to reach limiting friction, then the man himself would be on the verge of sliding.

Suppose in fact that the crate has mass 100 kg, and the coefficient of friction between it and the ground is 0.2. Suppose too that the corresponding figures for the man are 80 kg and 0.4. Then (see figure 14.9) $N = 100g$ and $R = 80g$, since there is no vertical motion. Therefore the limiting value of F is $0.2 \times 100g = 20g$, and the limiting value of E is $0.4 \times 80g = 32g$. Since $20g < 32g$, it is the crate that begins to slide, not the man, and this happens as soon as the tension in the rope exceeds $20g$ newtons.

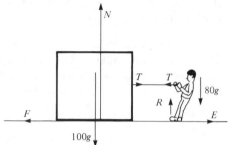

Fig. 14.9

However, if the man's 70 kg wife had climbed on top of the crate, then the combined weight of the crate and the woman would be $170g$ newtons: so N would be $170g$ and the limiting value of F would in consequence rise to $0.2 \times 170g = 34g$. So in that case the man would not be able to pull the crate plus his wife along: he would lose his footing first.

EXAMPLE A body of mass 3 kg is at rest on a horizontal table. The coefficient of friction between the body and the table is 0.5. A horizontal force P is applied to the body. Find the corresponding frictional force exerted by the table on the body if   (a) $P = 10$ newtons,   (b) $P = 20$ newtons.

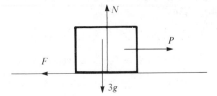

Fig. 14.10

Let F newtons be the frictional force, and N newtons the normal force. Since there is no vertical acceleration

$$N = \text{the weight} = 3g = 29.4 \, (\text{newtons})$$

So $$\text{limiting friction} = 0.5 \times 29.4$$

$$= 14.7 \, \text{newtons}$$

In (a), the frictional force needed to prevent motion is just 10 newtons, which is possible: so $F = 10$ newtons.

In (b), however, a frictional force of 20 newtons would be needed, which is too great: so F takes its limiting value of 14.7 newtons (and the body cannot be in equilibrium).

EXAMPLE A body of mass 5 kg is at rest on a rough horizontal plane, the coefficient of friction being 0.6. A force of P newtons at 30° above the horizontal acts on the body. Find the frictional force if $P = 20$, and find the value of P that produces limiting friction.

The forces acting on the body are shown in figure 14.11.

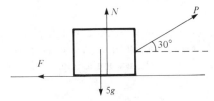

Fig. 14.11

Suppose first that $P = 20$. Resolving vertically, we have

$$N + 20 \sin 30° = 5g$$

i.e. $$N = 49 - 10 = 39$$

So $$\text{limiting friction} = 0.6 \times 39$$

$$= 23.4$$

Now the horizontal resolved part of the applied force $= 20\cos 30° = 17.3$.

Therefore the frictional force needed for equilibrium is 17.3, which is possible, and hence $F = 17.3$ (newtons).

We now suppose that friction is limiting, i.e. that $F = 0.6\,N$, but that the body is still in equilibrium. Then

$$P\cos 30° = F \qquad \text{and} \qquad P\sin 30° + N = 5g$$

and so

$$P\cos 30° = 0.6\,N = 0.6\times(5g - P\sin 30°)$$

i.e.

$$P\times(\cos 30° + 0.6\times\sin 30°) = 0.6\times 5g \Rightarrow P = 25.2\,(\text{newtons})$$

So if the applied force equals 25.2 newtons, the body will be on the verge of sliding, and if the force is any greater then the body will accelerate to the right.

The normal force N and the frictional force F are of course just components of the total contact force R. It is sometimes more convenient to deal with the resultant than with its components.

From figure 14.12, we can see that $\tan\phi = F/N$, where ϕ is the angle between R and the normal. Since F/N can never exceed μ, it is obvious that ϕ also can never exceed a certain maximum value, usually denoted by λ and called the *angle of friction*:

$$\tan\lambda = \text{maximum value of } (F/N) = \mu$$

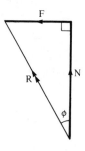

Fig. 14.12

EXAMPLE A particle of mass m rests on a rough plane inclined at an angle α to the horizontal (figure 14.13). If it is on the verge of sliding down the plane, prove that $\alpha = \lambda$, where λ is the angle of friction.

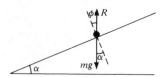

Fig. 14.13

The particle is in equilibrium, and so the two forces, R and mg, must act in exactly opposite directions, i.e. $\phi = \alpha$. But friction is limiting, i.e. $\phi = \lambda$. Hence $\alpha = \lambda$.

EXAMPLE A body of mass 5 kg rests on a rough plane inclined at 40° to the horizontal, the angle of friction being 17°. Find the least force up the line of greatest slope required   (a) to prevent the body sliding down,   (b) to get it sliding up.

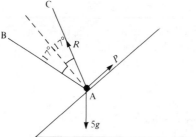

Fig. 14.14

(a) If there were no extra force, the body would accelerate down the plane (cf. the example above). Suppose therefore that we pull on the body with a force P just strong enough to produce limiting equilibrium: then the contact force R acts along AC (see figure 14.14). Figure 14.15 shows the triangle of forces. By the sine rule, therefore

$$P/(\sin 23°) = 5g/(\sin 107°) \implies P = 5g \times (\sin 23°)/(\sin 107°)$$

$$= 20.0\,(\text{N})$$

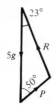

Fig. 14.15

(b) If P is now increased, the direction of R rotates until it points along AB, and the body is again in limiting equilibrium. Figure 14.16 shows the new triangle of forces. So by the sine rule

$$P = 5g \times (\sin 57°)/(\sin 73°) = 43.0\,(\text{N})$$

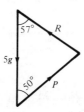

Fig. 14.16

It is clear from figures 14.15 and 14.16 that if the direction of P can be altered, then P can be made slightly smaller. Obviously P is least of all when perpendicular to R, and we then have

    (a) $P = 5g \times \sin 23° = 19.1$ and   (b) $P = 5g \times \sin 57° = 41.1$

EXERCISE 14B

1. A horizontal force of $10\,\text{N}$ will just move a block of mass $5\,\text{kg}$ on a horizontal surface. Find the coefficient of friction, and the acceleration when the applied force is increased by 30%.

2. A body of mass $3\,\text{kg}$ is at rest on a rough horizontal table, the coefficient of friction being 0.5. Find the acceleration produced by a horizontal force of $20\,\text{N}$, and the force required to produce an acceleration of $2\,\text{m}\,\text{s}^{-2}$.

3. A body of mass $9\,\text{kg}$ lies on rough horizontal ground. The coefficient of friction is $1/3$. What force acting upwards at $45°$ to the horizontal will produce limiting equilibrium?

4. A parcel of mass $2\,\text{kg}$ is initially at rest on a horizontal electric truck, with $\mu = 0.8$. Find the acceleration of the parcel if the truck accelerates   (a) at $2\,\text{m}\,\text{s}^{-2}$, and   (b) at $10\,\text{m}\,\text{s}^{-2}$.

5. A block of mass $4\,\text{kg}$ is placed on a plane inclined at $30°$ to the horizontal. If the coefficient of friction is 0.2, show that the block will slide down the slope. Find the least *horizontal* force needed to prevent it sliding down.

6. What horizontal force is needed in question 5
   (a) if the body is to slide up the plane,
   (b) if the frictional force is to vanish?

7. A crate of mass $30\,\text{kg}$ is resting in equilibrium on a rough plane inclined at $30°$ to the horizontal. Find   (a) the normal reaction,   (b) the frictional force,   (c) the least possible coefficient of friction.

8. A body of mass $5\,\text{kg}$ is on a rough plane inclined at $40°$ to the horizontal. The angle of friction is $30°$. Find the force along the line of greatest slope that will:
   (a) just prevent the body sliding down,
   (b) just get it sliding up.

9. Consider the body and plane defined in question 8. Find the magnitude and direction of the least force that will:
   (a) prevent the body sliding down the slope,
   (b) get it sliding up.

14.4 IMPULSE AND MOMENTUM

If a body of mass m is acted on by a constant force $\mathbf{P}$ over an interval of time t, then Newton's second law, $\mathbf{P} = m\mathbf{a}$, tells us that the acceleration $\mathbf{a}$ is constant. With the usual notation, therefore, $\mathbf{v} = \mathbf{u} + \mathbf{a}t \Rightarrow \mathbf{v} - \mathbf{u} = \mathbf{a}t$. Hence we derive the following important equation:

$$\mathbf{P}t = m\mathbf{v} - m\mathbf{u}$$

The quantity **P**t is called the *impulse* of the force **P** during the interval of time, and the quantity *m***v** is called the *momentum* of the body. The equation can therefore be rephrased as follows:

$$\text{impulse} = \text{final momentum} - \text{initial momentum}$$

Note that both impulse and momentum are vector quantities. They are usually measured in the same units, N s.

EXAMPLE A stationary ball of mass 0.14 kg receives an impulse of $+3.5\,\text{N s}$. Find the velocity acquired.

With the usual notation, $m = 0.14$, $u = 0$, and v must be found. Using the principle that impulse equals gain in momentum, we get

$$+3.5 = 0.14v - 0 \Rightarrow v = +25\,(\text{m s}^{-1})$$

EXAMPLE A body of mass 2 kg moving along a number line with velocity $+7\,\text{m s}^{-1}$ is subjected for 3 s to a constant force which raises its velocity to $+43\,\text{m s}^{-1}$. Find the force.

Initial momentum $= mu = +14$, and final momentum $= mv = +86$. Therefore gain in momentum $= +72\,\text{N s}$, and this must equal the impulse. So the force $= +72/3 = +24\,\text{N}$.

As you will have observed, the vectors involved in both these examples are one-dimensional. In the following examples, velocity, force, impulse, momentum are all two-dimensional.

EXAMPLE The velocity of a 10 kg body is $(\mathbf{i}+4\mathbf{j})\,\text{m s}^{-1}$ initially, but $(5\mathbf{i}+2\mathbf{j})$ after a constant force **P** has acted for 5 s. Find **P**.

Here $m = 10$, $t = 5$, $\mathbf{u} = \mathbf{i}+4\mathbf{j}$, $\mathbf{v} = 5\mathbf{i}+2\mathbf{j}$. Substituting into the equation $\mathbf{P}t = m\mathbf{v} - m\mathbf{u}$, we get

$$5\mathbf{P} = 10(5\mathbf{i}+2\mathbf{j}) - 10(\mathbf{i}+4\mathbf{j}) = 10(4\mathbf{i}-2\mathbf{j})$$

and so $$\mathbf{P} = 8\mathbf{i}-4\mathbf{j}\,(\text{N})$$

EXAMPLE As a result of a collision with another object, a body's velocity changes from

$$\begin{pmatrix}1\\4\end{pmatrix} \text{ to } \begin{pmatrix}5\\2\end{pmatrix}\,\text{m s}^{-1}.$$

If the body's mass is 10 kg, find the impulse of the contact force during the period of collision.

We have $\text{impulse} = \text{final momentum} - \text{initial momentum}$

$$= 10\begin{pmatrix}5\\2\end{pmatrix} - 10\begin{pmatrix}1\\4\end{pmatrix} = \begin{pmatrix}+40\\-20\end{pmatrix}\,\text{N s}$$

When two bodies collide (as in the last example), there is a contact force between them during the period of collision. This force is by no means constant: it starts at zero, and may then rise to a very high value before falling back to zero. The whole process of collision takes only a very short time, but because the average magnitude of the contact force is high the impulse produced is appreciable. It is this impulse that causes the bodies to rebound from each other. Now Newton's third law ensures that throughout the collision the contact forces on the two bodies are equal and opposite; this means that the impulse on the first body is equal and opposite to the impulse on the second body. The total impulse on the pair of bodies is therefore zero, and so the whole system suffers no overall change in momentum, i.e. the total momentum of the system is conserved.

Collisions provide the most obvious example of the conservation of momentum. But the total momentum of any system of objects will be conserved during any interval of time provided that the total impulse on the system during the interval is zero. This will be so whenever the only forces are *internal*—contact forces, for example, or tensions. It will also be so in effect whenever the impulses of any *external* forces can be ignored, either because the time interval is so short (as in a collision), or because the external forces are themselves small (the momentum of the solar system may be regarded as constant, for instance, although it is subject to small gravitational pulls from nearby stars).

EXAMPLE A body of mass $3\,\text{kg}$ is moving at $5\,\text{m}\,\text{s}^{-1}$. It strikes a stationary body of mass $2\,\text{kg}$, and they move on together. Find their common final speed.

Figure 14.17 shows the situation before and after the collision.

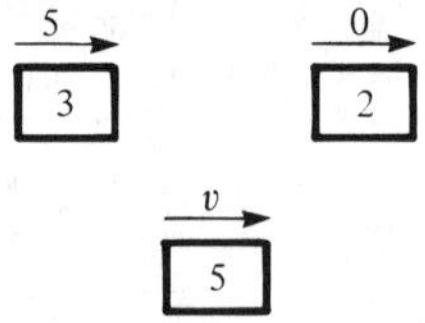

Fig. 14.17

$$\text{Momentum before} = +15+0 = +15\,\text{N}\,\text{s}$$
$$\text{Momentum after} = 5v\,\text{N}\,\text{s}$$

Since momentum is conserved,

$$5v = +15 \Rightarrow v = +3\ (\text{m}\,\text{s}^{-1})$$

EXAMPLE A body of mass $3\,\text{kg}$ moving at $4\,\text{m}\,\text{s}^{-1}$ strikes a body of mass $2\,\text{kg}$ moving at $4\,\text{m}\,\text{s}^{-1}$ in the opposite direction. If the heavier body's final velocity is zero, find the other body's velocity.

Figure 14.18 shows the position before and after. Note that in this case we have to decide which direction to count as positive.

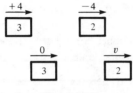

Fig. 14.18

$$\text{Momentum before} = +12+(-8) = +4\,\text{N s}$$

$$\text{Momentum after} \quad = 0+2v = 2v\,\text{N s}$$

So
$$2v = +4 \Rightarrow v = +2 \ (\text{m s}^{-1})$$

The final velocity of the 2 kg mass is therefore $2\,\text{m s}^{-1}$ to the right. If v had turned out negative (physically impossible in this case, of course), that would have indicated a velocity to the left.

EXERCISE 14C

1. What is the momentum of a mass of 0.49 kg moving at $4\,\text{m s}^{-1}$?

2. Arrange in order of magnitude the momentum of the following: a sprinter of mass 70 kg running at $10\,\text{m s}^{-1}$, a bullet of mass 30 grams moving at $600\,\text{m s}^{-1}$, a truck of mass 3000 kg moving at $10\,\text{m s}^{-1}$, and a ship of mass 2000 tonnes moving at $0.3\,\text{m s}^{-1}$.

3. What impulse is needed to accelerate a body of mass 3 kg from rest to $15\,\text{m s}^{-1}$?

4. A 750 kg car is brought to rest from a speed of $54\,\text{km h}^{-1}$. What impulse is required? If the process takes 3 s, what constant force is involved?

5. A cricket ball of mass 0.14 kg receives an impulse of $(2.1\mathbf{i}+2.8\mathbf{j})\,\text{N s}$. Find in vector form the velocity it acquires, and the magnitude of this velocity.

6. A squash ball of mass 0.03 kg and travelling with velocity $(10\mathbf{i}+8\mathbf{j})\,\text{m s}^{-1}$ rebounds from a wall with velocity $(-4\mathbf{i}+8\mathbf{j})\,\text{m s}^{-1}$. Find the impulse given by the wall to the ball, and the impulse given by the ball to the wall.

7. A hockey ball of mass 0.2 kg receives an impulse of 1.2 N s at a free hit. How fast does it begin moving?

8. A cricket ball of mass 0.5 kg and with initial velocity $32\mathbf{i}\,\text{m s}^{-1}$ receives an impulse of $3\mathbf{j}\,\text{N s}$. Find its subsequent velocity in vector form, and the speed.

9. A particle reaches a speed of $30\,\text{m s}^{-1}$ in 20 s under the action of a force of 10 N. Find its mass.

10. Two bodies of mass 4 kg meet head on at speeds of 3 and $7\,\text{m s}^{-1}$, and move on together. Find their common final speed.

11. A gun of mass $900 \, \text{kg}$ fires a shell of mass $2 \, \text{kg}$. If the gun recoils with an initial speed of $6 \, \text{m s}^{-1}$, what is its momentum? What therefore must the momentum of the bullet be? What is the speed of the bullet? Assume that all velocities are horizontal, and that friction is negligible.

12. A bullet moving at $550 \, \text{m s}^{-1}$ hits a stationary block of wood of mass $0.49 \, \text{kg}$, and becomes embedded in it. If the block is given a speed of $11 \, \text{m s}^{-1}$, find the mass of the bullet.

13. A railway truck of mass $1500 \, \text{kg}$ travelling at $5 \, \text{m s}^{-1}$ hits another truck of mass $1000 \, \text{kg}$ which is stationary. If the two trucks couple automatically on impact, what is their speed immediately afterwards?

14. A ball of mass $0.5 \, \text{kg}$ strikes an identical stationary ball at a speed of $10 \, \text{m s}^{-1}$. After impact, they continue with speeds v and $(v+5)$ respectively along the same line. Find v.

15. A stationary body of mass $5 \, \text{kg}$ bursts apart into two fragments of mass $3 \, \text{kg}$ and $2 \, \text{kg}$. If the velocity of the former is $12\mathbf{i}$, what is the velocity of the latter?

15 ALGEBRA III

15.1 SIMULTANEOUS EQUATIONS

You already know how to solve simultaneous equations like

$$x+y = 5, \quad 2x+3y = 13$$

It is easy to show that this pair of equations has one solution, namely $(x, y) = (2, 3)$. Geometrically, $x+y = 5$ and $2x+3y = 13$ are equations of straight lines, so that solving them simultaneously may be thought of as finding the coordinates of their point of intersection (see figure 15.1).

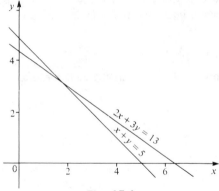

Fig. 15.1

We now consider how to solve two equations simultaneously, where one is linear but the second is a quadratic equation in x and y. An example of this type of problem might be to solve

$$2x-y = 4, \quad 3x^2+xy = 1$$

This is of course equivalent to finding the point (or points) of intersection of a straight line and a curve. Equations like this will usually result in two points of intersection. Although it is helpful to think of the general solution in geometrical terms, our methods of solution—just as with two linear equations—will be algebraic. A simple but reliable method for tackling such problems is outlined in the next paragraph.

Use the linear equation to obtain a formula for either y or x in terms of the other, and then substitute this formula into the quadratic equation, so that you are left with a quadratic equation in just one variable, say x. Solve for x, and use the formula to find the corresponding value(s) of y.

EXAMPLE Solve $2x - y = 4$, $3x^2 + xy = 1$.

From the linear equation, we get $y = 2x - 4$, and substitution then gives $3x^2 + x(2x - 4) = 1 \Rightarrow 5x^2 - 4x - 1 = 0$.

Factorising, we get

$$(x - 1)(5x + 1) = 0 \Rightarrow x = +1 \text{ or } -0.2$$

Now $x = +1 \Rightarrow y = -2$, and $x = -0.2 \Rightarrow y = -4.4$.

Therefore $(x, y) = (+1, -2)$ or $(-0.2, -4.4)$.

It is important in your answer to make it clear that $x = +1$ goes with $y = -2$ and not with $y = -4.4$.

Do *not*, for example, write $x = +1$ or -0.2, $y = -2$ or -4.4.

Writing your final answer in the standard form $(x, y) = (+1, -2)$ or $(-0.2, -4.4)$ avoids this pitfall, and also acts as a useful reminder that we are finding the points of intersection of a line and a curve.

EXAMPLE Solve $x + 3y = 5$, $x^2 + y^2 = 5$.

You will recognise $x^2 + y^2 = 5$ as the equation of a circle, with centre $(0, 0)$ and radius $\sqrt{5}$.

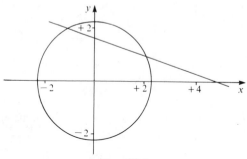

Fig. 15.2

From the linear equation, we get $x = 5 - 3y$, and substitution then gives $(5 - 3y)^2 + y^2 = 5$.

Hence $\qquad\qquad\qquad 10y^2 - 30y + 20 = 0$

i.e. $\qquad\qquad\qquad\qquad y^2 - 3y + 2 = 0$

$$(y - 1)(y - 2) = 0$$

$$y = 1 \text{ or } 2$$

Now $y = 1 \Rightarrow x = 5 - 3 = 2$, and $y = 2 \Rightarrow x = 5 - 6 = -1$.

Therefore $(x, y) = (2, 1)$ or $(-1, 2)$.

EXAMPLE Solve $3x = 2y$, $x^2 - xy + y^2 = 7$.

The linear equation gives $y = 3x/2$ (marginally easier than $x = 2y/3$), and so $x^2 - x(3x/2) + (3x/2)^2 = 7$.

Hence
$$x^2 - 3x^2/2 + 9x^2/4 = 7$$
$$7x^2/4 = 7$$
$$x^2 = 4$$

and so
$$x = \pm 2$$

Now $x = 2 \Rightarrow y = 3$, and $x = -2 \Rightarrow y = -3$; so $(x, y) = (\pm 2, \pm 3)$.

EXAMPLE A farmer wishes to use 160 m of fencing to construct three equal square enclosures together with one larger square enclosure. What must be the dimensions of the enclosures if their total area is to be 508 m²?

Suppose the smaller squares are x m by x m, while the larger square is y m by y m. Then we must solve simultaneously the following two equations:

$$12x + 4y = 160, \quad 3x^2 + y^2 = 508$$

The linear equation gives $y = 40 - 3x$, and substitution then gives $3x^2 + (40 - 3x)^2 = 508$.

Hence
$$3x^2 + (1600 - 240x + 9x^2) = 508$$
$$12x^2 - 240x + 1092 = 0$$
$$x^2 - 20x + 91 = 0$$
$$(x - 7)(x - 13) = 0$$
$$x = 7 \text{ or } 13$$

Now $x = 7 \Rightarrow y = 40 - 21 = 19$, and $x = 13 \Rightarrow y = 1$.

So the algebraic method yields two alternative solutions to the simultaneous equations: we find that $(x, y) = (7, 19)$ or $(13, 1)$. But $(13, 1)$ does not constitute a solution to the problem, since the three equal squares had to be smaller than the single square.

The problem therefore has a unique solution. The smaller squares must be 7 by 7 m, the larger square must be 19 by 19 m.

In some special cases, although the substitution method will work without difficulty, an *ad hoc* method can be devised which produces a solution more efficiently, or more elegantly. One such method is demonstrated in the next example.

EXAMPLE Solve $x - y = 4$, $x^2 + 2xy + y^2 = 64$.

The quadratic equation can be rewritten $(x+y)^2 = 64$.

Hence we must solve $x - y = 4$, $x + y = \pm 8$.

Adding, we get $2x = 4 \pm 8 \Rightarrow x = 6$ or $x = -2$.

Therefore, since $x - y = 4$, we have $(x, y) = (6, 2)$ or $(-2, -6)$.

EXAMPLE Solve $y = x^2 - 3x + 5$, $y = x + 1$. Interpret the result geometrically.

On this occasion, the substitution method is plainly the best.

We have
$$x^2 - 3x + 5 = x + 1$$
$$x^2 - 4x + 4 = 0$$
$$(x - 2)^2 = 0$$
$$\therefore x = 2$$

Now $x = 2 \Rightarrow y = 3$: so $(x, y) = (2, 3)$.

Note that we have just one solution, whereas we expect two solutions when dealing with a quadratic equation. The geometrical interpretation of this is that the line $y = x + 1$ *touches* the curve $y = x^2 - 3x + 5$, the point of contact being $(2, 3)$.

EXAMPLE Find the gradients of the tangents from the point $(0, 5)$ to the circle $x^2 + y^2 = 9$.

The line with gradient m through $(0, 5)$ has equation $y = mx + 5$. Now if this is to touch the circle, then when we solve simultaneously, we must get just one solution rather than two.

Substituting as usual, we have
$$x^2 + (mx + 5)^2 = 9$$
$$x^2 + m^2x^2 + 10mx + 25 = 9$$
$$(1 + m^2)x^2 + 10mx + 16 = 0$$

This quadratic equation will have repeated roots if its discriminant (see section 1.7) comes to zero, i.e. if
$$(10m)^2 - 64(1 + m^2) = 0$$
$$100m^2 - 64 - 64m^2 = 0$$
$$36m^2 = 64$$
$$m^2 = 64/36 = 16/9$$

Hence the tangents have gradient $+4/3$ and $-4/3$.

EXERCISE 15A

Solve the following equations, making careful checks of all your answers.

1. $x+y = 5$, $xy = 6$.

2. $2x-y = 3$, $x^2-2xy+24 = 0$.

3. $x-y = 1$, $y^2-xy+x^2 = 7$.

4. $x-y = 4$, $x^2+y^2 = 8$.

5. $x^2+2xy+y^2 = 9$, $x-y = 7$.

6. $x^2+y^2 = 25$, $x^2-y^2 = 7$.

7. A farmer uses 50 m of fencing to enclose a rectangular area against a long straight wall. What must be the dimensions of the enclosure if its area is to be 300 m²?

8. I think of two positive numbers. If the difference between them equals 12, and the sum of their squares equals 314, what are my two numbers?

9. The sum of two numbers equals 5, while the sum of their cubes equals 35. Find the two numbers.
Hint: $x^3+y^3 = (x+y)(x^2-xy+y^2)$.

10. Find the equations of the lines with gradient 2 that touch the curve $5x^2-y^2 = 5$.

15.2 THE REMAINDER THEOREM

In the calculation shown below, x^3-4x^2+7x+6 is being divided by $(x-3)$:

$$
\begin{array}{r}
x^2-\ x+\ 4 \\
x-3\overline{)\ x^3-\ 4x^2+7x+\ 6} \\
\underline{x^3-\ 3x^2} \\
-x^2+7x+\ 6 \\
\underline{-x^2+3x} \\
4x+\ 6 \\
\underline{4x-12} \\
18
\end{array}
$$

This calculation displays in highly condensed form the following sequence of identities:

$$x^3-4x^2+7x+6 = x^2(x-3)-x^2+7x+6$$

$$-x^2+7x+6 = -x\,(x-3)+4x+6$$

$$4x+6 = 4(x-3)+18$$

The final result may be written

$$x^3-4x^2+7x+6 = (x^2-x+4)(x-3)+18$$

In this identity, $(x^2 - x + 4)$ is called the *quotient*, and 18 is the *remainder*.

The main purpose of the *remainder theorem* is to enable us to find the remainder quickly, without going through the full process of division. Suppose we wish to find the remainder when $x^4 + 4x - 7$ is divided by $(x - 3)$. If we do the calculation as above to find the quotient and remainder, we will obtain an identity

$$x^4 + 4x - 7 = \text{quotient} \times (x - 3) + \text{remainder}$$

Now if we set x equal to 3 in this identity, we have

$$81 + 12 - 7 = (\text{value of quotient}) \times 0 + \text{remainder}$$

from which we can see that the remainder $= 86$.

Applying this procedure to any such algebraic expression, $f(x)$, divided by $(x - p)$, we obtain the identity

$$f(x) = \text{quotient} \times (x - p) + \text{remainder}$$

If we set $x = p$ in this identity, we then have

$$f(p) = (\text{value of quotient}) \times 0 + \text{remainder}$$

i.e. the remainder $= f(p)$.

Similarly, when $f(x)$ is divided by $(qx - p)$ we have

$$f(x) = \text{quotient} \times (qx - p) + \text{remainder}$$

You can see that in this case we must set $x = p/q$ rather than $x = p$, and we then have

$$f(p/q) = (\text{value of quotient}) \times 0 + \text{remainder}$$

i.e. the remainder $= f(p/q)$.

Note that none of this is applicable unless $f(x)$ is a *polynomial*, i.e. an expression of the form

$$ax^n + bx^{n-1} + \ldots + k$$

where $a, b, \ldots$ are all constant numbers, and the powers of x are all positive whole numbers. The highest power involved is called the degree of the polynomial: thus we say that $x^4 + 4x - 7$ is of degree 4, that $x - 3$ is of degree 1, that any constant is of degree 0.

We can now make a formal statement of the remainder theorem:

if a polynomial $f(x)$ is divided by $(qx - p)$, then the remainder is $f(p/q)$

EXAMPLE Find the remainder when $f(x) = 4x^5 - x^3 + 2x^2 + 7$ is divided by:
   (a) $(x-2)$,   (b) $(x+1)$,   (c) $(2x-1)$.

(a) The remainder $= f(2)$

$$= 128 - 8 + 8 + 7 = 135$$

(b) The remainder $= f(-1)$

$$= -4 + 1 + 2 + 7 = 6$$

(c) The remainder $= f(1/2)$

$$= 4/32 - 1/8 + 2/4 + 7 = 7.5$$

Note that when a polynomial is divided by $(qx-p)$, of degree 1, the remainder is a constant (i.e. of degree 0). But if the polynomial were divided by, say, (x^2+1), which is of degree 2, then the remainder would be of degree 1 or 0.

EXAMPLE When the polynomial $x^4 + 4x^2 + cx + d$ is divided by $(x^2 - 1)$ the remainder is $3x + 7$. Find c and d.

If we call the polynomial $f(x)$, then

$$f(x) = \text{quotient} \times (x^2 - 1) + 3x + 7$$

$$= \text{quotient} \times (x - 1)(x + 1) + 3x + 7$$

Setting $x = 1$ in this identity,

we obtain $f(1) = 0 + 3 \times 1 + 7 = 10$,

but also $f(1) = 1 + 4 + c + d = 5 + c + d$: so $c + d = 5$ **1**

Similarly $1 + 4 - c + d = f(-1) = 3 \times (-1) + 7$: so $c - d = 1$ **2**

Solving **1** and **2** simultaneously, we get $c = 3$, $d = 2$.

15.3 FACTORISATION AND THE SOLUTION OF EQUATIONS

You may object that the remainder theorem gives us a very easy and quick way of finding the remainder when a polynomial is divided by an expression of the form $(qx-p)$, but that it gives us no idea of the quotient. This is true: if the quotient is required, we are forced back to the long-division method used at the start of section 15.2. None the less, there are many situations where knowledge of the remainder alone is quite enough.

Particularly important is the case when the remainder equals zero. For then the divisor is a factor of the polynomial. The remainder theorem applied to this special case gives the following useful results, sometimes known as the *factor theorem*:

if $\qquad\qquad f(p) = 0$, then $(x-p)$ *is* a factor of $f(x)$

if $\qquad\qquad f(p) \neq 0$, then $(x-p)$ is *not* a factor of $f(x)$

The factor theorem may be used to test quickly whether $(x-p)$ is or is not a factor of $f(x)$, and thus may help us factorise $f(x)$ completely (if possible). Since the equation $f(x) = 0$ can be solved easily once $f(x)$ has been factorised, the factor theorem also helps in the solution of equations.

EXAMPLE Factorise $f(x) = 2x^3 - 5x^2 - 28x + 15$, and hence solve $f(x) = 0$.

The factor theorem says that $(x-p)$ will be a factor if and only if $f(p) = 0$. We test various possibilities.

$$f(+1) = +2-5-28+15 \neq 0: \quad \text{so } (x-1) \text{ is not a factor}$$

$$f(-1) = -2-5+28+15 \neq 0: \quad \text{so } (x+1) \text{ is not a factor}$$

Now neither $(x-2)$ nor $(x+2)$ can be factors of $f(x)$, since 2 is not a factor of 15: so there is no point in testing them.

$$f(+3) = +54-45-84+15 \neq 0: \quad \text{so } (x-3) \text{ is not a factor}$$

$$f(-3) = -54-45+84+15 = 0: \quad \text{so } (x+3) \text{ is a factor}$$

Having found one factor, we can continue testing for other factors in exactly the same manner, or we can long-divide $f(x)$ by the known factor $(x+3)$, and thus find the quotient $g(x)$, which is then itself tested for factors.

With practice, however, $g(x)$ may often be quite easily found by inspection. It is obvious that $g(x)$ must be of order 2, i.e.

$$f(x) = 2x^3 - 5x^2 - 28x + 15 = (x+3)(ax^2 + bx + c)$$

Now the coefficients in the two versions of $f(x)$ must agree. So

$$2 = a, \quad -5 = b+3a, \quad -28 = c+3b, \quad 15 = 3c$$

The first and last of these equations show that $a = 2$ and $c = 5$, and the second then shows that $b = -11$. The third equation can be used to check these results. Therefore

$$f(x) = (x+3)(2x^2 - 11x + 5) = (x+3)(x-5)(2x-1)$$

This method may seem rather complicated, but after a little practice the discovery of a, b, c can be done mentally. In any event, you can always fall back on long division, or you can continue with the factor theorem until further factors are found.

Suppose that you *did* decide to carry on testing for factors.

You would soon find that $f(+5) = 250-125-140+15 = 0$, thus discovering a second factor, $(x-5)$. It should then be obvious that

$$f(x) = 2x^3-5x^2-28x+15 = (x+3)(x-5)(Ax+B)$$

and now inspection of coefficients would show that $A = 2$ and $B = -1$, i.e. that the third factor was $(2x-1)$.

Once the factors have been found, by whatever method, you can immediately see that

$$f(x) = 0 \Rightarrow x = -3, 5, \text{ or } \tfrac{1}{2}$$

EXAMPLE Find the value of c if $(x-1)$ is a factor of x^3-x^2+cx+4. Factorise the expression with this value of c.

Let $f(x) = x^3-x^2+cx+4$.

Then $f(1) = 1-1+c+4 = c+4$. But since $(x-1)$ is a factor of $f(x)$, $f(1) = 0$ and so $c = -4$.

Hence

$$f(x) = x^3-x^2-4x+4$$
$$= (x-1)(x^2-4) \qquad \text{(by inspection)}$$
$$= (x-1)(x-2)(x+2)$$

EXAMPLE Factorise a^3+b^3.

If we set $a = -b$, the expression $= (-b)^3+b^3 = 0$. Hence $(a+b)$ must be a factor of a^3+b^3. We can now see (by inspection, or long-division) that a^3+b^3 equals $(a+b)(a^2-ab+b^2)$. Since the second bracket will not conveniently factorise further, it is customary to stop the process at this point.

In a similar way, we can establish the following list of well-known results:

$$a^3+b^3 = (a+b)(a^2-ab+b^2)$$
$$a^3-b^3 = (a-b)(a^2+ab+b^2)$$
$$a^2+b^2 \text{ cannot be factorised simply}$$
$$a^2-b^2 = (a-b)(a+b)$$
$$a^2+2ab+b^2 = (a+b)(a+b) = (a+b)^2$$
$$a^2-2ab+b^2 = (a-b)(a-b) = (a-b)^2$$
$$a^3+3a^2b+3ab^2+b^3 = (a+b)^3$$
$$a^3-3a^2b+3ab^2-b^3 = (a-b)^3$$

Although *ad hoc* methods are often necessary in problems involving factorisation, these standard results, or simple modifications such as $4a^2 - 9b^2 = (2a - 3b)(2a + 3b)$, are particularly useful. We shall see in the next section how the list can be extended and used in other applications.

EXERCISE 15B

1. Find the remainders when:
   (a) $x^3 + 3x^2 - 4x + 2$ is divided by $(x - 1)$
   (b) $x^5 + x - 9$ is divided by $(x + 1)$
   (c) $4x^3 - 5x + 4$ is divided by $(2x - 1)$

2. Find the value of t in each case if the given condition is satisfied:
   (a) $x^3 + tx^2 + 3x - 5$ leaves a remainder of -11 when divided by $(x + 2)$;
   (b) $x^4 + 2x^2 - 2tx + t^2$ leaves a remainder of 6 when divided by $(x - 1)$;
   (c) $x^5 + 2x^3 - 5x + 2t$ is exactly divisible by $(x + 1)$.

3. Factorise:
   (a) $x^3 + 4x^2 + x - 6$
   (b) $x^3 + 3x^2 - 4x - 12$
   (c) $2x^3 - 9x^2 + 7x + 6$

4. Find the values of a and b if $ax^4 + bx^3 - 5x + 3$ has remainder $3x + 7$ when divided by $(x^2 - 1)$.

5. Factorise:
   (a) $7x^3 + 21x^2$
   (b) $3x^2y + 2xy - y$
   (c) $49x^4 - 16y^2$
   (d) $ac + 2ad + 3bc + 6bd$
   (e) $p^2 + p - q - q^2$
   (f) $x^6 - 64$

6. Factorise $\cos^4\theta - \sin^4\theta$, and hence show that

$$\cos^4\theta - \sin^4\theta = \cos^2\theta - \sin^2\theta$$

for all values of θ.

15.4 THE BINOMIAL THEOREM

In the last section, we saw that

$$(a + b)^2 = a^2 + 2ab + b^2$$

and
$$(a + b)^3 = a^3 + 3a^2b + 3ab^2 + b^3$$

In fact, these identities are particular cases of a general theorem that enables us to expand $(a+b)^n$, where n is any positive integer. For example, suppose $n = 9$:

$$(a+b)^9 = (\underline{a}+b)(a+\underline{b})(\underline{a}+b)(a+\underline{b})(a+\underline{b})(\underline{a}+b)(a+\underline{b})(a+\underline{b})(\underline{a}+b)$$

When this product is multiplied out, we must take one of the terms, either a or b, from each bracket, and multiply these nine terms together to form a single term. For instance, if we take the a's and b's underlined, we get the single term $ababbabba = a^4b^5$. We then add together every possible such combination of a's and b's. A term like a^4b^5 will arise whenever we choose the b from 5 of the brackets, and of course the a from the other brackets. As you may remember, the number of ways of doing this is denoted by $^9C_5$ (refer back to section 13.5 if you have forgotten). Similarly, a term like a^3b^6 will arise $^9C_6$ times, and so on. The term a^9 will naturally arise only once, as will b^9. We thus have the following result:

$$(a+b)^9 = a^9 + {}^9C_1a^8b^1 + {}^9C_2a^7b^2 + {}^9C_3a^6b^3 + \ldots + {}^9C_8a^1b^8 + b^9$$

The *binomial theorem* is simply an extension of this:

$$(a+b)^n = a^n + {}^nC_1a^{n-1}b^1 + {}^nC_2a^{n-2}b^2 + {}^nC_3a^{n-3}b^3 + \ldots$$
$$+ {}^nC_ra^{n-r}b^r + \ldots + {}^nC_{n-1}a^1b^{n-1} + b^n$$

where n is any positive integer.

We make the following observations:

(1) since r takes all integer values from 0 to n, there are $(n+1)$ terms in the expansion of $(a+b)^n$;

(2) the degree of each term is $(n-r)+r = n$.

If we examine the coefficients, ^nC_r, in greater detail, we can build up a table known as *Pascal's triangle*:

$n = 1$						1		1						
$n = 2$					1		2		1					
$n = 3$				1		3		3		1				
$n = 4$			1		4		6		4		1			
$n = 5$		1		5		10		10		5		1		
$n = 6$	1		6		15		20		15		6		1	
$n = 7$	1	7		21		35		35		21		7		1

etc.

For practical calculations with relatively small values of n, this triangle provides an efficient way of finding the coefficients in the expansion of $(a+b)^n$. For example, by simply reading from the triangle, we can see that

$$(a+b)^5 = a^5 + 5a^4b + 10a^3b^2 + 10a^2b^3 + 5ab^4 + b^5$$

For larger values of n, it is better to calculate ^nC_r by the method of section 13.5. For example,

$$^9C_1 = 9, \quad {}^9C_2 = 9 \times 8 \div 2! = 36, \quad {}^9C_3 = 9 \times 8 \times 7 \div 3! = 84, \text{ and so on.}$$

We therefore have

$$(a+b)^9 = a^9 + 9a^8b + 36a^7b^2 + 84a^6b^3 + \ldots$$

The following examples illustrate the use of the theorem.

EXAMPLE Expand $(2x-5y)^4$.

Using Pascal's triangle, we find the expansion to be

$$(2x)^4 + 4(2x)^3(-5y) + 6(2x)^2(-5y)^2 + 4(2x)(-5y)^3 + (-5y)^4$$
$$= 16x^4 - 160x^3y + 600x^2y^2 - 1000xy^3 + 625y^4$$

EXAMPLE Obtain the first three terms of the expansion of $(1-3x)^{30}$ in ascending powers of x.

It is not practical to use Pascal's triangle here, since 30 is too large a value of n. So we must evaluate $^{30}C_r$, for $r = 0, 1, 2$.

Now $^{30}C_0 = 1$, $^{30}C_1 = 30$, and $^{30}C_2 = 30 \times 29 \div 2! = 435$. So

$$(1-3x)^{30} = 1 + 30(-3x) + 435(-3x)^2 + \ldots$$
$$= 1 - 90x + 3915x^2 + \ldots$$

EXAMPLE Expand $(1+x+x^2)^5$ in ascending powers of x as far as the term in x^3.

We regard $1+x+x^2$ as $1+(x+x^2)$. Then the required expansion equals

$$1 + 5(x+x^2) + 10(x+x^2)^2 + 10(x+x^2)^3 + \ldots$$
$$= 1 + 5(x+x^2) + 10(x^2+2x^3+\ldots) + 10(x^3+\ldots) + \ldots$$
$$= 1 + (5x+5x^2) + (10x^2+20x^3+\ldots) + (10x^3+\ldots) + \ldots$$
$$= 1 + 5x + 15x^2 + 30x^3 + \ldots$$

EXAMPLE Expand $(1+2x)^4$, and use the result to evaluate $(1.02)^4$, correct to 5 s.f.

$$(1+2x)^4 = 1 + 4(2x) + 6(2x)^2 + 4(2x)^3 + (2x)^4$$
$$= 1 + 8x + 24x^2 + 32x^3 + 16x^4$$

If we now set $x = 0.01$, we see that $(1.02)^4$ equals

$$1 + 8(0.01) + 24(0.0001) + 32(0.000\,001) + 16(0.000\,000\,01)$$
$$= 1 + 0.08 + 0.0024 + 0.000\,032 + 0.000\,000\,16$$
$$= 1.0824 \quad \text{(to 5 s.f.)}$$

EXERCISE 15C

1. Write down the expansions of:

(a) $(a+b)^5$ (b) $(2x+y)^4$

(c) $(3p-2q)^6$ (d) $(x-1/x)^4$

2. Write down the first three terms when each of the following is expanded in ascending powers of x:

(a) $(1+x)^{10}$ (b) $(1+3x)^{12}$

(c) $(1-x/2)^9$ (d) $(1+x)^{100}$

3. Find the given term in the following expansions:

(a) x^4 in the expansion of $(1+x)^{10}$

(b) t^3 in the expansion of $(3-2t)^5$

(c) the constant term in the expansion of $(x+1/x^2)^3$

(d) the term in the expansion of $(q+p)^6$ that has the greatest value, given that $p = 0.4$ and $q = 0.6$

4. (a) Expand $(1+x)^{10}$ as far as x^3, and deduce the value of $(1.01)^{10}$ to 4 s.f.

(b) Expand $(2+x)^8$ as far as x^4, and deduce the value of $(2.001)^8$ to 6 s.f.

(c) Expand $(1-x)^3$, and deduce the exact value of $(0.999)^3$.

(d) Expand $(100-x)^3$, and deduce the exact value of $99 \times 99 \times 99$.

5. Expand as far as the term in x^2:

(a) $(1+2x+3x^2)^4$

(b) $(1-x+x^2)^3$

6. Use the binomial theorem twice to evaluate exactly

$$(\sqrt{3}+\sqrt{2})^4 + (\sqrt{3}-\sqrt{2})^4$$

15.5 THE BINOMIAL SERIES

The binomial theorem states that

$$(a+b)^n = a^n + {}^nC_1 a^{n-1}b^1 + {}^nC_2 a^{n-2}b^2 + {}^nC_3 a^{n-3}b^3 + \ldots$$

where n must be a positive integer.

We now investigate whether this result can be modified so as to permit negative or fractional values of n.

Using the facts that

$$^{n}C_1 = {}^{n}P_1 \div 1! = n$$

$$^{n}C_2 = {}^{n}P_2 \div 2! = \frac{n(n-1)}{2!}$$

$$^{n}C_3 = {}^{n}P_3 \div 3! = \frac{n(n-1)(n-2)}{3!}$$

and so on, and setting $a = 1$, $b = y$, we obtain the following binomial equation:

$$(1+y)^n = 1 + ny + \frac{n(n-1)}{2!}y^2 + \frac{n(n-1)(n-2)}{3!}y^3 + \dots$$

The right-hand side of this equation is called a *binomial series*.

If n is a positive integer, then all powers of y higher than the nth in the series will have a coefficient which includes $(n-n)$ as one of its factors. So in this case, the series contains only a finite number of terms, and the binomial equation reduces to

$$(1+y)^n = 1 + ny + \frac{n(n-1)}{2!}y^2 + \dots + \frac{n(n-1)\dots 1}{n!}y^n$$

which of course is just the binomial theorem.

For example,

$$(1+y)^4 = 1 + 4y + \frac{(4)(3)}{2!}y^2 + \frac{(4)(3)(2)}{3!}y^3 + \frac{(4)(3)(2)(1)}{4!}y^4$$

$$+ \frac{(4)(3)(2)(1)(0)}{5!}y^5 + \frac{(4)(3)(2)(1)(0)(-1)}{6!}y^6 + \dots$$

$$= 1 + 4y + 6y^2 + 4y^3 + 1y^4 + 0y^5 + 0y^6 + \dots$$

$$= 1 + 4y + 6y^2 + 4y^3 + y^4$$

In contrast, when n is a negative integer, or fractional, then the expression $n(n-1)(n-2)(n-3)\dots$ never becomes zero, and therefore the binomial series never comes to an end. In other words, we are dealing with an infinite series, whose sum cannot be evaluated in any ordinary way.

When the binomial series is infinite, however, it can be shown that provided y lies between -1 and $+1$, we can safely use just the first few terms of the series, ignoring all subsequent terms, and that the binomial equation will then be approximately correct. The closer the value of y is to zero, and the more terms we take before truncating the series, the more accurate will be the approximation. The detailed proof of all this lies outside the scope of this book: you must take it on trust for the time being.

EXAMPLE Find the first four terms of the binomial expansion of $(1+y)^{-2}$. Hence find an approximate value of 1.1^{-2}.

$$(1+y)^{-2} = 1+(-2)y+\frac{(-2)(-2-1)}{2!}y^2+\frac{(-2)(-2-1)(-2-2)}{3!}y^3+\ldots$$

$$= 1+(-2)y+\frac{(-2)(-3)}{2!}y^2+\frac{(-2)(-3)(-4)}{3!}y^3+\ldots$$

$$= 1-2y+3y^2-4y^3+\ldots$$

We now set $y = 0.1$, noting that this value lies within the range of validity from -1 to $+1$, and obtain

$$1.1^{-2} \approx 1-2(0.1)+3(0.1)^2-4(0.1)^3$$

$$= 1-0.2+0.03-0.004$$

$$= 0.826$$

The correct value is about $0.826\,446\,281$: so our approximation is in error by less than 1%. If we needed a better approximation to the value of 1.1^{-2}, we would simply include a few more terms of the series in our calculations. For instance, the approximation based on the first six terms of the series is correct to 5 d.p.

EXAMPLE Obtain the first five terms of the binomial expansion of $(1+x)^{1/2}$. By making a suitable substitution for x, find the value of $\sqrt{0.98}$ correct to 7 d.p.

We write x in place of y in the binomial equation, and set $n = \frac{1}{2}$; then

$$(1+x)^{1/2} = 1+(1/2)x+\frac{(1/2)(-1/2)}{2!}x^2+\frac{(1/2)(-1/2)(-3/2)}{3!}x^3$$

$$+\frac{(1/2)(-1/2)(-3/2)(-5/2)}{4!}x^4+\ldots$$

$$= 1+\frac{1}{2}x-\frac{1}{8}x^2+\frac{1}{16}x^3-\frac{5}{128}x^4+\ldots$$

If we now set $x = -0.02$ (within the range of validity), we obtain

$$\sqrt{0.98} \approx 1+\frac{1}{2}(-0.02)-\frac{1}{8}(-0.02)^2+\frac{1}{16}(-0.02)^3-\frac{5}{128}(-0.02)^4$$

$$= 1-0.01-0.000\,05-0.000\,000\,5-0.000\,000\,006\,25$$

$$= 0.989\,949\,5 \quad \text{(correct to 7 d.p.)}$$

When obtaining a binomial series, you must take care to expand only expressions of the form $(1+y)^n$. When an expression is not in this form, some preliminary rearrangement will be necessary.

EXAMPLE Expand $1/(1-x)$ as a binomial series, and use the result to write $10/9$ as a recurring decimal.

Now $1/(1-x) = [1-x]^{-1} = [1+(-x)]^{-1}$. So we replace y by $-x$ in the binomial equation, and set $n = -1$. Then

$$\frac{1}{1-x} = 1+(-1)(-x)+\frac{(-1)(-2)}{2!}(-x)^2+\frac{(-1)(-2)(-3)}{3!}(-x)^3+\dots$$

$$= 1+x+x^2+x^3+x^4+x^5 \quad \text{and so on.}$$

Since $10/9 = 1/0.9$, we set $x = 0.1$ and obtain

$$10/9 = 1+0.1+0.01+0.001+0.0001+\dots = 1.\dot{1}$$

EXAMPLE Expand $(8+3x)^{1/3}$ up to the term in x^2, and state the range of values of x for which the expansion is valid.

Here we argue $(8+3x)^{1/3} = [8(1+3x/8)]^{1/3} = 2(1+3x/8)^{1/3}$, and concentrate on expanding $(1+3x/8)^{1/3}$. So writing $3x/8$ for y and setting $n = 1/3$, we obtain

$$(1+3x/8)^{1/3} = 1+(1/3)(3x/8)+\frac{(1/3)(-2/3)}{2!}(3x/8)^2+\dots$$

$$= 1+\frac{1}{8}x-\frac{1}{64}x^2+\dots$$

Therefore $(8+3x)^{1/3} = 2+\frac{1}{4}x-\frac{1}{32}x^2+\dots$

This expansion is valid provided that $3/8x$ lies between -1 and $+1$, i.e. provided that $-8/3 < x < +8/3$.

EXERCISE 15D

1. Expand the following in ascending powers of x, as far as the term in x^3:
   (a) $(1+x)^{-3}$ (b) $(1-2x)^{3/2}$
   (c) $(2+x)^{-1}$ (d) $(4-x)^{-1/2}$

2. Use the results in question 1 to find approximate values of (a) 1.02^{-3}, (b) $0.9^{3/2}$, (c) $10/21$, (d) $1/\sqrt{3}$.

3. Show that the expression $2x/(1-x^2)$ can be rewritten as $(1-x)^{-1}-(1+x)^{-1}$, and hence find the binomial expansion of $2x/(1-x^2)$. Check your answer by rewriting $2x/(1-x^2)$ as $2x(1-x^2)^{-1}$ and expanding that.

16 TRIGONOMETRY III

16.1 THREE DIMENSIONS

In three-dimensional problems, it is essential to draw clear diagrams, both three-dimensional ones (to give an overall picture) and plane sections (to help in the detailed working). You may find that three or even more diagrams, all very carefully lettered, are necessary when you are solving a single problem.

The most useful three-dimensional diagrams are isometric (rather than perspective). Figure 16.1 shows such a diagram of a square-based right pyramid.

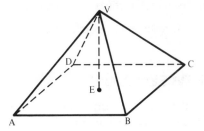

Fig. 16.1

Note the basic rules:

parallel lines (e.g. AD and BC) are drawn parallel,

vertical lines (e.g. VE) are drawn up/down the page,

hidden lines are shown dashed.

Plane sections are two-dimensional cuts through a three-dimensional object. Figure 16.2 shows one possible section of our pyramid.

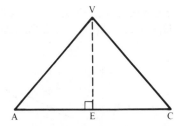

Fig. 16.2

Note that whereas isometric diagrams inevitably contain some distortion of shape and angle, accurate diagrams of plane sections do not. In many cases, of course, calculation based on freehand diagrams is easier than measurement from accurate diagrams.

EXERCISE 16A

In each question, draw an isometric diagram of the object, and also two plane sections, lettering all three carefully (with new letters introduced as necessary).

1. A cube ABCDPQRS whose base ABCD is horizontal.

2. A wedge ABCDEF with rectangular base ABCD and equal vertical edges AE and BF.

3. An equilateral triangle ABC, with C lying vertically above the point D, where ABD is a horizontal plane.

4. A regular tetrahedron ABCD, with ABC horizontal.

5. Two equal rectangular playing-cards standing on a horizontal table and leaning against each other as in a card-castle.

6. A prism ABCDEFPQRSTU whose ends ABCDEF and PQRSTU are regular hexagons, with the edges AP, BQ, etc., all vertical.

7. A bungalow, with rectangular ground plan, and sloping roof.

16.2 ANGLES BETWEEN LINES

What is meant by the angle between two non-parallel lines in three-dimensions? If they intersect, the answer is straightforward. For example, the angle between the lines AB and AV in figure 16.1 is BAV (or the associated obtuse angle). If the lines do not intersect, we simply translate one or both until they do: the angle between the new lines must equal the angle between the original lines, since translation preserves direction and therefore angle. For example, the angle between BC and AV equals the angle between AD and AV, i.e. angle DAV.

To calculate an angle in three dimensions, we may use either a plain trigonometrical method, or the vectorial method explained in section 9.4.

EXAMPLE ABCDEF is the wedge described in question 2 of exercise 16A, with AB = 4 cm, AD = 6 cm, AE = 3 cm. Calculate the angle between AB and DF (figure 16.3).

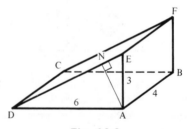

Fig. 16.3

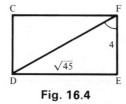

Fig. 16.4

AB and DF do not meet: so we translate AB to EF, and can then see that the required angle is angle EFD.

Now $DE = \sqrt{(3^2+6^2)} = \sqrt{45}$ cm,

and so
$$\text{angle EFD} = \arctan(ED/FE)$$
$$= \arctan(\sqrt{45}/4)$$
$$= 59.2° \quad (1\,\text{d.p.})$$

Alternatively, we take unit vectors **i, j, k** along AB, AD, AE.

Then $\mathbf{AB} = 4\mathbf{i}$ and $\mathbf{DF} = \mathbf{DC+CB+BF} = 4\mathbf{i}-6\mathbf{j}+3\mathbf{k}$.

Thus $\mathbf{AB\cdot DF} = 4\times4+0+0 = 16$, and $DF = \sqrt{(4^2+6^2+3^2)} = \sqrt{61}$,

and so
$$\text{angle EFD} = \arccos\left[(\mathbf{AB\cdot DF}) \div (AB\times DF)\right]$$
$$= \arccos\left[16 \div (4\sqrt{61})\right]$$
$$= 59.2°$$

EXERCISE 16B

1. If $AB = 7\,\text{cm}$ and $EV = 5\,\text{cm}$ in figure 16.1, calculate the angles between (a) AV and BC, (b) AV and BD.

2. Figure 16.5 shows a cuboid with $AB = 6\,\text{cm}$, $AD = 4\,\text{cm}$, $AE = 3\,\text{cm}$. Calculate the angles between (a) AC and HG, (b) AG and DH, (c) EG and CH.

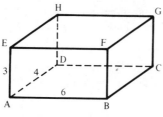

Fig. 16.5

3. Taking axes along AB, AD, AE in question 2, express the vectors **BC, CH, BH, CE**, in terms of **i, j, k**. Hence calculate the angles between (a) BC and CH, (b) CH and BH, (c) BH and CE.

16.3 LINE AND PLANE

Look back at figure 16.1: what is the angle between AV and the base ABCD? You should have little difficulty in seeing that it is angle VAE. But what is the angle between the line FA and the sloping plane CDEF in figure 16.3? This question is not so easy—if you think that angle AFC (or AFD or AFE) is the answer then you must think again!—and it shows the need for a proper definition of the angle between a line and a plane.

An angle measures the difference between two directions. The direction of the line FA is simply that of the vector **FA** (although we could equally well use the vector **AF** instead). Our difficulty is that the plane CDEF comprises indefinitely many directions, corresponding to the vectors **FC**, **FD**, **FN**, **FE**, etc. Which of these many vectors should we choose? Look again at figure 16.1: why did we choose **AE**, rather than any other vector in the plane of ABCD, such as **AB**?

You will remember (refer back to section 9.3 if not) that in two dimensions the projection of one vector on another is a number which may be positive, negative, or zero, i.e. it is a one-dimensional vector. We now extend this idea to three dimensions: in figure 16.1, the *projection* of the vector **AV** on the plane ABCD is **AE**.

More generally, the projection of a vector **QR** on a plane π is the vector **MN**, where M, N lie in π and QM, RN are both perpendicular to π. Finally, we define the angle between the line QR and the plane π to be the angle between the vector **QR** and its projection **MN**.

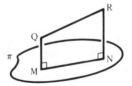

Fig. 16.6

We can now answer the question about the wedge. To find the angle between FA and CDEF, we must draw AN perpendicular to ED (and so to the plane ABCD). Then **FN** is the projection of **FA** on the plane, and the required angle is the angle between them, i.e. angle AFN.

EXAMPLE Calculate the angle between the edge AD and face ABC of the regular tetrahedron of side 6 cm shown in figure 16.7.

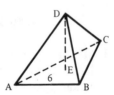

Fig. 16.7

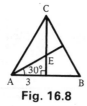

Fig. 16.8

Fig. 16.9

The projection of **AD** on ABC is **AE**, where E is the centroid of ABC, and the required angle is DAE. Figures 16.8 and 16.9 show two plane sections.

We can see from figure 16.8 that

$$AE \cos 30° = 3 \Rightarrow AE = 3/\cos 30°$$

and then from figure 16.9 that

$$\text{angle DAE} = \arccos[AE \div AD]$$
$$= \arccos[(3/\cos 30°) \div 6]$$
$$= 54.7° \quad (1 \text{ d.p.})$$

Notice the general rule:

if ϕ is the angle between the line QR and any plane π,

then $\phi = \arccos[MN \div QR]$,

where **MN** is the projection of the vector **QR** on the plane.

EXAMPLE I am standing with a rifle at A(3, −1, 0). A crow is perched at B(0, 2, 6). At what angle above the horizontal should I fire in order to shoot the crow, assuming that the bullet moves so fast that the effect of gravity may be ignored?

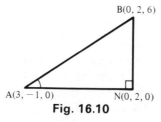

Fig. 16.10

We assume that the bullet travels along the straight line AB, and we calculate the angle AB makes with the horizontal plane $z = 0$. The projection of **AB** on the plane is **AN** (see figure 16.10). So the required angle is BAN.

Now
$$AB = -3i+3j+6k \Rightarrow AB = \sqrt{54}$$
and
$$AN = -3i+3j \Rightarrow AN = \sqrt{18}$$

So angle $BAN = \arccos[AN \div AB] = \arccos[1 \div \sqrt{3}] = 54.7° \quad (1 \text{ d.p.})$

EXERCISE 16C

Questions 1 to 5 refer to previous figures. In each case, copy the figure and calculate the angle between the given line and plane.

1. Figure 16.5: AG and ABCD.

2. Figure 16.5: AG and ABFE.

3. Figure 16.3: CE and ABCD.

4. Figure 16.3: CE and ABFE.

5. Figure 16.1, with AB = 8 cm, EV = 7 cm: AV and ABCD.

6. (a) Calculate the length of AN in figure 16.3.

   (b) Sketch triangle AFN. How long is FA? Why is angle ANF a right-angle?

   (c) Show by calculation that the angle between the line FA and the plane CDEF is about $32\frac{1}{2}°$.

7. A ski lift goes 268 m vertically upwards while going 456 m west and 723 m north. If it starts at O and finishes at P, choose suitable axes and find

   (a) the displacement vector **OP**,

   (d) the projection of **OP** on the horizontal plane,

   (c) the gradient of OP,

   (d) the angle OP makes with the horizontal.

16.4 ANGLES BETWEEN PLANES

What is the angle between the plane CDEF and the plane ABCD in figure 16.3? You should have little difficulty in seeing that it is an angle EDA (or FCB—they are obviously equal).

Now look at figure 16.11. What is the angle between VAB and ABCD? The plane VAB contains many lines, such as AV, AB, XV, etc. We can easily find the angle between any one of these and the plane ABCD. For instance, the angle between AV and ABCD is the angle between **AV** and its projection **AE**, i.e. the angle VAE. But which of these many lines must be chosen to give the angle between the *planes* VAB and ABCD?

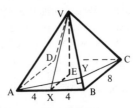

Fig. 16.11

The solution is to choose a line like XV that runs perpendicular to AB, the line of intersection of the two planes; note that in this case XV is also a line of greatest slope. Then the required angle is that between **XV** and its projection **XE**, i.e. angle VXE.

You will notice that both XV and XE are perpendicular to AB. When finding the angle between two planes, therefore, an alternative method is to choose two lines (one in each plane) in such a way that each is perpendicular to the line of intersection of the planes: then the angle between the planes will equal the angle between the two chosen lines.

EXAMPLE Given that in figure 16.11 ABCD is a square of side 8 cm and that EV = 7 cm, calculate (a) the angle between VAB and ABCD, and (b) the angle between VAB and VBC.

(a) The required angle is VXE = arccos [XE/XV]—see above. But since we do not know XV, it is easier to say

$$\text{angle VXE} = \arctan[EV \div XE] = \arctan(7/4) = 60.3° \quad (1\,\text{d.p.})$$

(b) The planes intersect along VB, so we find two lines, one in VAB and one in VBC, each of which is perpendicular to VB. The most convenient are YA and YC (see figure 16.11), and then the required angle equals the angle between these two lines, i.e. the angle AYC.

Now $AE = \sqrt{(16+16)}$ (by Pythagoras)

                 $= \sqrt{32} = 5.66\,\text{cm} \quad (3\,\text{s.f.})$

and so $AV = \sqrt{(32+49)}$ (again by Pythagoras)

                 $= 9\,\text{cm exactly}$

Thus angle VAX = VBX = arccos (4/9) = 63.6°,

and so $AY = 8 \sin 63.6° = 7.17\,\text{cm} \quad (3\,\text{s.f.})$

Finally (see figure 16.12), angle AYC = $2 \times$ AYE

                              $= 2 \times \arcsin[AE \div AY]$

                              $= 104.3° \quad (1\,\text{d.p.})$

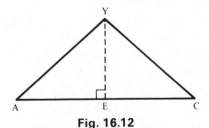

Fig. 16.12

In example (b), you may have expected the answer to be 90°, since angle ABC = 90°. But neither AB nor BC is perpendicular to BV, the line of intersection of the two planes. Also if EV were very small the two sloping faces would be almost horizontal, and would clearly be far from perpendicular to each other: this shows that the height of the pyramid affects the angle between its sloping faces—is it *possible* for this angle to be 90°?

In coordinate geometry, the angle between two planes can most easily be found by vectorial methods.

EXAMPLE What is the angle between the plane with equation $12x + 3y + 4z = 0$ and the plane $z = 0$?

We solve this problem by finding a vector perpendicular to each plane, and calculating the angle between these two vectors. The method of section 10.2 can be extended from two to three dimensions: hence the vector $\mathbf{n} = 12\mathbf{i} + 3\mathbf{j} + 4\mathbf{k}$ is perpendicular to the first plane, and of course the vector $\mathbf{k}$ is perpendicular to the second.

Now suppose the angle required is ϕ. Then

$$\mathbf{n} \cdot \mathbf{k} = \sqrt{(12^2 + 3^2 + 4^2)} \times 1 \times \cos\phi = 13\cos\phi$$

and $\mathbf{n} \cdot \mathbf{k} = 12 \times 0 + 3 \times 0 + 4 \times 1 = 4$

So $\cos\phi = 4/13 \Rightarrow \phi = 72.1°$ (1 d.p.)

EXERCISE 16D

Questions 1 to 5 refer to previous figures. In each case, name an angle between the given planes (with new letters introduced as necessary) and then calculate it.

1. Figure 16.3: CDEF and ABFE.

2. Figure 16.5: ABGH and ABCD.

3. Figure 16.5: BCHE and ADHE.

4. Figure 16.5: ABGH and CDEF.

5. Figure 16.7: ABC and ABD.

6. Find the angle between $x + 2y + 2z = 8$ and $z = 0$.

7. The lines AB, AD, and AE are mutually perpendicular and are taken as the x, y, z axes respectively. Given that AB = 6, AD = 4, and AE = 3, find the equation of the plane BED (hint: when y and z equal 0, x must equal 6). Hence calculate the angle between this plane and the plane ABD.

8. A hill has a gradient of 20% (i.e. 20 vertically per 100 *horizontally*). A road is to be built up the hill with gradient not exceeding 8%. What is the minimum angle the road can make with the line of greatest slope?

16.5 COMPOUND AND MULTIPLE ANGLES

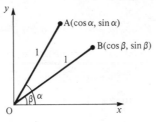

Fig. 16.13

In figure 16.13, $OA = OB = 1$;

so $$\mathbf{OA} \cdot \mathbf{OB} = OA \times OB \times \cos AOB$$

$$= 1 \times 1 \times \cos(\alpha - \beta)$$

But also $\mathbf{OA} = (\cos \alpha)\mathbf{i} + (\sin \alpha)\mathbf{j}$ and $\mathbf{OB} = (\cos \beta)\mathbf{i} + (\sin \beta)\mathbf{j}$;

so $$\mathbf{OA} \cdot \mathbf{OB} = (\cos \alpha \mathbf{i} + \sin \alpha \mathbf{j}) \cdot (\cos \beta \mathbf{i} + \sin \beta \mathbf{j})$$

$$= \cos \alpha \cos \beta + \sin \alpha \sin \beta$$

Therefore $\cos(\alpha - \beta) = \cos \alpha \cos \beta + \sin \alpha \sin \beta$.

EXAMPLE Express $\cos 15°$ in surd form.

We need to express $15°$ as the difference between two angles whose cosines and sines are known exactly: so we write $15 = 60 - 45$.

Then $$\cos 15° = \cos(60° - 45°)$$

$$= \cos 60° \cos 45° + \sin 60° \sin 45°$$

$$= \left(\frac{1}{2}\right)\left(\frac{1}{\sqrt{2}}\right) + \left(\frac{\sqrt{3}}{2}\right)\left(\frac{1}{\sqrt{2}}\right) = \frac{1 + \sqrt{3}}{2\sqrt{2}}$$

The formula $\cos(\alpha - \beta) = \cos \alpha \cos \beta + \sin \alpha \sin \beta$ can quite easily be modified to yield a number of other useful formulae.

Thus, replacing β by $-\beta$, we obtain the formula

$$\cos[\alpha - (-\beta)] = \cos \alpha \cos(-\beta) + \sin \alpha \sin(-\beta)$$

i.e. $$\cos(\alpha + \beta) = \cos \alpha \cos \beta - \sin \alpha \sin \beta$$

We now replace α by $(90° - \alpha)$ in this new formula, and obtain

$$\cos(90° - \alpha + \beta) = \cos(90° - \alpha)\cos \beta - \sin(90° - \alpha) \sin \beta$$

i.e. $$\sin(\alpha - \beta) = \sin \alpha \cos \beta - \cos \alpha \sin \beta$$

And finally, we replace β by $-\beta$, and obtain the formula

$$\sin(\alpha + \beta) = \sin \alpha \cos \beta + \cos \alpha \sin \beta$$

These four formulae, giving the cosines and sines of compound angles, are worth remembering:

$$\cos(\alpha - \beta) = \cos\alpha\cos\beta + \sin\alpha\sin\beta$$

$$\cos(\alpha + \beta) = \cos\alpha\cos\beta - \sin\alpha\sin\beta$$

$$\sin(\alpha - \beta) = \sin\alpha\cos\beta - \cos\alpha\sin\beta$$

$$\sin(\alpha + \beta) = \sin\alpha\cos\beta + \cos\alpha\sin\beta$$

EXAMPLE Prove that $\cos 2\alpha = \cos^2\alpha - \sin^2\alpha$ and that $\sin 2\alpha = 2\sin\alpha\cos\alpha$.

Setting β equal to α in the formula for $\cos(\alpha + \beta)$, we obtain

$$\cos 2\alpha = \cos\alpha\cos\alpha - \sin\alpha\sin\alpha = \cos^2\alpha - \sin^2\alpha$$

Similarly, the formula for $\sin(\alpha + \beta)$ gives us

$$\sin 2\alpha = \sin\alpha\cos\alpha + \cos\alpha\sin\alpha = 2\sin\alpha\cos\alpha$$

EXAMPLE Prove that the angle between the two lines $y = 2x$ and $3y = x$ equals $45°$ exactly.

Suppose that the line $y = 2x$ makes an angle α with the x-axis; then $\tan\alpha = $ the line's gradient $= 2$.

Similarly, we see that $\tan\beta = \frac{1}{3}$, where of course β is the angle between the line $3y = x$ and the x-axis.

Now the angle between the lines is $(\alpha - \beta)$. So using two of the formulae established above, we argue as follows:

$$\tan(\alpha - \beta) = \frac{\sin(\alpha - \beta)}{\cos(\alpha - \beta)} = \frac{\sin\alpha\cos\beta - \cos\alpha\sin\beta}{\cos\alpha\cos\beta + \sin\alpha\sin\beta}$$

$$= \frac{\tan\alpha - \tan\beta}{1 + \tan\alpha\tan\beta} \quad \text{(dividing top and bottom by } \cos\alpha\cos\beta)$$

$$= \frac{2 - \frac{1}{3}}{1 + \frac{2}{3}} = 1 \text{ exactly}$$

So the tangent of the angle between the lines equals 1, and so the angle itself, which is obviously acute, must equal $45°$.

This example has thrown up another useful formula:

$$\tan(\alpha - \beta) = \frac{\tan\alpha - \tan\beta}{1 + \tan\alpha\tan\beta}$$

from which $\tan(\alpha + \beta) = \dfrac{\tan\alpha + \tan\beta}{1 - \tan\alpha\tan\beta}$ follows immediately

EXAMPLE Prove that $\tan 22\frac{1}{2}° = \sqrt{2}-1$.

Setting β equal to α in the formula for $\tan(\alpha+\beta)$, we obtain

$$\tan 2\alpha = \frac{\tan\alpha+\tan\alpha}{1-\tan\alpha\tan\alpha} = \frac{2\tan\alpha}{1-\tan^2\alpha} = \frac{2t}{1-t^2} \quad \text{where } t = \tan\alpha$$

So if $\alpha = 22\frac{1}{2}°$, then

$$\frac{2t}{1-t^2} = \tan 45° = 1$$

i.e. $$t^2+2t-1 = 0 \Rightarrow t = \frac{-2\pm\sqrt{8}}{2} = -1\pm\sqrt{2}$$

Now α is acute, and so $\tan\alpha$ must be positive. We therefore reject the negative root of the quadratic equation, and conclude that $\tan 22\frac{1}{2}°$ does indeed equal $\sqrt{2}-1$.

EXAMPLE Express $3\cos x+4\sin x$ in the form $r\cos(x-\alpha)$, and hence solve the equation $3\cos x+4\sin x = 2.5$.

Now $r\cos(x-\alpha) = r\cos x\cos\alpha+r\sin x\sin\alpha$. Comparing this expression with $3\cos x+4\sin x$, we see that r and α must be chosen so that

$$r\cos\alpha = 3 \quad \text{and} \quad r\sin\alpha = 4$$

So r and α are the polar coordinates of the point $(3, 4)$.

Therefore

$$r = \sqrt{(3^2+4^2)} = 5 \quad \text{(we prefer the positive value)}$$

and $$\alpha \text{ (clearly acute)} = \arctan(4/3) = 53.1° \text{ (1 d.p.)}$$

So $3\cos x+4\sin x = 5\cos(x-\alpha)$, where $\alpha = 53.1°$ approximately.

To solve the equation is now quite simple:

$$3\cos x+4\sin x = 2.5 \Rightarrow 5\cos(x-\alpha) = 2.5$$

$$\cos(x-\alpha) = 2.5/5 = 0.5$$

$$x-53.1° = 60°, 300°, \text{ etc.}$$

$$x = 113.1°, 353.1°, \text{ etc.}$$

EXERCISE 16E

1. By giving α and β appropriate values in one of the compound angle formulae, confirm that $\cos^2\theta + \sin^2\theta = 1$.

2. Prove that $\cos 2\alpha = 2\cos^2\alpha - 1 = 1 - 2\sin^2\alpha$.

3. Express $\cos 75°$ and $\sin 75°$ in surd form, and use your results to verify that $\cos^2 75° + \sin^2 75° = 1$ exactly.

4. If $\tan\alpha = 5/4$ and $\tan\beta = 4/5$, investigate the values of $\tan(\alpha-\beta)$ and $\tan(\alpha+\beta)$, and comment on your results.

5. Prove that $\cos 70° + \cos 50° = \cos 10°$, by expressing 70 and 50 as $60+10$ and $60-10$, and using the appropriate compound angle formulae. Check this result on your calculator.

6. Show that $\cos 2\alpha = \dfrac{1-t^2}{1+t^2}$ and $\sin 2\alpha = \dfrac{2t}{1+t^2}$, where $t = \tan\alpha$.

7. Express $7\cos x - 24\sin x$ in the form $r\cos(x+\alpha)$, and hence solve the equation $7\cos x - 24\sin x = -7$.

17   CALCULUS III

17.1 VOLUMES OF REVOLUTION

Before starting this section, you may find it helpful to re-read section 11.3. You will notice that figure 17.1 is very similar to figure 11.2, but the curve's equation is $y = f(x)$ instead of $v = f(t)$.

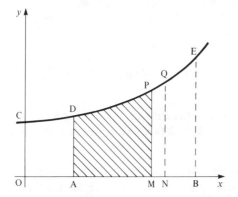

Fig. 17.1

Imagine now that the shaded region AMPD is rotated through an angle of 360° about Ox, i.e. about AM. Can you see that a solid shape will be formed, of the kind produced by a lathe? The line Ox will be an axis of symmetry, and if the solid were cut perpendicular to this axis, the cross-section would be a circle, centre on the axis. The problem before us is to find the *volume* of a solid generated in this manner.

In figure 17.1, D is a fixed point on the curve, and P is a variable point, as in section 11.3: OA $= a$, OM $= x$, and MP $= y = f(x)$. AD is a fixed (left-hand) boundary of our region, whereas we imagine MP to be a movable (right-hand) boundary. So the volume V depends on x, and we say $V = F(x)$.

Now suppose that x is increased by a small amount, which we shall call δx: obviously V also increases by a very small amount, which we shall call δV. Looking at the figure, we see that $\delta x = $ MN, and that δV is the volume generated when MNQP is rotated through 360° about MN. Now since MN is meant to be so very small, this volume is very nearly the result of just rotating a rectangle MP × MN about MN, which would give a coin-like cylindrical volume of radius y and thickness δx, i.e. δV very nearly equals $\pi y^2 \delta x$. In other words, $dV \div \delta x$ very nearly equals πy^2, i.e. $\pi[f(x)]^2$, and the discrepancy becomes indefinitely small as MN is made indefinitely small. This argument (which runs

237

parallel, you notice, to the argument in section 11.3) demonstrates that dV/dx, the rate of change of V, does exactly equal πy^2. We need not spell out the rest of the argument as we did in section 11.3, but can say immediately that if we now fix the position of MP, so that $OM = b$, then

$$V = \int_a^b \pi y^2 \, dx$$

In practice, we must replace the y in this formula by $f(x)$—and of course square it—*before* attempting to evaluate the integral. Note that it would be quite wrong to say $\int \pi y^2 \, dx = [\pi y^3/3]$: the right hand side equals $\int \pi y^2 \, dy$, and *not* $\int \pi y^2 \, dx$.

Let us now consider a numerical example. We shall find the volume of the cone formed by rotating the line $y = 3x$ from $x = 0$ to $x = 10$ about the x-axis. In this case, $f(x) = 3x$, and

$$V = \int_0^{10} \pi (3x)^2 \, dx = \int_0^{10} \pi \times 9x^2 \, dx = \pi \left[3x^3 \right]_0^{10}$$

taking the constant π outside the square brackets, which is permissible and often convenient. Thus $V = 3000\pi$. You should check this result, using the formula $V = \frac{1}{3}\pi r^2 h$ for the volume of a cone.

If we rotate the same line segment about the y-axis (can you visualise the resulting solid?), then of course the formula for the volume has to be altered: x and y must be interchanged, and a and b are now the limiting values of y. Thus

$$\text{volume} = \int_0^{30} \pi (y/3)^2 \, dy = \pi \left[y^3/27 \right]_0^{30} = 1000\pi$$

In both these examples, the answers can be found, or checked, without integration, but with a curve this is not usually so.

EXAMPLE (a) Find the volume generated when $y = x^3$, from $(1, 1)$ to $(2, 8)$, is rotated about the x-axis.

(b) Find the volume generated when $y = x^2$, from $(0, 0)$ to $(3, 9)$, is rotated about the y-axis.

(a) $\text{Volume} = \int_1^2 \pi y^2 \, dx = \pi \int_1^2 x^6 \, dx = \pi \left[x^7/7 \right]_1^2 = 127\pi/7$

(b) $\text{Volume} = \int_0^9 \pi x^2 \, dy = \pi \int_0^9 y \, dy = \pi \left[y^2/2 \right]_0^9 = 81\pi/2$

EXERCISE 17A

1. Find the volume generated when the given curves, between the given values of x, are rotated about the x-axis:

   (a) $y = 2x$, $x = 0$ to $x = 3$

   (b) $y = x+1$, $x = 2$ to $x = 3$

   (c) $y = \sqrt{x}$, $x = 4$ to $x = 9$

   (d) $y = x^2$, $x = 1$ to $x = 2$

2. Find the volume generated when the region enclosed between $y = 1-x$ and the two axes is rotated about the x-axis.

3. Find the volume generated when $y = x^4$ between the origin and $(2, 16)$ is rotated about the *y-axis*.

4. The rim of a wheel is formed by rotating the region enclosed between $y+x = 4$, $y-x = 4$, and $x = 3$, about the x-axis. What is the volume?

5. Establish the formula $V = \frac{1}{3}\pi r^2 h$ for the volume of a cone by considering the rotation about the x-axis of a certain line through the origin.

6. Find the volume of the sphere of radius 5 cm formed by rotating the semi-circle $y = \sqrt{(25-x^2)}$ about the x-axis.

17.2 TRAPEZIUM RULE

It is often impossible, or very difficult, to find the area under a graph by integration. For example, figure 17.2 represents the graph of $y = \sqrt{(100+x^2)}$, and so the shaded area equals $\int_5^9 \sqrt{(100+x^2)}\, dx$, an integral we do not know how to find.

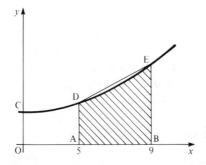

Fig. 17.2

It is, however, obvious that the area of the trapezium ABED would provide a reasonable approximation to the required area, and obvious too that since the line-segment DE lies wholly above the curve itself, the approximation will in this case be too big.

Now $AD = \sqrt{(100+25)} = \sqrt{125}$ and $BE = \sqrt{181}$.

Thus $ABED = \frac{1}{2}(AD+BE) \times AB$

$$= \frac{1}{2}(\sqrt{125}+\sqrt{181}) \times 4 = 49.27 \quad (4\,\text{s.f.})$$

The correct value is 48.9732 to 6 s.f., and you will see that our approximation is less than 1% out. Such a small error would be of no consequence in many applications, but if a more accurate result is essential, then we simply subdivide the region into several thinner sections and apply the trapezium rule to each. To illustrate this process, we will use two sections, each 2 units wide:

$$\text{area} \approx \frac{1}{2}(\sqrt{125}+\sqrt{149}) \times 2 + \frac{1}{2}(\sqrt{149}+\sqrt{181}) \times 2$$

$$= 49.05 \quad (4\,\text{s.f.}), \text{ a very good approximation}$$

EXAMPLE Find $\displaystyle\int_{10}^{30} 1/x\,dx$, using the trapezium rule with five sections, each 4 units wide.

$$\text{Area} \approx \frac{1}{2}(1/10 + 1/14) \times 4 + \ldots + \frac{1}{2}(1/26 + 1/30) \times 4$$

$$= 1.110 \quad (4\,\text{s.f.})$$

Write this calculation out in full if you do not find it clear. You may find it easier to use letters rather than numbers. We have five trapezia, each of width 4. If we use the letters a, b, c, d, e, f to denote the six values of y involved in the calculation, then we have

$$\text{area} \approx \frac{1}{2}(a+b) \times 4 + \frac{1}{2}(b+c) \times 4 + \frac{1}{2}(c+d) \times 4 + \frac{1}{2}(d+e) \times 4 + \frac{1}{2}(e+f) \times 4$$

$$= \frac{1}{2}(a+2b+2c+2d+2e+f) \times 4$$

The correct value of the area in this example is 1.099 (to 4 s.f.), and so once again our estimate would be close enough for most purposes—and if not, we could take more sections, say 20 sections each of width 1 unit (which would in fact give 1.099 to 4 s.f.).

In both the problems tackled above, our difficulty lay in the fact that we could not integrate the functions. Scientists will often face another difficulty, trying to evaluate an area under a graph when they know of no formula for the function and must rely solely on observed values. In this case, the trapezium rule is a great help.

EXAMPLE Find the area under the graph given by the following table of observed values:

x	0	1	2	3	4	5	6
y	0	95	182	262	336	405	463

We obviously divide the region into six sections, each 1 unit wide. Using the notation adopted in the last example, we have

$$\text{area} \approx \tfrac{1}{2}(a+2b+2c+2d+2e+2f+g) \times 1$$

where $a = 0$, $b = 95$, $c = 182$, $d = 262$, $e = 336$, $f = 405$, and $g = 463$. Hence the area equals 1510 (to 3 s.f.).

EXERCISE 17B

1. Estimate the following integrals, using the number of sections specified:

(a) $\displaystyle\int_0^{90} \sin x° \, dx$ (9)

(b) $\displaystyle\int_0^{10} \sqrt{(1+x)} \, dx$ (10)

(c) $\displaystyle\int_5^9 \sqrt{(100+x^2)} \, dx$ (8)

2. Find the areas under the graphs given by the following tables:

(a)

x	0	3	6	9	12	15	18
y	6.37	7.11	8.00	9.11	10.58	12.80	17.58

(b)

p	0	1	2	3	4	5	6	7
q	17	21	23	22	18	13	7	0

(c)

v	0	10	20	30	40	50	60
p	18.2	16.7	15.4	14.3	13.3	12.5	11.8

3. The velocity of a tram, t s after starting, is given by the formula $v = 8 \sin^2 t° \, \text{m s}^{-1}$, $0 \leqslant t \leqslant 90$. How far does it travel in the first 90 s?

17.3 MID-ORDINATE RULE AND SIMPSON'S RULE

The trapezium rule, applied to the shaded region in figure 17.3, gives $\frac{1}{2}(AD+BE) \times AB$ as its approximate area. The rule in effect takes the average height of the graph between the points D and E to be equal to $\frac{1}{2}(AD+BE)$, the average value of the two end ordinates AD and BE.

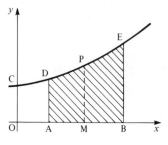

Fig. 17.3

We now consider two other useful rules for estimating the average height of part of a graph.

The *mid-ordinate rule* takes MP, the ordinate exactly mid-way between AD and BE, as the estimate of average height. This is best illustrated by means of an example.

EXAMPLE Find $\displaystyle\int_{10}^{30} 1/x \, dx$, using the mid-ordinate rule.

We divide the region into five sections (just as we did when applying the trapezium rule to this same problem), each 4 units wide. The first section lies between $x = 10$ and $x = 14$, and we estimate its average height to be the height half way across, i.e. 1/12. Similarly, we estimate the average heights of the other sections to be 1/16, 1/20, 1/24, and 1/28. So we have

$$\text{area} \approx (1/12 + 1/16 + 1/20 + 1/24 + 1/28) \times 4$$

$$= 1.093 \quad (4\,\text{s.f.})$$

Note that this estimate based on the mid-ordinate rule is rather better than our previous estimate based on the trapezium rule, and no more difficult to obtain. However, the mid-ordinate rule is less satisfactory when calculating an area from a table of values, and therefore you need to be familiar with both techniques.

The third method of estimating the average height is called *Simpson's rule*. This rule takes the average height to be $\frac{1}{6}(AD+4MP+BE)$. Since this formula takes account of the two end ordinates *and* of the mid-ordinate, it very often gives a closer approximation than the other two rules. It is quite a bit more tricky to use, however, and the extra accuracy may not be worth the extra trouble.

EXAMPLE Find $\int_{10}^{30} 1/x \, dx$, using Simpson's rule.

Once again, we will divide the region into five sections, each 4 units wide. The first section lies between $x = 10$ and $x = 14$. The two end ordinates of this section equal $1/10$ and $1/14$, and the mid-ordinate equals $1/12$: so we estimate its average height to be $\frac{1}{6}(1/10 + 4/12 + 1/14)$. We deal with the other sections in a similar manner. So we have

area $\approx \frac{1}{6}(1/10 + 4/12 + 1/14) \times 4$

$\qquad + \frac{1}{6}(1/14 + 4/16 + 1/18) \times 4$

$\qquad\qquad + \frac{1}{6}(1/18 + 4/20 + 1/22) \times 4$

$\qquad\qquad\qquad + \frac{1}{6}(1/22 + 4/24 + 1/26) \times 4$

$\qquad\qquad\qquad\qquad + \frac{1}{6}(1/26 + 4/28 + 1/30) \times 4$

$= 1.099$ (4 s.f.)

If we use the letters a to k to denote the eleven values of y involved in this calculation, then we have

area $\approx \frac{1}{6}(a + 4b + c + c + 4d + e + \ldots + i + 4j + k) \times 4$

$\qquad = \frac{1}{6}(a + 4b + 2c + 4d + 2e + 4f + 2g + 4h + 2i + 4j + k) \times 4$

EXERCISE 17C

1. Use (i) the mid-ordinate rule, and (ii) Simpson's rule, to estimate the integrals in question 1 of exercise 17B.

2. Estimate the following integrals, using (i) the mid-ordinate rule, and (ii) Simpson's rule:

(a) $\int_0^1 \sqrt{(10 + 4x)} \, dx$
(b) $\int_{10}^{100} \log_{10} x \, dx$

3. Answer question 3 of exercise 17B using (i) the mid-ordinate rule, and (ii) Simpson's rule.

17.4 MORE ADVANCED RESULTS

We stated in section 4.3 that the derivatives of $\sin x$ and $\cos x$ are $+\cos x$ and $-\sin x$ respectively (provided that x is measured in radians), and we outlined an informal demonstration of these facts in section 12.7. So what about the derivative of $\tan x$?

Before answering this question, we will develop a couple of useful rules to help us differentiate complicated functions of x.

Suppose that $y = u+v$, where u and v are functions of x. Then of course $y' = u'+v'$. We have constantly been using this rule.

For example, suppose $u = x^4$, $v = x^3$, and $y = x^4+x^3 = u+v$.

Then $$y' = 4x^3+3x^2 = u'+v'$$

But now suppose that $y = uv$, i.e. that y equals the product of u and v (rather than their sum): it is natural to imagine that y' might simply equal the product of u' and v', but unfortunately this is not so.

For example, if $u = x^4$, $v = x^3$, and $y = uv = x^7$,

then $y' = 7x^6$, whereas $u'v' = (4x^3)(3x^2) = 12x^5$.

The correct rule is rather more complicated:

$$\text{if } y = uv, \text{ then } y' = u'v+uv'$$

Thus (with the same u and v as above) we have

$$y' = u'v+uv' = (4x^3)(x^3)+(x^4)(3x^2) = 4x^6+3x^6 = 7x^6$$

which of course is correct.

EXAMPLE Find the derivative of $\sin x \cos x$.

Let $u = \sin x$, $v = \cos x$, $y = uv = \sin x \cos x$.

Then $$y' = u'v+uv' = (+\cos x)(\cos x)+(\sin x)(-\sin x)$$
$$= \cos^2 x-\sin^2 x$$

There is a similar (but even more complicated!) rule to deal with the case when y is the quotient of two functions of x:

$$\text{if } y = u/v, \text{ then } y' = (u'v-uv')/v^2$$

EXAMPLE Find the derivative of $\tan x$.

Let $u = \sin x$, $v = \cos x$, $y = u/v = \sin x/\cos x = \tan x$.

Then

$$y' = (u'v-uv')/v^2 = \frac{(+\cos x)(\cos x)-(\sin x)(-\sin x)}{(\cos x)^2}$$

$$= \frac{\cos^2 x+\sin^2 x}{\cos^2 x} = \frac{1}{\cos^2 x} = \sec^2 x$$

Therefore the derivative of $\tan x$ is $\sec^2 x$ (x in radians).

There are two other important functions whose derivatives are worth remembering, although at this stage we must simply state the results without proof:

the derivative of ln x is 1/x and the derivative of e^x is e^x

The basic functions that we can now differentiate are:

(1) the powers of x (and remember that such functions as $1/x$ and $\sqrt{x}$ can be regarded as powers of x),

(2) the trigonometrical functions ($\sin x$, $\cos x$, $\tan x$),

(3) the functions connected with e ($\ln x$, e^x).

Furthermore, by making use of the sum, product, and quotient rules, and of the chain rule, we can differentiate many functions that are built up from these basic functions.

EXAMPLE   Differentiate (a) $\ln(5x+12)$, (b) $e^x(x^2+3x)$, and (c) $\dfrac{x+1}{x-1}$.

(a) Let $u = 5x+12$, and $y = \ln u = \ln(5x+12)$.

Then $$\frac{dy}{dx} = \frac{dy}{du} \times \frac{du}{dx} = 1/u \times 5 = \frac{5}{5x+12}$$

(b) Now let $u = e^x$, $v = x^2+3x$, $y = uv = e^x(x^2+3x)$.

Then $\quad y' = u'v+uv' = e^x(x^2+3x)+e^x(2x+3) = e^x(x^2+5x+3)$

(c) Now finally let $u = x+1$, $v = x-1$, $y = \dfrac{u}{v} = \dfrac{x+1}{x-1}$.

Then $$y' = \frac{u'v-uv'}{v^2} = \frac{1(x-1)-(x+1)1}{(x-1)^2} = \frac{-2}{(x-1)^2}$$

EXAMPLE   Calculate $\displaystyle\int_{10}^{30} 1/x \, dx$.

To integrate $1/x$, we need to find a function whose derivative equals $1/x$: $\ln x$ will do admirably.

So $$\int_{10}^{30} 1/x \, dx = \Big[\ln x\Big]_{10}^{30} = \ln 30 - \ln 10$$

$$= 3.401\,197\,382 - 2.302\,585\,093 = 1.0986 \quad (5\,\text{s.f.})$$

EXAMPLE Find y given that $dy/dx = \cos 3x$ (x in radians).

We need a function whose derivative equals $\cos 3x$. Now the chain rule tells us that $(\sin 3x)' = 3 \cos 3x$, which is 3 times too great.

Therefore $$y = \tfrac{1}{3} \sin 3x + c$$

EXAMPLE Find $\int e^{2x}\, dx$.

We need a function whose derivative equals e^{2x}. The chain rule tells us that $D(e^{2x}) = 2e^{2x}$, which is twice what we want.

Therefore $$\int e^{2x}\, dx = \tfrac{1}{2}e^{2x} + c$$

EXERCISE 17D

1. Differentiate:
   - (a) $1/(7x+24)$, $\sqrt{(7x+24)}$
   - (b) $\sin(7x+24)$, $\cos(7x+24)$, $\tan(7x+24)$
   - (c) $\ln(7x+24)$, $e^{(7x+24)}$

2. Differentiate uv and u/v, where $u = x^3 - 1$, $v = x^3 + 1$. Then find and classify the stationary points on the curves $y = uv$ and $y = u/v$.

3. Integrate:
   - (a) $1/(7x+24)$, $\sqrt{(7x+24)}$
   - (b) $\sin(7x+24)$, $\cos(7x+24)$
   - (c) $e^{(7x+24)}$

4. Find the second derivative of $y = \sin(nx+\varepsilon)$, where n and ε are constants. Hence show that this function satisfies the equation $y'' + n^2 y = 0$.

5. Find the maximum and minimum values of $8 \cos x + 15 \sin x$:
   - (a) by expressing the function in the form $r \cos(x-\alpha)$,
   - (b) by differentiating and locating the stationary points.

6. Differentiate $\ln(\cos x)$ by using the chain rule, and hence integrate $\tan x$.

7. Differentiate $x(\ln x - 1)$ by using the product rule, and hence integrate $\ln x$.

8. Use the fact that $\cos 2x = 2\cos^2 x - 1$ to express $\cos^2 x$ in terms of $\cos 2x$, and find a similar expression for $\sin^2 x$. Hence evaluate the following definite integrals:
   - (a) $\displaystyle\int_0^{\pi/2} \cos^2 x\, dx$
   - (b) $\displaystyle\int_0^{\pi/2} \sin^2 x\, dx$

9. Draw a graph of the function e^x against x as accurately as possible, and confirm by drawing several tangents that $D(e^x) = e^x$.

<table>
<tr><td>**18**</td><td># MECHANICS V</td></tr>
</table>

18.1 WORK

When an object's position changes, then any forces acting on it are said to do work. The amount of work done may be positive, zero, or negative.

Suppose for example that a box of mass 10 kg is dragged along a distance of 4 m by an applied force of 35 newtons, against a frictional force of 20 newtons, as in figure 18.1.

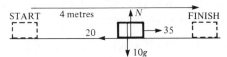

START   4 metres N FINISH

20   35

$10g$

Fig. 18.1

We would say in this case that the applied force does positive work: it is 'successful'—its direction and the direction of motion are in agreement. The frictional force, on the other hand, does negative work: it is 'unsuccessful'—its direction and the direction of motion are in disagreement. The weight and the normal force do zero work: they are 'neutral'.

How is work measured? We multiply the magnitude of the force by the distance involved. When standard units are in use (newtons and metres), the unit of work is the joule (abbreviated to J). Thus in our example

$$\text{the work done by the applied force} = 35\,N \times 4\,m = +140\,J$$

$$\text{the work done by the frictional force} = -20 \times 4 = -80\,J$$

$$\text{and the total work done} = +140 + (-80) + 0 + 0 = +60\,J$$

Suppose now that the applied force acts at 25° above the horizontal (figure 18.2). Its components parallel to and perpendicular to the direction of motion are $35 \cos 25°$ and $35 \sin 25°\,N$.

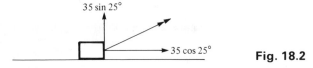

$35 \sin 25°$

$35 \cos 25°$

Fig. 18.2

$$\text{The total work done by these} = (35 \cos 25° \times 4) + 0$$

$$= 35 \times 4 \times \cos 25°$$

$$= +127\,J \quad (3\,s.f.)$$

Imagine now a man holding a heavy box above his head. His hands push up on the base of the box with a force to balance the box's weight. If the box is held absolutely still, the force P does zero work, because the box is motionless.

Fig. 18.3

In practice, of course, the box will be moving rapidly up and down through very small distances as a result of the action of the man's muscles. His muscles are constantly in motion, and the forces in them do a significant amount of work. This is why the man soon becomes hot and tired, and why, if asked, he would probably say that he was working hard.

Figure 18.2 showed a situation where an applied force was acting at an angle to the direction of motion. We now consider another such case.

Suppose that the same box (of mass 10 kg) slides from A to B, a distance of 6 m, down a smooth slope inclined at an angle of 30° to the horizontal (figure 18.4). The two forces acting on the box are the normal reaction N and the weight $10g$. The force N acts perpendicular to the direction of motion, and therefore does zero work. The weight acts at an angle of 60° to the direction of motion: so its components parallel to and perpendicular to the motion are $10g \cos 60°$ and $10g \sin 60°$.

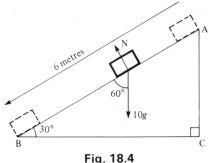

Fig. 18.4

$$\text{The total work done by the weight} = (10g \cos 60° \times 6) + 0$$

$$= 10g \times 6 \times \cos 60°$$

$$= +294 \, \text{J}$$

Instead of splitting the weight into components parallel and perpendicular to the motion, we might try splitting the displacement **AB** into components parallel to and perpendicular to the weight, i.e. **AC** and **CB**. The magnitude of the displacement **AC** is 6 cos 60°, of course, and so the work done by the weight if the box moved from A to C would be (10g × 6 cos 60°). Can you see that the work done by the weight as the box moved on from C to B would be zero? Therefore the total work done would be 10g × 6 × cos 60°, which is exactly the answer obtained earlier on.

You will notice that work is not a vector quantity. The work done in any situation is positive or negative (or zero), but has no direction. In the case of the box sliding down the slope, for instance, the work done by the weight is simply +294 J: the weight acts in a particular direction, and the motion is in a particular direction, but the work done is not in any particular direction.

On the contrary, work is a scalar quantity. In fact, as you may already have spotted, there is a connection between work done and the idea of a scalar product studied in chapter 9. It is this connection that provides us with the formal definition of work:

> the work done by a constant force **P** as the object
> involved moves through a displacement **s** is the scalar
> product of **P** and **s**, i.e. **P · s**

For instance, in the example above, **P** is the weight and **s** is the displacement from A to B, the angle between them being 60°. So

$$\text{the work done} = \mathbf{P} \cdot \mathbf{s} = |\mathbf{P}| \times |\mathbf{s}| \times \cos 60°$$

$$= 10g \times 6 \times \cos 60°$$

$$= +294\,\text{J}$$

EXAMPLE The upper end of a 13 m chute is 5 m above the lower end. A block of mass 30 kg slides down against a frictional force of 60 N. Calculate the work done by   (a) the block's weight,   (b) the frictional force, and   (c) both together. When the block has reached the bottom, it is hauled up to the top again by an applied force of 200 N acting straight up the plane, the friction being unaltered (except of course in direction). Calculate the work done by (d) the applied force,   (e) the weight,   (f) the friction, and   (g) all the forces involved.

By Pythagoras in triangle OPR (see figure 18.5), OP = $\sqrt{(13^2 - 5^2)}$ = 12 m.

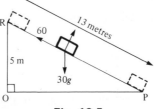

Fig. 18.5

(a) The work done by the weight $= 30g \times 5 = +1470\,\text{J}$

This calculation could have been tackled vectorially. We set up axes along OP and OR; as usual, **i** and **j** are unit vectors in directions OP and OR.

Then the weight $= -30g\mathbf{j}$, and the displacement $= 12\mathbf{i} - 5\mathbf{j}$.

So   the work done $=$ force $\cdot$ displacement

$$= (-30g\mathbf{j}) \cdot (12\mathbf{i} - 5\mathbf{j})$$

$$= 0 + 30g \times 5 = +1470\,\text{J}$$

(b) The angle between the frictional force and the displacement **RP** is $180°$.

So   the work done $=$ force $\cdot$ displacement

$$= 60 \times 13 \times \cos 180°$$

$$= 60 \times 13 \times (-1) = -780\,\text{J}$$

(c) The total work done $= +1470 - 780 = +690\,\text{J}$

(d) The angle between the applied force of $200\,\text{N}$ and the displacement **PR** is $0°$ (figure 18.6).

So   the work done $= 200 \times 13 \times \cos 0°$

$$= 200 \times 13 \times (+1) = +2600\,\text{J}$$

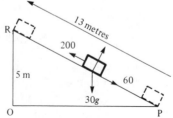

Fig. 18.6

(e) As before, the work done by the block's weight equals $(-30g\mathbf{j}) \cdot (-12\mathbf{i} + 5\mathbf{j}) = -1470\,\text{J}$.

(f) The angle between the frictional force and the direction of motion is again $180°$ (it always is, of course), and so the work done equals $-780\,\text{J}$, as before.

(g) The work done by the normal reaction is zero.

So   the total work done $= +2600 - 1470 - 780 + 0$

$$= +350\,\text{J}$$

EXERCISE 18A

1. A body of mass $7\,\text{kg}$ falls vertically through a distance of $5\,\text{m}$ against air resistance of $12\,\text{N}$. Find   (a) the work done by the weight,   (b) the work done by air resistance, and   (c) the total work done.

2. A boy of mass 50 kg bounces off a trampoline, rising 3 m into the air. Find the work done by his weight (a) on the way up, (b) on the way down, (c) overall.

3. A sledge weighing 2000 N is given a good shove and slides down a slope for a distance of 10 m. If the angle of slope is arcsin (1/100), and the resisting force is 300 N, find (a) the work done by the weight, (b) the work done by the resisting force, and (c) the total work done.

4. A small ball of mass 0.5 kg is attached to one end of a light rod, of length 3 m, which can rotate freely about a horizontal axis at the other end. Initially the ball is vertically above the axis. Find the work done by the weight as the ball falls to its lowest position (it follows a semi-circular path, of course). If the ball completes a full circle, how much work does its weight do in all? Explain why the tension or thrust of the rod does zero work as the ball travels round an arc of the circle.

5. In each case, the given constant force **P** acts on a particle. Find the work done by **P** when the particle moves through the given displacement **s**, assuming the units to be newtons and metres.

   (a) $\mathbf{P} = 12\mathbf{i}$, $\mathbf{s} = 5\mathbf{i}$

   (b) $\mathbf{P} = 5\mathbf{i}$, $\mathbf{s} = 12\mathbf{j}$

   (c) $\mathbf{P} = 2\mathbf{i} + 3\mathbf{j}$, $\mathbf{s} = 4\mathbf{i} + \mathbf{j}$

   (d) $\mathbf{P} = 2\mathbf{i} + 3\mathbf{j}$, $\mathbf{s} = 4\mathbf{i} - 5\mathbf{j}$

   (e) $\mathbf{P} = 3\mathbf{i} - \mathbf{j}$, $\mathbf{s} = -2\mathbf{i} - 6\mathbf{j}$

   (f) $\mathbf{P} = \mathbf{i} + 2\mathbf{j} + 3\mathbf{k}$, $\mathbf{s} = 4\mathbf{i} - \mathbf{j} + 2\mathbf{k}$

   (g) $\mathbf{P} = 4\mathbf{i} + 3\mathbf{j} - \mathbf{k}$, $\mathbf{s} = 2\mathbf{i} - \mathbf{j} + 5\mathbf{k}$

   Illustrate your answers in (a) to (e) with sketches, showing the particle in an initial position, in an intermediate position (with the force marked in), and in its final position.

6. A particle is tied to one end of an elastic string, whose other end is fixed. The string has been stretched by 30 cm and the tension is 10 N. If the particle is now allowed to move until the string becomes slack, find the work done by the tension, assuming that you can use the average value of the tension in your calculations.

18.2 KINETIC ENERGY

We now return to our very first example, the box being dragged along by an applied force (see figure 18.1). Since the applied force of 35 N is greater than the frictional force of 20 N, the box will accelerate. This corresponds to the fact that the total work done ($35 \times 4 - 20 \times 4$ J) is positive: positive work causes a gain in speed.

Alternatively, we may argue as follows. The work done by the applied force is 140 J. Some of this (80 J in fact) can be regarded as work done *against* friction. The surplus of 60 J is what causes the gain in speed. But what is the precise connection between work and motion?

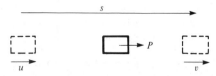

Fig. 18.7

If a body of mass m is acted on by a constant force P, and moves a distance s under its influence (as in figure 18.7), then Newton's second law, $P = ma$, tells us that the acceleration a is constant. With the usual notation, therefore,

$$v^2 = u^2 + 2as \Rightarrow \tfrac{1}{2}v^2 - \tfrac{1}{2}u^2 = as$$

Hence we derive the following important equation:

$$Ps = \tfrac{1}{2}mv^2 - \tfrac{1}{2}mu^2$$

The quantity Ps is of course just the work done by the force. The quantity $\tfrac{1}{2}mv^2$ is called the *kinetic energy* (K.E.) of the body. The equation can therefore be rephrased as follows:

work done = final K.E. − initial K.E.

Note that both work and K.E. are scalar quantities. They are usually measured in the same units, joules.

We have established the equation only for the case of a single force acting in the direction of motion, but it can quite easily be shown to apply also when there are several forces, and when the motion is in two or three dimensions. The principle that

total work done = gain in K.E.

is indeed fundamental to Newtonian mechanics, and holds under all circumstances.

EXAMPLE A mass of 9 kg is moving at $10\,\mathrm{m\,s^{-1}}$: what is its K.E.? If its K.E. were 648 J, what would be its speed?

The kinetic energy $= \tfrac{1}{2} \times 9 \times 10^2 = 450\,\mathrm{J}$.

If K.E. $= 648$, then $\tfrac{1}{2} \times 9 \times v^2 = 648$, and so $v = 12$ $(\mathrm{m\,s^{-1}})$.

EXAMPLE The start of a 100 m switchback track is 20 m above the finish. A car of mass 0.5 tonne starts from rest, and runs down the track against a constant resisting force of 340 newtons. What is its final speed? At the finish, the track levels out, and the brakes are applied to bring the car to rest within a further 10 m. Calculate the necessary braking force, assumed constant.

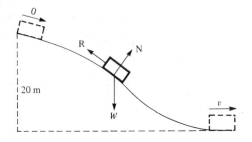

Fig. 18.8

We consider first the 100 m descent (see figure 18.8):

$$\text{work done by } W = 500g \times 20$$
$$= +98\,000\,\text{J}$$

$$\text{work done by } R = -340 \times 100$$
$$= -34\,000\,\text{J}$$

and

$$\text{work done by } N = 0\,\text{J}$$

So

$$\text{total work done} = 98\,000 - 34\,000$$
$$= +64\,000\,\text{J}$$

The initial K.E. $= 0$

and final K.E. $= \frac{1}{2} \times 500 \times v^2$ (where v is final speed)
$$= 250v^2$$

Therefore $64\,000 = 250v^2 - 0 \Rightarrow v = 16 \;(\text{m s}^{-1})$.

We now consider the braking stage; since the track is horizontal here, the weight does zero work. The work done by the stopping force (S newtons, let us say) equals $-S \times 10\,\text{J}$. The initial K.E. equals $64\,000\,\text{J}$, and the final K.E. equals zero, of course.

So $\qquad -10S = 0 - 64\,000 \Rightarrow S = 6400$ (newtons)

The braking force thus equals $(6400 - 340) = 6060$ newtons.

EXAMPLE A body of mass $\frac{1}{2}$ unit is at $(2, -1, 4)$ with a velocity of $(3\mathbf{i} + 2\mathbf{j} - \frac{1}{2}\mathbf{k})$. A force of $(-\mathbf{i} + 3\mathbf{j} + 2\mathbf{k})$ displaces it to $(4, 15, 11)$. Calculate its final speed, assuming the data to be given in standard units.

The displacement $= (4\mathbf{i} + 15\mathbf{j} + 11\mathbf{k}) - (2\mathbf{i} - \mathbf{j} + 4\mathbf{k})$
$$= (2\mathbf{i} + 16\mathbf{j} + 7\mathbf{k})$$

and so work done $= (-\mathbf{i} + 3\mathbf{j} + 2\mathbf{k}) \cdot (2\mathbf{i} + 16\mathbf{j} + 7\mathbf{k})$
$$= -2 + 48 + 14 = +60\,\text{J}$$

Now initial speed $=$ magnitude of initial velocity
$$= \sqrt{(3^2 + 2^2 + \tfrac{1}{2}^2)} = \sqrt{13\tfrac{1}{4}}\,\text{m s}^{-1}$$

and suppose the final speed to be $v\,\mathrm{m\,s^{-1}}$. Then

$$60 = \tfrac{1}{2} \times \tfrac{1}{2} \times v^2 - \tfrac{1}{2} \times \tfrac{1}{2} \times 13\tfrac{1}{4}$$

and so $\qquad v^2 = 240 + 13\tfrac{1}{4} = 253\tfrac{1}{4} \Rightarrow v = \text{nearly } 16\,(\mathrm{m\,s^{-1}})$

EXERCISE 18B

1. What is the kinetic energy of a mass of 0.49 kg moving with a speed of $4\,\mathrm{m\,s^{-1}}$?

2. Arrange in order of magnitude the kinetic energy of the following: a sprinter of mass 70 kg running at $10\,\mathrm{m\,s^{-1}}$, a bullet of mass 30 grams moving at $600\,\mathrm{m\,s^{-1}}$, a truck of 3000 kg moving at $10\,\mathrm{m\,s^{-1}}$, and a ship of 2000 tonnes moving at $0.3\,\mathrm{m\,s^{-1}}$.

3. What work is needed to accelerate a body of mass 3 kg from rest to $15\,\mathrm{m\,s^{-1}}$?

4. A 750 kg car is brought to rest from a speed of $54\,\mathrm{km\,h^{-1}}$. What work is required? If the process takes 25 m, what constant force is involved?

5. An 800 kg car travelling at $20\,\mathrm{m\,s^{-1}}$ collides head on with a 1000 kg car travelling at $16\,\mathrm{m\,s^{-1}}$. If both cars are brought to a standstill, how much kinetic energy is lost in the collision? Compare your answer with the loss of kinetic energy when an 1800 kg limousine travelling at $36\,\mathrm{m\,s^{-1}}$ hits a large tree.

6. A 160 000 tonne tanker must reduce speed from $5\,\mathrm{m\,s^{-1}}$ to $1\,\mathrm{m\,s^{-1}}$. If the maximum stopping force is 320 kN, how many kilometres are needed for the manoeuvre?

7. A shell is fired with muzzle velocity of $1600\,\mathrm{m\,s^{-1}}$ at an angle of 30° above the horizontal. What is its initial kinetic energy? What is the kinetic energy when it reaches the highest point of its trajectory, and when it returns to ground level? How would your answers be affected if air resistance were taken into account?

8. A body of mass 1 unit is at $(3, 5)$ with a velocity of $(4\mathbf{i} - 3\mathbf{j})$. A force of $(3\mathbf{i} + 2\mathbf{j})$ displaces it to $(43, 9)$. Find its final speed.

9. A particle on a vertical z-axis falls from $z = 22$ to $z = 3$ under the action of its own weight and of a resisting force equal to 45. If its initial and final speeds are 15 and 23 respectively, find its mass (assuming the data to be given in standard units).

10. Find the speed of the small ball mentioned in question 4 of exercise 18A when it reaches its lowest position, if (a) it starts from rest, and (b) it starts with a speed of $2\,\mathrm{m\,s^{-1}}$.

18.3 **POTENTIAL ENERGY**

If a steel ball of mass 5 kg is held 10 m above ground level, the ball has no kinetic energy—indeed it has no energy at all in the ordinary sense of that term. If the ball is now allowed to fall to the ground, the amount of work done by the weight is $5g \times 10 = +490$ J. If we ignore air resistance, therefore, its kinetic energy on impact also equals 490 J. Equally, if we threw the ball up from ground level with kinetic energy of 490 J, it would rise to a height of 10 m above ground level, at which moment it would have lost all its kinetic energy, and would then fall back to the ground again, arriving with its initial kinetic energy of 490 J.

In a sense, therefore, we can store 490 J of kinetic energy in the ball simply by holding it 10 m above ground level. Since this is not actual kinetic energy (kinetic means connected with motion, and the ball is held stationary), but can easily and efficiently be converted into kinetic energy (by letting the ball fall to the ground), we call it *potential energy* (P.E.), and of course we measure it in joules.

More generally, if a body of mass m kg is held h m above a fixed level, then its potential energy is said to be mgh J. Note that the concept of potential energy is relative to some fixed level. For instance, if a platform of height 2 m was directly under the steel ball, we might have regarded the level of the platform, rather than ground level, as our fixed level—and in that case, the potential energy of the steel ball would have been $5g \times 8 = +392$ J, rather than $+490$. As we shall see in a moment, however, this relative nature of potential energy does not matter at all, since we are always dealing with a *change* in potential energy, and the change (whether gain or loss) is the same whatever fixed level is chosen.

EXAMPLE A mass of 10 kg is moved from point A (9 m above ground level) to point B (5 m above ground level). What is the potential energy at A and at B, and what is the loss of potential energy when the move is made? Answer these questions taking the fixed level to be   (a) the ground, and   (b) a platform 2 m above the ground.

(a) P.E. at A $= 10g \times 9 = +90g$ J

and at B $= 10g \times 5 = +50g$ J

Therefore loss $= 90g - 50g = 40g$ J

(b) P.E. at A $= 10g \times 7 = +70g$ J

and at B $= 10g \times 3 = +30g$ J

Therefore loss $= 70g - 30g = 40g$ J

You will see that although the individual values of potential energy depend on whether we regard the ground or the platform as the fixed level, the loss of potential energy is the same in each case.

It is possible to store energy in other easily convertible forms. For instance, refer back to your solution to question 6 of exercise 18A (if you did not tackle that question, do so now). You should have found that as the string contracts to its natural length, the work done by the tension equals $+1.5\,\mathrm{J}$. So we can say that when the string is stretched, its elastic potential energy is $+1.5\,\mathrm{J}$. This is one example of the very many forms of potential energy used by scientists and engineers. In this course, however, we confine our attention to gravitational potential energy, i.e. the P.E. associated with weights.

The essential feature of (gravitational) potential energy is that it may be converted into kinetic energy, and vice versa. In any mechanical system, the total stock of energy is conserved, i.e. does not change, unless work (positive or negative) is done by non-P.E. forces such as friction (scientists in fact believe that energy is conserved in every conceivable circumstance, but they count heat, light, mass, etc., as forms of energy). We can often solve problems by considering the total stock of energy.

EXAMPLE A cyclist and his machine have a joint mass of $95\,\mathrm{kg}$. He rides down a $200\,\mathrm{m}$ hill inclined at $4°$ to the horizontal, exerting a forward force of $25\,\mathrm{N}$ against a frictional force of $35\,\mathrm{N}$. If his initial speed is $4\,\mathrm{m\,s^{-1}}$, what is his final speed v?

The work done by the driving force is $25 \times 200 = +5000\,\mathrm{J}$: this is positive, and so increases the total energy. The work done by friction is $-35 \times 200 = -7000\,\mathrm{J}$: this is negative, and so decreases the total. Altogether there is a loss of energy equalling $2000\,\mathrm{J}$.

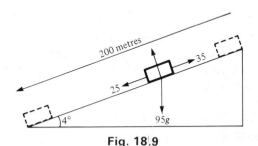

Fig. 18.9

So $\text{final (K.E.} + \text{P.E.)} = \text{initial (K.E.} + \text{P.E.)} - 2000\,\mathrm{J}$

i.e. $\text{final K.E.} = \text{initial K.E.} + \text{loss in P.E.} - 2000\,\mathrm{J}$

$= (\tfrac{1}{2} \times 95 \times 16) + (95g \times 200 \sin 4°) - 2000\,\mathrm{J}$

$= 11\,748.7\,\mathrm{J}$

So $\tfrac{1}{2} \times 95 \times v^2 = 11\,748.7 \Rightarrow v = 15.7\,\mathrm{m\,s^{-1}}$ (3 s.f.)

EXAMPLE The hammer in a pile-driving mechanism is allowed to fall vertically through a height of 5 m so as to strike the top of the pile. The masses of the hammer and pile are 300 kg and 700 kg respectively. If the hammer does not rebound on impact, calculate the speed with which the pile begins to move (take g to be $10\,\mathrm{m\,s^{-2}}$), and the loss of energy caused by the impact. If the pile is driven 9 cm into the ground, find also the resistance to motion (assumed to be constant).

During its fall, the hammer loses P.E. and gains K.E., but there is no overall change in energy. So if v is the hammer's speed just before impact

$$\text{gain in K.E.} = \text{loss in P.E.} \Rightarrow \tfrac{1}{2}mv^2 = mg \times 5 \Rightarrow v = 10$$

During the impact, a certain amount of energy is lost (or rather, some mechanical energy is converted into heat and noise). Momentum is conserved, however, provided that the impact lasts for such a short period of time that the impulses of the external forces can be ignored. So if V is the common speed of hammer and pile just after impact

$$\text{final momentum} = \text{initial momentum} \Rightarrow 1000V = 300v \Rightarrow V = 3$$

Therefore the pile begins to move at a speed of $3\,\mathrm{m\,s^{-1}}$.

The loss of kinetic energy caused by the impact

$$
\begin{aligned}
&= (\text{K.E. just before}) - (\text{K.E. just after})\\
&= \tfrac{1}{2} \times 300 \times v^2 - \tfrac{1}{2} \times 1000 \times V^2\\
&= 15\,000 - 4500 = 10\,500\,\mathrm{J}
\end{aligned}
$$

If we assume that the impact lasts for a very short period of time (as we have already done), then there is no time for potential energy to be lost during the impact, and so the total loss of (mechanical) energy is 10.5 kJ.

During the final phase of the motion, K.E. and P.E. are lost, because the resisting force R is doing negative work. Therefore

$$
\begin{aligned}
R \times 0.09 &= (\text{loss in K.E.}) + (\text{loss in P.E.})\\
&= 4500 + 1000g \times 0.09 = 5400
\end{aligned}
$$

and so $R = 60\,000$.

So the resistance to motion is $6g$ kN.

EXERCISE 18C

1. A skier of mass 75 kg comes down a ski-run of length 1000 m and average slope 1 in 12. What is his loss in P.E.?

2. Calculate his speed at the bottom if he starts from rest, and the resistance to motion is negligible.

3. As question 2, with average resistance $= 46.25\,\text{N}$.

4. As question 3, with initial speed $= 20\,\text{m s}^{-1}$.

5. A car of mass 1200 kg goes up a hill of length 800 m and average inclination to the horizontal of $10°$. Its speed at the foot of the hill is $30\,\text{m s}^{-1}$ and at the top is $10\,\text{m s}^{-1}$. If the average resistance to motion is 500 N, calculate the average tractive force exerted by the engine.

6. A lead block of mass 1 kg rests on a rough horizontal surface, the coefficient of friction being 0.5. A plasticine pellet of mass 50 grams travelling horizontally at $147\,\text{m s}^{-1}$ smacks straight into one face of the block. Show that the combined mass begins to move at $7\,\text{m s}^{-1}$, and find out how far it slides before coming to rest.

7. If the pellet described in question 6 had collided head-on with a lead sphere of mass 1 kg suspended from a girder by means of a steel wire of length 10 m, show that the wire would have swung sideways through an angle of about $41°$.

18.4 POWER AND EFFICIENCY

If I station myself behind a car and exert a steady push on its rear end, it will start moving (provided that the brakes are off and my push is strong enough to overcome friction). So my applied force will do positive work.

Suppose, for instance, that the force is a constant 240 N. During the first second the car might move only 5 cm, in which case the work done would be $240 \times 0.05 = 12\,\text{J}$. But as time passed, the car would pick up speed and would therefore travel further and further each second. So the work done per second would gradually increase. The distances travelled in successive seconds might be say 5 cm, 15 cm, 25 cm, 35 cm, and so on. In this case, the work done in successive seconds would be 12 J, 36 (i.e. 240×0.15) J, 60 (i.e. 240×0.25) J, 84 J, and so on. In other words, the rate of working would be increasing all the time, although the applied force remained constant. In practice, of course, the magnitude of my push would tend to diminish as the car gathered speed, and so my rate of working would eventually level off, the maximum value depending on my strength and general physical condition.

The technical term for rate of working is *power*, and the standard unit is the *watt* (W), defined as follows:

$$1 \text{ watt equals } 1 \text{ joule per second}$$

In our example, the average power developed during the first four 1 s intervals would therefore be 12 W, 36 W, 60 W, and 84 W.

The watt is named after James Watt (1736–1819), the inventor of the modern steam-engine and a pioneer in the science of energy. The unit was not devised or used until 1882, when it was defined with reference to electricity, as 'the power conveyed by a current of an Ampère through the difference of potential of a Volt'. The unit in common use at that time was the horse-power, equal to 746 W (which is in fact about $1\frac{1}{3}$ times the actual power of a horse). This unit is still used today in some applications.

The power being developed (by a force P) at any instant of time is defined to be the scalar product of the force **P** and the velocity **v** of the object on which the force is acting. If force and velocity are in the same direction, as is often the case, you simply multiply their magnitudes together to find the power.

EXAMPLE   A workman on a building site hauls up a load of 40 kg by means of a rope. If the load rises at a steady speed of $1\,\mathrm{m\,s}^{-1}$, find the power developed by the workman.

Since the load is not accelerating, the force exerted by the workman must equal the weight of the load (ignoring the possible effects of friction), i.e. $P = 40g$. And he must haul in his end of the rope at a speed of $1\,\mathrm{m\,s}^{-1}$, i.e. $v = 1$. Furthermore, P and v are obviously in the same direction.

So   the power developed $= Pv = 40g \times 1 = 392\,\mathrm{W}$

In section 18.3, we used the principle that during any interval of time the total work done by all the various forces acting on a mechanical system equals the increase in the total energy (K.E. + P.E.) of the system. It follows that the total power developed at any instant of time equals the rate of increase in total energy. Power and rate of change of energy are therefore usually measured in the same units, watts.

EXAMPLE   A man operates a tackle as shown in figure 18.10 to lift a load of 50 kg. He pulls with a steady force of 400 N, causing the load to rise at a steady speed of $0.6\,\mathrm{m\,s}^{-1}$. Find the power developed by the man and the rate at which the load is gaining in energy, and account for the discrepancy.

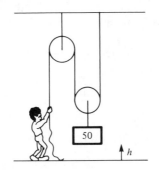

Fig. 18.10

Because of the design of the tackle, the part of the rope held by the man must be moving at twice the speed of the load itself, i.e. at $1.2\,\mathrm{m\,s^{-1}}$.

Therefore the power developed by the man $= 400 \times 1.2 = 480\,\mathrm{W}$.

Since the load is moving at a constant speed, its kinetic energy does not change. But the potential energy is increasing, since the load is gaining height. If we choose the ground as our fixed level, then the P.E. at any instant equals $50g \times h\,\mathrm{J}$, and its rate of increase equals $50g \times \mathrm{d}h/\mathrm{d}t$, i.e. $50g \times 0.6\,\mathrm{W}$.

So the load is gaining energy at a rate of $0 + 50g \times 0.6 = 294\,\mathrm{W}$.

You will see that the man is putting energy into the system at a faster rate (480 W) than the system appears to be gaining in energy (294 W). This is because energy is being wasted by the mechanism itself: some is lost because of friction, some because the pulleys and ropes all weigh something (even if not very much), some maybe for other reasons.

We say that the *efficiency* of a contrivance equals the effective power output divided by the total power input. In this particular case, the efficiency $= 294/480 = 61\%$ approximately.

The makers claim that a BMW 320i can accelerate from 0 to $100\,\mathrm{km\,h^{-1}}$ in $10\,\mathrm{s}$: this represents an average acceleration of approximately $2.8\,\mathrm{m\,s^{-2}}$. Since the mass of the car is about $1350\,\mathrm{kg}$ when fully laden, the tractive force required must be about $3750\,\mathrm{N}$ (provided we confine our attention to quite low speeds, when air resistance is not substantial). So if the car was travelling at $50\,\mathrm{km\,h^{-1}}$ (about $30\,\mathrm{m.p.h.}$), the power developed by the tractive force would be very roughly $52\,\mathrm{kW}$. Since the engine of this car is theoretically capable of generating $92\,\mathrm{kW}$, we see that quite a high proportion of the power developed is wasted.

EXAMPLE   A pump draws water from a tank $3\,\mathrm{m}$ below the level of a fountain, at a rate of $5\,\mathrm{kg\,s^{-1}}$, and squirts it out into the fountain at a speed $8\,\mathrm{m\,s^{-1}}$. What power is being developed by the pump?

Every second, $5\,\mathrm{kg}$ of water is being given a speed of $8\,\mathrm{m\,s^{-1}}$ and raised a distance of $3\,\mathrm{m}$. Therefore

$$\text{the increase in K.E.} = \tfrac{1}{2} \times 5 \times 8^2 = 160\,\mathrm{J}$$

and $\text{the increase in P.E.} = 5g \times 3 = 147\,\mathrm{J}$

The power developed is therefore $160 + 147 = 307\,\mathrm{W}$.

In practice, the pump will have to develop more power than $307\,\mathrm{W}$, since the efficiency of the system will be less than 100%.

EXAMPLE When a car of mass 1350 kg is going at 120 km h^{-1}, the effective power output of its engine is 52 kW and air resistance amounts to 1020 N. If the car is moving at this speed on a flat road, find its instantaneous acceleration. Also find the angle of slope of the steepest hill this car could manage at 120 km h^{-1}.

$$\text{tractive force} = (52\,\text{kW})/(120\,\text{km h}^{-1})$$

$$= (52\,\text{W})/(120\,\text{m h}^{-1})$$

$$= \frac{52}{120/3600}\,\text{N}$$

$$= 1560\,\text{N}$$

If a is the acceleration, then the equation of motion is

$$1560 - 1020 = 1350a \;\Rightarrow\; a = 0.4$$

Thus the car's instantaneous acceleration will be 0.4 m s^{-2}.

Note that this positive acceleration means that the speed will immediately increase. Therefore the air resistance will also increase, but the tractive force will decrease (unless the power output can be increased): so the acceleration will fall.

We now suppose that the car is driving up a hill whose angle of slope is α, and that it could not manage a steeper hill. The component of the car's weight acting down the hill will be $1350g \sin \alpha$, and of course the car's acceleration will be zero. Therefore the equation of motion is

$$1560 - 1020 - 1350g \sin \alpha = 0 \;\Rightarrow\; \sin \alpha = 0.4/g$$

Therefore the maximum angle is $\arcsin(0.4/g)$, i.e. about 2°.

EXERCISE 18D

1. A gymnast of mass 60 kg climbs a 6 m rope in 5 s. At what average rate must he be working?

2. A labourer picks up one brick (of mass 1.5 kg) from the ground every 3 s and lobs it into a skip, whose top edge is 2 m above ground level. At what average rate is he working?

3. A fire engine discharges water at a rate of 5000 litres per minute. What power must the engine develop if the speed of the water is 20 m s^{-1}?

4. If the effective power output of a car's engine is 52 kW, and air resistance equals $1.2v^2$ N when the car is travelling at v m s^{-1}, find its maximum speed on a flat road.

5. A hand crane is used to raise a load of 100 kg against gravity at a speed of 5 cm s^{-1}. The operator winds the crank at a speed of 3 m s^{-1}, exerting a force of 20 N. What is the efficiency of this crane?

6. If the theoretical 'horse' pulls a barge along a canal at a steady speed of 7.2 km h^{-1}, calculate the water resistance. Assuming that the resistance remains constant, find how fast an ordinary horse might be expected to pull this barge.

7. A car of mass 1000 kg has an engine capable of developing an effective power output of 45 kW when the car is travelling at 90 km h^{-1}. If the car is going at this speed up a hill whose angle of slope is $\arcsin(1/49)$, and if the non-gravitational resisting forces amount to 800 N, find the car's greatest possible acceleration.

19 ALGEBRA IV

19.1 FUNCTIONS

Throughout this book, we have made frequent mention of functions: but what precisely is a function?

Suppose that we have two sets (called X and Y, say), and also some rule (called f, say) linking the elements of X to the elements of Y. Then if every single element of X is linked to precisely one element of Y, we say that f is a *function* (or transformation or mapping) of X into Y. The first set is referred to as the *domain* of the function, the second set as its *co-domain*.

If x is a typical element of the domain of a function f, then its partner in the co-domain is technically known as its *image* under f: it is written $f(x)$ and is very often denoted by another letter (such as y).

Here are some examples of arithmetical functions. In each case, the domain is $\mathbb{R}$ (the set of real numbers), as is the co-domain.

$$y = x, \quad y = x^2, \quad y = x^3 + 4x - 7, \quad y = \sin x, \quad y = \ln x$$

The first of these is the identity function, the second and third (and first) are polynomials, the fourth and fifth are what are called *transcendental* functions.*

An x–y equation does not necessarily correspond to a function. For instance, if $x + y = 1$, then y is indeed a function of x, but if $x^2 + y^2 = 1$, then y is not a function of x.

Strictly speaking, every element in the domain of a function is meant to have an image. But for the sake of convenience, we can use a domain some of whose elements do not have an image. For instance, if $f(x) \equiv 1/x$ we might choose $\mathbb{R}$ as the domain, even though 0 has no image: we would then say that f was not defined at 0.

---

*Other examples of transcendental functions are $\cos x$ and e^x. The characteristic feature of a transcendental function is (roughly speaking) that the connection between x and its image y cannot be expressed by means of an equation involving only a finite sequence of the elementary arithmetical operations (adding, subtracting, multiplying, dividing, squaring and cubing and so on, square-rooting and so on). Thus even the most powerful calculator (or computer) could never find the value of $\cos 40°$ or $\ln 2$ precisely; the calculator contents itself with performing a finite number of elementary calculations, and displaying an answer that is wrong but near enough for most practical purposes.

Not all functions, of course, are arithmetical. In chapter 6, we considered linear transformations, such as rotations and reflections: these are geometrical functions. The domain is the x–y plane, often denoted by $\mathbb{R}^2$, since position in it is specified by two elements of $\mathbb{R}$.

Suppose that f and g are defined as follows:

$$f: x \to 2x + 1, \qquad g: x \to 3x - 2, \quad \text{where } x \in \mathbb{R}.$$

Then we may say that $fg(5) = f(13)$ since $g(5) = 13$

$$= 27$$

and more generally $fg(x) = f(3x - 2)$

$$= 2(3x - 2) + 1 = 6x - 3$$

Note that the value of $fg(x)$ is uniquely defined for all $x \in \mathbb{R}$ and so fg is a function with domain $\mathbb{R}$.

EXAMPLE The functions f and g are defined as $f: x \to 5x$ and $g: x \to x^2$ where $x \in \mathbb{R}$. Define fg and gf similarly.

We have $fg(x) = f(x^2) = 5x^2$ and $gf(x) = g(5x) = (5x)^2 = 25x^2$.

So the definitions are $fg: x \to 5x^2$ and $gf: x \to 25x^2$, where in each case $x \in \mathbb{R}$.

EXAMPLE Find the inverse of the function $f: x \to 2x + 3$.

We need to find a function g such that fg is the identity function, i.e. $fg(x) = x$.

So $2g(x) + 3 = x \Rightarrow 2g(x) = x - 3 \Rightarrow g(x) = (x - 3)/2$.

Therefore the inverse function g is defined as $g: x \to (x - 3)/2$.

Note incidentally that $gf(x) = g(2x + 3) = (2x + 3 - 3)/2 = x$, and so gf is also the identity function. Therefore each function is the inverse of the other, as is always the case, in fact.

EXAMPLE Find f^{-1} given that $f(x) = 5 - x$ (the inverse of a function f is usually denoted by f^{-1}).

We want $ff^{-1}(x)$ to equal x, so $5 - f^{-1}(x) = x \Rightarrow f^{-1}(x) = 5 - x$. You will notice that in this case f is self-inverse.

As you may remember, $\ln x$ and e^x are inverse functions. What is the connection between their graphs? The two graphs are sketched in figure 19.1 Do you see that one may be obtained from the other by reflection in the line $y = x$?

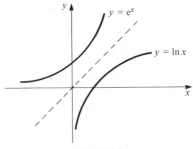

Fig. 19.1

You should sketch the graphs of $y = 2x+3$ and $y = (x-3)/2$, and also the graphs of $y = x^2$ (for positive x) and $y = \sqrt{x}$.

If we can find the inverse of the function f, then we should have no difficulty in solving an equation of the form $f(x) = a$ where a is some number. For instance, $\ln x = 4 \Rightarrow x = e^4 = 54.6$. Unfortunately, inverses are not always easy to find, and so we are sometimes driven to solving an equation by graphical means.

To solve an equation graphically, you should if possible rearrange it in the form $f(x) = ax+b$, where f is a function whose graph will be fairly easy to draw accurately.

You then draw the graph of $y = f(x)$ and the graph of $y = ax+b$, and read off the x-values at the points where the graphs cross.

EXAMPLE Solve the equation $x \sec x = 1$, where x is measured in radians.

Although $x \sec x = 1$ is in the form $f(x) = ax+b$, it is better to rearrange it as $\cos x = x$, since $y = \cos x$ is much easier to draw than $y = x \sec x$. Figure 19.2 shows a rough sketch of $y = \cos x$ and $y = x$, which makes it plain that there is only one solution to the equation, lying somewhere between $x = 0.5$ and $x = 1$. To solve the equation more precisely, you should draw the two graphs as accurately as you can for values of x between 0.5 and 1. Your answer should be about 0.74.

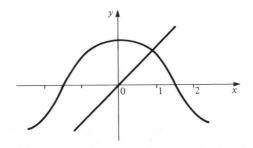

Fig. 19.2

EXERCISE 19A

1. Do the following equations give y as a function of x?

   $2x + 3y = 1$, $xy = 1$, $x = y^2$, $x = \sin y$

2. If $f(x) = 4x$, $g(x) = 1 + x^2$, $h(x) = 1/x$, find $fg(x)$, $gf(x)$, $gh(x)$, $hg(x)$, $hf(x)$, $fh(x)$, and give suitable domains for all nine functions.

3. Find the inverses of the following functions:

   $x \to 3x - 5$, $x \to 1/x$ $(x \neq 0)$, $x \to x/(1-x)$ $(x \neq 1)$,

   and give the domains of the three inverse functions.

4. The *range* of a function f is the set of all its images (for instance, $+1$ belongs to the range of $x \to e^x$ since $0 \to +1$, but -1 does not). Explain why the domain and range of f become the range and domain of f^{-1} respectively.

5. Explain how (if at all) the domain of each of the following functions needs to be restricted if a proper inverse function is to exist:

   $x \to x^2$, $x \to \sin x$, $x \to \cos x$, $x \to 2^x$.

6. Solve the following equations graphically:

   $\ln x = 3 - x$, $x e^x = 1$, $x^4 = 10x + 1$, $\cos x = \tan x$.

19.2 RATIONAL FUNCTIONS

A rational function equals one polynomial divided by another: for instance, $(x+1)/(x-1)$ is a rational function.

If we have to sketch the graph of such a function, $y = f(x)$, there are a number of questions that are almost always worth asking, except in the simplest cases.

(1) Are there any rogue x-values for which y is undefined?

(2) How does y behave near the rogue x-values, if any? For instance, if $y = 1/x$, then y behaves very badly near $x = 0$, shooting off to infinity.

(3) How does y behave as x becomes very large (positive or negative)?

(4) Where does the graph cut the axes?

(5) How many points are there on the graph at each y-level? And are there any exceptions?

EXAMPLE Sketch the graph of $y = \dfrac{x+1}{x-1}$.

We will answer the five questions, one by one.

(1) There is a rogue value, $x = 1$. If you try substituting 1 for x, you get $y = 2/0$, which means nothing.

(2) If x is very slightly greater than 1, then $(x-1)$ is very small and positive, and so y is very large and positive. Similarly, if x is just less than 1, y is very large and negative.

(3) If x becomes very large, whether positive or negative, then $(x+1)$ and $(x-1)$ both become very large numbers, close together, and so y becomes very nearly equal to 1.

(4) When $x = 0$, $y = -1$, and when $y = 0$, $x = -1$.

(5) $y = (x+1)/(x-1) \Rightarrow y(x-1) = (x+1)$. Now if $y = 1$, this equation reduces to $x-1 = x+1$, which obviously has no solutions. But if y is given any other value, the equation has precisely one solution for x. Therefore there is one point on the graph at every y-level except $y = 1$, where there are no points.

Now that we have the answers to questions 1 to 5, the graph is quite easy to sketch, as in figure 19.3

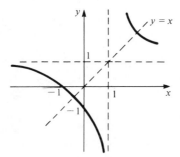

Fig. 19.3

The two lines $x = 1$ and $y = 1$ are specially related to the graph. We may think of them as tangents to the graph 'at infinity': such lines are called *asymptotes*.

Once a graph has been sketched, or drawn accurately, it can be used to solve equations or inequalities.

EXAMPLE Solve $\dfrac{x+1}{x-1} = x$ and $\dfrac{x+1}{x-1} > 0$.

To solve the equation, we simply superimpose the graph of $y = x$ on the graph that we have already drawn: this has been done in figure 19.3. We need the values of x at the points where the straight line and curve intersect. Reading from the graph, we find that $x = -0.4$ or $+2.4$.

The inequality can also be solved by inspecting the graph. We find that $x < -1$ or $x > +1$.

EXAMPLE Sketch the graph of $y = \dfrac{x^2-1}{x^2+1}$.

y is defined for all values of x, since x^2+1 never equals 0.

If x becomes very large, then as in the previous example y becomes very nearly equal to 1.

When $x = 0$, $y = -1$, and when $y = 0$, $x = -1$ or $+1$.

Finally, $y = (x^2-1)/(x^2+1) \Rightarrow y(x^2+1) = x^2-1$. If $y = +1$, this equation reduces to $x^2+1 = x^2-1$, which obviously has no solutions. If y is given any other value, however, we get a quadratic equation in x, which must have either two real roots or none. So there are either two points or no points on the graph at every y-level. (Is this true even in the special case $y = -1$?)

The graph is sketched in figure 19.4. As you see, there is only one asymptote, the line $y = +1$, and $x = 0$ is an axis of symmetry.

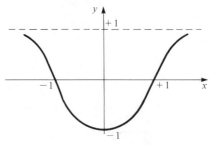

Fig. 19.4

EXERCISE 19B

Draw the graphs of $y = f(x)$, marking in any asymptotes. Also solve the equations and inequalities as indicated in each case.

1. $y = (2x+3)/x$;   solve $(2x+3)/x = x$, $(2x+3)/x < 0$.

2. $y = x^2/(x-1)$;   solve $x^2/(x-1) = 5$, $x^2/(x-1) > 0$.

3. $y = x/(x^2-1)$;   solve $x/(x^2-1) = 2x$, $x/(x^2-1) < 0$.

4. $y = 2/(x^2+1)$;   solve $2/(x^2+1) = 1$, $2/(x^2+1) > x$.

5. $y = x^3/(x^2+1)$;   solve $x^3/(x^2+1) = 2$, $x^3/(x^2+1) < x$.

19.3 STRAIGHT LINE GRAPHS

The simplest graphs of all are straight lines. These correspond to equations of the form $y = mx+c$. The quantity m equals the gradient of the line, found as shown in figure 19.5, and c is the intercept made by the line on the y-axis.

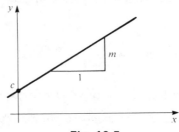

Fig. 19.5

Unfortunately, many quantities in science are connected by non-linear relationships, which means that the graph is a curve rather than a straight line. If the equation is of the form $y = af(x) + b$, however, where a and b are constants, then we can quite easily convert the graph into a straight line, by means of a simple trick.

For instance, suppose that the x–y equation is $y = 3x^2 + 5$. Then instead of plotting y against x, which would of course produce a curve, we set $Y = y$ and $X = x^2$, and plot Y against X. Since the X–Y equation is $Y = 3X + 5$, we get a straight line, with a gradient of 3 and intercept of 5. This will probably be much more useful and convenient than the curve.

EXAMPLE The quantities v and t, some values of which are shown in the table, are known to be related by an equation of the form $v = a/t + b$, where a and b are constants.

t	1	2	3	4	5
v	64	34	24	19	16

By drawing a suitable graph, find a and b.

We set $V = v$ and $T = 1/t$, and construct a new table:

T	1.00	0.50	0.33	0.25	0.20
V	64	34	24	19	16

The graph of V against T is shown in figure 19.6. Since $V = aT + b$, we can find a and b by reading off the gradient and intercept. We see that

$$a = 48/0.8 = 60, \quad \text{and} \quad b = 4$$

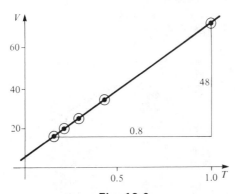

Fig. 19.6

In this example, the points that have been plotted really do lie on a straight line. But more often the values of the quantities have been obtained by experiment, and are therefore subject to experimental errors of one sort or another. Therefore when we plot the points, they will probably not lie on an exact straight line. In this case, we have to draw the straight line that seems to fit the plotted points as closely as possible, and we use this line in any subsequent calculations.

EXAMPLE The quantities x and y, some approximate values of which are shown in the table, are known to be related by an equation of the form $y = cx^n$, where c and n are unknown constants.

x	10	15	20	25	30
y	1.99	1.60	1.36	1.26	1.18

By drawing a suitable graph, estimate c and n.

The trick this time is slightly different. First of all, we modify the equation $y = cx^n$ by taking the logarithms of both sides, as we did in section 8.6. We obtain

$$\log y = \log(cx^n) = n\log x + \log c$$

If we now set $Y = \log y$, $X = \log x$, and $C = \log c$, the equation $y = cx^n$ becomes $Y = nX + C$, which will give a straight line graph.

The values of X and Y are shown in the following table:

X	1.00	1.18	1.30	1.40	1.48
Y	0.30	0.20	0.13	0.10	0.07

The points are shown plotted in the figure, and a straight line has been drawn to fit them as closely as possible.

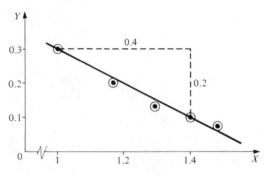

Fig. 19.7

The equation of this line is of course $Y = nX + C$.

So the gradient $= n = -0.2/0.4 = -0.5$.

Now the point given by $X = 1.00$, $Y = 0.30$ lies on the line; so substituting these values into the equation, we find that $\log c = C = 0.80$, and so $c \approx 6.3$.

EXERCISE 19C

In each case, the quantities shown in the table are known to be related by an equation of the form indicated. Draw a suitable graph to estimate the unknown constants (a, b, c, or n) as accurately as the figures allow.

1. $y = ax^3 + b$

x	4	5	6	7	8
y	101	223	405	659	997

2. $y = a\sqrt{x} + b$

x	1.0	1.5	2.0	2.5	3.0
y	5.5	6.4	7.2	7.8	8.4

3. $y = a\,\mathrm{e}^x + b$

y	0.1	0.2	0.3	0.4	0.5
x	3.65	3.41	2.92	2.36	2.20

4. $y = cx^n$

x	2	3	4	5	6
y	1.4	2.2	3.2	4.1	5.2

19.4 GRAPHS OF INEQUALITIES

If an inequality involves only one variable, x say, then its solution set can be represented by a set of points on a single axis. For instance, the solution set of the inequality $x^2 < 9$ is the set $P = \{x: -3 < x < +3\}$, and the graph is very simple: it is just the segment of the x-axis running from -3 to $+3$. One-dimensional inequalities like this have made occasional appearances in the pages of this book: quadratic inequalities were discussed in section 1.9, for instance.

In this section, however, we are concerned with inequalities that involve two variables, x and y say. The graph is now a set of points in the x–y plane, i.e. in $\mathbb{R}^2$.

EXAMPLE Sketch the sets $Q = \{(x, y) : x + y < 5\}$

and $R = \{(x, y) : x^2 + y^2 > 25\}$

and indicate the set $Q \cap R$ on the diagram.

The set Q contains all the points on the lower side of the straight line $x + y = 5$. The set R contains all the points outside the circle $x^2 + y^2 = 25$, i.e. the circle with centre $(0, 0)$ and radius 5.

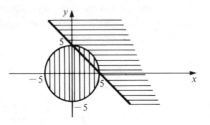

Fig. 19.8

Look at figure 19.8. Note carefully how the shading has been done. You will see that Q' and R', the complements of Q and R, have been shaded distinctively, rather than Q and R themselves. This is usually the best and clearest method.

$Q \cap R$ is the region that is left unshaded: it is a half-plane with an almost complete circular bite taken out of it.

EXAMPLE Draw the sets $P = \{(x, y) : x \geqslant 0 \text{ and } y \geqslant 0\}$

$Q = \{(x, y) : x + 3y \leqslant 31\}$

$R = \{(x, y) : 4x + y \leqslant 44\}$

and locate the position in $P \cap Q \cap R$ where x and y are whole numbers and $s = x + y$ takes its greatest value.

Set P contains all points in the first quadrant, while Q and R contain all points on or below the lines $x + 3y = 31$ and $4x + y = 44$.

The unshaded quadrilateral in figure 19.9 (including its four boundaries) represents the set $P \cap Q \cap R$.

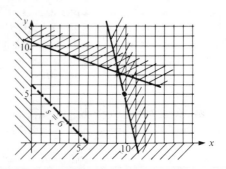

Fig. 19.9

How do we set about finding the point (x, y) where s takes its greatest value? If we were unrestricted in our choice of point, then obviously we could make s as large as we liked. But in fact we are restricted to points inside the quadrilateral whose coordinates are whole numbers: these are the only permitted positions. The broken line marks those where $s = 6$. Clearly the line $s = 7$ would be parallel to $s = 6$ and a little further away from the origin; $s = 8$ would be further away still; and so on. To find the point where s is maximised, we simply translate the broken line further and further away from the origin until we reach the last and therefore best permitted position (the easiest way to do this in practice is to use a set-square and ruler). In this case, the answer turns out to be just inside the north-east corner of the quadrilateral at $(9, 7)$: it is marked with a dot in the figure. So 16 is the greatest possible value of s.

EXERCISE 19D

1. In four separate small diagrams, indicate the following sets
   (a) $P \cap Q$, (b) $P' \cap Q$, (c) $P \cap Q'$, (d) $P' \cap Q$,
   where $P = \{(x, y): y > x\}$ and $Q = \{(x, y): x + y > 0\}$.

2. Sketch the sets $\quad P = \{(x, y): y > x^2\}$
   $$\text{and} \quad Q = \{(x, y): y < 6 - x\}$$
   and calculate the area of $P \cap Q$.

3. Draw the set $S = \{(x, y): xy \geqslant 10\}$, and determine the least possible value of $x^2 + y^2$ at points within this set.

4. A, B, C are fixed points in a plane. P is a variable point in this plane. The sets α, β, γ are defined as follows: $\alpha = \{P: PB < PC\}$, $\beta = \{P: PC < PA\}$, $\gamma = \{P: PA < PB\}$. Draw a figure showing the three sets as clearly as possible, and describe the set $\alpha \cap \beta \cap \gamma$.

5. A group of 5 brothers can all play the trumpet and drum, but of course no boy can play both simultaneously. Every boy playing a trumpet gives the group 2 units of joy, whereas a drum gives only 1: they aim to get at least 6 units of joy in all. If x is the number of trumpets in action, and y the number of drums, write down two inequalities satisfied by x and y, apart from $x \geqslant 0$ and $y \geqslant 0$, and draw a graph illustrating the situation.
   Their playing gives the neighbours $2x^2 + y^2$ units of pain: for example, if 3 boys play the trumpet and 1 the drum (which is a possibility), the neighbours suffer 19 units of pain. By considering all the possibilities, find out how many of the brothers should play a trumpet, and how many a drum, assuming (a) they like the neighbours, (b) they don't.

6. In an examination paper lasting 2 hours, there are questions of two sorts: hard (each takes 5 minutes and is worth 5 marks) and easy (each takes 1 minute and is worth 3 marks). A girl always gets right any questions she attempts; so she naturally hopes to win the prize, but you need at least 150 marks to have any chance of that, and moreover you must do more hard questions than easy ones in order to qualify. If she does x hard questions and

y easy ones, then obviously $x, y \geqslant 0$: write down three other inequalities that x and y must satisfy, and draw their graphs, using a large enough scale to make everything clear. How many hard and how many easy questions should the girl plan to do?

19.5 ARITHMETIC AND GEOMETRIC PROGRESSIONS

Consider this sequence of numbers: 3, 5, 7, 9, 11, 13, ...

The first term equals 3. Thereafter, each term is obtained by adding on 2, so that the difference between successive terms is always 2. Such a sequence is called an *arithmetic progression* (A.P.).

The first term is often denoted by the letter a, and the common difference by the letter d. Thus in our example, $a = 3$, $d = 2$.

What is the 100th term in this progression?

To reach the 100th term, we start with 3 and then add on 2 again and again, 99 times in all: so the 100th term $= 3 + 99 \times 2 = 201$.

More generally, we can say that $T_n = a + (n-1)d$.

What then is the sum of the first 100 terms of this progression?

We have $S_{100} = 3 + 5 + 7 + \ldots + 199 + 201$

Now it is evident that
$$3 + 201 = 204 = 102 + 102$$
$$\text{and} \quad 5 + 199 = 204 = 102 + 102$$
$$\text{and} \quad 7 + 197 = 204 = 102 + 102 \quad \text{and so on.}$$

Therefore each of the terms in S_{100} may be replaced by 102 without altering the total, i.e. $S_{100} = 100 \times 102 = 10\,200$.

In general $\qquad S_n = \dfrac{n}{2} \times (a+l) \qquad\qquad$ where l is the last term

$$= \frac{n}{2} \times [2a + (n-1)d] \qquad \text{since } l = a + (n-1)d$$

EXAMPLE The 3rd and 7th terms of an A.P. are 10 and 22. Find the 20th term and the sum of the first 20 terms. Also find out how many terms must be taken to sum to 175.

We have $T_3 = 10$ and $T_7 = 22$: but $T_7 - T_3 = 4d$, and so $d = 3$.

So $a = T_1 = T_3 - 2d = 10 - 6 = 4$.

Therefore $\qquad\qquad T_{20} = a + 19d = 4 + 57 = 61$

and $\qquad\qquad S_{20} = \dfrac{n}{2} \times (a+l) = 10 \times (4+61) = 650$

Suppose that $S_n = 175$: then $\dfrac{n}{2} \times [2a + (n-1)d] = 175$

i.e.
$$n \times (8 + 3n - 3) = 350$$
$$3n^2 + 5n - 350 = 0$$
$$(n - 10)(3n + 35) = 0$$

So we see that 175 is the sum of the first 10 terms of the A.P.

Now consider this new sequence: 3, 15, 75, 375, 1875, …

The first term equals 3. Thereafter, each term is obtained by multiplying by 5, so that the ratio of successive terms is always 5. Such a sequence is called a *geometric progression* (G.P.).

The first term is often denoted by a (as with the A.P.) and the common ratio by r. Thus in our example, $a = 3$, $r = 5$.

What is the 20th term in this progression?

To reach the 20th term, we start with 3 and then multiply by 5 again and again, 19 times in all: so the 20th term $= 3 \times 5^{19}$.

More generally, we can say that $T_n = a \times r^{n-1}$.

And what is the sum of the first 20 terms of this progression?

We have $S_{20} = 3 + 15 + 75 + \ldots + T_{19} + T_{20}$.

Now it is evident that $\quad 4T_{20} = 5T_{20} - T_{20} = T_{21} - T_{20}$

$$\text{and} \quad 4T_{19} = 5T_{19} - T_{19} = T_{20} - T_{19}$$

$$\vdots$$

$$\text{and} \quad 4T_1 = 5T_1 - T_1 = T_2 - T_1$$

So adding up, we have

$$4S_{20} = (T_{21} - T_{20}) + (T_{20} - T_{19}) + \ldots + (T_3 - T_2) + (T_2 - T_1)$$

i.e. $\qquad 4S_{20} = T_{21} - T_1$

and so $\qquad S_{20} = \dfrac{T_{21} - T_1}{4}$.

In general, $S_n = \dfrac{T_{n+1} - T_1}{r - 1} = \dfrac{a(r^n - 1)}{r - 1}$ since $T_{n+1} = ar^n$.

EXAMPLE   The 1st and 4th terms of a G.P. are 4 and 108. Find the common ratio, and the sum of the first 8 terms. Also find how many terms must be taken before the sum exceeds one million.

We have $T_1 = 4$ and $T_4 = 108$: but $T_4 \div T_1 = r^3$, and so $r = 3$.

Therefore
$$S_8 = \frac{a(r^n - 1)}{r - 1} = \frac{4(3^8 - 1)}{3 - 1} = 13\,120$$

Suppose that $S_n = 10^6$: then $2(3^n - 1) = 10^6$

i.e. $3^n = 500\,001$

$$n = \log 500\,001 / \log 3 \approx 11.9$$

So the sum of the first 12 terms will exceed one million.

In both examples of geometrical progressions that we have so far considered, the terms have all been positive, and have become greater and greater: this is because $r > 1$. If $r < 0$, then the terms will alternate in sign; while if $-1 < r < +1$, then they will become closer and closer to zero.

EXAMPLE Find the 100th term of the G.P. with $a = 8$ and $r = 0.6$, and also find the sum of the first 99 terms.

To find S_{99}, we use a slightly modified version of the formula for S_n, which is rather more convenient than the original version when $r < +1$, and is obviously equivalent.

We have $T_{100} = ar^{n-1} = 8 \times 0.6^{99} \approx 8.71 \times 10^{-22}$

and $S_{99} = \dfrac{a(1 - r^n)}{1 - r} = \dfrac{8(1 - 0.6^{99})}{1 - 0.6} \approx \dfrac{8}{1 - 0.6} = 20$

We have given 20 as the value of S_{99}. In fact, however, the true value must be a tiny amount less than 20, but the difference is far too small to register on a calculator. It should be clear that if we had been finding the sum of an even larger number of terms, the answer would have been even closer to 20. We say therefore that the *sum to infinity* of this progression equals 20.

In general, $S_\infty = \dfrac{a}{1 - r}$ (provided $-1 < r < +1$).

EXERCISE 19E

1. State whether each of the following might be part of an A.P. or a G.P., and if so, give d or r and the next two terms:

(a) 6, 12, 18, 24, ...   (b) 6, 12, 24, 48, ...

(c) $+6, -12, +18, -24, ...$ (d) $+6, -12, +24, -48, ...$

(e) 6, 3, 1.5, ...   (f) 6, 3, 0, ...

2. Show that T_{18} is the first negative term in the A.P. 50, 47, 44, etc., and find how many terms must be taken for the sum to be just negative.

3. Find the sum of all the whole numbers between 1 and 1000 that are exactly divisible by 7, and also the sum of just the odd numbers in this category.

4. Explain how 20 and 80 might be the 3rd and 5th terms of either of two different G.P.s. Find the sum of the first 10 terms in each case.

5. I invest £1000 in a building society on 1 January 1984, and plan to do the same in succeeding years. If the society pays compound interest at 8% per annum, which they add to my account every 31 December, find the total amount invested on 2 January 2000.

6. Find the sum to infinity of the following G.P.s:
   (a) 4, 2, 1, …   (b) 4, −2, 1, …

19.6 MATHEMATICAL INDUCTION

Look at the following series: 16, 88, 736, …

You will probably not be able to spot how it is constructed.

The rule in fact is that $T_n = 9^n + 7$: thus $T_1 = 9 + 7$, $T_2 = 81 + 7$, $T_3 = 729 + 7$, and so on.

But you may notice that the terms given are all divisible by 8, and the suspicion may form in your mind that conceivably 8 goes into all the terms in this sequence, without exception.

How can we set about proving the correctness of this suspicion?

To do so, we really need to establish the truth of every single one of the following infinite sequence of propositions:

p_1 the proposition that 8 goes into T_1

p_2 the proposition that 8 goes into T_2

and so on, *ad infinitum.*

Well, p_1 says that 8 goes into T_1, which is obviously true. In the same way, we could establish that p_2 was true, that p_3 was true, and so on and so on. But we cannot possibly establish the truth of an *infinite* number of propositions one by one like this. Instead, we use the method of *mathematical induction.*

We establish   (a) that p_1 is true, and then   (b) that (for every n) $p_n \Rightarrow p_{n+1}$.

We can then safely conclude that all the propositions are true.

(a) We have already established that p_1 is true.

(b) Now   8 goes into $9^n + 7$

$\Rightarrow$ 8 goes into $9^{n+1} + 63$ (multiplying by 9)

$\Rightarrow$ 8 goes into $9^{n+1} + 7$ (subtracting 56)

   i.e. $p_n \Rightarrow p_{n+1}$

Hence we are entitled to conclude, by mathematical induction, that all the propositions are true.

EXAMPLE Prove (by mathematical induction) that the sum of the first n odd numbers is n^2.

We have to prove the following sequence of propositions:

p_1 the proposition that $1 = 1^2$

p_2 the proposition that $1+3 = 2^2$

p_3 the proposition that $1+3+5 = 3^2$

and so on.

(a) The proposition p_1 is obviously true.

(b) We begin by noting that the nth odd number is $(2n-1)$.

Now $1+3+5+\ldots+(2n-1) = n^2$

$$\Rightarrow 1+3+5+\ldots+(2n-1)+(2n+1) = n^2+(2n+1)$$
$$= (n+1)^2$$

i.e. $p_n \Rightarrow p_{n+1}$

Hence we may conclude that all the propositions are true.

EXAMPLE Prove that $1^2+2^2+3^3+\ldots+n^2 = n(n+1)(2n+1)/6$.

We have to prove the following sequence of propositions:

p_1 the proposition that $1^2 = (1 \times 2 \times 3)/6$

p_2 the proposition that $1^2+2^2 = (2 \times 3 \times 5)/6$

p_3 the proposition that $1^2+2^2+3^2 = (3 \times 4 \times 7)/6$

and so on.

(a) p_1 is plainly true.

(b) Now $1^2+2^2+\ldots+n^2 = n(n+1)(2n+1)/6$

$$\Rightarrow 1^2+2^2+\ldots+n^2+(n+1)^2 = n(n+1)(2n+1)/6+(n+1)^2$$
$$= (n+1)[n(2n+1)/6+(n+1)]$$
$$= (n+1)(2n^2+7n+6)/6$$
$$= (n+1)(n+2)(2n+3)/6$$

i.e. $p_n \Rightarrow p_{n+1}$

Hence we may conclude that all the propositions are true.

EXERCISE 19F

Prove the following by induction, n being any positive integer.

1. That $n^3 + 5n$ is divisible by 6.

2. That $1 \times 2 + 2 \times 3 + \ldots + n(n+1) = n(n+1)(n+2)/3$.

3. That $1^3 + 2^3 + 3^3 + \ldots + n^3 = \frac{1}{4}n^2(n+1)^2$.

4. That the derivative of x^n is nx^{n-1} (use the product rule).

5. That $f_1 + f_2 + f_3 + \ldots + f_n = f_{n+2} - 1$, where f_1, f_2, f_3, etc., are the Fibonacci numbers (0, 1, 1, 2, 3, 5, 8, etc.).

6. That $\sum_{r=0}^{n} 2^r = 2^{n+1} - 1$ (the left-hand side means $2^0 + 2^1 + \ldots + 2^n$).

19.7 COMPLEX NUMBERS

Gerolamo Cardano (1501–76), an Italian mathematician of the greatest distinction, pointed out that the square root of -1 is not $+1$ or -1, but is 'of hidden nature'. So even a simple quadratic equation like $x^2 + 1 = 0$ has no solutions in the system of ordinary real numbers. To overcome this snag, mathematicians from that time onwards have enriched the number system by adding to it what they call imaginary numbers. These totally new objects include the number i whose key property is that $i^2 = -1$ (this number is in fact often denoted by the letter j), together with multiples of i such as 3i or $-i$. Real numbers and imaginary numbers combined form the system of *complex numbers*.

Thus $3 + 4i$ is a complex number: we refer to 3 as its *real part*, and 4i as its *imaginary part*.

Arithmetic in the complex number system is exactly as in ordinary arithmetic, with the one extra rule that $\underline{i^2 = -1}$.

EXAMPLE Find the sum and product of $(8 + 3i)$ and $(3 + 4i)$.

$$(8 + 3i) + (3 + 4i) = 11 + 7i$$
$$(8 + 3i) \times (3 + 4i) = 24 + 32i + 9i + 12i^2$$
$$= 24 + 32i + 9i - 12$$
$$= 12 + 41i$$

Subtraction is just as simple, but division calls for rather more subtlety, as the following example demonstrates.

EXAMPLE Calculate $(8+3i)$ divided by $(3+4i)$.

We have

$$\frac{8+3i}{3+4i} = \frac{(8+3i)(3-4i)}{(3+4i)(3-4i)}$$

$$= \frac{24-32i+9i-12i^2}{9-12i+12i-16i^2}$$

$$= \frac{36-23i}{25} = 1.44-0.92i$$

The crucial step in this calculation comes at the very start, when we multiply the top and bottom of the fraction by $(3-4i)$. The two complex numbers $(3+4i)$ and $(3-4i)$ are termed *conjugates* of each other: multiplying them together results in a real number, which is the secret of success in our calculation.

EXAMPLE Solve the equation $z^2-4z+5 = 0$.

Since the discriminant of the quadratic expression z^2-4z+5 is negative ($b^2-4ac = 16-20 = -4$), this equation has no real roots. Nevertheless, we proceed to 'solve' it in the normal manner. Using the formula, we obtain

$$z^2-4z+5 = 0 \Rightarrow z = \frac{+4\pm\sqrt{(16-20)}}{2}$$

$$= \frac{4\pm\sqrt{(-4)}}{2} = \frac{4\pm2i}{2} = 2\pm i$$

So the two complex roots of the equation are $(2+i)$ and $(2-i)$. Note that these are conjugates of each other (which in fact is always the case if the equation itself has real coefficients).

We represent real numbers by means of points on a number *line*. Complex numbers can be represented by points on a number *plane*. For example, the number $2+i$ is represented by the point $(2,1)$, the number $2-i$ by the point $(2,-1)$, and so on (figure 19.10).

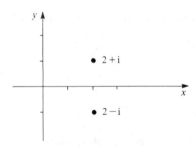

Fig. 19.10

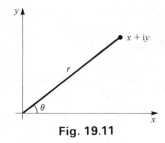

Fig. 19.11

In general, the point (x, y) (where of course x and y are just ordinary real numbers) represents the complex number $z = x + iy$ (figure 19.11).

If the polar coordinates of the point are (r, θ), then $x = r \cos \theta$ and $y = r \sin \theta$. So $z = r(\cos \theta + i \sin \theta)$.

The expression $\cos \theta + i \sin \theta$ crops up so frequently that it is normally abbreviated as cis θ. Thus $z = r \operatorname{cis} \theta$.

The distance r is called the *modulus* of z, and usually written $|z|$.

The angle θ is called the *argument* of z, and is written $\arg(z)$.

EXAMPLE Find the modulus and argument of the following complex numbers:

(a) i, (b) -1, (c) $3 + 4i$.

In any question like this, it is essential to draw a diagram, usually known (after its inventor) as an Argand diagram.

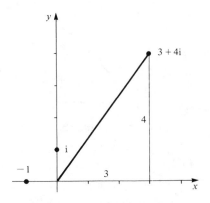

Fig. 19.12

(a) We see clearly from figure 19.12 that the modulus of i equals 1 and the argument equals $\pi/2$ (radians). So $i = 1 \operatorname{cis}(\pi/2)$.

(b) Similarly, we see that $|-1|$ equals 1 and $\arg(-1)$ equals π. So $-1 = 1 \operatorname{cis}(\pi)$.

(c) We see that $|3 + 4i| = 5$, and $\arg(3 + 4i) = \arctan(4/3)$.

The modulus–argument form of a complex number provides us with a particularly easy way of multiplying and dividing. This is due to the important fact that $\operatorname{cis}\theta \times \operatorname{cis}\phi = \operatorname{cis}(\theta+\phi)$. To prove it

$$\operatorname{cis}\theta \times \operatorname{cis}\phi = (\cos\theta+i\sin\theta) \times (\cos\phi+i\sin\phi)$$

$$= \cos\theta\cos\phi+i\cos\theta\sin\phi+i\sin\theta\cos\phi-\sin\theta\sin\phi$$

$$= (\cos\theta\cos\phi-\sin\theta\sin\phi)+i(\sin\theta\cos\phi+\cos\theta\sin\phi)$$

$$= \cos(\theta+\phi)+i\sin(\theta+\phi) = \operatorname{cis}(\theta+\phi)$$

It follows that

$$\operatorname{cis}(\theta-\phi) \times \operatorname{cis}\phi = \operatorname{cis}(\theta-\phi+\phi) = \operatorname{cis}\theta$$

i.e. that $\operatorname{cis}\theta \div \operatorname{cis}\phi = \operatorname{cis}(\theta-\phi)$.

So we have the following two rules of thumb:

to *multiply* complex numbers, multiply moduli and *add* arguments

to *divide* complex numbers, divide moduli and *subtract* arguments

EXAMPLE Calculate (a) $(1+i)^7$, (b) $(i+i)^7 \div (1-i)^3$.

To perform these calculations efficiently, we need $(1+i)$ and $(1-i)$ in modulus–argument form. Figure 19.13 shows that $|1+i|$ equals $\sqrt{2}$ and that $\arg(1+i)$ equals $\pi/4$. Similarly, $|1-i|$ equals $\sqrt{2}$ and $\arg(1-i)$ equals $-\pi/4$.

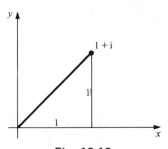

Fig. 19.13

(a) $(1+i)^7 = (1+i) \times (1+i) \times \ldots \times (1+i)$

$$= \sqrt{2}\operatorname{cis}(\pi/4) \times \sqrt{2}\operatorname{cis}(\pi/4) \times \ldots \times \sqrt{2}\operatorname{cis}(\pi/4)$$

$$= (\sqrt{2})^7 \times \operatorname{cis}(\pi/4+\pi/4+\ldots+\pi/4)$$

$$= 8\sqrt{2}\operatorname{cis}(7\pi/4)$$

$$= 8\sqrt{2}(\cos 7\pi/4+i\sin 7\pi/4)$$

$$= 8\sqrt{2}\left(\frac{1}{\sqrt{2}} - \frac{i}{\sqrt{2}}\right) = 8-8i$$

(b) $(1+i)^7 \div (1-i)^3 = [8\sqrt{2}\,\text{cis}\,(7\pi/4)] \div [2\sqrt{2}\,\text{cis}\,(-3\pi/4)]$

$$= 4\,\text{cis}\,(7\pi/4 + 3\pi/4)$$
$$= 4\,\text{cis}\,(10\pi/4)$$
$$= 4(\cos 10\pi/4 + i \sin 10\pi/4)$$
$$= 4(0 + i)$$
$$= 4i$$

This example demonstrates the truth of *De Moivre's theorem*, which states that $(\text{cis}\,\theta)^n = \text{cis}(n\theta)$, where n is any positive integer.

EXAMPLE Show that $\text{cis}\,(\pi/3)$ and $\text{cis}\,(5\pi/3)$ are both cube roots of -1.

If $z = \text{cis}\,(\pi/3)$,   then $z^3 = \text{cis}\,(3\pi/3)$ by De Moivre's theorem
$$= \text{cis}\,(\pi) = -1$$

so $\text{cis}\,(\pi/3)$ definitely is a cube root of -1.

We proceed in precisely the same way to demonstrate that $\text{cis}\,(5\pi/3)$ is also a cube root of -1. Since we knew all along that -1 was a cube root of -1, we see that in fact -1 has three cube roots, which are shown in figure 19.14. This is quite general: any complex number (other than 0) has two square roots, three cube roots, and so on.

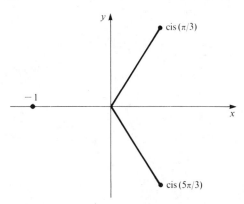

Fig. 19.14

EXAMPLE Find the square roots of -1.

Suppose that $z = r\,\text{cis}\,\theta$ is a square root of -1.

Then $r^2\,\text{cis}\,(2\theta) = -1 = 1\,\text{cis}\,(\pi)$. So one obvious possibility is that $r = 1$ and $\theta = \pi/2$, i.e. one square root of -1 is $1\,\text{cis}\,(\pi/2) = i$.

What about the other square root? Well, -1 also equals $1\,\text{cis}\,(3\pi)$. So another possibility is that $r = 1$ and $\theta = 3\pi/2$: i.e. the second square root of -1 is $1\,\text{cis}\,(3\pi/2) = -i$. This, of course, is what we expected.

EXERCISE 19G

1. Find $(2-5i)+(4+6i)$, $(3+i)+(-2+i)$, $i+(4-i)$.

2. Find $(3+7i)-(2-9i)$, $(5-2i)-3$, $6-(1+2i)$.

3. Find $i\times(3+4i)$, $(2+3i)\times(4-i)$, $(1+i)\times(1-i)$.

4. Write down the conjugates of $(2+i)$, $(4-3i)$, $5i$, 4.

5. Find $(4-2i)\div(2+i)$, $3\div(4-3i)$, $(1-5i)\div5i$, $(2+3i)\div4$.

6. Solve the following equations:
    (a) $z^2+6z+10 = 0$
    (b) $z^2-2z+5 = 0$
    (c) $z^2-4z+13 = 0$

7. Represent the following complex numbers in modulus–argument from, and illustrate in an Argand diagram:
    (a) $+1-i$
    (b) $-1+i$
    (c) $-1-i$

8. Find z^2, z^3, z^4, etc.,   (a) if $z = i$, and   (b) if $z = 1+i$.

9. Find the square and cube roots of the complex number $+1$, and illustrate in an Argand diagram.

20 MECHANICS VI

20.1 EXTENDED BODIES

In the earlier chapters on mechanics in this book, we confined our attention to objects which had a certain mass but whose size was either very small or could safely be ignored (what mathematicians refer to as particles). This final chapter is devoted to the behaviour of bodies extended in space.

An extended body (such as an elephant or a steel girder) differs from a particle in two important respects:

(1) it may be able to rotate in space, as well as moving from side to side or up and down;

(2) a force acting on an extended body has a turning effect, which depends not only on the magnitude of the force but also on its line of action.

20.2 TURNING EFFECT OF A FORCE

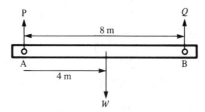

Fig. 20.1

Figure 20.1 represents a light rigid girder, held in position by pins inserted at A and B, where $AB = 8\,m$, and supporting a weight of $12\,kN$. The downward pull on the girder must be balanced by the combined effect of upward forces at A and B, as in the figure. If the weight hangs exactly half way between A and B, then is it obvious that P and Q must both equal $6\,kN$ (since $P = Q$ by symmetry, and $P+Q = 12$)?

If you think of the pin at A as a pivot, then the weight W has a tendency to turn the girder clockwise about the pivot, and this must be balanced by the anti-clockwise effect of the supporting force at B (since P clearly has zero effect). Similarly, if the pin at B is thought of as the pivot, then W has an anti-clockwise turning effect which is balanced by the clockwise turning effect of P (and now it is Q that has zero effect).

The technical term for the turning effect of a force is *moment*, and experiments show that the moment of a force F about a point is $F \times d$, where d is the distance from the point to the line of action of the force. The SI unit is the newton metre (Nm).

Thus in our example

the moment of W about A $= 12\,\text{kN} \times 4\,\text{m} = 48$ units clockwise

the moment of Q about A $= Q \times 8 = 8Q$ units anti-clockwise

the moment of P about A $= P \times 0 = 0$

Since the moments must cancel out, we see that $8Q = 48$.

Thus $Q = 6$, as we saw earlier. And $P + Q = 12 \Rightarrow P = 6$.

Since it is in any case obvious that $Q = 6$, this argument may seem absurdly elaborate. But now consider figure 20.2, which shows the same girder but with the weight hanging from a point 6m from A.

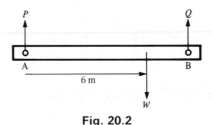

Fig. 20.2

Since we can no longer appeal to symmetry, the use of moments is essential:

the moment of W about A $= 12 \times 6 = 72$ units clockwise

the moment of Q about A $= Q \times 8 = 8Q$ units anti-clockwise

the moment of P about A $= 0$

So we have $8Q = 72 \Rightarrow Q = 9\,\text{kN}$, and $P + Q = 12 \Rightarrow P = 3\,\text{kN}$.

Notice that we could just as well have 'taken moments' about B. The calculations would then have gone as follows:

the moment of W about B $= 12 \times 2 = 24$ anti-clockwise

the moment of P about B $= P \times 8 = 8P$ clockwise

the moment of Q about B $= 0$

So we have $8P = 24 \Rightarrow P = 3\,\text{kN}$, as before.

Suppose now that the load is split into two equal parts, at distances of 5m and 7m from A respectively (figure 20.3). What will the forces P and Q be in these new circumstances?

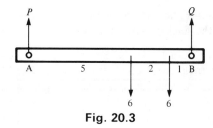

Fig. 20.3

If we take moments about A, then P will have zero moment and so only Q will appear in our calculations to begin with; but if we take moments about B, then it will be the other way round. Let us (more or less arbitrarily) decide to take moments about A. Then we have

the moment of the left-hand weight $= 6 \times 5 = 30$ clockwise

the moment of the right-hand weight $= 6 \times 7 = 42$ clockwise

the moment of $P = 0$, and the moment of $Q = 8Q$ anti-clockwise

Therefore $8Q = 30 + 42 = 72 \Rightarrow Q = 9\,\text{kN}$, and $P = 3\,\text{kN}$.

Two points are worth noting.

(1) The weights in figure 20.3 are equal but their moments about A are different. This is so because their lines of action are at different distances from A.

(2) The values of P and Q in figure 20.3 turn out to be the same as in figure 20.2. This demonstrates that the combined effect of the two weights in figure 20.3 is the same as the effect of the single weight in figure 20.2. We return to this point in the next section.

Suppose next that the 12 kN is split into unequal parts, as in figure 20.4. What supporting forces must the pins now exert on the girder?

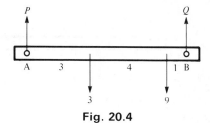

Fig. 20.4

We decide to take moments about A:

the moment of the 3kN weight $= 3 \times 3 = 9$ clockwise

the moment of the 9 kN weight $= 9 \times 7 = 63$ clockwise

the moment of $P = 0$, and the moment of $Q = 8Q$ anti-clockwise

Therefore $8Q = 9 + 63 = 72 \Rightarrow Q = 9\,\text{kN}$, and $P = 3\,\text{kN}$.

Once again, observe that the combined effect of the two weights is exactly the same as that of the single weight in figure 20.2.

To save ourselves from having to say clockwise and anti-clockwise all the time, we normally use the convention that an anti-clockwise moment counts as positive and a clockwise moment as negative, or vice versa, whichever seems more convenient.

EXAMPLE   Figure 20.5 represents a light plank resting on supports at A and B, and supporting two loads as shown. Find the support forces, and find also the single load that would be equivalent to the two given loads. If a third load W is imposed at C and just causes the plank to tip up, find W.

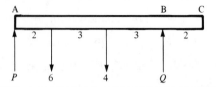

Fig. 20.5

We take moments about A, counting clockwise as positive. We have:

the total moment of the two loads $= (+6 \times 2) + (+4 \times 5) = +32$,

the moment of $P = 0$, and the moment of $Q = -Q \times 8 = -8Q$.

Since the sum of the moments must be zero (taking sign into account), we see that $32 - 8Q = 0 \Rightarrow Q = 4$, and so $P = 6$.

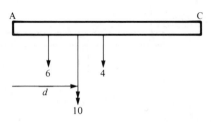

Fig. 20.6

The magnitude of the single load equivalent to the two loads combined must obviously be 10. Suppose that its line of action is d units to the right of A (figure (20.6)), then

$$+10 \times d = +32 \Rightarrow d = 3.2$$

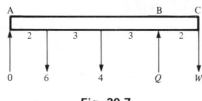

Fig. 20.7

Imagine now that the third load W is added to the system (figure 20.7). The fact that the plank is *just* tilting means that it is still in equilibrium but that the support force at A has become zero. So taking moments about B (and still counting clockwise as positive), we have

$$(+W \times 2) + (-6 \times 6) + (-4 \times 3) = 0 \Rightarrow 2W = 48 \Rightarrow W = 24$$

EXERCISE 20A

In each case, draw a clear figure showing all the forces involved, together with any relevant distances, and state whether you are counting anti-clockwise or clockwise as positive.

1. A window cleaner sits on a light plank supported by means of two ropes. The plank is horizontal, and the ropes hang vertically 6 m apart. If the man's weight is 720 N, find the tensions in the ropes   (a) when he sits 2 m from the left-hand rope, and   (b) when he sits 1 m from it.

2. A light bar of length 4 m is hinged at one end, and is supported horizontally by a vertical force acting at its other end. Find this support force if loads of 4, 3, and 2 kN are placed at distances of 1, 2, and 3 m from the hinge. Find also the (vertical) force exerted by the hinge on the bar.

3. A light girder of length 6 m is hinged at one end, and is supported horizontally by a vertical force acting at a point d m from the hinge. If the girder is subject to a vertical load of 2 kN at its mid-point, find the support force, and the force exerted by the hinge (stating whether up or down),   (a) when $d = 6$,   (b) when $d = 3$,   (c) when $d = 1$.

4. A crowbar is used to turn a ship's capstan when the power on board fails. Two men push horizontally, the first at a distance of 3 m from the axis of the capstan and with a force of 300 N, the second at a distance of 2 m and with a force of 200 N. What single force would be equivalent to their combined push?

20.3 CENTRE OF GRAVITY

We found in section 20.2 that two forces acting in the same direction but with different lines of action are equivalent to a single force in that direction. For instance, the two loads in figure 20.3 or in figure 20.4 are equivalent to the single load in figure 20.2.

This fact enables us to deal with the weight of an extended body. We have been assuming that the girders and planks and so on have all been light, i.e. that their weight was negligible in comparison with the other forces. That may be a plausible assumption when a girder is supporting a load of 12 kN (equivalent to about 1 tonne); but the weight of a girder can very often not be neglected.

Each physical particle of an object such as a girder is affected by the gravitational field of the Earth. Unless the object is very large indeed, the forces involved form a system of parallel forces (they all point vertically downwards). By repeatedly replacing two forces in the system by an equivalent single force, the whole system can eventually be reduced to one single force. Like the original individual forces, it will point vertically downwards, its magnitude will be the sum of their magnitudes, and it will have a definite line of action.

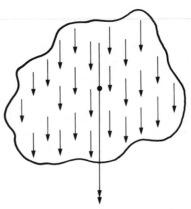

Fig. 20.8

This single force is called the weight of the whole object. Moreover, if the object is rigid, the line of action of its weight always passes through a definite point in the object, however much the object is turned around in space. This point is called the *centre of gravity* of the object.

The centre of gravity of an object coincides with its centre of mass, and the two terms tend therefore to be used interchangeably, although they are by no means synonymous.

If the object has a regular shape, and if its density is uniform (i.e. its mass is evenly spread out), then the centre of mass/gravity will coincide with the geometrical centre of the object (sometimes called its centroid). For instance, the centre of gravity of a uniform rectangular lamina (a lamina is an object that is so thin that its thickness can be neglected) is at its centre, and likewise a circular lamina; the centre of gravity of a uniform triangular lamina is at the point where the medians cut; and so on. Later on in this section, we will consider how to find the centre of gravity of less regular shapes. The centre of gravity of a very irregularly shaped object may be in a surprising position: for instance, the centre of gravity of a high-jumper employing a flop technique may pass *under* the bar, even when the jumper himself passes over it.

EXAMPLE When the very ends of a wooden beam AB are placed on two trestles, the support forces at A and B are 120 and 280 N. If the length of the beam is 10 m, find where its centre of gravity is.

Figure 20.9 shows the situation. The beam's centre of gravity clearly lies somewhere along its length, at G say, d m from A, and the weight of the beam is clearly 400 N.

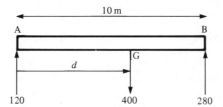

Fig. 20.9

We take moments about A, counting clockwise as positive. The moment of the support force at A equals zero, the moment of the force at B equals -280×10, and the moment of the weight equals $+400 \times d$. Since the total moment must be zero, we have

$$400d - 2800 = 0 \Rightarrow d = 7$$

So the centre of gravity is 7 m from A, 3 m from B.

EXAMPLE The beam described in the last example is now supported by a single trestle placed under its mid-point. If the beam balances when a child sits at one end of it, find the weight of the child.

Suppose the child weighs W N. In this example, it is best to take moments about the mid-point of the beam, since then the unknown support force has zero moment.

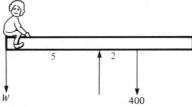

Fig. 20.10

We have $800 - 5W = 0 \Rightarrow W = 160$

So the child weighs 160 N (and the support force provided by the trestle must be $400 + 160 = 560$ N).

We now turn our attention to laminae. Since the mass in them is not confined to a straight line, we have to consider moments about axes, rather than about a point. For convenience, we arrange things so that the lamina is horizontal.

EXAMPLE Find the centre of gravity of a uniform lamina made of two squares joined together as in figure 20.11.

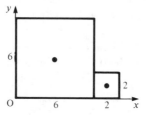

Fig. 20.11

We set up coordinate axes Ox, Oy to help us in our calculations.

Since the lamina is of uniform density, weight must be proportional to area. So the weight of the larger square will be 36 units, acting at its centre of gravity $(3, 3)$. The weight of the smaller square will be 4 units, acting at $(7, 1)$. The weight of the whole thing is then 40 units. Let us suppose that its centre of gravity is (X, Y).

In figure 20.12, the weights of the two parts of the object (36 and 4 units) are indicated by ordinary arrows, while the weight of the complete object (40 units) is indicated by a double arrow.

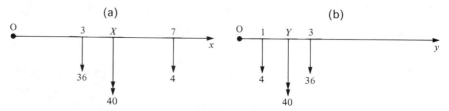

Fig. 20.12

The moment of the whole weight about any axis must equal the sum of the moments of the two part weights.

So taking moments about Oy, we have

$$40 \times X = 36 \times 3 + 4 \times 7$$

$$40X = 136 \Rightarrow X = 3.4$$

and taking moments about Ox, we have

$$40 \times Y = 36 \times 3 + 4 \times 1$$

$$40Y = 112 \Rightarrow Y = 2.8$$

Thus the centre of gravity is at $(3.4, 2.8)$.

These calculations can be more concisely laid out as follows:

$$40 \times (X, Y) = 36 \times (3, 3) + 4 \times (7, 1) = (136, 112)$$

$$\Rightarrow (X, Y) = (3.4, 2.8)$$

Instead of regarding an object as being the sum of two parts, it may sometimes be more convenient to think of it as one part minus another.

EXAMPLE Find the centre of gravity of the uniform lamina indicated in figure 20.13.

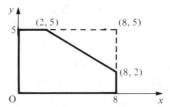

Fig. 20.13

We regard the awkward shape as being an 8×5 rectangle minus a triangle.

The weight of the rectangle $= 40$ units, and its centre of gravity is at $(4, 2.5)$. The weight of the triangle $= 9$ units, and its centre of gravity is at the centroid of $(2, 5)$, $(8, 5)$ and $(8, 2)$, i.e. at $(6, 4)$.

So $$31 \times (X, Y) = 40 \times (4, 2.5) - 9 \times (6, 4) = (106, 64)$$

$$\Rightarrow (X, Y) = (106/31, 64/31)$$

One advantage of this form of layout is that the question whether a moment is positive or negative is automatically taken care of.

EXAMPLE Isolated masses of $7\,\text{kg}$, $4\,\text{kg}$, $6\,\text{kg}$, and $3\,\text{kg}$ are located at $(5, 3)$, $(-6, 2)$, $(-3, -7)$, and $(1, -1)$ respectively. Find their centre of gravity.

The weights are $7g$, $4g$, $6g$, $3g$, and the total weight is $20g$. Suppose that the centre of gravity is (X, Y). Then

$$20g \times (X, Y) = 7g \times (5, 3) + 4g \times (-6, 2) + 6g \times (-3, -7) + 3g \times (1, -1)$$

$$\Rightarrow 20(X, Y) = 7(5, 3) + 4(-6, 2) + 6(-3, -7) + 3(1, -1) = (-4, -16)$$

$$\Rightarrow \quad (X, Y) = (-1/5, -4/5)$$

Observe how g can be cancelled out, thereby making the calculation much simpler. Our calculation then relates to masses as well as to weights, which demonstrates what was said earlier, that the centre of gravity and centre of mass coincide.

In cancelling g, we are of course assuming that g is the same for all the individual masses. But if they were so widely dispersed that g varied from one to the other, then the centre of gravity and the centre of mass would not coincide.

EXERCISE 20B

1. An 11 m log is slung from two vertical chains attached to its two ends. If the tensions in the chains are 600 N and 720 N, find the centre of gravity of the log.

2. A uniform steel bar of length 4 m and weight 220 N has an attachment of weight 30 N welded to one end. Where is the centre of gravity of the whole article?

3. A thin rigid rod AD is held horizontally by means of two pegs at B and C, the rod passing under the peg at B and over the peg at C. The distances are as follows: AB = BC = 1 m, CD = 8 m. If the vertical forces exerted by the pegs on the rod are in the ratio 3:4, find the rod's centre of gravity.

4. An L-shaped lamina, 50 cm high and 40 cm wide, is constructed by joining together eight uniform 10×10 cm squares. Where is its centre of gravity?

5. A 3, 4, 5 triangle is formed from a 12 cm piece of uniform wire. Where is its centre of gravity?

6. A uniform quadrilateral lamina has corners at $(0,0)$, $(9,0)$, $(9,2)$, $(0,8)$. Where is its centre of gravity?

7. Isolated masses of 1 kg, 2 kg, 3 kg, and 4 kg are located at $(0,0)$, $(7,-3)$, $(-3,4)$, and $(-2,-1)$ respectively. Find their centre of mass.

20.4 RESULTANTS AND COUPLES

If the lines of action of two forces intersect at a point, then the line of action of the resultant obviously passes through that point, and its magnitude and direction are found by vector addition, as we saw in chapter 7.

EXAMPLE Find the resultant of the following two forces:

P, of magnitude 3 N, acting due east, along $y = 2$,

and **Q**, of magnitude 4 N, acting due north, along $x = 6$.

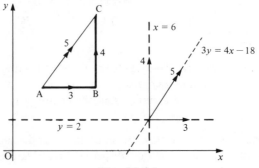

Fig. 20.14

The lines of action intersect at the point $(6, 2)$: therefore the resultant's line of action passes through this point (figure 20.14). We represent the forces **P** and **Q** by the displacements **AB** and **BC**; then **AC** gives the magnitude and direction of the resultant. The line of action, therefore, is the line with gradient $4/3$ that passes through $(6, 2)$. Its equation is $3(y-2) = 4(x-6)$, i.e. $3y = 4x-18$.

Notice that in this example, we have made no use of the principle of moments. If the lines of action are parallel, however, then we do need this principle.

EXAMPLE Find the resultant of the following two forces:

> **P**, of magnitude $3\,\text{N}$, acting due south, along $x = 2$,
>
> and **Q**, of magnitude $4\,\text{N}$, acting due north, along $x = 6$.

In this example, the lines of action do not intersect but are parallel (figure 20.15). The resultant is clearly a force of magnitude $1\,\text{N}$, acting due north, but its line of action is not so clear.

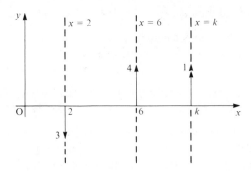

Fig. 20.15

Suppose the line of action has equation $x = k$. Then the moment of the resultant about the origin will be $1 \times k$ (counting anti-clockwise as positive), and this must equal the sum of the moments of the two component forces; so

$$1 \times k = (-3 \times 2) + (+4 \times 6)$$
$$\Rightarrow k = 18$$

So the resultant is a force of $1\,\text{N}$ acting due north along $x = 18$.

EXAMPLE Investigate the following system of three forces:

> **P**, of magnitude $3\,\text{N}$, acting due south, along $x = 2$,
>
> **Q**, of magnitude $4\,\text{N}$, acting due north, along $x = 6$,
>
> **R**, of magnitude $1\,\text{N}$, acting due south, along $x = 8$.

Once again, the lines of action are parallel (figure 20.16), but this time the resultant is zero, since $3 + 1 = 4$. So the system has no overall translational effect.

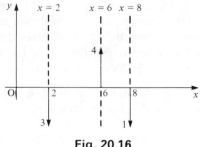

Fig. 20.16

It does have a turning effect, however, as we see by taking moments about any point. If we choose the origin, and count anti-clockwise as positive:

$$\text{total moment} = (-3 \times 2) + (+4 \times 6) + (-1 \times 8) = +10$$

If we were to choose some other point, say $(1, 0)$, we would, perhaps rather surprisingly, get the same result:

$$\text{total moment} = (-3 \times 1) + (+4 \times 5) + (-1 \times 7) = +10$$

Check these calculations carefully, and by trying points other than $(0, 0)$ and $(1, 0)$ convince yourself that the moment of this system is the same, no matter which point is chosen.

This system of forces, therefore, has zero translational effect, but has a constant non-zero turning effect about every point, which is called the *torque* of the system.

The simplest system of this kind is a *couple*, which is a pair of equal forces, acting along parallel lines but in opposite directions (figure 20.17). The torque of a couple is Fd, where F is the magnitude of each of the forces and d is the distance between their lines of action.

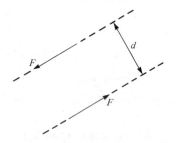

Fig. 20.17

The analysis of systems of forces in three dimensions is quite hard. But in two dimensions, it can be shown that any system is either

(1) equivalent to a single non-zero force, or

(2) equivalent to a non-zero couple, or

(3) in equilibrium.

EXAMPLE Investigate the system shown in figure 20.18.

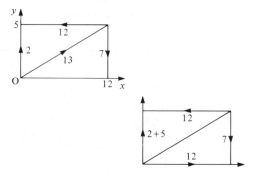

Fig. 20.18

The force of 13 along the diagonal can be resolved into components of 12 along the x-axis and 5 along the y-axis. You can then see that the translational effect of the system is zero. But the moment about the origin is not zero:

$$\text{total moment} = (+12 \times 5) + (-7 \times 12) = -24$$

So this system is equivalent to a couple with a torque of -24.

EXAMPLE A uniform rectangular lamina ABCD is suspended by means of a string attached to the corner A. If $AB = 2\,m$ and $AD = 3\,m$, find the angle that AD makes with the vertical when the system is in equilibrium.

There are just two forces acting on the lamina: its weight W acting downwards through X, the point where the diagonals meet, and the tension T in the string acting through A (figure 20.19).

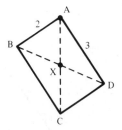

Fig. 20.19

The system must have zero resultant: so W and T must act in opposite directions, i.e. T must pull vertically upwards. The system must also have zero torque: so the lines of action of W and T must coincide, i.e. AX must be vertical.

Thus the required angle $= \text{CAD} = \arctan(2/3) = 33.7°$ (1 d.p.)

This example illustrates the useful two-force principle:

> if two forces are in equilibrium, then they must be equal and opposite, and their lines of action must coincide

EXAMPLE A light rod AOB is bent at O into a rigid L shape, where OA = 15 cm and OB = 10 cm. Masses of 30 kg and 20 kg are welded on to A and B, and the thing is hung from a string tied on at O. Find the angle that OA makes with the vertical in equilibrium.

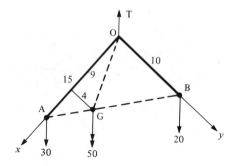

Fig. 20.20

The weight at A = 30 units, the weight at B = 20 units, and clearly the tension = 50 units. To get a two-force system, we replace the two separate weights by a single equivalent weight acting at the centre of gravity $G(X, Y)$. So

$$50(X, Y) = 30(15, 0) + 20(0, 10) = (450, 200) \Rightarrow (X, Y) = (9, 4)$$

Using the two-force principle, we see that OG must be vertical, and so the required angle is AOG = $\arctan(4/9) = 24.0°$ (1 d.p.).

EXAMPLE Figure 20.21 represents a 10 m ladder leaning against a vertical wall, and shows the system of forces acting on the ladder. Find the values of N, S, and F that produce equilibrium, if the ladder makes an angle of 70° with the horizontal ground.

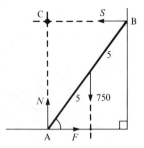

Fig. 20.21

The system must have zero resultant, so resolving vertically and horizontally we find that $N = 750$ and $F = S$.

The system must also have zero torque, so taking moments about the foot of the ladder we find that

$$S \times 10 \sin 70° - 750 \times 5 \cos 70° = 0 \Rightarrow S = 136.5 \quad (4 \text{ s.f.})$$

Since we know that $F = S$, we have solved the problem.

This example will serve to remind you of an important fact: that when calculating the moment of a force about a point, you must always use the distance from the point to the force's line of action, *not* the distance from the point to the force's point of application. Thus the moment of S about A is $S \times AC$, *not* $S \times AB$.

EXERCISE 20C

1. Two forces, of magnitude 5 and 15 N, act due east and due north, along $y = 4$ and $x = 3$. Find their resultant.

2. Forces **P** and **Q**, of magnitude 5 and 15 N, act due east along $y = 4$ and $y = -3$. Find their resultant.

3. Answer question 2 if **P** now acts in the opposite direction.

4. The diameter of the top of a jar of marmalade is 6 cm. To open it, a man exerts an overall tangential force of 20 N with his fingers. What is the torque?

5. $AB = 3$ m, $BC = 4$ m, $CA = 5$ m. A force of 3 N acts along AB, and in that direction; likewise, forces of 4 N and 5 N act along BC and CA. Show that this system is equivalent to a couple, and find its torque.

6. A wire AOB of uniform density is bent at O into an L-shape, where $OA = 40$ cm and $OB = 60$ cm, and is hung from a string tied on at O. Find the angle that OA makes with the vertical when the system is in equilibrium.

20.5 EQUILIBRIUM

When an extended body rests in equilibrium under the action of a system of forces, then the resultant of the system must be zero and the torque must be zero.

EXAMPLE A uniform beam OA is hinged at O so that it is free to rotate up or down, but is maintained in a horizontal position by a light wire, one end of which is tied to the beam at A and the other to a hook B situated vertically above O. If $OA = 4$ m, $OB = 3$ m, and the weight of the beam is 450 N, find the tension in the wire, and the magnitude of the reaction at the hinge.

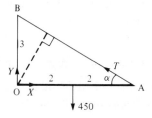

Fig. 20.22

The situation is shown in figure 20.22. The weight of the beam acts vertically downwards through its mid-point, and the tension in the wire acts along the line of the wire. The reaction at the hinge acts through O but its direction is unknown: we therefore represent it by horizontal and vertical components, X and Y.

The resultant of the force system is zero: so

$$X = T\cos\alpha \qquad \text{and} \qquad Y + T\sin\alpha = 450$$

And the torque is zero: so taking moments about O

$$450 \times 2 = T \times 4\sin\alpha$$

Now simple trigonometry tells us that

$$\tan\alpha = 3/4, \quad \cos\alpha = 4/5, \quad \sin\alpha = 3/5$$

Therefore we easily calculate that $T = 375$, $X = 300$, $Y = 225$.

Thus the tension in the wire is 375 N, and the magnitude of the reaction at the hinge is $\sqrt{(300^2 + 225^2)}$, i.e. 375 N.

EXAMPLE A uniform rod AB of length 50 cm is supported by light wires OA and OB of length 30 and 40 cm. At what angle to the vertical will AB rest in equilibrium?

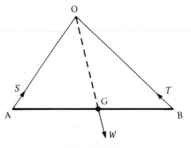

Fig. 20.23

There are three forces acting on the rod: its weight W, and the tensions S and T in the wires (figure 20.23). The resultant of the system must be zero, and so must the torque. Now the moment of S and T about O is zero, since O lies on their lines of action. Therefore the moment of the weight about O must also be zero, i.e. its line of action must pass through O. So OG is vertical. The required angle is thus AGO, which can be found most easily from an accurate drawing (it comes to about 74°).

This example illustrates the useful three-force principle

> if three forces are in equilibrium, then their lines of action
> must meet in a point (or be parallel)

EXAMPLE The lower end of a light rod rests on rough horizontal ground, while the upper end rests against a smooth vertical wall. The rod is held in position by a wire in tension, as shown in figure 20.24. Show that the frictional force between the ground and the rod must be zero.

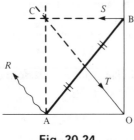

Fig. 20.24

There are three forces acting on the rod: *R*, *S*, and *T*.

To start with, we do not know the direction in which *R* acts. This is indicated in the figure by marking in *R* with a wavy arrow.

S is known to act horizontally, however, since the wall is smooth, and the lines of action of *S* and *T* intersect at C. Therefore *R*'s line of action also passes through C. But simple geometry shows that AOBC is a rectangle, and therefore AC is vertical. Thus there is no frictional element in *R*.

EXAMPLE An aluminium ladder stands on rough horizontal ground and leans against a smooth vertical garden wall. When the foot of the ladder is 8 m from the wall, the top of the ladder reaches a point on the wall 15 m above ground level. The mass of the ladder is 30 kg, and the ladder's centre of mass is at its mid-point. Find the frictional and normal component of the reaction between the ground and ladder. If the coefficient of friction is 0.4, determine whether a gardener of mass 70 kg can climb up the ladder to within 1 m of the wall in order to pick apricots.

The forces on the ladder are shown in figure 20.25.

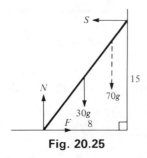

Fig. 20.25

The system must have zero resultant: so $N = 30g$ and $F = S$. And the system must have zero torque: so taking moments about the foot of the ladder, we have $S \times 15 = 30g \times 4$.

Therefore $N = 30g$ and $F = 8g$.

We now suppose that the gardener is standing on the ladder 1 m from the wall, and see what values of F and N are required. If F/N turns out to be greater than 0.4, we shall have to conclude that the gardener cannot in fact approach the wall so close.

The calculations are similar to those performed above. We have: $N = 100g$, $F = S$, and $S \times 15 = 30g \times 4 + 70g \times 7$.

Hence $N = 100g$ and $F = 122g/3 \Rightarrow F/N = 1.22/3 \approx 0.407$.

So the gardener cannot quite get within reach of the apricots.

EXAMPLE The gardener decides to pull a heavy cubical crate from one part of his garden to another. To do this, he ties a rope to the top of the crate, and pulls horizontally, hoping that the crate will slide along rather than tip over. If the crate is uniformly loaded, and the coefficient of friction between it and the ground is 0.4, will the gardener succeed in his plan?

Let us suppose that the gardener pulls more and more strongly in an effort to make the crate move, but that what happens is that it begins to tip over rather than slide. Figure 20.26 shows the moment when it is just on the point of tipping over; note that the normal force between the crate and the ground is concentrated at the front edge of the crate.

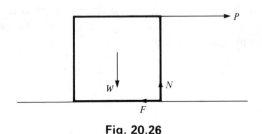

Fig. 20.26

The system of forces must have zero resultant: so

$$N = W \quad \text{and} \quad F = P$$

And it must have zero torque: so

$$P \times 2 = W \times 1$$

Therefore $F/N = P/W = 0.5$. Since the coefficient of friction is only 0.4, we see that F/N could never have such a high value as 0.5, and so the crate will slide rather than tip over. The gardener cannot get at the apricots, but he can move the crate.

EXERCISE 20D

1. A uniform girder AB of weight 500 N is freely hinged at A to a warehouse wall, and is held up in a horizontal position by a chain that is attached to the mid-point of the girder. If the girder supports a load of 5 kN at B, and the chain makes an angle of 45° with the horizontal, find the tension in the chain and the reaction at the hinge.

2. A log AB hangs from two chains OA and OB, where AB = 10 m, and OA = OB = 7 m. If the log hangs in equilibrium at an angle of 70° with the vertical, find, by drawing, the position of its centre of gravity.

3. A uniform ladder leans against a vertical smooth wall at an angle of 70° to the not very rough horizontal pavement upon which the foot of the ladder rests. If the weight of the ladder is 600 N, and the coefficient of friction is only 0.1, find the weight of the apprentice needed to stand on the bottom rung in order to prevent slipping.

SUPPLEMENTARY QUESTIONS

EXERCISE 1S

1. Draw the graph of $y = x^2 - 2$ for values of x from -3 to $+3$. On the same axes draw $y = x$. Show that you can use the two graphs to solve the equation $x^2 - x - 2 = 0$, and give the solutions.

2. Draw the graph of $y = x^2 + 2x - 1$ for values of x from -3 to $+3$. On the same axes draw $y = 3x + 2$. What equation is satisfied by the x-values at the points of intersection, and what are the solutions of that equation?

3. Draw the graph of $y = -x^2$. On the same axes plot a straight line that will enable you to solve $x^2 + 2x - 1 = 0$, and solve this equation.

4. Draw the graph of $y = x - 4 + 5/x$ for values of x from $+1/2$ to $+5$. Use the graph to solve the equation $x + 5/x = 6$.

Write down the expansions of the following:

5. $(2x - 5)(x + 4)$

6. $(3x + 4)(x - 7)$

7. $(3x - 8)(2x + 3)$

8. $(5x + 7)(4x + 1)$

9. $(x^2 - 3x)(x + 4)$

10. $(x^2 - x)(x + 1)$

Solve the following equations:

11. $(x - 8)(x + 3) = 0$

12. $(x - 4)(x - 9) = 0$

13. $(2x + 7)(3x + 1) = 0$

14. $(4x + 5)(5x + 4) = 0$

15. $(x^2 + 1)(x^2 - 1) = 0$

16. $(x^3 - 1)(x^3 + 1) = 0$

What must be added to the following expressions to give a perfect square?

17. $x^2 + 10x$

18. $x^2 + 18x$

19. $x^2 - x$

20. $x^2 - 3x$

Factorise the following:

21. $x^2 - 5x - 6$

22. $x^2 - 6x - 16$

23. $2x^2 - 5x + 2$

24. $2x^2 - 3x - 14$

25. $4x^2 + 13x + 10$

26. $2x^2 - 7x + 6$

27. $3x^2 + 10x - 8$

28. $3x^2 + 17x + 10$

Solve the following equations by factorisation:

29. $5x^2 + 7x - 6 = 0$ **30.** $3x^2 + x - 24 = 0$

31. $6x^2 - 11x + 4 = 0$ **32.** $12x^2 - 23x + 10 = 0$

33. $2x^2 + 7x - 15 = 0$ **34.** $18x^2 - 27x - 56 = 0$

Solve the following equations by the formula, giving your answers to 3 d.p.:

35. $x^2 + 2x - 4 = 0$ **36.** $x^2 - 3x + 1 = 0$

37. $2x^2 + 5x + 1 = 0$ **38.** $3x^2 - 10x + 6 = 0$

39. $5x^2 - 3x - 3 = 0$ **40.** $4x^2 + 9x - 1 = 0$

Find the sum and product of the roots of the following equations:

41. $x^2 - 3x - 5 = 0$ **42.** $x^2 + 6x - 2 = 0$

43. $5x^2 + 4x + 1 = 0$ **44.** $4x^2 - 7x + 2 = 0$

Calculate the values of $1/\alpha + 1/\beta$ and of $\alpha^2 + \beta^2$, where α and β are the roots of the following equations:

45. $x^2 + 4x - 2 = 0$ **46.** $x^2 - 5x - 4 = 0$

47. $2x^2 - 6x + 1 = 0$ **48.** $3x^2 + 6x + 2 = 0$

Find quadratic equations whose roots are   (a) 5α and 5β, and   (b) $1 - \alpha$ and $1 - \beta$, where α and β are the roots of the following equations:

49. $x^2 - 3x - 1 = 0$ **50.** $x^2 + 4x + 1 = 0$

51. $5x^2 + x - 2 = 0$ **52.** $4x^2 - 3x + 1 = 0$

Find the values of c that cause the following equations to have repeated roots:

53. $x^2 - 2cx + 9 = 0$ **54.** $x^2 + 3x + (2 + c^2) = 0$

55. $x^2 + cx + (2c + 5) = 0$ **56.** $x^2 - (c + 1)x + (c^2 - 5) = 0$

Calculate the discriminant of the following, and determine whether or not they can be factorised:

57. $30x^2 - 7x - 18$ **58.** $24x^2 - 33x + 10$

59. $14x^2 + 27x + 12$ **60.** $15x^2 + 43x - 16$

By completing the square, find   (a) the axis of symmetry, and   (b) the highest or lowest point, on the following graphs. Also sketch the graph in each case, marking in the points (if any) where the graph cuts the axes:

61. $y = x^2 + 6x - 8$ **62.** $y = x^2 + 10x + 3$

63. $y = 7 + 4x - x^2$ **64.** $y = 2 - 8x - x^2$

Solve the following inequalities:

65. $(x + 3)(x - 7) \geqslant 0$ **66.** $(x + 5)(x - 1) \geqslant 0$

67. $(2x - 1)(x - 4) \leqslant 0$ **68.** $(x + 4)(2x + 1) \leqslant 0$

Prove that the following inequalities hold for all values of x:

69. $x^2 - 10x + 40 \geqslant 15$

70. $x^2 + 6x + 12 \geqslant 3$

71. $1 + 4x - x^2 \leqslant 5$

72. $4 - 8x - x^2 \leqslant 20$

EXERCISE 2S

What are the x–y coordinates of P (to 3 s.f.) if r and θ are:

1. 4 and $50°$
2. 6 and $55°$

3. 7.62 and $73.4°$
4. 11.9 and $26.1°$

5. 4 and $90°$
6. 3 and $0°$

7. 5 and $180°$
8. 7 and $270°$

9. 4.57 and $164.2°$
10. 8.39 and $243.7°$

11. 0.0264 and $293.4°$
12. 26.6 and $336.8°$

Find the values of the stated quantities (rounding as appropriate, and taking θ to be acute), and in each case check your results by using an alternative method:

13. $r = 4$, $x = 3$; θ, y
14. $r = 6$, $y = 4$; θ, x

15. $r = 5.72$, $y = 2.36$; θ, x
16. $r = 4.61$, $x = 1.72$; θ, y

17. $x = 12.6$, $y = 17.4$; r, θ
18. $x = 0.241$, $y = 0.179$; r, θ

Express the following in terms of the sine or cosine of an acute angle:

19. $\cos 143°$ | **20.** $\cos 127°$ | **21.** $\sin 243°$ | **22.** $\sin 194°$

23. $\cos 316°$ | **24.** $\cos 334°$ | **25.** $\sin 321°$ | **26.** $\sin 339°$

27. $\cos 247°$ | **28.** $\cos 206°$ | **29.** $\sin 112°$ | **30.** $\sin 97°$

31. $\cos 287°$ | **32.** $\sin 264°$ | **33.** $\sin 164°$ | **34.** $\cos 196°$

35. $\cos 537°$ | **36.** $\sin 648°$ | **37.** $\sin 847°$ | **38.** $\cos 1394°$

Solve the following equations (to 1 d.p.), in each case for $0° \leqslant \theta < 360°$:

39. $\cos \theta = -0.843$
40. $\cos \theta = -0.629$

41. $\sin \theta = +0.743$
42. $\sin \theta = +0.267$

43. $\cos \theta = +0.804$
44. $\cos \theta = +0.408$

45. $\sin \theta = -0.367$
46. $\sin \theta = -0.960$

47. $\cos \theta = +0.267$
48. $\sin \theta = +0.762$

49. $\sin \theta = -0.814$
50. $\cos \theta = -0.973$

Express the following in terms of the tangent of an acute angle:

51. $\tan 137°$ | **52.** $\tan 112°$ | **53.** $\tan 237°$ | **54.** $\tan 198°$

55. $\tan 297°$ | **56.** $\tan 327°$ | **57.** $\tan 593°$ | **58.** $\tan 687°$

Solve the following equations (to 1 d.p.), in each case for $0° \leqslant \theta < 360°$:

59. $\tan \theta = +0.731$ **60.** $\tan \theta = +0.672$

61. $\tan \theta = -1.843$ **62.** $\tan \theta = -2.416$

63. $\cot \theta = -0.762$ **64.** $\cot \theta = +2.731$

65. $\sec \theta = -3.619$ **66.** $\operatorname{cosec} \theta = +1.728$

67. By sketching the cosine and sine graphs, demonstrate that $\cos \theta = \sin(90-\theta)$ for all θ.

68. Demonstrate similarly that $\cot \theta = \tan(90-\theta)$.

Convert the following polar-form vectors to column form:

69. $[4, 25°]$ **70.** $[6, 65°]$

71. $[7.5, 136°]$ **72.** $[8.2, 157°]$

73. $[0.431, -143.8°]$ **74.** $[0.263, -154.2°]$

75. $[274, -64.2°]$ **76.** $[861, -31.4°]$

Convert the following column-form vectors to polar form:

77. $\begin{pmatrix} 5 \\ 6 \end{pmatrix}$ **78.** $\begin{pmatrix} -5 \\ +8 \end{pmatrix}$ **79.** $\begin{pmatrix} +2.4 \\ -3.2 \end{pmatrix}$ **80.** $\begin{pmatrix} 3.2 \\ 5.6 \end{pmatrix}$

81. $\begin{pmatrix} -724 \\ +387 \end{pmatrix}$ **82.** $\begin{pmatrix} -1200 \\ -1100 \end{pmatrix}$ **83.** $\begin{pmatrix} -0.012 \\ -0.065 \end{pmatrix}$ **84.** $\begin{pmatrix} -0.063 \\ +0.087 \end{pmatrix}$

85. In triangle ABC (figure 2.16), find (without calculator or tables) the exact lengths of   (a) CD,   (b) AD,   (c) AB,   (d) BC.

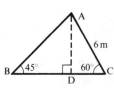

Fig. 2.16

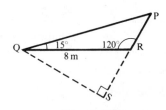

Fig. 2.17

86. In triangle PQR (figure 2.17), find (without calculator or tables) the exact lengths of   (a) RS,   (b) QS,   (c) PS,   (d) PR,   (e) PQ.

87. The sides AD and BC of the trapezium ABCD are parallel. AB and AD equal 8 and 12 m respectively, and angles A and D are 60° and 45°. Prove that BC equals $(8-4\sqrt{3})$ m exactly, and hence find the exact area of the trapezium.

88. Prove that the area of a regular hexagon inscribed in a circle of radius 24 cm is exactly $864\sqrt{3}$ cm^2, and find a similar exact expression for the area of a regular octagon inscribed in a circle of radius 23 cm. Which of the two has the greater area?

89. If $\cos \theta = 1/3$ and θ is acute, find the exact value of $\sec \theta$, and hence of $\tan \theta$.

90. If $\tan \theta = 7/24$ and θ is acute, find the exact value of $\sec \theta$, and hence of $\cos \theta$ and $\sin \theta$.

91. If $\sin \theta = 0.5$ and θ is obtuse, find the exact value of $\cot \theta$.

92. If $\sec \theta = \sqrt{3}$, find the two possible exact values of $\tan \theta$, and hence of $\sin \theta$.

Prove the following identities:

93. $\cos \theta \operatorname{cosec} \theta = \cot \theta$

94. $\cot \theta \cos \theta \sin \theta = \cos^2\theta$

95. $\cot \theta \sec \theta = \operatorname{cosec} \theta$

96. $\tan \theta \operatorname{cosec} \theta = \sec \theta$

97. $(1 - \cos^2\theta)(1 + \tan^2\theta) = \tan^2\theta$

98. $(1 + \tan^2\theta)(\sin^2\theta - 1) + 1 = 0$

99. $\sin^2\theta + 4\cos^2\theta = 1 + 3\cos^2\theta$

100. $3\sin^2\theta - \cos^2\theta = \sin^2\theta + 2 - 3\cos^2\theta$

101. $1 + \tan \theta = \sec \theta(\cos \theta + \sin \theta)$

102. $\cos \theta (\tan \theta + \cot \theta) = \operatorname{cosec} \theta$

103. $(1 + \cos \theta)/\sin \theta = \sin \theta/(1 - \cos \theta)$

104. $(1 - \cos^2\theta)/\tan \theta = \cot \theta/\operatorname{cosec}^2\theta$

Solve the following equations, in each case for $0° \leqslant \theta < 360°$, rounding to 1 d.p. where necessary:

105. $\tan^2\theta = 2$
106. $\sin^2\theta = 0.9$
107. $\sin 3\theta = 1$
108. $\cos 4\theta = 1$
109. $\sec 2\theta = 2$
110. $\cot 2\theta = -1$
111. $\sin^2\theta = \cos^2\theta$
112. $\sin^2\theta = 2\sin \theta \cos \theta$
113. $2\cos^2\theta = \sin \theta + 1$
114. $2\cos^2\theta = \sin \theta - 1$
115. $6\sec^2\theta = 5\tan \theta + 10$
116. $\sec \theta + 2\tan^2\theta = 13$

In the following questions, the four letters r, θ, s, and A, refer to the four quantities radius, angle (in radians), arc length, and area, of a sector. In each case, two of these quantities are given. Find the two unknown quantities.

117. $r = 8$, $\theta = 1.5$
118. $r = 200$, $\theta = \pi/4$
119. $r = 50$, $s = 60$
120. $r = 6$, $s = 9$
121. $r = 4$, $A = 20$
122. $r = 10$, $A = 17$

123. A paper sector of radius 12 cm and angle $\pi/3$ radians is rolled round to form a circular cone. Find the base radius of this cone.

124. A circular cone has a base radius of 3 cm and a vertical height of 4 cm. What are the radius and angle (in radians) of the sector needed to make the curved surface of this cone?

Solve the following equations, in each case for $0 \leqslant \theta < 2\pi$, giving your answers as an exact multiple of π:

125. $\cos \theta = +0.5$ **126.** $\sin \theta = -0.5$

127. $\sin 4\theta = -1$ **128.** $\cos 3\theta = +1$

Solve the following equations, in each case for $0 \leqslant \theta < 2\pi$, giving your answers rounded to 3 d.p.:

129. $100 \cos^2\theta - 20 \cos \theta - 3 = 0$ **130.** $2 \tan^2\theta - 5 \tan \theta + 2 = 0$

131. $\theta = 2 \sin \theta$ **132.** $\theta = \cos \theta$

EXERCISE 3S

Find the displacements from the first point to the second, and also find the magnitude and gradient in each case:

1. P(3, 5), Q(4, 4)   **2.** P(3, 5), O(0, 0)

3. S(−5, 7), T(7, −5)   **4.** U(4.5, 1.5), V(6.5, −0.5)

5. W(−3, −1), X(−5, 1.2)   **6.** Y(p, q), Z(−q, p)

Write down unit vectors which are parallel to the following vectors, and in each case write down two unit vectors which are perpendicular to the given vectors:

7. $\begin{pmatrix} 4 \\ 3 \end{pmatrix}$ **8.** $\begin{pmatrix} -3 \\ +4 \end{pmatrix}$ **9.** $\begin{pmatrix} 7 \\ 24 \end{pmatrix}$ **10.** $\begin{pmatrix} 5 \\ 12 \end{pmatrix}$

11. $\begin{pmatrix} +3 \\ -1 \end{pmatrix}$ **12.** $\begin{pmatrix} 2 \\ 1 \end{pmatrix}$ **13.** $\begin{pmatrix} -24 \\ +7 \end{pmatrix}$ **14.** $\begin{pmatrix} 1 \\ 1 \end{pmatrix}$

15. $\begin{pmatrix} 21 \\ 20 \end{pmatrix}$ **16.** $\begin{pmatrix} -8 \\ +6 \end{pmatrix}$ **17.** $\begin{pmatrix} -35 \\ +12 \end{pmatrix}$ **18.** $\begin{pmatrix} -1 \\ -2 \end{pmatrix}$

If m_1 and m_2 are gradients of perpendicular vectors, write down m_2 given that m_1 equals:

19. 3   **20.** 2   **21.** $1\frac{1}{2}$ **22.** $2\frac{3}{4}$

23. −4   **24.** −7   **25.** $-1\frac{1}{4}$ **26.** −1.2

27. 0.7   **28.** 0.3   **29.** ∞ **30.** $-\infty$

Write down and simplify the equations of the lines through the given point and with the given gradient:

31. (3, 9), 5   **32.** (2, 7), 4

33. $(-1, -5), -2$ **34.** $(-1, -3), 3$

35. $(-4, 7), -1/3$ **36.** $(-2, 5), -1/2$

Write down and simplify the equations of the lines through the given points:

37. $(1, 3)$ and $(2, 5)$ **38.** $(2, 4)$ and $(3, 9)$

39. $(-2, 4)$ and $(3, 6)$ **40.** $(-1, 3)$ and $(4, 7)$

41. $(0, 7)$ and $(-6, 0)$ **42.** $(0, 5)$ and $(-4, 0)$

43. $(-3, -2)$ and $(-5, -4)$ **44.** $(-2, -7)$ and $(-5, -6)$

45. $(11, 6)$ and $(11, 5)$ **46.** $(-2, 9)$ and $(3, 9)$

47. $(4, -3)$ and $(-3, -3)$ **48.** $(-2, -7)$ and $(-2, 8)$

Find the gradients of the following lines (where a, b, and c are constants):

49. $y - 4 = 2x$ **50.** $y - 7 = 5x$

51. $3x + 7y = 19$ **52.** $3y + 2x = 15$

53. $x - 11y - 7 = 0$ **54.** $2x - 3y = 6$

55. $(y - 3)/5 = (x - 2)/7$ **56.** $(3 - x)/2 - (2 + y)/3 = 0$

57. $4x - 7y = a$ **58.** $(y - a)/3 = (x - b)/4$

59. $3x + 2y = b$ **60.** $7x - 9y = c$

Find lines through the given point, (a) parallel and (b) perpendicular to the given line:

61. $(-5, 7), 3x + 4y = 12$ **62.** $(-2, -3), 5x - 2y + 1 = 0$

63. $(0, 0), 4x + 7y = 9$ **64.** $(-1, -1), 3x - 8y + 1 = 0$

65. $(2, 5), 2x + 3y = 1$ **66.** $(1, -1), 3x - 7y = 2$

Find two mediators of the triangle with the given vertices, and hence find the circumcentre:

67. $(5, 8), (5, -2), (-3, 0)$ **68.** $(2, -1), (0, 7), (8, 7)$

Find the orthocentre of the given triangle:

69. $(12, 8), (6, 0), (6, 12)$ **70.** $(0, 1), (2, 0), (2, 3)$

Find two medians of the given triangle, and hence find the centroid:

71. $(-4, 6), (-2, 4), (-6, 2)$ **72.** $(1, 1), (3, -1), (5, 3)$

73. **a**, **b**, **c** are the position vectors of A, B, C respectively. What are the position vectors of:

    (a) the point dividing BC in the ratio $1 : 2$,

    (b) the point dividing CA in the ratio $2 : 1$,

    (c) the point dividing AB in the ratio $3 : 2$?

74. **p, q, r** are the position vectors of P, Q, R respectively. What are the position vectors of:

(a) the point dividing PQ in the ratio $1:5$,

(b) the point dividing RQ in the ratio $4:1$,

(c) the point dividing PR in the ratio $0:1$?

Write down the centroids of the following triangles:

75. $(3, 1), (2, 5), (-2, 0)$ **76.** $(4, 1), (2, 3), (3, 2)$

77. $(-3, -4), (-6, -6), (12, 21)$ **78.** $(-5, -7), (4, 6), (2, 2)$

79. $(0, 3), (-5, 7), (4, 11)$ **80.** $(0, 0), (3, 5), (-6, -2)$

EXERCISE 4S

Use the method of section 4.1 to find the gradient of the chord joining the given points on the given curve:

1. $(-1, 3)$ and $(2, 12)$, $y = 3x^2$

2. $(-2, 8)$ and $(1, 2)$, $y = 2x^2$

3. Find the gradient of the chord joining $(p, 1/p)$ and $(q, 1/q)$ on the curve $y = 1/x$. Don't forget that $(p-q) = -(q-p)$. Hence find the gradient of the chord joining the two points on the curve at $x = 1/2$ and $x = 6$.

4. Find the gradient of the chord joining $(p, \sqrt{p})$ and $(q, \sqrt{q})$ on the curve $y = \sqrt{x}$. Note that $(q-p) = (\sqrt{q} - \sqrt{p})(\sqrt{q} + \sqrt{p})$. Hence find the gradient of the chord joining the two points on the curve at $x = 1$ and $x = 4$.

Differentiate the given $f(x)$ in each case, and find the gradient of $y = f(x)$ at the given point:

5. $x^2 - 5x - 2$, $(2, -8)$ **6.** $x^2 + 3x + 7$, $(3, 25)$

7. $3x^2 + 4x + 9$, $(-3, 24)$ **8.** $2x^2 - 7x + 1$, $(-1, 10)$

9. $4 - 5x^2$, $(-1, -1)$ **10.** $2 + 3x - 3x^2$, $(1/2, 11/4)$

Find the gradient of the given curve at each of the two points where it cuts the x-axis, and show that the angle between the curve and the axis is the same at these points:

11. $y = 3x^2 - 12x$ **12.** $y = 3x^2 - 12$

13. $y = x^2 - 5x + 4$ **14.** $y = x^2 - 5x - 6$

Find where the given curve meets $y = 6x$, drawing a rough sketch in each case, and find the gradient of the curve at these points of intersection:

15. $y = 2x^2$ **16.** $y = 3x^2$

17. $y = x^2 + 5$ **18.** $y = x^2 + 6x - 1$

Find dy/dx in the following cases:

19. $y = (x+3)(x-5)$

20. $y = (2x-7)(3x+10)$

21. $y = (x+1)^2$

22. $y = (x+1)^3$

23. $y = 2x^4+7x+1$

24. $y = 5x^3-x^2-9x$

25. $y = 3/x$

26. $y = 1-1/x$

27. $y = (2x-1)^2/x$

28. $y = (x^2-1)^2/x^2$

What is the gradient of the curve at the given point, and what is the equation of the tangent at this point?

29. $y = 2x^3-3x^2$, $(2,4)$

30. $y = x^6+x^7$, $(-1,0)$

31. $y = x^2-1/x$, $(1,0)$

32. $y=x^3+3/x$, $(1,4)$

What is the gradient of the curve at the given point? Find the equations of the tangent and the normal at this point.

33. $y = 5-x^2$, $(2,1)$

34. $y = 3-x+x^2$, $(3,9)$

35. $y = 3x+8/x$, $(2,10)$

36. $y = 6/x-x^3$, $(1,5)$

37. Find y' given that $y = 3\cos x+4\sin x$, where x is in radians. Draw the graph of y against x for values of x between 0 and 2π, and superimpose the graph of y' against x.

38. Find y' given that $y = \cos x-\sin x$, where x is in radians. Draw the graph of y against x for values of x between 0 and 2π, and superimpose the graph of y' against x.

Find dx/dt in the following cases:

39. $x = u^3$, $u = t^2$

40. $x = 4+u$, $u = t+6$

41. $x = u^2+4u+1$, $u = 3t$

42. $x = 5-2u+u^2$, $u = t+1$

Differentiate the following:

43. $(ax+b)^5$

44. $(px+q)^n$

45. $(3+x-x^2)^3$

46. $(5+2x+x^2)^4$

Find dy/dx in each case, and calculate the gradient of the curve at the given point, and the equation of the tangent there:

47. $y^2 = x^3$, $(4,8)$

48. $y^3 = x^2$, $(8,4)$

49. $x^2+2y^2 = 3$, $(1,1)$

50. $2x^2-3y^2 = 5$, $(2,-1)$

Find an approximate value of the following expressions for the given values of x, using the method of small increments, and also find a more accurate value using a calculator:

51. x^3+5x^2-3, $x = 1.01$

52. x^2-4x+7, $x = 12.5$

53. x^2+x^3, $x = 1001$

54. x^4-x^3, $x = 98$

55. Find the approximate percentage increase in the total surface area of a cube if the edges of the cube increase in length by 3%.

56. Find the approximate percentage decrease in the weight of a solid metal cube if cold weather causes all its linear dimensions to decrease by 1.5%.

Sketch the graph of the given curve by finding for what values of x the function is increasing or decreasing:

57. $y = 4 + 3x - x^2$ **58.** $y = 2x^2 + 8x + 5$

59. $y = 3x - x^3$ **60.** $y = 4x^3 + 30x^2$

61. A car, travelling up a hill, starts free-wheeling, and t s later it has travelled x m, where $x = 15t - t^2$. Say for what period of time x is increasing.

62. T, the percentage of time wasted in a certain factory, is given as $T = 2t + 64/t^2$, where t $(1 < t < 12)$ is the length of each shift in hours. Say for what values of t the value of T is increasing.

Find the turning points of the given functions, and discuss their nature:

63. $12x - x^3$ **64.** $x^3 - 3x^2$

65. $x^2 + 6x + 3$ **66.** $8x - 5 - x^2$

67. A rectangular box has a square base of side x cm, and its volume is 500 cm³. It has no top. Show that the area of board needed to make the base and the four sides is given by $A = x^2 + 2000/x$. What value of x will make A a minimum, and what will then be the dimensions of the box?

68. A closed rectangular box has a square base of side x cm, and its surface area is 150 cm². Show that its height is $37.5/x - x/2$, and obtain an expression for V, its volume. For what value of x will that volume V be a maximum, and what will be the maximum value?

69. The operating costs of an ocean liner are of two kinds: fuel costs of £$v^2/2$ per hour (v knots being the ship's speed), and other costs of £200 per hour. Show that the cost £C per nautical mile is given by the formula $v/2 + 200/v$, and hence find the most economical operating speed.

70. The girth plus length of a box-shaped parcel sent through the post must not exceed 300 cm. If one end of the parcel is a square measuring x cm by x cm, show that the greatest length allowed is $(300 - 4x)$ cm, and find an expression for V the volume. Hence find the optimum dimensions.

Find the stationary points and points of inflection (if any) of the following, and sketch the graphs:

71. $y = x + x^3$ **72.** $y = 3x^2 + x^3$

73. $y = x^3 - 12x + 16$ **74.** $y = 12x - 4x^3$

EXERCISE 5S

In questions 1 to 16 and 23 to 24, the four letters t, v, u, a have their usual meanings. In questions 31 to 42, take g to be $9.8 \, \text{m/s}^2$. Note: $18 \, \text{km/h} = 5 \, \text{m/s}$.

1. $u = +0.5$, $v = +1.7$, $t = 0.3$; find a.

2. $u = +1.3$, $v = +2.1$, $t = 4$; find a.

3. $u = +10.2$, $v = +6.6$, $t = 0.9$; find a.

4. $u = +3.72$, $v = +2.15$, $t = 3.14$; find a.

5. $u = -1.4$, $v = +0.6$, $t = 0.5$; find a.

6. $u = -0.7$, $v = +2.1$, $t = 4$; find a.

7. $u = +1.2$, $a = +0.6$, $t = 3$; find v.

8. $u = +0.8$, $a = +1.4$, $t = 2$; find v.

9. $v = +8$, $a = +1.5$, $t = 3$; find u.

10. $v = +3.4$, $a = +0.2$, $t = 8$; find u.

11. $u = +1.7$, $v = +2.3$, $a = +2$; find t.

12. $u = +2.76$, $v = +1.32$, $a = -1.5$; find t.

13. $u = 5$, $a = 2$: draw the v–t graph between $t = 0$ and $t = 6$, and find the distance travelled.

14. $u = 40$, $a = -3$: draw the v–t graph between $t = 0$ and $t = 10$, and find the distance travelled.

15. A vehicle accelerates at $1 \, \text{m/s}^2$ from rest to a speed of $16 \, \text{m/s}$, and then decelerates at $2 \, \text{m/s}^2$ until once again at rest. Draw a v–t graph, and find the distance travelled.

16. A Lotus approaches a corner at $50 \, \text{m/s}$. The driver decelerates uniformly for $5 \, \text{s}$, goes at the lower speed for $5 \, \text{s}$, and then accelerates uniformly for $5 \, \text{s}$ to return to his original speed. Sketch the v–t graph, and find the lower speed, given that the car travels $650 \, \text{m}$ during the $15 \, \text{s}$.

17. What acceleration does a force of $5 \, \text{N}$ give a mass of $2 \, \text{kg}$?

18. What acceleration does a force of $0.4 \, \text{N}$ give a mass of $500 \, \text{grams}$?

19. What force is needed to accelerate a mass of $1.5 \, \text{tonnes}$ at $0.5 \, \text{m/s}^2$?

20. What force is needed to accelerate a mass of $200 \, \text{grams}$ at $1.5 \, \text{m/s}^2$?

21. What mass is accelerated at $0.1 \, \text{m/s}^2$ by a force of $2 \, \text{N}$?

22. What mass is accelerated at $0.6 \, \text{m/s}^2$ by a force of $0.15 \, \text{N}$?

23. $u = +0.5$, $v = +2.5$, $t = 20$; find P if $m = 5$.

24. $u = +1.3$, $v = +2.8$, $t = 3$; find P if $m = 0.2$.

25. What force is needed to accelerate a mass of 1.5 tonnes from 9 km/h to 36 km/h in 30 s?

26. What force is needed to decelerate a mass of 0.5 tonne from 27 km/h to 9 km/h in 1 minute?

27. A force of 2 N changed the speed of an object from 2 m/s to 2.3 m/s over 10 s. What was the mass of the object?

28. A force of 0.5 N changed the speed of an object from 5 m/s to 15 m/s over 1.5 s. What was its mass?

29. A force of 500 N acts on a mass of 3 tonnes for 20 s. Its original speed is 2 m/s. What is its final speed?

30. A force of 0.15 N acts on a mass of 50 grams for 3 s. Its original speed is 1.5 m/s. What is its final speed?

31. Find the weight (in newtons) of (a) 3 kg, (b) 0.55 kg, (c) 200 grams, (d) 0.5 tonne.

32. Find the weight of (a) 4 kg, (b) 0.2 kg, (c) 0.5 gram, (d) 2 tonnes.

33. What mass has a weight of (a) 30 N, (b) 1 kN, (c) 0.1 N?

34. What mass has a weight of (a) 50 N, (b) 550 N, (c) 0.5 N?

35. A 2 kg mass hangs on a rope. What is the tension in the rope when the mass is (a) at rest, (b) accelerating up at $3 \, m/s^2$, (c) accelerating down at $3 \, m/s^2$?

36. A crate of supplies of total mass 50 kg is being lowered to the ground by winch from a helicopter. What is the tension in the winch cable when the crate is (a) accelerating down at $2 \, m/s^2$, (b) moving down at a steady speed, (c) decelerating at $4 \, m/s^2$?

37. A 4 kg mass hangs on a rope. Find the acceleration (and say whether it is up or down) when the tension in the rope is (a) 30 N, (b) 40 N, (c) 50 N.

38. A mass of 500 kg hangs on a wire. Find the acceleration (and say whether it is up or down) when the tension in the wire is (a) 3000 N, (b) 5000 N, (c) 7000 N.

39. A submarine of mass 4000 tonnes is patrolling at a steady depth below the surface. What must be the upward buoyancy force exerted by the water? If this force is reduced by 10% owing to a change in the density of the water, what is the consequent downward acceleration of the boat?

40. The captain of a submerged midget submarine finds that he is accelerating upwards at $0.2 \, m/s^2$. What is the buoyancy force if the mass of the boat is 100 tonnes, and how many tonnes of water must the captain allow to flood into the ballast tanks to achieve a proper trim?

41. A balloon of mass 1 tonne is moving down with an acceleration of $1 \, \text{m/s}^2$. Calculate the upward force exerted by the air. When it is moving down at $30 \, \text{m/s}$, ballast of $200 \, \text{kg}$ is dropped out. When does the balloon stop descending (if the air continues to exert the same upward force)?

42. A balloon of mass $1200 \, \text{kg}$ carries additional ballast of mass $300 \, \text{kg}$. Calculate the upward buoyancy force if the balloon is descending with an acceleration of $0.5 \, \text{m/s}^2$. When the speed of descent is $20 \, \text{m/s}$, all the ballast is thrown overboard. What will now be the balloon's deceleration, and when will it stop descending? Assume that the buoyancy force remains the same.

EXERCISE 6S

1. Find $\begin{pmatrix} 2 & 1 \\ 1 & 4 \end{pmatrix} + \begin{pmatrix} 3 & -3 \\ 0 & 2 \end{pmatrix}$ **2.** Find $\begin{pmatrix} 0 & 1 \\ 3 & 4 \end{pmatrix} + \begin{pmatrix} 1 & 2 \\ 0 & -6 \end{pmatrix}$

3. Find $\begin{pmatrix} -2 & 3 \\ 4 & -2 \end{pmatrix} - \begin{pmatrix} 1 & 4 \\ 0 & -6 \end{pmatrix}$

4. Find $\begin{pmatrix} 3 & 6 & 4 \\ -2 & -3 & 1 \\ 4 & 0 & 6 \end{pmatrix} - \begin{pmatrix} -1 & 2 & 1 \\ 0 & 4 & 3 \\ 5 & 1 & 7 \end{pmatrix}$

Multiply (or explain why the calculation is not possible):

5. $\begin{pmatrix} 2 & 1 \\ 3 & -1 \end{pmatrix} \begin{pmatrix} 1 \\ -2 \end{pmatrix}$ **6.** $(1 - 2) \begin{pmatrix} 2 & 1 \\ 3 & -1 \end{pmatrix}$

7. $(1 \quad 6 \quad -3) \begin{pmatrix} 6 \\ 1 \\ 4 \end{pmatrix}$ **8.** $\begin{pmatrix} 6 \\ 1 \\ 4 \end{pmatrix} (1 \quad 6 \quad -3)$

9. $(1 \quad 3)(3 \quad -1)$ **10.** $(2) \begin{pmatrix} 4 & 3 \\ 1 & -1 \end{pmatrix}$

11. $\begin{pmatrix} 0 & -1 \\ 1 & 0 \end{pmatrix} \begin{pmatrix} 0 & 1 & 0 & 1 \\ 0 & 0 & 1 & 1 \end{pmatrix}$ **12.** $\begin{pmatrix} 0 & 1 \\ 1 & 0 \end{pmatrix} \begin{pmatrix} 0 & 2 & 0 & 2 \\ 0 & 0 & 2 & 2 \end{pmatrix}$

Find the determinants of the following matrices; say whether the matrix is singular, and find the inverse if it exists:

13. $\begin{pmatrix} 1 & -1 \\ 1 & 1 \end{pmatrix}$ **14.** $\begin{pmatrix} 1 & -1 \\ -1 & 1 \end{pmatrix}$ **15.** $\begin{pmatrix} 2 & 1 \\ 4 & 3 \end{pmatrix}$ **16.** $\begin{pmatrix} 0 & -1 \\ 1 & 1 \end{pmatrix}$

17. $\begin{pmatrix} -3 & -5 \\ 4 & 7 \end{pmatrix}$ **18.** $\begin{pmatrix} 3 & -5 \\ -4 & 7 \end{pmatrix}$ **19.** $\begin{pmatrix} 2 & 1 \\ 1 & 0 \end{pmatrix}$ **20.** $\begin{pmatrix} 0 & -1 \\ -1 & 0 \end{pmatrix}$

What transformations are represented by the following matrices?

21. $\begin{pmatrix} 3 & 0 \\ 0 & 2 \end{pmatrix}$ **22.** $\begin{pmatrix} -2 & 0 \\ 0 & -2 \end{pmatrix}$ **23.** $\begin{pmatrix} 3 & 4 \\ -4 & 3 \end{pmatrix}$ **24.** $\begin{pmatrix} 1 & -2 \\ 0 & 1 \end{pmatrix}$

25. $\begin{pmatrix} 1 & 0 \\ 3 & 1 \end{pmatrix}$ **26.** $\begin{pmatrix} 0 & -3 \\ -3 & 0 \end{pmatrix}$ **27.** $\begin{pmatrix} -2 & 1 \\ 0 & -2 \end{pmatrix}$ **28.** $\begin{pmatrix} 2 & 4 \\ 1 & 2 \end{pmatrix}$

Evaluate the following matrix products, and interpret the results geometrically (e.g. reflection in $y = 0$ followed by reflection in $y = x$ is equivalent to a positive quarter turn):

29. $\begin{pmatrix} 0 & -1 \\ 1 & 0 \end{pmatrix}\begin{pmatrix} -1 & 0 \\ 0 & 1 \end{pmatrix}$ **30.** $\begin{pmatrix} -1 & 0 \\ 0 & 1 \end{pmatrix}\begin{pmatrix} 0 & -1 \\ 1 & 0 \end{pmatrix}$

31. $\begin{pmatrix} -1 & 0 \\ 0 & -1 \end{pmatrix}\begin{pmatrix} -1 & 0 \\ 0 & -1 \end{pmatrix}$ **32.** $\begin{pmatrix} 1 & 2 \\ 0 & 1 \end{pmatrix}\begin{pmatrix} 1 & 3 \\ 0 & 1 \end{pmatrix}$

Find in each case the matrix that maps AB on to CD:

33. A(2, 5), B(1, 3), C(3, −1), D(4, 2)

34. A(3, −2), B(−2, 2), C(1, 6), D(6, 1)

35. Find the area of triangle ABC as defined in question 33.

36. Find the areas of ABC and ABCD as defined in question 34.

EXERCISE 7S

By drawing give the polar form of:

1. $[3, 0°] + [4, 120°]$ **2.** $[2, 90°] + [5, −70°]$

3. $[4, 40°] + [5, 130°]$ **4.** $[3, −60°] + [4, −160°]$

By calculation give the polar form of:

5. $[3, 0°] + [4, 120°]$ **6.** $[2, 90°] + [5, −70°]$

7. $[4, 40°] + [5, 130°]$ **8.** $[3, −60°] + [4, −160°]$

9. Forces of 3 N and 5 N act at an angle of 70° to each other. Find the magnitude of their resultant and the angle it makes with the first force, (a) by drawing and (b) by calculation.

10. Forces of 2 N and 6 N act at an angle of 110° to each other. Find the magnitude of their resultant and the angle it makes with the first force, (a) by drawing and (b) by calculation.

11. Find, by drawing, the magnitude of the resultant of the forces shown in figure 7.11, and the angle it makes with the 3 N force.

12. Find, by drawing, the magnitude of the resultant of the forces shown in figure 7.12, and the angle it makes with the 5 N force.

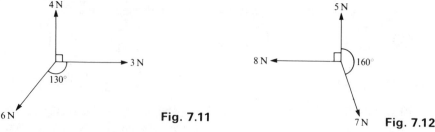

Fig. 7.11   Fig. 7.12

13. Answer question 11 by calculation.

14. Answer question 12 by calculation.

15. My cross-channel ferry is heading south-east towards Calais at a speed of 20 knots. I walk on deck from the starboard to the port side at a speed of 4 knots. Find, by drawing, my resultant velocity.

16. My executive jet heads in direction 120° at an air speed of 300 m/s. The air's velocity is 100 m/s in direction north. Find, by drawing, my ground speed.

17. Answer question 15 by calculation.

18. Answer question 16 by calculation.

19. I travel 20 miles east, and then a further 15 miles in a different direction. I end up south-east of my starting point. Find, by drawing, the two possible directions for the second leg of the journey.

20. A submarine steers on a course of 270° at a speed of 25 knots and at a depth of 300 feet. At that depth, the current is known to flow due south. The boat's navigational equipment shows that her actual direction of travel is 250°. What must be the speed of the current?

21. Two forces of 0.5 N at 80° to each other act on a body of mass 200 grams. Find its acceleration.

22. A barge of mass 0.6 tonne is pulled by two forces of 300 N, acting at 50° on either side of the fore-and-aft line. Find its acceleration, neglecting water resistance.

23. A mass of 5 kg hangs on a string of length 1.5 m, tied to a fixed point. A horizontal force pulls the mass a horizontal distance 50 cm sideways. Find, by drawing, (a) the angle the string now makes with the vertical, (b) the tension in the string, (c) the horizontal force.

24. A 200 gram mass is suspended from a hook by a thread of length 60 cm. If a horizontal force pulls the mass a horizontal distance 10 cm sideways, find, by drawing, (a) the angle the thread makes with the vertical, (b) the tension in the thread, (c) the horizontal force.

25. Answer question 23 by calculation.

26. Answer question 24 by calculation.

27. A mass of 2 kg hangs by strings of length 60 cm and 90 cm from two hooks on the same level a distance of 1.2 m apart. By drawing, find   (a) the angles the strings make with the vertical,   (b) the tensions in the strings.

28. A mass of 0.5 tonne hangs by strings of length 5 m and 7 m from two hooks on the same level a distance 10 m apart. By drawing, find   (a) the angles the strings make with the vertical,   (b) the tensions in the strings.

29. A mass is supported by two strings at 90° in which the tensions are 5 N and 7 N. Find the mass by calculation.

30. A mass is supported by two ropes at 90° in which the tensions are 2 kN and 3 kN. Find the mass by calculation.

31. (a) A 200 kg mass is moving on a smooth horizontal plane, pulled by an 80 N horizontal force. Find the acceleration and the normal force from the ground.
(b) If the 80 N pull is now at 40° to the ground, find the new acceleration and normal force.
(c) If a frictional force of 20 N is added to situation (a), find the acceleration and normal force.
(d) If a frictional force of 20 N is added to situation (b), find the acceleration and normal force.

32. (a) A 500 gram mass is moving on a smooth horizontal plane, pulled by a 0.2 N horizontal force. Find the acceleration and the normal force from the plane.
(b) If the 0.2 N force is now at 30° to the horizontal, find the new acceleration and normal force.
(c) If a frictional force of 0.05 N is added to situation (a), find the acceleration and normal force.
(d) If a frictional force of 0.05 N is added to situation (b), find the acceleration and normal force.

33. (a) In figure 7.13 we have a mass of 200 kg. If $P = 80\,(N)$ and the mass has acceleration 0.15 m/s², find R and F.
(b) If P remains 80 but now pulls up at an angle of 35° and if the acceleration is 0.25 m/s², find R and F.

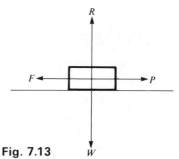

Fig. 7.13

34. (a) In figure 7.13 we now have a mass of 800 grams.   If $P = 2.5\,(N)$ and the mass has acceleration 1.2 m/s², find R and F.
(b) If P remains 2.5 but now pulls up at an angle of 25° and if the acceleration is 0.4 m/s², find R and F.

35. (a) A 5 kg mass sits on a rough plane at $35°$ to the horizontal. Find the friction and the normal force.
(b) If the maximum frictional force available is reduced to 20 N, what will be the acceleration?

36. (a) A 500 gram mass sits on a rough plane at $50°$ to the horizontal. Find the friction and the normal force.
(b) If the maximum frictional force available is reduced to 2 N, what will be the acceleration?

37. A 10 kg mass is moving down a slope of $35°$ with an acceleration of $2.2 \, \text{m/s}^2$. Find the frictional force and the normal force.

38. A 500 gram mass is sliding down an incline of $18°$ with an acceleration of $1.9 \, \text{m/s}^2$. Find the frictional and normal forces.

39. What is the steepest slope (give the angle to the horizontal) up which an engine of mass 2 tonnes can go with a driving force of 600 N (and no resistance)?

40. What is the steepest gradient that can be tackled by a vehicle of mass 500 kg with a driving force of 400 N if the resistance is negligible?

41. The resistance to motion of a 1.5 tonne engine is 120 N/tonne. The engine goes up a slope of 1 in 100 with an acceleration of $0.04 \, \text{m/s}^2$. Calculate the driving force. What would be the acceleration (with the same driving force and resistance) (a) on the flat and (b) going down the same slope?

42. The resistance to motion of a 3 tonne lorry is 100 N/tonne. The lorry goes up a slope of 1 in 40 with an acceleration of $0.06 \, \text{m/s}^2$. Calculate the driving force. What would be the acceleration (with the same driving force and resistance) (a) on the flat and (b) going down the same slope?

EXERCISE 8S

Simplify each of the following:

1. $\sqrt{72}$

2. $\sqrt{75}$

3. $\sqrt{(4/9)}$

4. $\sqrt[3]{(64/27)}$

5. $\sqrt{3} \times \sqrt{27}$

6. $5\sqrt{2} \div \sqrt{8}$

7. $\sqrt{200} \div \sqrt{(1/4)}$

8. $\sqrt{8} \times \sqrt{6} \div \sqrt{75}$

9. $\sqrt{8} + \sqrt{128} - 2\sqrt{32}$

10. $\sqrt{125} + \sqrt{45} - 3\sqrt{20}$

11. $\sqrt{12} - 5\sqrt{48} + 10\sqrt{9}$

12. $\sqrt{343} - \sqrt{28} - \sqrt{175}$

13. $(2\sqrt{3} + 4)^2$

14. $(\sqrt{11} + \sqrt{8})(\sqrt{11} - \sqrt{8})$

15. $(3\sqrt{2} + 5\sqrt{3})(5\sqrt{2} - 2\sqrt{3})$

16. $(2 - \sqrt{3})^3$

Find the values of:

17. $8^{2/3}$

18. $27^{-4/3}$

19. $100^{3/2}$

20. $1000^{-1/3}$

21. $(3\frac{3}{8})^{5/3}$

22. $(1\frac{7}{9})^{1/2}$

23. $(12\frac{1}{4})^{3/2}$

24. $(5\frac{1}{16})^{1/4}$

25. $(1.69)^{-1/2}$

26. $(0.125)^{-2/3}$

27. $(0.001)^{4/3}$

28. $(0.25)^{-3/2}$

Simplify the following expressions as far as possible:

29. $3pq \times 5r^3 \times (pr^2)^{-1}$

30. $9s^2t \times 16st^3 \times (12st)^{-2}$

31. $4a^2 \times 5a^4b \div (10a^3b^2)$

32. $c^2d \times 12c^3d^5 \times (2c^2d^2)^{-3}$

33. $2^{3t} \times 4^{-2t} \times 8^{t+3}$

34. $3^{5m} \times 9^{2m} \div 27^{3m}$

35. $3^n \times 4^{-n} \times 12^n$

36. $5^{2t} \times 2^{4t} \times 10^{-3t}$

Without using calculating aids, solve the following equations:

37. $4s^{-2/3} = 1/25$

38. $0.1t^{3/2} = 0.0008$

39. $2 \times 4^{5x} = 8^{4x+1}$

40. $3^{2x} \times 27^{x-1} = 9^6$

41. $9^p - 4 \times 3^p + 3 = 0$ (substitute $q = 3^p$)

42. $4^n - 3 \times 2^{n+1} + 8 = 0$

43. $\sqrt{(x+5)} = 5 - \sqrt{x}$ (square both sides)

44. $\sqrt{(x+1)} + \sqrt{(x-2)} = 3$

In each case, find dy/dx and solve the equation $dy/dx = 0$:

45. $y = \sqrt{x} - x\sqrt{x}$

46. $y = \sqrt[3]{x^2} + x/3$

47. $y = (x+1) \div \sqrt{x}$

48. $y = (x^3\sqrt{x} + 6) \div \sqrt{x}$

49. Square $(\sqrt{a} - \sqrt{b})$, and hence find $\sqrt{(5 - 2\sqrt{6})}$.

50. Work out $(\sqrt{2} - 1)^3$, and hence find $\sqrt[3]{(7 - 5\sqrt{2})}$.

51. Find integers x and y such that $4^x \times 3^y = 24^{18}$.

52. If $2^{x+y} = 1$ and $10^{3x-y} = 100$, find 3^{x+y} and x^y.

Solve the following equations using the decimal-search method (and a calculator), with all intermediate results carefully tabulated, and final answers accurate to 3 s.f.:

53. $0.735^n = 0.527$

54. $0.914^n = 0.346$

55. $x^3 + 7x = 10$

56. $x^3 - 5x^2 = 462$

57. $\cos\theta - \sin\theta = 0.34$ (given that θ is acute)

58. $\sin\theta + \tan\theta = 1.58$ (given that θ is acute)

By taking logarithms of both sides, solve the following equations, giving your answers correct to 5 s.f.:

59. $4^x = 7$ **60.** $53^x = 419$

61. $17^x = 0.614$ **62.** $0.154^x = 0.0318$

63. Solve $(0.3)^x = (0.4)^{x+5}$ (to 4 s.f.)

64. Solve $(0.1)^x = (0.2)^3$ (to 5 s.f.)

65. Solve $4^x \times 9^x = 216$ (exactly)

66. Solve $4^x \times 9^x = 10^{x+1}$ (to 3 s.f.)

67. £P invested at $r\%$ per annum compound interest will amount to £$P(1+r/100)^n$ after n years. After how long will £150 invested at 9% have trebled in value?

68. After how long will £6000 invested at 7% compound interest amount to £8000? What sum invested for the same period of time and at the same rate of interest would amount to £9000?

Write down the values of the following logarithms:

69. $\log_3 9$ **70.** $\log_{64} 8$ **71.** $\log_{\sqrt 2} 4$ **72.** $\log_{100} 10$

73. Express $\log 108$ in terms of $\log 2$ and $\log 3$.

74. Express $\log 375$ in terms of $\log 3$ and $\log 5$.

75. Given that $\log 2 = 0.301\,03$ and $\log 3 = 0.477\,12$ (each to 5 d.p.), evaluate $\log 12$, $\log(3/4)$, and $\log 10.125$, all to 4 d.p.

76. Given the values of $\log 2$ and $\log 3$ (as in question 75), evaluate $\log 18$, $\log(4/9)$, and $\log 6.75$, all to 4 d.p.

77. Simplify $(\log x^3) \div (\log x^2)$.

78. Simplify $\log x^4 + \log x^3 + \log x^2 + \log x$.

79. Find x if $(\log_{10} x)^2 - \log_{10} x = 0$.

80. Find x if $(\log_{10} x)^2 - 3\log_{10} x + 2 = 0$.

81. Given that $u^t = 25$, find $\log_5 u$ in terms of t.

82. Given that $v^t = 1/4$, find $\log_8 v$ in terms of t.

83. The function f if given by $f:x \to 10^x$. Express the inverse function f^{-1} in the same way. Find $f(2.5)$, and write down the values of $f^{-1}(100)$ and $f^{-1}(0.1)$.

84. The function g is given by $g:x \to e^x$. Express the inverse function g^{-1} in the same way. Find $g(2.5)$, and write down the values of $g^{-1}(100)$ and $g^{-1}(0.1)$.

85. $f(x) = x^x$, $g(x) = (x^x)^x$, $h(x) = x^{(x^x)}$. Calculate the values of f, g, and h for $x = 1, 2, 3$.

EXERCISE 9S

Express each of the following vectors in terms of the base vectors $\mathbf{a} = \mathbf{i} + 2\mathbf{j}$ and $\mathbf{b} = 3\mathbf{i} - \mathbf{j}$:

1. $5\mathbf{i} + 3\mathbf{j}$ **2.** $2\mathbf{i} - 3\mathbf{j}$
3. $-3\mathbf{i} + 8\mathbf{j}$ **4.** $\mathbf{i} + 16\mathbf{j}$
5. $10\mathbf{i} + 7\mathbf{j}$ **6.** $7\mathbf{i} - 10\mathbf{j}$

Calculate the following scalar products:

7. $[3, 35°] \cdot [5, 75°]$

8. $[4, 30°] \cdot [7, 80°]$

9. $[2.64, 162.7°] \cdot [3.47, 23.8°]$

10. $[471, 5.7°] \cdot [532, -8.8°]$

11. $[0.418, -104.8°] \cdot [0.516, 97.3°]$

12. $[12, 143.7°] \cdot [53, -162.7°]$

13. to 18. Sketch the vectors given in questions 7 to 12, and in each case calculate the projection of the first vector on the second.

In each of the following questions calculate the scalar product of the two vectors, and deduce the projection of the first vector on the second:

19. $4\mathbf{i} - \mathbf{j}$ and $2\mathbf{i} + \mathbf{j}$ **20.** $7\mathbf{i} + 3\mathbf{j}$ and $3\mathbf{i} - 4\mathbf{j}$
21. $24\mathbf{i} + 7\mathbf{j}$ and $\mathbf{i} + 7\mathbf{j}$ **22.** $3\mathbf{i} - 20\mathbf{j}$ and $2\mathbf{i} + 2\mathbf{j}$
23. $-6\mathbf{i} + 2\mathbf{j}$ and $4\mathbf{i} + 4\mathbf{j}$ **24.** $4\mathbf{i} + 6\mathbf{j}$ and $-8\mathbf{i} - 6\mathbf{j}$
25. $9\mathbf{i} + 7\mathbf{j} - 8\mathbf{k}$ and $2\mathbf{i} - 2\mathbf{j} - \mathbf{k}$ **26.** $3\mathbf{i} - 4\mathbf{j} + 7\mathbf{k}$ and $6\mathbf{i} + 3\mathbf{j} + 2\mathbf{k}$

27. P is at $(0, 10)$ and Q at $(3, 4)$. Calculate the scalar product $\mathbf{OP} \cdot \mathbf{OQ}$, and hence the projection of $\mathbf{OP}$ on $\mathbf{OQ}$, illustrating your result in a freehand diagram. Then use Pythagoras' theorem to find the distance from P to the line OQ.

28. As question 27, but with P at $(7, 1)$ and Q at $(4, -3)$.

29. The three points $A(4, 9)$, $B(10, 1)$, $C(8, 10)$ form the triangle ABC. Calculate the projection of $\mathbf{AC}$ on $\mathbf{AB}$, illustrating your result in a freehand diagram. Then use Pythagoras' theorem to find the distance from C to AB, and hence find the area of the triangle ABC.

30. As question 29, but with A at $(2, 7)$, B at $(26, 14)$, and C at $(4, 18)$.

Calculate the angles between the following pairs of vectors, illustrating your answers with sketches:

31. $2\mathbf{i} + \mathbf{j}$ and $\mathbf{i} + 3\mathbf{j}$ **32.** $3\mathbf{i} + 2\mathbf{j}$ and $\mathbf{i} + 4\mathbf{j}$
33. $-2\mathbf{i} + 3\mathbf{j}$ and $2\mathbf{i} + \mathbf{j}$ **34.** $\mathbf{i} - 2\mathbf{j}$ and $\mathbf{i} + 3\mathbf{j}$
35. $-2\mathbf{i} + \mathbf{j}$ and $-3\mathbf{i} - 4\mathbf{j}$ **36.** $-\mathbf{i} - 2\mathbf{j}$ and $-2\mathbf{i} + \mathbf{j}$

Calculate the angles between the following vectors:

37. $\mathbf{i}+2\mathbf{j}+3\mathbf{k}$ and $2\mathbf{i}+3\mathbf{j}+\mathbf{k}$

38. $2\mathbf{i}+3\mathbf{j}+5\mathbf{k}$ and $3\mathbf{i}+5\mathbf{j}+2\mathbf{k}$

39. $\mathbf{i}-3\mathbf{j}+6\mathbf{k}$ and $-2\mathbf{i}+2\mathbf{j}+\mathbf{k}$

40. $3\mathbf{i}-2\mathbf{j}-\mathbf{k}$ and $-4\mathbf{i}+3\mathbf{j}-2\mathbf{k}$

41. The point O is the mid-point of AB, and C is a fourth point. By expressing the vectors **AC** and **BC** in terms of **OA** and **OC**, (a) prove that if OC is perpendicular to OA then $\mathbf{AC}\cdot\mathbf{AC}$ must equal $\mathbf{BC}\cdot\mathbf{BC}$, (b) state and prove the converse theorem.

42. A, B, C, D are four points, with position vectors **a**, **b**, **c**, and **d**. Show that if AB is perpendicular to CD then $\mathbf{a}\cdot\mathbf{c}+\mathbf{b}\cdot\mathbf{d}$ must equal $\mathbf{b}\cdot\mathbf{c}+\mathbf{a}\cdot\mathbf{d}$, and establish the corresponding result if AC is perpendicular to BD. Hence prove that if AB is perpendicular to CD and AC is perpendicular to BD, then AD must also be perpendicular to BC.

Use the cosine rule to calculate:

43. b if $c = 2.84$, $a = 4.32$, $B = 65.7°$

44. c if $a = 3.15$, $b = 3.94$, $C = 48.3°$

45. q if $p = 0.0784$, $r = 0.126$, $Q = 124.7°$

46. x if $y = 832$, $z = 967$, $X = 143.4°$

47. A if $a = 2.37$, $b = 1.76$, $c = 2.62$

48. C if $a = 3.45$, $b = 4.18$, $c = 2.87$

49. Q if $p = 17.6$, $q = 23.4$, $r = 14.4$

50. U if $w = 0.783$, $u = 1.24$, $v = 0.852$

51. The smallest angle if $x = 5.72$, $y = 6.83$, $z = 4.18$

52. The largest angle if $l = 8.53$, $m = 2.05$, $n = 8.28$

Use the sine rule to calculate:

53. b if $a = 6.73$, $A = 56.7°$, $B = 43.4°$

54. a if $b = 4.87$, $A = 73.9°$, $B = 38.3°$

55. a if $c = 18.3$, $A = 26.3°$, $B = 47.2°$

56. r if $p = 0.0316$, $P = 126.8°$, $Q = 17.4°$

57. B if $a = 6.73$, $b = 5.39$, $A = 56.7°$

58. B if $c = 7.86$, $b = 4.32$, $C = 74.3°$

59. B (acute) if $a = 6.73$, $b = 7.39$, $A = 56.7°$

60. A (obtuse) if $a = 8.47$, $c = 7.86$, $C = 54.3°$

61. R if $p = 263$, $q = 223$, $P = 116.7°$

62. Z (acute) if $x = 3470$, $y = 5643$, $X = 24.7°$

Calculate the areas of the triangles if:

63. $a = 2.75$, $b = 7.62$, $C = 76.3°$

64. $b = 57.3$, $c = 83.2$, $A = 107.8°$

65. $p = 457$, $q = 319$, $R = 28.9°$

66. $q = 5.4196$, $r = 7.3285$, $P = 132.5°$

67. ABC is a triangle in which angle A equals 80°, AB = 7 units, and AC = 10 units. Use the cosine rule to calculate the length BC, and then the sine rule to find angles B and C.

68. AD is the internal bisector of angle A of the triangle ABC defined in question 67, the point D lying on BC. Calculate the length AD, and the ratio BD/DC.

69. M is the mid-point of the side PR of the triangle PQR. If PQ = 5, QR = 7, RP = 6 units, use the cosine rule twice to calculate   (a) angle P,   (b) the length of the median QM.

70. ABCD is a quadrilateral. Angle A equals 60°, AB = 4, BC = 5, CD = 2, DA = 3 units. Find BD and then angle C (using the cosine rule twice), and hence the area of the quadrilateral.

EXERCISE 10S

Find the coordinates of the point P when:

1. A is $(2, 7)$, B is $(4, 11)$, and $\mathbf{AP} = 2\mathbf{AB}$

2. A is $(3, -1)$, B is $(5, 3)$, and $\mathbf{AP} = 3\mathbf{AB}$

3. A is $(-4, 2)$, B is $(8, 6)$, and $\mathbf{AP} = 2\mathbf{BP}$

4. A is $(-12, 0)$, B is $(0, 16)$, and $\mathbf{AP} = \frac{3}{4}\mathbf{AB}$

5. If R is $(-2, 5)$ and S is $(4, -3)$, find the coordinates of (a) the point T between R and S such that RT = 5, and (b) the point U on RS produced such that RU = 15.

6. If A is $(-1, 3)$ and B is $(6, -21)$, find the coordinates of (a) the point C between A and B such that AC = 5, and (b) the point D on AB produced such that BD = 15.

7. Given $\mathbf{r} = \begin{pmatrix} 1 \\ 2 \end{pmatrix} + t \begin{pmatrix} -4 \\ 3 \end{pmatrix}$ is the equation of a line, find how far it is along the line from the point $(1, 2)$ to the point where $t = 3$. Find also the two points on the line which are 10 units from $(1, 2)$.

8. Given $\mathbf{r} = \begin{pmatrix} -1 \\ 4 \end{pmatrix} + t \begin{pmatrix} 5 \\ 12 \end{pmatrix}$ is the equation of a line, find how far it is along the line from the point $(-1, 4)$ to the point where $t = 2$. Find also the two points on the line which are 13 units from $(-1, 4)$.

9. Write down vectors normal to: $y = 7x$, $x = 2y$, $2x+y = 0$, $3x+9y = 7$, $-2x+5y = 11$, $-6x-19y = 15$.

10. Write down vectors normal to: $y = 3x$, $5y = -x$, $4x-9y = 7$, $3x+11y = 2$, $12x-7y+15 = 0$, $12x-3y+1 = 0$.

11. Find the distance from the point $(2, 7)$ to the line joining $(1, 3)$ and $(5, 6)$.

12. Find the distance from the point $(-1, 3)$ to the line joining $(4, 7)$ and $(-1, -5)$.

Find the equations of the circles with centre and radius as given, expanding the brackets and simplifying in each case:

13. (a) $(3, 5)$, $r = 5$ (b) $(-3, 4)$, $r = 1$

14. (a) $(-2, -7)$, $r = 0.5$ (b) $(4, -3)$, $r = 1.5$

Find the centre and radius of the following circles:

15. (a) $x^2+y^2 = 25$ (b) $x^2+4x+y^2 = 21$

     (c) $x^2+y^2-4x-10y = 7$ (d) $x^2+y^2-2x+2y = 7$

16. (a) $x^2+y^2 = 4x-6y+3$ (b) $x^2+y^2+16x-2y = 19$

     (c) $4x^2+4y^2 = 4x+4y+7$ (d) $3x^2+3y^2-6x-8y = 1$

17. Calculate the coordinates of the foot of the perpendicular
    (a) from $(3, 4)$ to $9x+12y = 0$,
    (b) from $(-1, 3)$ to $3x-4y-10 = 0$.

18. Calculate the coordinates of the foot of the perpendicular
    (a) from $(1, -2)$ to $5x+12y = 150$,
    (b) from $(11, 9)$ to $y = x$.

19. Find the perpendicular distance from $A(-1, 3)$ to each of the following lines: $3y = 4x-5$, $7x-24y = 1$, $5x+12y = 5$.

20. Find the distance from $A(-1, 3)$ to each of the following lines: $6x+8y = 1$, $2x-y = 5$, $3x+y-2 = 0$.

21. Find the distance from $B(1, 2)$ to each of the following lines: $3x+4y = 5$, $8x+6y = 1$, $5x = 12y+1$.

22. Find the distance from $C(2, -3)$ to each of the following lines: $7x+24y-15 = 0$, $2x+y = 1$, $2x-3y = 5$.

23. For what values of c is the line $y = 3x+c$ a tangent to the circle $(x-2)^2+(y+3)^2 = 10$?

24. For what values of d is the line $x+2y = d$ a tangent to the circle $(x+1)^2+(y-2)^2 = 5$?

25. Find the equation of the tangent to the circle $(x-1)^2+(y-2)^2 = 25$ at the points $(4, 6)$, $(-4, 2)$, $(-2, 6)$, and $(1, -3)$.

26. Find the equation of the tangent to the circle $(x+3)^2+(y-1)^2 = 169$ at the points $(9, 6)$, $(2, -11)$, $(-15, -4)$, and $(-8, 13)$.

27. Find the equation in the form $\mathbf{r} = \mathbf{a}+t\mathbf{m}$ of the perpendiculars through $(1, 5)$ to the following lines: (a) $y = 3x+12$ and (b) $x+2y = 1$. Hence find the coordinates of the images of the point $(1, 5)$ when reflected in each of these lines.

28. As question 27, but with: (a) $3x-5y-12 = 0$, and (b) $5x+7y+34 = 0$.

29. Find the equations of the tangents to the following circles, in each case with the given gradient:

(a) $x^2+y^2 = 25$; $4/3$

(b) $x^2+y^2+2x+8y = 8$; $-3/4$

(c) $x^2+y^2+6x-2y = 615$; $-24/7$

(d) $x^2+y^2+8x-10y-8 = 0$; 0

30. As question 29, but:

(a) $x^2+y^2 = 25$; $-3/4$

(b) $x^2+y^2+4x-6y = 12$; $3/4$

(c) $x^2+y^2-2x+6y = 615$; $7/24$

(d) $x^2+y^2+2x-12y-12 = 0$; ∞

The conditions to be satisfied by $P(x, y)$ are as stated in each of the following questions. Find the equation of the locus, and state whether the locus is a straight line, a circle (in which case give its centre and radius), or some other curve.

31. A is $(-1, 5)$, B is $(-3, 1)$; $AP = BP$.

32. A is $(-1, -2)$, B is $(-4, 1)$; $AP = BP$.

33. A is $(-3, 0)$, B is $(0, 6)$; $AP = 2BP$.

34. A is $(-1, -2)$, B is $(3, 2)$; $BP = 3AP$.

35. A is $(1, 2)$, l is the line $y = 3x$; the distance AP equals the distance from P to l.

36. A is $(-2, 5)$, l is the line $x+y = 1$; the distance AP equals the distance from P to l.

37. P is equidistant from the two lines $x+7y-9 = 0$ and $5x+5y = 1$.

38. P is equidistant from the two lines $3x+y+1 = 0$ and $x-3y = 5$.

Express the following lines in vector form:

39. (a) $3y = x-1$ (b) $2y+3x = 1$

40. (a) $3y+4x+5 = 0$ (b) $y = \frac{1}{2}(4-x)$

Express the following lines in x–y form:

41. (a) $\mathbf{r} = (3t-1)\mathbf{i}+(2t-2)\mathbf{j}$ (b) $\mathbf{r} = (1.5-2t)\mathbf{i}+(2+2.5t)\mathbf{j}$

42. (a) $\mathbf{r} = (3t-2)\mathbf{i}+(4t+2)\mathbf{j}$ (b) $\mathbf{r} = -2t\mathbf{i}-(1-t)\mathbf{j}$

Express the following lines in x–y form:

43. (a) $\mathbf{r} = \begin{pmatrix} 1 \\ 2 \end{pmatrix} + t\begin{pmatrix} 1 \\ -3 \end{pmatrix}$ (b) $\mathbf{r} = \begin{pmatrix} -3 \\ 5 \end{pmatrix} + t\begin{pmatrix} 2 \\ 4 \end{pmatrix}$

44. (a) $\mathbf{r} = \begin{pmatrix} -3 \\ 2 \end{pmatrix} + t\begin{pmatrix} 1 \\ 4 \end{pmatrix}$ (b) $\mathbf{r} = \begin{pmatrix} -4 \\ -5 \end{pmatrix} + t\begin{pmatrix} -2 \\ 3 \end{pmatrix}$

45. Where does the line $\mathbf{r} = (2-3t)\mathbf{i} + (1+t)\mathbf{j}$ cut the circle $x^2 + y^2 = 25$?

46. Where does the line $\mathbf{r} = (1-t)\mathbf{i} + (2+3t)\mathbf{j}$ cut the ellipse $3x^2 + 4y^2 = 25$?

Find where the following pairs of lines meet:

47. $\mathbf{r} = (3+t)\mathbf{i} + (3+2t)\mathbf{j}$ and $\mathbf{r} = 2t\mathbf{i} + (3+t)\mathbf{j}$

48. $\mathbf{r} = (2t-2)\mathbf{i} + (1+3t)\mathbf{j}$ and $\mathbf{r} = (3+4t)\mathbf{i} + (4t-4)\mathbf{j}$

49. $\mathbf{r} = \begin{pmatrix} 1 \\ 3 \end{pmatrix} + t\begin{pmatrix} 3 \\ -4 \end{pmatrix}$ and $\mathbf{r} = \begin{pmatrix} -2 \\ 5 \end{pmatrix} + t\begin{pmatrix} 3 \\ -5 \end{pmatrix}$

50. $\mathbf{r} = \begin{pmatrix} -1 \\ 2 \end{pmatrix} + t\begin{pmatrix} 1 \\ 3 \end{pmatrix}$ and $\mathbf{r} = \begin{pmatrix} 3 \\ 2 \end{pmatrix} + t\begin{pmatrix} -4 \\ -6 \end{pmatrix}$

EXERCISE 11S

1. A point moves along a straight line Ox so that its position $x = F(t)$ after t s is given by:
(a) $t^2 + 6t$,   (b) $5t - t^3$,   (c) $t(2t-3)^2$,   (d) $24t - 3t^2$.
In each case, find the velocity $v = f(t)$, and find $f(4)$.

2. As question 1, but with $F(t)$ defined as:
(a) $7t - t^2$,   (b) $t^3 + 9t$,   (c) $(t+1)^3$,   (d) $4t^3 - 30t^2$.

3. A point moves along a straight line Ox so that its velocity $v = G(t)$ after t s is given by:
(a) $7t + 3$,   (b) $(2t-1)^2$,   (c) $t^4 - 3t^2$,   (d) $45 - 5t^2$.
In each case, find the acceleration $a = g(t)$, and find $g(2)$.

4. As question 3, but with $G(t)$ defined as:
(a) $24 - 10t$,   (b) $5t^2 + t^3$,   (c) $t^2/5 + 9$,   (d) $8t - t^2$.

5. A spherical balloon is being deflated so that its radius after t minutes is $(5-t)$ m. What is the volume, and what is the rate of decrease of volume, in terms of t? What is the greatest rate of decrease?

6. A circular town is expanding so that its radius after t years is $(2+t/2)$ km. What is its area, and what is the rate of expansion, in terms of t? What can you say about the rate of expansion in the distant future?

7. If a point moves along Ox so that its velocity $v = F'(t)$ and its starting position c are as given, what is its position $x = F(t)$ after t s, and at the stated time?

(a) $v = 4t - 5$, $c = 5$; after 4 s

(b) $v = 3t^2 + 4t$, $c = 9$; after 1 s

8. As question 7, but with the following data:

(a) $v = 18 - 6t$, $c = 10$; after 5 s

(b) $v = 12t^3 + 12t^2$, $c = 20$; after 2 s

(c) $v = t^3 - t^4$, $c = 7500$; after 10 s

9. If a point moves along Ox so that its acceleration $a = G'(t)$ and its starting velocity u are as given, what is its velocity $G(t)$ after t s, and at the stated time?

(a) $a = 2t + 5$, $u = 3$; after 10 s

(b) $a = 9.8$, $u = 0$; after 5 s

10. As question 9, but with the following data:

(a) $a = 20 - 6t$, $u = 10$; after 5 s

(b) $a = (3t + 1)^2$, $u = 0$; after 1 s

(c) $a = t^3/8$, $u = 8$; after 4 s

11. A tank is being filled with water at a rate which, t minutes after starting $(0 \leqslant t \leqslant 10)$, is $2 - t^3/500$ m³/minute. How much water enters the tank altogether?

12. A tank is being emptied at a rate which, t minutes after starting $(0 \leqslant t \leqslant 10)$, is $20 - 2t$ m³/minute. How much water leaves in the 10 minutes? If, however, the tank contained only 75 m³ initially, how long would it take to empty?

13. Find the areas underneath the following graphs between the given limits:

(a) $y = 4x$; $x = 2$ to $x = 5$

(b) $y = 6x^2$; $x = 1$ to $x = 3$

(c) $y = x^2 + 5$; $x = -3$ to $x = +6$

14. As question 13:

(a) $y = 6x$; $x = 5$ to $x = 10$

(b) $y = 7x^6$; $x = 1$ to $x = 2$

(c) $y = 16 - x^3$; $x = -2$ to $x = +2$

15. Evaluate the following definite integrals, and sketch in each case the region whose area has been found:

(a) $\displaystyle\int_0^2 4x^3 \, dx$,   (b) $\displaystyle\int_{-1}^{+2} (x+1)^2 \, dx$,   (c) $\displaystyle\int_1^2 (x - 1/x)^2 \, dx$.

16. As question 15:

(a) $\displaystyle\int_{1/4}^{1/2} (1/x^3)\,dx,$ (b) $\displaystyle\int_{0}^{1} (3x-1)^2\,dx,$ (c) $\displaystyle\int_{-3}^{+3} (27-3x^2)\,dx.$

17. Sketch the curve $y = x^2-3x$ for x between -1 and $+4$. Find the area enclosed between the curve and the x-axis.

18. Sketch the curve $y = (x-1)(x-5)$ for x between 0 and 6. Find the area enclosed between the curve and the x-axis.

19. Sketch the curve $y = x^5-32$, and find the area enclosed between the curve and the two axes.

20. Sketch the curve $y = 4x-x^3$, and find the total area enclosed between the curve and the x-axis. Explain why this cannot be calculated by a single definite integral.

21. Find y, given that dy/dx equals

(a) $4x^3$,   (b) $10x-x^2$,   (c) $(x^3+1)/x^2$.

22. Find y, given that dy/dx equals

(a) $6x^5$,   (b) x^4+7x,   (c) $(5x^2-2)^2$.

23. Find equations for the following curves, where dy/dx is as given, and the given point lies on the curve:

(a) $6x$; $(0,5)$

(b) $3x^3$; $(1,2)$

(c) $(\sqrt{x}-1)^2$; $(4,-1)$

24. As question 23:

(a) $3x^2$; $(0,10)$

(b) $5x$; $(-1,-2)$

(c) $3/x^3$; $(-2,1)$

25. Find these indefinite integrals (not forgetting $+c$):

(a) $\displaystyle\int x^5\,dx,$ (b) $\displaystyle\int (2x+3)^2\,dx,$ (c) $\displaystyle\int \frac{x+1}{\sqrt{x}}\,dx.$

26. As question 25:

(a) $\displaystyle\int 3x^4\,dx,$ (b) $\displaystyle\int x^{-7}\,dx,$ (c) $\displaystyle\int (2\sqrt{x}-3x)^2\,dx.$

27. A continuous curve, passing through the origin, has gradient $dy/dx = x$ when $x \leqslant 1$, and $dy/dx = x^2$ when $x > 1$. What is the value of y when $x = 1$ and when $x = 2$? What is the area enclosed between the curve, the x-axis, and $x = 2$?

EXERCISE 12S

In question 1 to 20, the five letters t, v, u, a, s have their usual meanings, and you should assume forward motion. In other questions, take g to be $9.8\,\text{m/s}^2$ when necessary and appropriate.

1. $s = 10$, $u = 4$, $v = 3$; find a.

2. $s = 5$, $u = 2$, $v = 8$; find t.

3. $s = 6$, $u = 4$, $a = -0.5$; find v.

4. $s = 300$, $u = 20$, $a = 0.4$; find t.

5. $s = 10$, $u = 0.5$, $t = 12$; find v.

6. $s = 50$, $u = 1.5$, $t = 16$; find a.

7. $s = 20$, $v = 3$, $a = 0.2$; find u.

8. $s = 15$, $v = 0.8$, $a = -0.3$; find t.

9. $s = 1000$, $v = 5$, $t = 180$; find u.

10. $s = 2$, $v = 0.2$, $t = 3$; find a.

11. $s = 1$, $a = -0.1$, $t = 4$; find u.

12. $s = 200$, $a = -2$, $t = 5$; find v.

13. $u = 3.7$, $v = 2.4$, $a = -0.21$; find s.

14. $u = 11.73$, $v = 8.62$, $a = -0.145$; find t.

15. $u = 0.65$, $v = 1.32$, $t = 7.13$; find s.

16. $u = 18.97$, $v = 32.45$, $t = 63.14$; find a.

17. $u = 6.84$, $a = 0.01$, $t = 16.3$; find s.

18. $u = 1.23$, $a = -0.023$, $t = 6.14$; find v.

19. $v = 5.23$, $a = 0.125$, $t = 3.78$; find s.

20. $v = 0.864$, $a = -0.023$, $t = 23.6$; find u.

21. I drop a pebble down a well. It takes 2.1 s to reach the bottom. How deep is the well?

22. I throw a pebble down a well 25 m deep. It takes 1.9 s to reach the bottom. How fast did I throw it?

23. I throw a pebble up at 3 m/s from a window. How long is it before the pebble hits the ground 10 m below?

24. A bird drops a stone which hits the ground at 25 m/s. How high was the bird?

25. My cross-bow fires a bolt from ground level vertically upwards at 72 m/s. How high does the bolt rise (you must ignore air resistance), and when does it hit the ground?

26. Find the velocity of the bolt in question 25 when it reaches a point 200 m above ground level. Hence find for how long the bolt remains above the 200 m level.

27. I fling a pebble up and catch it 4 s later. How fast did I fling it, and how high did it rise?

28. On another planet I fling a stone up at 5 m/s. After 3 s I see it descending at 2 m/s. How high is it now, and what is g on the planet?

29. I throw up a stone at 12 m/s and 1 s later another at 10 m/s. When and where do they collide?

30. As question 29, but with 15 m/s, 1.5 s, and 13 m/s.

31. A train passes through station A at 36 km/h and heads east towards station B, which is 630 m away. Two seconds later another train travelling west at a steady 90 km/h passes through B. If the first train is decelerating at 0.1 m/s² find when and where they meet.

32. As question 31, but with 27 km/h, 343 m, 3 s, 108 km/h, and 0.05 m/s².

33. A ball bearing is dropped from 3 m above the floor. How high does it rise if it rebounds with 0.4 of its speed on impact?

34. As question 33, but with 2.5 m and 0.8.

35. A lift accelerates from rest at 0.8 m/s² for 5 s, travels at a steady speed for 10 s, then decelerates at 1.6 m/s² till it stops. Sketch the velocity–time graph and use its area to find the total distance gone.

36. As question 35, but with 0.6 m/s², 4 s, 15 s, and 0.4 m/s².

37. A train is braking, and has steady deceleration. It has a speed of 72 km/h at one kilometre post, and 54 km/h at the next. What is the deceleration (in m/s²), and how long will it now be till the train stops?

38. As question 37, but with 91 and 74 km/h.

Find v and x (if $v = u$ and $x = 0$ initially) given that:

39. (a) $a = 2 + 5t$, $u = -3$ (b) $a = (2t+1)(t-2)$, $u = 2$

40. (a) $a = 20 - 2t$, $u = 40$ (b) $a = t(t+1)(t-1)$, $u = 0$

41. My acceleration rises steadily from 1 m/s² to 4 m/s² over 5 s, and then falls steadily to 3 m/s² over the next 10 s. If my speed was 6 m/s initially, what is it finally?

42. As question 41, but with 2 m/s², 6 m/s², 3 s, 5 m/s², 6 s, and 1 m/s.

43. Find the velocity vector **v** if the position vector **r** is:

     (a) $(2t+1)\mathbf{i} + (3-4t)\mathbf{j}$ (b) $t^2\mathbf{i} + t^2\mathbf{j}$ (c) $t^3\mathbf{i} + \mathbf{j}$

44. Find the velocity vector **v** if the position vector **r** is:

(a) $(1-3t)\mathbf{i}+(2+5t)\mathbf{j}$,   (b) $t^2\mathbf{i}+t^3\mathbf{j}$,   (c) $(1+t)(\mathbf{i}+t\mathbf{j})$.

45. Find the acceleration vector **a**, given **r** as in question 43.

46. Find the acceleration vector **a**, given **r** as in question 44.

47. If $\mathbf{v} = 2t\mathbf{i}+3\mathbf{j}$, find **r** if $\mathbf{r}_0 = \mathbf{i}+\mathbf{j}$.

48. If $\mathbf{v} = 3t\mathbf{i}+2\mathbf{j}$, find **r** if $\mathbf{r}_0 = \mathbf{i}-\mathbf{j}$.

49. If $\mathbf{v} = \mathbf{i}+2t\mathbf{j}$, find **r** if $\mathbf{r} = \mathbf{0}$ when $t = 2$.

50. If $\mathbf{v} = (t-1)(\mathbf{i}-t\mathbf{j})$, find **r** if $\mathbf{r} = \mathbf{i}$ when $t = 1$.

51. A varying force acting on a 3 kg mass produces a velocity $\mathbf{v} = t^2\mathbf{i}-t\mathbf{j}\,\text{m/s}$. Find the acceleration and hence the force. What are the magnitude and direction of the force when $t = 0.8\,\text{s}$ and when $t = 1.2\,\text{s}$?

52. As question 51, but with 0.2 kg, $\mathbf{v} = (t+1)(\mathbf{i}+t\mathbf{j})$, and $t = 0.2$ and $0.9\,\text{s}$.

53. Calculate the greatest height, time of flight, and horizontal range, of projectiles whose initial velocities have (in m/s) the following horizontal and vertical components:

(a) $\begin{pmatrix} 10 \\ 5 \end{pmatrix}$,   (b) $\begin{pmatrix} 100 \\ 20 \end{pmatrix}$,   (c) $\begin{pmatrix} 1 \\ 50 \end{pmatrix}$.

54. As question 53, but with:

(a) $\begin{pmatrix} 5 \\ 10 \end{pmatrix}$,   (b) $\begin{pmatrix} 20 \\ 100 \end{pmatrix}$,   (c) $\begin{pmatrix} 50 \\ 1 \end{pmatrix}$.

55. A gun's muzzle velocity is 40 m/s. Find the greatest height, time of flight, and horizontal range, if the gun is fired at an angle to the horizontal of:

(a) 10°,   (b) 30°,   (c) 60°,   (d) 80°.

56. As question 55, but with 30 m/s and angles of:

(a) 15°,   (b) 35°,   (c) 55°,   (d) 75°.

57. Take the x-axis horizontally and y-axis vertically up. A gun is fired from O horizontally at 300 m/s. Find t and y when $x = 600$. Also find t and x when $y = -10$.

58. As question 57, but with 200 m/s, $x = 300$, $y = -15$.

59. A projectile is fired from O (with axes as in question 57). After 4 s it hits the (horizontal) ground 50 m from O. Find the velocity and speed of projection. Also find the direction of motion when $t = 1.6\,\text{s}$.

60. As in question 59, but with 5 s, 30 m and $t = 3\,\text{s}$.

61. A mortar has a maximum range of 1000 m on level ground. If the target is only 800 m away, find the two possible angles of projection.

62. As question 61, but with 2000 m and 1200 m.

63. Find the maximum horizontal range of an anti-tank weapon whose muzzle velocity is 200 m/s (taking g to be 10 m/s²). If the angle of projection is set at arctan 0.6, show that the projectile will hit a tank situated at $(3000, 270)$, where the axes are arranged in the usual manner.

64. Find the maximum horizontal range of a weapon whose muzzle velocity is 280 m/s (taking g to be 9.8 m/s²). If the angle of projection is set at arctan 0.4, show that the projectile will hit a target at $(4000, 440)$, with the usual axes.

65. What other angle of projection will do for the weapon in question 63?

66. What other angle of projection will do for the weapon in question 64?

67. Find the radial acceleration of a particle moving with a speed of 6 m/s in a circle of radius 3 m.

68. As question 67, but with 5 m/s and 2 m.

69. A child ties a toy of mass 500 grams to a string and swings the toy round and round in a horizontal circle of radius 0.5 m at a steady speed. If the breaking load of the string is 49 N, what is the maximum safe speed?

70. As question 69, but with 600 grams, 0.8 m, and 48 N.

71. An object of mass 2 kg is attached by an inextensible light wire of length 25 m to a fixed point A, and is set rotating at a steady speed in a horizontal circle of radius 15 m whose centre O lies vertically beneath A. Find the tension in the wire (taking g to be 9.8 m/s²) and the speed of the object.

72. As question 71, but with a circle of radius 7 m.

73. I am bicycling at 10 km/h due south. The wind appears to come at 5 km/h from the east. Calculate the true speed and direction of the wind.

74. As question 73, but with speeds of 12 and 4 km/h.

75. I am bicycling at 15 km/h due east, and the wind appears to be coming at 8 km/h from the north-east. By drawing, find the true speed and direction of the wind. How will the wind seem if I speed up to 20 km/h?

76. As question 75, but with 22 km/h due north, 10 km/h from the north-west, and the speed reduced to 16 km/h.

77. A leaves $(1, 2)$ with steady velocity $-2\mathbf{i} - 3\mathbf{j}$, and at the same time B leaves $(3, -8)$ with velocity $-3\mathbf{i} + 2\mathbf{j}$. Do they collide? If so, when and where?

78. As question 77, but with B starting (a) from $(4, -12)$, (b) from $(4, -13)$.

79. A stream is flowing at 2 m/s. Superman can swim at 3 m/s in still water. He wants to swim straight across the stream, a distance of 30 m. In which direction should he point, and how long will he take?

80. As question 79, but with 5 m/s, 4 m/s and 20 m.

81. Paris to Geneva is 400 km on a bearing of 137°. A plane can fly at 350 km/h in still air. If a gale blows from the north at 80 km/h, find, by drawing, how long it takes to fly there and back.

82. Repeat question 81 if the gale now blows at 120 km/h.

83. I am at $(1, 2)$ travelling with velocity $4\mathbf{i} + 3\mathbf{j}$. An interceptor is at $(12, 0)$. If he travels at a speed of 10 units, find, by drawing, in which direction he should move to catch me, and how long he will take.

84. As question 83, but with $(2, -1)$, $2\mathbf{i} - 3\mathbf{j}$, $(20, 0)$, and a speed of 12 units.

85. In question 83, write down my coordinates after time t, and hence my distance from $(12, 0)$ at that time. Since this must be $10t$ at the moment of interception, write down an equation for t and solve it. Hence calculate the answers to question 83.

86. Solve question 84 by calculation, as in question 85.

EXERCISE 13S

On a car journey there are two towns to be driven through. I am equally likely to lose 1, 2, 3, or 4 minutes in town A, and 1, 2, 3, 4, 5, or 6 minutes in town B. Draw a figure like figure 13.6 (p. 179) and use it to find:

1. Pr(I am more than 6 minutes late in all)

2. Pr(I am less than 3 minutes late in all)

3. Pr(the amounts of time lost in A and B are the same)

4. Pr(I lose more time crossing B than crossing A)

5. Pr(I arrive exactly 4 minutes late)

6. Pr(I arrive exactly 5 minutes late)

A *date* consists of a whole number from 1 to 31 inclusive followed by a whole number from 1 to 12 inclusive: thus $(2, 6)$ is a date, corresponding to the 2nd of June. The events E, F, G are defined as follows:

>   E that the date corresponds to a day in 1983
>   F that the date corresponds to a day in 1984
>   G that the date corresponds to a Saturday or Sunday

If one date is randomly chosen, find:

7. Pr(E)   **8.** Pr(F)   **9.** Pr(E and G)

10. Pr(F and G)   **11.** Pr(E or F)   **12.** Pr(E and F)

In the modern pentathlon, there are five events. An athlete has a 3/4 chance of winning the 1st event, likewise the 2nd, but a 4/5 chance of winning the 3rd, likewise the 4th and 5th. He gets 5 points for a win, 2 otherwise. Draw a tree diagram, and use it to find:

13. Pr(he wins all the events)

14. Pr(he does not win any event)

15. Pr(he scores just 22 points in all)

16. Pr(he scores just 13 points in all)

17. Pr(he won events 3 to 5 | he has scored 22 points)

18. Pr(he won event 1 | he has scored 13 points)

The weather on any particular day may be good or bad, the probabilities being 1/3 and 2/3 respectively. If good, then the probability that the next day's weather is good equals 0.6, and the probability that the next day's weather is bad equals 0.4. If bad, on the other hand, then the probability that the next day's weather is good equals 0.2, and the probability that the next day's weather is bad equals 0.8. Draw a tree diagram showing the possibilities for four successive days (Monday, Tuesday, Wednesday, Thursday), and use it to find:

19. Pr(Wednesday's weather is good | Monday's was good)

20. Pr(Wednesday's weather is good | Monday's was bad)

21. Pr(Thursday's weather is good | Monday's was good)

22. Pr(Thursday's weather is good | Monday's was bad)

23. Pr(Monday's weather was good | Tuesday's is good)

24. Pr(Monday's weather was good | Tuesday's is bad)

25. Pr(Monday's weather was good | Thursday's is good)

26. Pr(Monday's weather was good | Thursday's is bad)

Find the following:

27. $^7P_2$ **28.** $^7P_5$ **29.** $^6P_6$ **30.** $^6P_3$

31. $^nP_2$ (assuming $n \geqslant 2$)   **32.** $^nP_3$ (assuming $n \geqslant 3$)

33. Find n if $^nP_2 = 56$.   **34.** Find n if $^nP_3 = 720$.

Find the following:

35. $^7C_2$ **36.** $^7C_5$ **37.** $^6C_6$ **38.** $^6C_3$

39. $^nC_2$ **40.** $^nC_3$ **41.** $^7C_7$ **42.** $^7C_0$

43. Find n if $^nC_2 = 36$.   **44.** Find n if $^nC_3 = 10$.

45. Verify that $^8C_0 + {}^8C_1 + {}^8C_2 + \ldots + {}^8C_7 + {}^8C_8 = 256$.

46. Verify that $^8C_3 + {}^8C_4 = {}^9C_4$ and that $^9C_3 + {}^9C_4 = {}^{10}C_4$.

47. A teacher has seven tickets for a concert, and plans to take six pupils with him. Since all ten boys and five girls in his class want to come, the composition of the party is to be decided by lot. How many possible parties are there if:

(a) everybody is to have an equal chance,
(b) there are to be three boys and three girls?

48. The teacher often invites his fifteen pupils (see question 47) to tea, seating them at a circular table (he himself never takes tea) and always ensuring that every boy sits next to a girl. The most senior girl is naturally allowed the most comfortable chair. How many possible seating arrangements are there?

49. By a curious chance, the initial letters of the girls' Christian names will form the word EXTRA, and the boys' initials the word ORDINARILY. How many anagrams does each word have?

50. How many anagrams does the word EXTRAORDINARILY have?

51. A grocer knows that, on average, one in forty of the eggs sold in his shop will prove to be bad. When a customer buys a dozen eggs, what are the probabilities that he gets (a) at least one bad egg, (b) just three bad eggs?

52. One of the grocer's customers (see question 51) buys a dozen eggs each week, but if two or more of them prove to be bad, he refuses to pay his bill. What is the probability that in the course of four weeks, he pays (a) all four bills, (b) just two bills, (c) no bills?

53. In a large school, 50% of the pupils are boys, 50% are girls. If a students' committee of five is chosen at random, what is the probability that three or more will be boys?

54. In a large urban area, 20% of all potential jurors are biased against young people. If a jury of twelve is chosen at random, what is the probability that a majority (i.e. seven or more) will be biased?

55. A bag contains five identical balls, except that two are white and three are black. A random sample of two balls is taken from the bag (without replacement), and the random variable x equals the proportion of white balls in this sample. Find $E(x)$ and $E(x^2)$.

56. A bag contains ten identical balls, except that three are white and seven are black. A random sample of two balls is taken from the bag (without replacement), and the random variables x and y are defined as follows: $x =$ the proportion of white balls in the sample, $y =$ the proportion of black balls. Calculate $E(x)$, $E(y)$, $E(x+y)$, $E(xy)$. Confirm that $E(x+y)$ equals $E(x)+E(y)$, and explain why $E(xy)$ does not equal $E(x) \times E(y)$ in this case.

57. In a two-person game, I choose a positive whole number and my opponent does likewise. If both the numbers are odd, I pay him £6, and if both are even I pay him £4; otherwise, he pays me £5. The random variable z is defined as my profit in a single game. Show that $E(z) = 9x+9y-20xy-4$, where $x = \Pr(I$ choose an odd number$)$, and $y = \Pr($he chooses an odd number$)$. Hence show that if my policy is to choose odd numbers with a probability of 9/20, I am bound to make a profit (in the long run) of at least 5 p per game, whatever policy he adopts.

58. Analyse a game similar to that described in question 57, where the rules are as follows: I pay my opponent £8 if both numbers are odd and £2 if both are even; otherwise, he pays me £5.

EXERCISE 14S

1. I buy half a kilo of sweets in a store and go down in the lift with the box hanging from my finger. The lift has a downward acceleration of $1\,\mathrm{m\,s^{-2}}$ at the start, and a retardation of $2\,\mathrm{m\,s^{-2}}$ at the end. How heavy does the parcel seem, in newtons, at the start and at the end?

2. Still carrying my half-kilo of sweets, I enter another store and take the lift up to the restaurant on the top floor. The weight of the sweets seems to be $5.5\,\mathrm{N}$ at the start of the ascent, and $3.6\,\mathrm{N}$ at the end. What are the initial acceleration and final retardation of this lift?

3. A taut string passes over a rough peg, and has masses of $10\,\mathrm{kg}$ and $4\,\mathrm{kg}$ tied to its ends. The peg's roughness means that the tension on the $10\,\mathrm{kg}$ side is $7\,\mathrm{N}$ greater than on the $4\,\mathrm{kg}$ side. Find the acceleration of the masses.

4. A light rope is slung over a smooth beam, with one boy hanging on to either end. The heavier boy (of mass $60\,\mathrm{kg}$) is found to descend with acceleration $2\,\mathrm{m\,s^{-2}}$. Find the tension in the rope, and the mass of the lighter boy to the nearest kilogram.

5. In a shipyard a winch is used to haul two trucks each of mass $3\,\mathrm{tonnes}$, coupled together one behind the other, along a level stretch of track, the resisting force on each being $0.8\,\mathrm{kN}$. What is the tension in the winch cable, and in the coupling, when the acceleration produced is $0.5\,\mathrm{m\,s^{-2}}$?

6. A tug towing three barges in line ahead has an acceleration of $0.02\,\mathrm{m\,s^{-2}}$. The mass of each barge is $80\,\mathrm{tonnes}$, and the water resistance on each is $12.5\,\mathrm{kN}$. If the three tow-ropes (connecting the tug to the first barge, the first barge to the second, and the second to the third) are horizontal, find the tension in each.

7. A block of mass $30\,\mathrm{kg}$ can just be moved on a rough horizontal table by a horizontal force of $98\,\mathrm{N}$. What is the coefficient of friction? And what will be the acceleration of the block if the applied force is increased by 60%?

8. A block of mass 6 kg lies on a rough horizontal table, the coefficient of friction being 0.4. What will be the frictional force if we apply a horizontal force of (a) 20 N, (b) 30 N, and what will be the resulting acceleration in each case?

9. A crate of mass 20 kg sits on rough horizontal ground, the coefficient of friction being 0.4. What will be its acceleration if (a) we pull at an angle of 30° above the horizontal, and (b) we push at an angle of 30° below the horizontal, in each case with a force of 110 N?

10. As question 9, but with the angle changed to 10°.

11. A mass of 25 kg resting on a plane surface begins to slip when the surface is tilted at an angle of 30° to the horizontal. What is the coefficient of friction, and what minimum applied force parallel to the line of greatest slope will be needed to maintain equilibrium if the angle of tilt is increased to 45°?

12. An object resting on an inclined plane begins to slip when the angle of inclination is 25°. What is the coefficient of friction, and what will be the object's acceleration if the angle is doubled?

13. A boulder lies on rough horizontal ground, the angle of friction being 15°. If the weight of the boulder is 300 N, what is the least horizontal force needed to get it moving?

14. What will be the acceleration of the boulder referred to in question 13 if a horizontal force of 100 N is applied?

15. By considering the triangle of forces, find what is the least force in any direction that will get the boulder of question 13 moving.

16. Repeat question 15 if the ground slopes at 10°.

17. In a game of croquet, a ball of mass 0.8 kg is given an impulse of 4 N s. What speed is imparted to it?

18. In a game of bowls, a wood of mass 1.2 kg is moving at $3 \, \text{m s}^{-1}$: what is its momentum? It strikes a stationary wood lying precisely in its path, and their speeds after impact are 0.5 and $2.4 \, \text{m s}^{-1}$: what is the mass of the second wood?

19. A brick of mass 3 kg falls into a pond with a speed of $6 \, \text{m s}^{-1}$. If its speed immediately after hitting the water surface is 60% less, find the impulse.

20. A cricket ball of mass 160 grams reaches a batsman at speed $7 \, \text{m s}^{-1}$ and is driven straight back at speed $18 \, \text{m s}^{-1}$. Find the impulse on the ball. If contact between bat and ball lasts for 0.1 s, find the average force between them.

21. A stationary body of mass 300 kg bursts into two parts of mass 200 and 100 kg. If the velocity of the former is $(2\mathbf{i} - 3\mathbf{j}) \, \text{m s}^{-1}$, what is the velocity of the latter?

22. A body of mass 8 kg bursts into two equal parts whose velocities are $(3\mathbf{i}+4\mathbf{j})$ and $(4\mathbf{i}+\mathbf{j})\,\mathrm{m\,s}^{-1}$. What was the velocity of the original body?

23. A batsman receives a ball of mass 160 grams moving at $15\,\mathrm{m\,s}^{-1}$ and hits it at $20\,\mathrm{m\,s}^{-1}$ towards square leg, at $90°$ to its original direction. Find the magnitude and direction of the impulse given to the ball, assuming it is moving horizontally just before and just after being struck.

24. As question 23: find the magnitude of the impulse, assuming that the ball is moving horizontally before being struck, but leaves the bat at $\arccos(0.6)$ to the horizontal.

EXERCISE 15S

Solve the following simultaneous equations:

1. $x-y = 2,\ xy = 15$
2. $x+2y = 7,\ 3x^2+2xy = 9$
3. $2x+3y = 5,\ 2x^2+3xy = 15$
4. $2x+y = 9,\ 4x^2-4xy+y^2 = 25$
5. $1/x+1/y = 5/6,\ xy = 6$
6. $5x-2y = 4,\ 3x^2-4y^2 = 2$
7. $2x+5y+1 = 0,\ 3x^2-10xy = 32$
8. $x^2-2xy+2y^2 = 10,\ 2x-y = 1$
9. $2x+3y = 7,\ 4x^2+6xy = 7$
10. $2x^2-4xy+3y^2 = 6,\ 2x-3y = 0$

11. The hypotenuse of a right-angled triangle is 29 cm and its perimeter is 70 cm. Find its area.

12. In statistics mode my calculator gives Σx (the sum of the numbers entered), and also Σx^2 (the sum of their squares). I enter the number p five times in succession, and then the number q three times in succession. If Σx equals 20 and Σx^2 equals 320, find the possible values of p and q.

13. Ben (aged 14) and James (aged 15) both think of a number. When each boy multiplies his number by his own age, the sum of their results is 421. When each boy squares his number, the sum of the results is again 421. By solving two simultaneous equations, prove that in fact Ben *must* be thinking of his own age, and likewise James.

14. I have two reels of thin wire. Type A's resistance is $0.20\,\Omega\,\mathrm{m}^{-1}$, type B's is $0.25\,\Omega\,\mathrm{m}^{-1}$. I snip off two pieces, $x\,\mathrm{m}$ of A and $y\,\mathrm{m}$ of B. The total resistance of these when connected in series is $5\,\Omega$, but in parallel is only $1.2\,\Omega$. Find the possible values of x and y. Non-physicists should note that resistances R_1 and R_2 connected in series gives a resistance of R_1+R_2, and in parallel give a resistance of $R_1R_2/(R_1+R_2)$.

15. Prove that the line $2x-y = 1$ touches the curve $y = x^2$.

16. Prove that the line $2x-y = 3$ touches $x^2-y^2 = 3$.

17. Find the equations of the lines with gradient 4 that touch the curve $2x^2+y^2 = 9$.

18. Find the gradient of the tangent from the point $(0,6)$ to the curve $xy = 12$.

What is the remainder when:

19. $2x^3-6x+5$ is divided by $(x-1)$?

20. x^4-6x^3+x+1 is divided by $(x+2)$?

21. $16x^3-10x+7$ is divided by $(2x+1)$?

22. $37x^2+8x-2$ is divided by $(10x-1)$?

23. Find the value of k if $(x-1)$ divides $7x^2-kx+9$.

24. Find the value of k if $(x-3)$ divides x^3+kx^2+x+6.

25. Find the values of b and c if both $(x+3)$ and $(x-4)$ are factors of $x^3+bx^2+cx+12$.

26. Find the values of b and c if the expression x^3+bx^2+cx-9 is exactly divisible by (x^2-9).

27. When ax^2+bx-3 is divided by $(x-1)$ the remainder is -6. If $(x-3)$ is a factor, find a and b.

28. The expression ax^2+5x+c leaves remainder -4 when divided by $(x+1)$ and remainder 0 when divided by $(x+2)$. Find a and c.

29. Factorise $18x^3-39x^2+2x+24$ completely, given that $(2x-3)$ is one of its factors.

30. Factorise $x^3+6x^2y+11xy^2+6y^3$ completely, given that $(x+2y)$ is one of its factors.

31. Factorise   (a) $3x^3-12xy^2$ (b) $(a-b)^2-(c-d)^2$

32. Factorise   (a) p^4-16q^6 (b) $(2x^2+x)^2-1$

33. Simplify as far as possible $p+q-(p^3-q^3)/(p^2-q^2)$.

34. Simplify $(y-2ap)/(x-ap^2) = (y-2aq)/(x-aq^2)$.

Solve the equations:

35. $x^3-3x^2-4x+12 = 0$

36. $x^3-4x^2+x+6 = 0$

37. $2x^3-x^2-2x+1 = 0$

38. $3x^3-20x^2+23x+10 = 0$

39. Show that $(x-a)$ is a factor of $(x-b)^7+(b-a)^7$.

40. For what values of n is $(x+1)$ a factor of x^n+1?

41. When the expression x^3+bx^2+2x+1 is divided by $(x-2)$, the remainder is three times the remainder when the divisor is $(x-1)$. Find b.

42. Show that $(x-1)^2$ is a factor of x^3-4x^2+5x-2.

43. Expand $(3+2x)^3$.

44. Expand $(x+1/x)^5$.

45. Find the coefficient of x^4 in $(1-3x)^7$.

46. Find the coefficient of x^2 in $(1-x+2x^2)^5$.

47. Evaluate $(\sqrt{7}+\sqrt{3})^5 - (\sqrt{7}-\sqrt{3})^5$.

48. Evaluate $(\sqrt{7}+\sqrt{3})^6 + (\sqrt{7}-\sqrt{3})^6$.

49. Find the value of $(1.99)^4$ to 5 s.f.

50. Use the binomial theorem to evaluate 98^5 exactly.

Expand the following in ascending powers of x, as far as the term in x^3:

51. (a) $(1+x)^{-1}$ (b) $(1-4x)^{1/2}$

52. (a) $(1-3x)^{-2}$ (b) $(1+x)^{-1/2}$

Use the results in questions 51 and 52 to find approximate values of:

53. (a) $10/11$ (b) $\sqrt{0.96}$

54. (a) 0.85^{-2} (b) $1\div\sqrt{0.99}$

By giving y and n suitable values, use the linear approximation $(1+y)^n = 1+ny$ to find approximate values of:

55. (a) 1.07^4 (b) $\sqrt{1.2}$ (c) $1/0.97$

56. (a) 0.95^8 (b) $\sqrt{1.08}$ (c) $1/1.008$

57. Show that the function $f(x) = (7x-6)/(2-3x+x^2)$ can be expressed as $1/(1-x)-8/(2-x)$, and hence find the binomial expansion of $f(x)$ as far as the term in x^3.

58. Express the function $f(x) = 5/(1-x-6x^2)$ in partial fractions, i.e. in the form $A/(1+2x)+B/(1-3x)$, where A and B are constants, and hence obtain the binomial expansion of $f(x)$ as far as the term in x^4.

59. Find the first four terms when $(1+x)/(1-x)$ is expanded in ascending powers of x.

60. Find the first four terms when $(1+5x)\sqrt{(9-3x)}$ is expanded in ascending powers of x.

EXERCISE 16S

OADBC is a pyramid with OC perpendicular to the rectangular base OADB, and $OA = 4i$, $OB = 5j$, $OC = 3k$. Before you attempt any of the questions in this exercise, be sure to make a sketch of the pyramid.

Express the following vectors in terms of i, j, and k:

1. BD   **2.** AD   **3.** AC   **4.** BC   **5.** AB   **6.** DC

Calculate the angles between the following pairs of lines:

7. OC and AC   **8.** OC and BC

9. OC and AB   **10.** OC and DC

11. OD and DC   **12.** AB and DC

Calculate the angles between the following lines and planes:

13. BC and OADB   **14.** AC and OADB

15. DC and OAC   **16.** DC and OBC

Calculate the angles between the following pairs of planes:

17. ACD and OADB   **18.** BCD and OADB

19. Show that the equation $x/4 + z/3 = 1$ is satisfied by the coordinates of A, C, and D, and is thus the equation of the plane ACD. Hence write down a vector perpendicular to ACD.

20. Write down the equation of the plane BCD, and hence a vector perpendicular to the plane.

21. Calculate the angle between the planes ACD and BCD.

22. Show that the equation $x/4 + y/5 + z/3 = 1$ is satisfied by the coordinates of A, B, and C, and is thus the equation of the plane ABC. Hence write down a vector perpendicular to this plane.

23. Calculate the angle between the planes ACD and ABC.

24. Calculate the angle between the planes BCD and ABC.

25. Express $\sin 15°$ in surd form, and use your result to verify that $\cos 30° = 1 - 2\sin^2 15°$ exactly.

26. Express $\tan 15°$ and $\tan 75°$ in surd form, and use your results to verify that $\tan 15° \times \tan 75° = 1$ exactly.

27. Show that the angle between the lines $y = 2x$ and $y = x$ is $\arctan(1/3)$.

28. Show that the angle between the lines $y = 3x$ and $x + y = 0$ is $\arctan(2)$.

29. Prove that $\sin 50° + \sin 10° = \cos 20°$ by means of a suitable compound angle formula, and check on your calculator.

30. Prove that $\cos 60° - \cos 80° = 2\sin 70° \sin 10°$ by means of a suitable compound angle formula, and check on your calculator.

31. Use the fact that $\tan 2\theta = 2t/(1-t^2)$, where $t = \tan\theta$, to solve the equation $\tan 2\theta = 3\tan\theta$.

32. Solve the equation $\cos 2\theta + \sin 2\theta = 1$, by using the facts that $\cos 2\theta = (1-t^2)/(1+t^2)$ and $\sin 2\theta = 2t/(1+t^2)$, where $t = \tan\theta$.

33. Express $5\cos x - 12\sin x$ in the form $r\cos(x+\alpha)$, where $r > 0$ and α is acute.

34. Express $3\sin x + \cos x$ in the form $r\sin(x+\alpha)$, where $r > 0$ and α is acute.

35. Express $8\cos x + 15\sin x$ in the form $r\cos(x-\alpha)$, and hence solve the equation $8\cos x + 15\sin x = 7$.

36. Express $15\sin x - 8\cos x$ in the form $r\sin(x-\alpha)$, and hence solve the equation $15\sin x - 8\cos x = 8$.

37. Express $\sin x + \cos x$ in the form $r\sin(x+\alpha)$, and use your result to sketch the graph of $y = 2 + \sin x + \cos x$.

38. Express $2\cos x - \sin x$ in the form $r\cos(x+\alpha)$, and use your result to sketch the graph of $y = 4 + 2\cos x - \sin x$.

EXERCISE 17S

Find the volume generated when the given curve, between the given values of x, is rotated through $360°$ about the x-axis:

1. $y = 4x$; $x = 0$ to $x = 6$ **2.** $y = 3x/2$; $x = 0$ to $x = 2$

3. $y = x\sqrt{x}$; $x = 1$ to $x = 3$ **4.** $y = 1/x$; $x = 1$ to $x = 2$

5. $y = x^3$; $x = 0.9$ to $x = 1.1$ **6.** $y = x^2$; $x = 11$ to $x = 13$

Find the volume generated when the region enclosed between the given curve and the positive halves of the two axes is rotated about the x-axis:

7. $y = 1 - x^2$ **8.** $y = 4 - x^2$

9. $y = 2 - \sqrt{x}$ **10.** $y = 1 - \sqrt{x}$

11. Find the volume generated when $y = x^2$ between the origin and $(3,9)$ is rotated about the *y-axis*.

12. Find the volume generated when $y = 2 - x^2$ between $(0,2)$ and $(1,1)$ is rotated about the *y-axis*.

13. Find the volume generated when the region enclosed between $y = x - x^2$ and the x-axis is rotated about that axis.

14. Find the volume generated when the region enclosed between $y = 1 - x^2$ and the x-axis is rotated about that axis.

Estimate the following integrals, using (a) the trapezium rule, (b) the mid-ordinate rule, and (c) Simpson's rule, with 10 sections in each case:

15. $\displaystyle\int_0^{60} \tan x° \, dx$ **16.** $\displaystyle\int_0^{50} \cos x° \, dx$

17. $\displaystyle\int_0^5 \sqrt{(1+2x)} \, dx$ **18.** $\displaystyle\int_1^2 \sqrt{(1+x^2)} \, dx$

Find the areas under the graphs given by the following information:

19. $y = 1, 5, 10, 10, 5, 1$ when $x = 0, 2, 4, 6, 8, 10$.

20. $y = 1, 6, 15, 20, 15, 6, 1$ when $x = 0, 10, 20, 30$, etc.

21. $q = 6, 28, 88, 180, 247, 260, 133, 42, 11, 5$ when $p = 0, 0.1, 0.2$, etc.

22. $v = 5.27, 5.68, 6.25, 7.21, 8.02, 8.71, 8.42$ when $u = 0, 1, 2$, etc.

23. The velocity of a car at time t s is given by the formula $v = \sqrt{(64-t^2)} \, \mathrm{m\,s}^{-1}$ $(0 \leqslant t \leqslant 8)$. How far does it travel between $t = 0$ and $t = 8$?

24. The acceleration of a car, t s after starting from rest, is given by the formula $a = \sqrt{(1000-t^3)} \, \mathrm{m\,s}^{-2}$ $(0 \leqslant t \leqslant 10)$. How fast is it going after 10 s?

Find dy/dx in the following cases:

25. $y = (x+3)(x-5)$ **26.** $y = (2x-7)(3x+10)$

27. $y = (x^2+x)(2x-7)$ **28.** $y = (2x^2+3x)(x^2+x+4)$

Find dy/dx in the following cases:

29. $y = (1+x^2)/(1-x^2)$ **30.** $y = (1-x^3)/(1+x^2)$

31. $y = (3x-5)/(x-1)$ **32.** $y = (x^2-x-4)/(2x-1)$

Find dy/dx in the following cases (where x is in radians):

33. $y = \sin(2x+1)$ **34.** $y = \cos(3x-4)$

35. $y = \cos^2 x$ **36.** $y = \tan^2 x$

37. $y = \cos x(1+\sin x)$ **38.** $y = \sin x(\cos x + \sin x)$

39. $y = \sec x$ **40.** $y = \cot x$

Find dy/dx in the following cases:

41. $y = \ln(3x-1)$ **42.** $y = e^{2x}$

43. $y = \ln(x^2)$ **44.** $y = (\ln x)^2$

45. $y = xe^x$ **46.** $y = x \ln x$

Calculate the following integrals (where x is in radians):

47. $\displaystyle\int_0^{\pi/2} \cos x \, dx$ **48.** $\displaystyle\int_0^{\pi/2} \sin x \, dx$

49. $\displaystyle\int_{\pi/3}^{\pi/2} \sin x \, dx$ **50.** $\displaystyle\int_{\pi/6}^{\pi/3} \cos x \, dx$

51. $\displaystyle\int_0^{\pi/2} (3\cos x + 4\sin x)\,dx$ **52.** $\displaystyle\int_0^{\pi/2} (4\cos x - 3\sin x)\,dx$

53. $\displaystyle\int_1^2 \cos(2x+1)\,dx$ **54.** $\displaystyle\int_0^2 \sin(3x-2)\,dx$

Calculate the following integrals:

55. $\displaystyle\int_0^2 1/(x+1)\,dx$ **56.** $\displaystyle\int_1^3 1/(2x-1)\,dx$

57. $\displaystyle\int_0^1 e^{2x}\,dx$ **58.** $\displaystyle\int_0^1 e^{4x}\,dx$

59. $\displaystyle\int_2^3 e^{2x+1}\,dx$ **60.** $\displaystyle\int_0^4 e^{3x+2}\,dx$

EXERCISE 18S

Unless otherwise stated, all forces (P or $\mathbf{P}$) are in newtons, displacements (s or $\mathbf{s}$) in metres, velocities (v or $\mathbf{v}$) in metres per second, masses (m) in kilograms, work and energy in joules. Take g as $9.8\,\mathrm{m\,s^{-2}}$, and give answers that are not exact to 3 significant figures. $\mathbf{j}$ denotes the upward vertical unit vector.

Calculate the work done given the following values of P and s:

1. 40, 5   **2.** 30, 6   **3.** 50, -4 **4.** -40, 3

5. A horizontal force of $50\,\mathrm{N}$ acts on a mass of $10\,\mathrm{kg}$ resting on a horizontal floor. The mass is pushed $8\,\mathrm{m}$ against a frictional force of $18\,\mathrm{N}$. Calculate the work done by the applied force and by the friction, and the total work done.

6. As question 5, but applied force $= 70\,\mathrm{N}$, mass $= 15\,\mathrm{kg}$, displacement $= 14\,\mathrm{m}$, frictional force $= 25\,\mathrm{N}$.

7. A parachutist of mass $80\,\mathrm{kg}$ falls freely for $200\,\mathrm{m}$. Calculate the work done by gravity.

8. He then falls a further $400\,\mathrm{m}$ with the parachute open, against an average resistance of $1100\,\mathrm{N}$. Calculate the work done by the resistance.

9. Calculate the total work done in the $400\,\mathrm{m}$ fall of question 8.

10. Calculate the total work done in the $600\,\mathrm{m}$ fall of questions 7 and 8.

11. A toboggan of mass $25\,\mathrm{kg}$ runs down a hill of average inclination $7°$ for $150\,\mathrm{m}$. The average resistance is $5\,\mathrm{N}$. Calculate the work done by gravity.

12. Calculate the work done by the resistance in question 11.

13. Calculate the total work done in question 11.

14. If the ground continues horizontally, calculate the distance required for the toboggan of question 11 to come to a stop, assuming unchanged resistance.

Calculate the work done in each case, illustrating your answers with sketches:

15. $\mathbf{P} = 3\mathbf{i}, \ \mathbf{s} = -4\mathbf{i}$ **16.** $\mathbf{P} = -4\mathbf{i}, \ \mathbf{s} = 3\mathbf{j}$

17. $\mathbf{P} = 2\mathbf{i} - \mathbf{j}, \ \mathbf{s} = 3\mathbf{i} + 4\mathbf{j}$ **18.** $\mathbf{P} = 3\mathbf{i} + \mathbf{j}, \ \mathbf{s} = -\mathbf{i} + 5\mathbf{j}$

19. $\mathbf{P} = -2\mathbf{i} + \mathbf{j}, \ \mathbf{s} = 3\mathbf{i} + \mathbf{j}$ **20.** $\mathbf{P} = 4\mathbf{i} - 2\mathbf{j}, \ \mathbf{s} = \mathbf{i} + 5\mathbf{j}$

Calculate the K.E. in each case:

21. $m = 4, \ v = 5$ **22.** $m = 5, \ v = 4$

23. $m = 2.5 \times 10^{-4}, \ v = 5.6 \times 10^{3}$ **24.** $m = 1.73 \times 10^{7}, \ v = 0.274$

25. An object of mass 3 kg moves in a straight line from O to P, where OP equals 12 m. If the object is subject to a constant force of 5 N acting in the direction OP, and the object's speed at O is $6\,\mathrm{m\,s}^{-1}$, calculate its speed at P.

26. A constant force of 8 N acts on a mass of 5 kg, increasing its speed from $4\,\mathrm{m\,s}^{-1}$ to $7\,\mathrm{m\,s}^{-1}$. Calculate the distance covered, assuming that the direction of the force and the direction of motion are the same.

27. A brick of mass 5 kg rests on a horizontal plane. A force of $(30\mathbf{i} + 40\mathbf{j})\,\mathrm{N}$ is applied to it, where $\mathbf{i}$ is a horizontal unit vector. Explain why the brick stays in contact with the plane. The brick moves through the displacement $5\mathbf{i}\,\mathrm{m}$, against a frictional force of $-8\mathbf{i}\,\mathrm{N}$. Find the total work done by the forces, and hence the velocity acquired by the brick.

28. A football of mass 0.43 kg is kicked with velocity $(22\mathbf{i} + 5\mathbf{j})\,\mathrm{m\,s}^{-1}$ from the penalty spot, 11 m from the goal line, where $\mathbf{i}$ is the unit vector pointing straight towards the goal. The overall force acting on the ball during its flight equals $(-0.6\mathbf{i} - 4.2\mathbf{j})\,\mathrm{N}$. If the ball enters the goal 1.28 m above the line, calculate its speed at that moment.

29. A roller-skater of mass 50 kg skates up a slope of length 10 m, ending 4 m above his starting point. What is his gain in P.E.?

30. The skater in question 29 then skates down the slope, starting from rest. What is his speed at the bottom of the slope (ignore rolling resistance)?

31. The skater of questions 29 and 30 changes to skates which are subject to a rolling resistance of 40 N. What speed does he need at the bottom of the slope in order just to reach the top without any additional effort on his part?

32. The skater of questions 29 to 31 finally skates down the slope, starting with a speed of $5\,\mathrm{m\,s}^{-1}$ at the top. What is his speed at the bottom?

33. Taking the mass of the Earth to be $6.0 \times 10^{24}\,\mathrm{kg}$ and its average distance from the Sun to be $1.5 \times 10^{11}\,\mathrm{m}$, calculate its kinetic energy due to its motion round the Sun.

34. The intrinsic energy E of a mass m at rest is given by the formula $E = mc^{2}$ (where c is the velocity of light). Calculate what mass has an intrinsic energy equal to the kinetic energy of the Earth, taking c to be $3.0 \times 10^{8}\,\mathrm{m\,s}^{-1}$.

35. A stream flows down the side of a mountain. The water enters a hydro-electric power station, where it drives a turbine and flows on into a reservoir. The turbine drives a generator. The electricity produced is distributed via the National Grid for industrial and domestic use, but at night when demand for energy is low it is used to drive a pump which pumps water from the reservoir into another reservoir much higher up the mountain. Explain the various conversions of energy involved in this whole process.

36. A ship coming alongside a jetty is brought to rest by means of a steel hawser. The hawser is not quite strong enough, however, and breaks under the strain. The broken hawser whips about very violently. Explain the various energy conversions.

37. A railway truck of mass 2000 kg moving along the track with a speed of $3 \, \text{m s}^{-1}$ collides with a stationary truck of mass 3000 kg. Assuming that the coupling mechanism means that they move on at a common speed, calculate the loss of (kinetic) energy caused by the collision.

38. Is more kinetic energy lost if two cars, each of mass 1500 kg and moving at 54 km/h, collide head on, or if a single car of mass 1500 kg, moving at 108 km/h, collides with an immovable obstacle?

39. Two objects of masses 5 and 3 kg lie on a smooth horizontal table, connected by a string, which is slack to begin with. If the smaller mass is projected away from the larger with a speed of $4 \, \text{m s}^{-1}$, find the loss of kinetic energy when the string suddenly becomes taut.

40. A device of mass 8 kg moving at a speed of $40 \, \text{m s}^{-1}$ suddenly explodes into two bits, of mass 5 kg and 3 kg. If the smaller part's velocity after the explosion is $100 \, \text{m s}^{-1}$ in the original direction of motion, find the energy supplied by the explosion.

41. A bullet of mass 100 grams is fired horizontally into a wood block of mass 4 kg which is suspended from a rigid bar by means of a steel wire of length 8 m. The bullet instantly becomes embedded in the block, and the wire (now supporting the bullet as well as the block) swings sideways through an angle of 12°. Find the speed of the block immediately after the impact, and hence the speed of the bullet immediately before the impact.

42. The bullet and block are as in question 41, except that the bullet's speed immediately before impact is now known to be $90 \, \text{m s}^{-1}$. Find the angle through which the wire will swing.

43. A man runs up a flight of steps which rise at an angle of 30° to the horizontal. If his speed is a steady $1.6 \, \text{m s}^{-1}$ and he weighs 700 N, find the power he must be generating.

44. If I can generate 600 W and weigh 600 N, how fast can I run up a hill inclined at 15° to the horizontal?

45. A sack of mass 50 kg is deposited on a conveyor belt which is driven at a steady $0.6\,\mathrm{m\,s^{-1}}$. If $0.1\,\mathrm{s}$ elapses before the sack picks up full speed, show that the average force on the sack during this period must be 300 N. Hence calculate the additional power that must be generated by the motor.

46. Find the power output in the situation described in question 45, and hence find the efficiency.

47. A car with an effective power output of 36 kW has a maximum speed on the flat of 108 km/h. Find the magnitude of the force resisting motion. What extra power would be needed to maintain the same speed up a hill inclined at an angle $\arcsin(0.05)$ to the horizontal, if the car's weight is 8 kN?

48. A car can generate 42 kW at 126 km/h. If the resisting forces at this speed amount to 900 N, and the car's weight is 10 kN, find the angle of the steepest incline that the car can manage at this speed.

49. When the man raises a load at a steady speed by means of the pulley system shown in figure 18.11, the tension in the rope on the far side of either pulley is only 80% of the tension on the near side. If the weight of the pulley wheels and the rope itself can be neglected, show that the efficiency of the mechanism is 72%.

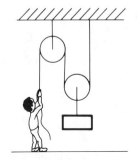

Fig. 18.11

50. Two wedges are used to raise a load, as shown in figure 18.12. If the efficiency is 80%, and the angle of the wedge is 15°, find the value of L/P.

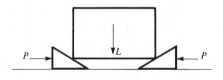

Fig. 18.12

EXERCISE 19S

Which of the following equations give y as a function of x?

1. $2x - y = 7$ **2.** $x = 4 + 3y$

3. $2y = 3 - xy$ **4.** $x + \tan y = 0$

5. $y^3 = x$ **6.** $x = e^y$

What is the range of the following functions, where the domain in each case is $\mathbb{R}$ (with x restricted as shown)?

7. $y = \log x$ $(x > 0)$ **8.** $y = \sin x$ (x in radians)

9. $y = 1 + x^2$ **10.** $y = 2x - x^2$

11. $y = \sqrt{(x^2)} - x$ **12.** $y = 1/x^2$ $(x \neq 0)$

Find $fg(x)$ and $gf(x)$, where $f(x)$ and $g(x)$ are as given:

13. $f(x) = 2x + 3$, $g(x) = 4 - x$

14. $f(x) = 3 + 5x$, $g(x) = 1 - 3x$

15. $f(x) = x^2 + 3x + 4$, $g(x) = 2x$

16. $f(x) = 2 - 4x + x^2$, $g(x) = 10x$

Find the inverses of the following functions:

17. $f(x) = 1 - x$ **18.** $f(x) = 3 - 2x$

19. $f(x) = 4 + 2/x$ **20.** $f(x) = 5 - 1/x$

Solve the following equations graphically:

21. $x^3 = 5 - x$ **22.** $x^4 = 2x - 1$

23. $x \log x = 1$ **24.** $\cos x + \sin x = 1$

Sketch the graphs of the following equations, marking in any asymptotes:

25. $y = 2x/(x - 2)$ **26.** $y = 6x/(x + 3)$

27. $y = 5x/(x^2 + 1)$ **28.** $y = 4/(x^2 + 1)$

29. $y = x^3/(x - 2)$ **30.** $y = (x^2 + 1)/(x + 1)$

Solve graphically the following equations and inequalities:

31. $2x/(x - 2) = 3$, $2x/(x - 2) < 0$

32. $6x/(x + 3) = 3$, $6x/(x + 3) < x$

33. $5x/(x^2 + 1) = 2$, $5x/(x^2 + 1) > x$

34. $4/(x^2 + 1) = x$, $4/(x^2 + 1) > 2$

35. $x^3/(x - 2) = -1$, $x^3/(x - 2) < 0$

36. $(x^2 + 1)/(x + 1) = 2$, $(x^2 + 1)/(x + 1) < x$

In each case, the quantities shown in the table are known to be related by an equation of the form indicated. Draw a suitable graph to estimate the unknown constants (a, b, c, or n) as accurately as the figures allow:

37. $y = ax^2 + b$

x	1.0	1.1	1.2	1.3	1.4
y	120	183	252	327	408

38. $y = \sqrt{(ax+b)}$

x	16	18	20	22	24
y	11.0	11.7	12.4	13.0	13.6

39. $y = a \log x + b$

x	2	3	4	5	6
y	0.1	3.1	5.3	6.8	8.2

40. $y = cx^n$

x	0.3	0.4	0.5	0.6	0.7
y	0.4	0.9	1.8	3.0	4.8

In four separate small diagrams, indicate the following four sets (a) $P \cap Q$, (b) $P' \cap Q$, (c) $P \cap Q'$, (d) $P' \cap Q'$, where P and Q are as indicated in each case:

41. $P = \{(x, y): y > 2x\}$ and $Q = \{(x, y): y < 1\}$

42. $P = \{(x, y): x+y < 2\}$ and $Q = \{(x, y): y < x\}$

43. $P = \{(x, y): x > 3\}$ and $Q = \{(x, y): x < 1\}$

44. $P = \{(x, y): x+y < 1\}$ and $Q = \{(x, y): x+y < 3\}$

45. $P = \{(x, y): xy < 1\}$ and $Q = \{(x, y): x+y < 0\}$

46. $P = \{(x, y): x^2+y^2 < 4\}$ and $Q = \{(x, y): y < x-2\}$

47. Draw the set $\{(x, y): y \geqslant x \text{ and } 2 \leqslant x \leqslant 5\}$, and determine the least and greatest possible values of $x+y$ at points within this set.

48. Draw the set $\{(x, y): y \geqslant 2 \text{ and } x \geqslant 1 \text{ and } x+y \leqslant 10\}$, and determine the least and greatest possible values of $3x+4y$ at points within this set.

49. Draw the set $\{(x, y): y \leqslant 5-x^2\}$, and determine the greatest possible value of $x+y$ at points within this set.

50. Draw the set $\{(x, y): y \geqslant -x^2\}$, and determine the least possible value of $x+y$ at points within this set.

51. A, B, C are fixed points in a plane, forming the equilateral triangle ABC. The set α is defined as $\{P: \text{angle } BPC < 90°\}$, where P is a variable point in the plane. Sets β and γ are defined likewise. Draw a figure showing the sets as clearly as possible, and indicate the set $\alpha \cap \beta \cap \gamma$.

52. A, B, C are three non-collinear fixed points in a plane. The set α is defined as $\{P: BP + PC > BC\}$, where P is a variable point in the plane, and sets β and γ are defined likewise. Draw a figure showing one of these sets as clearly as possible, and describe the set $\alpha \cap \beta \cap \gamma$.

The sequences in the following questions are either arithmetic or geometric progressions. In each case, say which type of progression it must be, give d or r, find the next two terms, calculate the 20th term, and give a formula for the nth term.

53. 4, 3, 2, 1,...

54. 7, 12, 17, 22,...

55. 5, 10, 20, 40,...

56. 8, 4, 2, 1,...

57. to 60. Calculate the sum of the first 20 terms of the progressions given in questions 53 to 56, and give a formula for the sum of the first n terms.

61. Given that the numbers 6, x, y, 39 are in arithmetic progression, find x and y.

62. Given that 10, x, y, z, 70 are in arithmetic progression, find x, y, and z.

63. Given that 27, x, y, 64 are in geometric progression, find x and y.

64. Given that 25, x, y, z, 3.24 are in geometric progression, find x, y, and z.

65. How many odd numbers (starting with 1) must be taken before the total exceeds 1000?

66. How many even numbers (starting with 2) must be taken before the total exceeds 1000?

67. How many terms of the geometric progression 1, 1/2, 1/4,... must be taken before the total exceeds 1.999?

68. How many terms of the geometric progression 5, 15, 45,... must be taken before the sum exceeds one million?

69. Find the sum to infinity of the following G.P.s:

   (a) 36, 12, 4,...   (b) 1000, 100, 10,...

70. Find the sum to infinity of the following G.P.s:

   (a) 250, -50, 10,...   (b) 0.4, 0.04, 0.004,...

Prove the following by induction, n being any positive integer:

71. That $1^2 + 3^2 + 5^2 + \ldots$ to n terms $= \frac{1}{3}n(4n^2 - 1)$.

72. That $1/(1 \times 2) + 1/(2 \times 3) + \ldots$ to n terms $= n/(n+1)$.

73. That $49^n - 1$ is divisible by 48.

74. That $49^n - 48n - 1$ is divisible by 48^2.

75. That $\sum\limits_{r=1}^{n+1} r = \frac{1}{2}(n+1)(n+2)$.

76. That $\quad 1 \times n + 2 \times (n-1) + 3 \times (n-2) + \ldots + (n-1) \times 2 + n \times 1 \quad$ equals $\frac{1}{6}n(n+1)(n+2)$.

77. That the H.C.F. of f_n and f_{n+1} equals 1, where f_1, f_2, f_3, etc. are the Fibonacci numbers.

78. That the maximum number of regions formed when n lines are drawn in a plane equals 2^n.

79. That a connected network with n nodes ($n > 1$), of which exactly two are odd nodes, is traversable.

80. That a connected network with n nodes, of which all are even nodes, is traversable.

Find the sum and product of the following complex numbers:

81. $(4 - 7i)$ and $(5 + 3i)$

82. $(3 + 6i)$ and $(2 - i)$

83. $(1 + i)$, $(2 + 3i)$, and $(5 - 4i)$

84. $(2 + 5i)$, $(1 - i)$, and $(-3 - i)$

85. Calculate 10i divided by $(1 + 3i)$.

86. Calculate $(3 + 4i)$ divided by $(2 + i)$.

Solve the following quadratic equations, and show their roots in an Argand diagram:

87. $z^2 - 6z + 13 = 0$

88. $z^2 + 2z + 10 = 0$

89. $z^2 + iz + 2 = 0$

90. $z^2 - 3iz + 4 = 0$

Express the following complex numbers in modulus–argument form, and illustrate in an Argand diagram:

91. 3, 5i, $4 - 4i$

92. -1, $-3 - 3i$, $4 + 3i$

Calculate:

93. (a) $(1 + i\sqrt{3})^3$ (b) $(1 + i\sqrt{3})^6$

94. (a) $(\sqrt{3} - i)^6$ (b) $(\sqrt{3} - i)^9$

EXERCISE 20S

In the following questions, the diagrams represent a light beam AB in equilibrium under the action of various forces as shown. Find the unknown quantities in each case, if AB = 10 units.

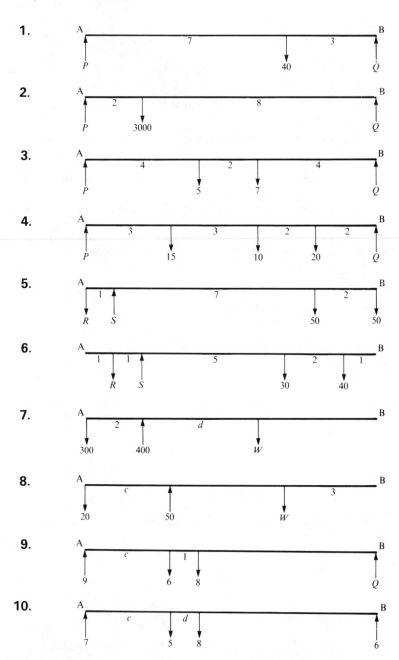

11. An unevenly loaded beam AB of length 4 m is supported in a horizontal position by two vertical forces, 3 N at A and 5 N at B. Find the single force equivalent to these two.

12. Various loads hang from a light girder AB of length 6 m. The girder itself is held horizontally by means of bolts inserted at A and B, which exert vertical support forces of 2 kN and 3 kN respectively. Find the single force equivalent to these two support forces.

13. Four vertical loads of 2, 4, 6, and 8 N act at $(1,0)$, $(2,0)$, $(3,0)$, and $(4,0)$ respectively. Find the single load equivalent to them all.

14. Five vertical loads of 1, 3, 5, 7, and 9 N act at $(1,0)$, $(2,0)$, $(3,0)$, $(4,0)$, and $(5,0)$ respectively. Find the single load equivalent to them all.

15. A 6 m beam AB is placed symmetrically (and horizontally) on two trestles which are 4 m apart. When a load of 400 N is hung from B, the forces exerted by the nearer and further trestles are 590 and 50 N respectively. Find the weight of the beam, and the position of its centre of gravity.

16. Show that the maximum load that could be hung from B without causing the beam in question 15 to tip over is 600 N. If the load at B is removed, what is the maximum load that can be hung from A?

17. Two uniform metal rods each of length 1 m are welded end to end. If the density of one rod is one-third that of the other, where is the centre of gravity of the whole thing?

18. Two uniform rectangular metal plates measuring 5×3 m and 5×2 m are butt welded to form a 5×5 m square plate. Where is its centre of gravity?

19. A uniform rectangular plate OABC has a 2×2 m square cut away from corner B. If OA = 6 m and OC = 4 m, where is the centre of gravity of the resulting shape?

20. A uniform square plate OABC has three 10×10 cm squares cut away from corners A, B, and C. If OA = OC = 30 cm, where is the centre of gravity of the resulting shape?

21. A uniform triangular lamina has corners at $(0,0)$, $(5,0)$, and $(4,6)$. Where is its centre of mass?

22. A uniform quadrilateral lamina has corners at $(0,0)$, $(9,0)$, $(3,9)$, and $(0,3)$. Where is its centre of mass?

23. Isolated masses of 2 kg, 3 kg, 5 kg, and 5 kg are located at $(-1,6)$, $(-1,1)$, $(4,5)$, and $(3,7)$ respectively. Find their centre of mass.

24. Isolated masses of 4 kg, 6 kg, 6 kg, 7 kg, and 7 kg are located at $(0,0)$, $(3,-4)$, $(1,6)$, $(-2,8)$, and $(2,1)$ respectively. Find their centre of mass.

Find the resultant (i.e. the magnitude and the line of action) of each of the following systems of forces:

25. **P**, of magnitude 5 N, acting due east, along $y = 3$,
  Q, of magnitude 12 N, acting due north, along $x = 1$.

26. **P**, of magnitude 24 N, acting due east, along $y = 4$,
  Q, of magnitude 7 N, acting due south, along $x = 3$.

27. **P**, of magnitude 1 N, acting due north, along $x = 5$,
  Q, of magnitude 3 N, acting due south, along $x = 7$,
  R, of magnitude 2 N, acting due east, along $y = 8$.

28. **P**, of magnitude 5 N, acting due east, along $y = 6$,
  Q, of magnitude 9 N, acting due west, along $y = 4$,
  R, of magnitude 3 N, acting due south, along $x = 7$.

Show that the resultant of each of the following systems is zero, and find the torque:

29. **P**, of magnitude 4 N, acting due east, along $y = 1$,
  Q, of magnitude 7 N, acting due west, along $y = 7$,
  R, of magnitude 3 N, acting due east, along $y = 10$.

30. **P**, of magnitude 2 N, acting due south, along $x = 1$,
  Q, of magnitude 3 N, acting due south, along $x = 4$,
  R, of magnitude 5 N, acting due north, along $x = 10$.

31. Forces each of magnitude 10 N act along AB, BC, and CA, where ABC is an equilateral triangle of side 2 m. Show that this system is equivalent to a couple, and find its torque.

32. AB = 5 cm, BC = 12 cm, and CA = 13 cm. Forces of 10 N and 24 N act along AB and BC (in those directions). What further force acting along CA is needed to make the resultant of the system equal to zero, and what is then the torque?

33. A wire AOB of uniform density is bent at O into an L shape, where OA = 40 cm and OB = 30 cm, and is hung from a string tied on at O. Find the angle that OA makes with the vertical when the system is in equilibrium.

34. As question 33, but with OA = 20 cm and OB = 50 cm.

35. A uniform plane lamina ABC hangs in equilibrium from a string tied on at B. If AB = AC and angle A is a right-angle, find the angle that AB makes with the vertical.

36. A light square lamina ABCD has masses of 2, 3, and 4 attached at B, C, and D. If it hangs in equilibrium from a string tied on at A, find, by accurate drawing or by calculation, the angle that AD makes with the vertical.

37. A uniform girder OA of weight 500 N is hinged freely at O, and is held in a horizontal position by a light chain running from A to a point B vertically above O. A load of 500 N hangs from A. If OA = OB = 4 m, find the tension in the chain, and the magnitude of the reaction at the hinge.

38. As question 37, but with a load of 1000 N hanging from A, and with OB = 7.5 m.

39. A horizontal cantilever AB is built rigidly into a stone wall at A, and carries a load of 400 kg at B. If the cantilever is assumed to be a uniform structure of mass 100 kg and length 4 m, find the support force and torque exerted by the wall at A.

40. As question 39, but with four loads of 100 kg at distances of 1, 2, 3, and 4 m from A, instead of the single load of 400 kg at B.

41. The boom OA of a derrick is freely hinged at O, and held up at an angle of 45° to the vertical by a horizontal wire connected at A. The boom may be taken as a uniform beam of weight 3 kN and length 10 m. If a load of 5 kN is slung from A, find the tension in the wire, and the magnitude of the reaction at O.

42. As question 41, but with an angle of 30° and with a load of 7 kN.

43. A uniform bar AB of length 2 m is supported in equilibrium by light wires OA and OB of length 160 and 140 cm. Find by accurate drawing the angle between AB and the vertical.

44. A beam AB of length 5 m is slung from chains OA and OB each of length 5 m. Assuming the chains are light, find the position of the centre of gravity of the beam if it hangs in equilibrium at an angle of 80° to the vertical.

45. The lower end of a uniform ladder rests on smooth horizontal ground, while the upper end rests against a smooth vertical wall. The ladder is inclined at 70° to the horizontal, and is kept in position by a horizontal rope pulling the foot of the ladder in towards the wall. If the weight of the ladder is 500 N, find the tension in the rope.

46. As question 45, but with a man weighing 750 N standing   (a) at the foot of the ladder, and   (b) at the top.

47. A uniform boom OA is freely hinged at O, and is kept in position by a wire AB, as shown in figure 20.27. By accurate drawing (or otherwise), find the angle between the reaction at O and the horizontal BC.

48. As question 47, but with a load equal to the weight of the boom hung at A.

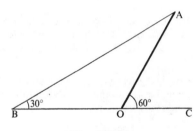

Fig. 20.27

EXAMINATION QUESTIONS

EXERCISE 1X

1. Solve the equation $\dfrac{1}{x}+\dfrac{1}{3x-2} = 2$.

[UL]

2. For what values of x is it true that $6+5x-x^2 > 0$? Illustrate your answer with a sketch of the graph of the function f, where $f(x) = 6+5x-x^2$.

Give a simpler description of the set $\{x: f(x) < 12\}$.

[SMP]

3. Find the range of values of x for which

$$(x-2)(2x+1) < 3.$$

[MEI]

4. A cyclist finds that, by increasing his usual average speed by $2\,\mathrm{km/h}$, he saves one hour over a distance of $100\,\mathrm{km}$.

Take his usual average speed to be $x\,\mathrm{km/h}$. Write down expressions in terms of x for his usual time, his new speed and his new time. Deduce an equation for x and simplify it.

Solve this equation to find his usual average speed, giving the answer in km/h correct to one decimal place. Show that this answer satisfies the original problem by calculating the old and new times taken in hours to two decimal places.

[MEI]

5. The perimeter of a given triangle whose sides are in the ratio $3:4:5$ is greater by 4 metres than that of a given square. The area of the square is greater by $25\,\mathrm{m}^2$ than that of the triangle. Find the lengths of the sides of the square and of the triangle.

6. Calculate to two significant figures the sides of a rectangle whose perimeter is 24 metres and area 26 square metres.

[MEI]

7. The height in metres of a stone above ground level t second after being thrown, until it hits the ground, is given by

$$h = 80+15t-5t^2.$$

(a) State the height from which it was thrown.

(b) Calculate, to the nearest tenth of a second, when it hits the ground.

(c) Rewrite h in the form $5[B-(A-t)^2]$, stating the values of the positive numbers A and B.

(d) Hence, or otherwise, state when the stone is highest and give this height.

(e) Find the height after 0.8 second and calculate for how long it is above this.

[SMP]

8. On squared paper, with a scale of 1 cm to 1 unit, draw the graphs of the line $y = 2(x-1)$ and the curve $y^2 = 4x$ between $x = 0$ and $x = 4$. Hence obtain approximate values of the solutions of the simultaneous equations $y = 2(x-1)$ and $y^2 = 4x$. Verify that the values of x thus obtained are approximate values of the roots of the equation

$$x^2-3x+1 = 0.$$

Find the corresponding equation in y of which the roots are the ordinates (values of y) of the points of intersection.

[MEI]

9. State the coordinates of the points where the graph of $y = (x-2)(3-x)$ cuts (a) the x-axis, (b) the y-axis.

Sketch the graph, and indicate on your diagram how it can be used to estimate the roots of the equation $(x-2)(3-x) = -3$.

Solve the equation algebraically, giving your answers corrected to 1 decimal place.

[SMP]

10. (i) Factorise x^2-6x+8.

(ii) Rewrite x^2-6x+8 in the form $(x-a)^2-b$.

(iii) For the graph of $y = x^2-6x+8$ write down the coordinates of (a) the vertex, (b) the points where the curve meets the x-axis and the y-axis.

(iv) Draw a sketch of the graph and show clearly on it your answers to part (iii).

[SMP]

11. Express the equation $y = x^2 - 6x + 7$ in the form $y = (x-a)^2 - b$. Sketch the graph of this equation, and state fully the transformation which maps the graph of $y = x^2$ onto the graph of $y = x^2 - 6x + 7$.

Solve the equation $x^2 - 6x + 7 = 0$, giving your answers correct to 3 significant figures.

[SMP]

12. Express $2x^2 + 6x + 1$ in the form $a(x+h)^2 + k$ where a, h, k are rational numbers. This expression is denoted by $E(x)$.

Find:

(a) the minimum value of $E(x)$,
(b) the solution set of $E(x) = 0$,
(c) the solution set of $E(x) \geqslant 9$.

Sketch the graph of $E(x)$ for real values of x and show clearly on it your answers to parts (a), (b), (c).

[SMP]

13. (a) Factorise the quadratic function $f(x)$, where $f(x) = 5x^2 - 7x - 6$.

(b) If x is real, find the set of values of x for which $f(x) < 0$.

(c) Given that $A = \{-2, -1, 0, 1, 2\}$ state the elements $x \in A$ for which $f(x) < 0$.

[UL]

14. (a) Factorise the quadratic expression y where

$$y = 6x^2 - 17x + 7.$$

Hence, given that $x \in \mathbb{R}$, find the set of values of x for which $y > 0$.

(b) If $P = \{(x, y) : y = 6x^2 - 17x + 7\}$ and $Q = \{(x, y) : y = 7 - x\}$, find the two members of $P \cap Q$.

(c) Sketch, with the same axes, the graphs of $y = 6x^2 - 17x + 7$ and $y = 7 - x$, indicating clearly the two members of $P \cap Q$.

[UL]

15. A quadratic polynomial function is given by

$$f : x \rightarrow x^2 - x - 6.$$

(a) Factorise $f(x)$.

(b) Draw the graph of $y = f(x)$ for $-3 \leqslant x \leqslant 4$.

(c) Solve the equation $f(x) = 0$.

(d) Express $f(x)$ in the form $(x-p)^2 + q$ and

show clearly the significance of p and q on your graph.

(e) What are the sum and product of the roots of the equation $f(x) = -4$?

(f) Explain, by reference to the graph, why it is that for every equation $x^2 - x - 6 = k$ the sum of the roots is the same, whatever the value of k.

[SMP]

16. (a) $f(x) = 9 + 12x - 4x^2$. The roots of the quadratic equation $f(x) = 0$ are p and q.

Explain why $\dfrac{p+q}{2} = 1.5$.

(b) Hence write down the axis of symmetry of the graph of the function f.

(c) For what value of x is $f(x)$ greatest?

(d) Hence calculate the greatest value of $f(x)$.

(e) State the value of $f(x)$ when $x = 0$.

(f) Write down the factors of $12x - 4x^2$ and hence give another value of x for which $f(x)$ has the same value as in part (e).

(g) Calculate the roots of $f(x) = 0$, correct to one place of decimals.

Show your answers to parts (b) to (g) on a sketch-graph of the function f.

[SMP]

17. (i) Solve the equation $2x^2 - 3x - 9 = 0$.

(ii) Hence write down the equation of the axes of symmetry of the graphs of

(a) $y = 2x^2 - 3x - 9$,
and (b) $y = 2x^2 - 3x + 5$.

Explain why the sum of the roots of the equation $2x^2 - 3x + 5 = 0$ is the same as the sum of the roots in part (i).

(iii) The graph of $y = 25x^2 + bx + c$ has $x = 2$ as an axis of symmetry. Write down the value of b.

Given also that a zero of $25x^2 + bx + c$ is 3.4, write down the other zero, and hence find the value of c.

[SMP]

18. Find numbers A, B and C such that

$$3x^2 + 12x \equiv A(x+B)^2 - C$$

for all values of x.

Explain why $(x+B)^2$ is never negative, deduce the least value of $3x^2 + 12x$, and state the value of x for which this occurs.

cont.

Using the first part, or otherwise, find, if possible, values of x to two decimal places for which

(i) $3x^2 + 12x = 17$,
(ii) $3x^2 + 12x + 17 = 0$.

If in either case there is no value of x, say so.

[MEI]

19. Find the range of values of q for which the roots of the equation

$$x^2 - 6x + q^2 - 7 = 0 \quad \text{are real.}$$

If q is a positive integer, list the values of q for which the roots of the equation are real and of the same sign, giving reasons for your answer.

[AEB 1980]

20. Given that α and β are the roots of the equation

$$x^2 + 5x + 3 = 0,$$

find an equation with integer coefficients whose roots are α^2 and β^2.

[UL]

21. The roots of a quadratic equation differ by three and their product is twice their sum. Find the two quadratic equations satisfying these conditions.

[AEB 1982]

22. (a) Find the set of values of k for which the equation $x^2 + kx + 2k - 3 = 0$ has no real roots.

When $k = 7$, the roots of the equation $x^2 + kx + 2k - 3 = 0$ are α and β, where $\alpha > \beta$.

(b) Write down the values of $(\alpha + \beta)$ and $\alpha\beta$.

(c) Form an equation with integral coefficients whose roots are α/β and β/α.

(d) Prove that $\alpha - \beta = \sqrt{5}$.

[UL]

23. The roots of the quadratic equation

$$(2k+1)x^2 + 4(k-1)x + k = 0$$

are α and β.

(a) Find the values of k for which α and β are equal.

(b) The roots of the equation $x^2 + qx + r = 0$ are $\dfrac{1}{\alpha}$ and $\dfrac{1}{\beta}$.

Given that $k \neq 0$, find q and r in terms of k.

[AEB 1982]

24. (a) The roots of the equation $x^2 + px - q = 0$, where p and q are non-zero constants, are α and β. Express $(\alpha - 3\beta)(\beta - 3\alpha)$ in terms of p and q.

Hence find the condition for one root of the equation to be equal to three times the other root.

Given that this condition holds, determine the sign of q.

(b) State the condition for the equation $ax^2 + bx + c = 0$ to have equal roots and state a value of these roots.

Hence, or otherwise, find the values of k for which the equation

$$(k+2)x^2 + (4k+2)x + 3k + 4 = 0$$

has equal roots.

[JMB]

25. Show that

$$x^2 - 4x + 3 = 0 \Leftrightarrow x = 4 - 3/x.$$

Draw, on the same axes with -3 to 10 for domain and range, graphs of $y = 4 - 3/x$ and of $y = x$.

State the quadratic equation whose roots are the points of intersection of the graphs.

A flow chart for finding a root of this equation is:

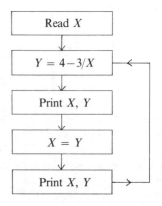

Take $X = 0.5$ and write down the first five pairs of values printed out. Treating each pair of values as the coordinates of a point, plot these five points on your graph, joining each to the next by a straight line. (Note that the effect is to move successively horizontally from curve to line, then vertically from line to curve.) Without further calculation, show on your graph the next 3 points which would be given by this process, labelling them *A*, *B*, *C*.

Write down, correct to 2 significant figures, the hundredth pair of coordinates that would be printed.

[SMP]

EXERCISE 2X

1. At 1300 hours two hikers, *P* and *Q*, leave a camp *C* and begin to cross a flat plain. Hiker *P* walks steadily at 7 km/h on a bearing of 080° and hiker *Q* walks steadily at 5 km/h on a bearing of 020°. At 1400 hours the hikers, *P* and *Q*, are at points *A* and *B* respectively. Calculate the distance and bearing of *B* from *A*.

Hiker *P* now changes course and walks steadily at 7 km/h on a bearing of 010° while hiker *Q* remains at the point *B*.

Calculate the time, to the nearest minute, at which hiker *P* is due East of *B*.

[AEB 1981]

2. (i) Give definitions of $\sin\theta$ and $\cos\theta$ which are valid for any angle.

(ii) State the values of (a) $\sin 100°$, (b) $\cos 140°$, (c) $\sin 200°$, (d) $\cos 320°$, in terms of sines or cosines of acute angles, paying particular attention to whether they are positive or negative.

(iii) A formula for the depth of water in a tidal channel is $y = 5 + 3\cos(30t)°$ in metres, where *t* is the number of hours after noon on Monday.

State the next times of High Water and Low Water after noon on Monday and the depth of water at these times. Calculate also, to the nearest five minutes, the times on Monday afternoon between which the channel is closed to navigation for a vessel drawing 3 metres.

[MEI]

3. The depth of water *d* metre in a tidal channel at *x* hour after midnight is given by the formula

$$d = 3 + 2\cos(30x + 60)°.$$

Copy and complete the following table for evaluating *d* at hourly intervals from midnight

to noon.

x	0	1	2	3	4	5	6
$30x + 60$	60	90	120	150	180		
$\cos(30x+60)°$	0.5	0	−0.5				
d		4	3	2			

x	7	8	9	10	11	12
$30x + 60$						
$\cos(30x+60)°$						
d						

Plot *d* against *x* accurately on squared paper and so draw a graph showing the depth of water during this time.

(i) State the times of high tide and low tide.

(ii) Read from your graph the times between which a boat drawing 1.5 m of water will be aground if it is moored in this channel.

[MEI]

4. Copy and complete the following table of values for the graph of $y = 10 + 5\sin(30x)°$ in the interval $0 \leqslant x \leqslant 12$.

x	0	1	2	3	...
$30x$	0	30	60	90	
$5\sin(30x)°$	0	2.5	4.33		
y	10	12.5	14.33	...	

Plot the resulting curve accurately on graph paper, using one centimetre as unit for both *x* and *y*.

The graph represents the cross-section at a certain instant of a sea wave. *y* metre is the depth of water above the point of a flat sea bed *x* metre horizontally from a fixed point.

A succession of waves like the one plotted is moving steadily parallel to the *x*-axis.

If there is a wreck on the sea bed with a mast extending 8 m vertically above the sea bed, estimate from your graph for what percentage of the time the tip of the mast is visible above the water.

[MEI]

5. On the same diagram, sketch the graphs of

$$y = \sin 2x \quad \text{and} \quad y = \cos 3x$$

for *x* between 0° and 180°.

cont.

Hence state the number of solutions to the equation

$$\sin 2x = \cos 3x$$

in the interval $0° \leqslant x \leqslant 180°$.

By using the relation $\sin 2x = \cos(90° - 2x)$, find these solutions by calculation

[SMP]

6.   Taking a scale of 2 cm to represent 30° on the x-axis and 2 cm to represent 1 unit on the y-axis, draw the graphs of

$$y = 2\sin 2x \quad \text{and} \quad y = 3\cos 3x,$$

plotting the values of y for which $x = 0°$, 15°, 30°, 45°, 60°, 75°, 90°, 105°, 120°, 135°, 150°, 165° and 180°.

From your graphs estimate

(i) the solutions to the equation

$$2\sin 2x = 3\cos 3x$$

in the range 0° to 180°,

(ii) the ranges of values of x between 0° and 180° for which $2\sin 2x > 3\cos 3x$.

Use your graphs to sketch the curve

$$y = 2\sin 2x + 3\cos 3x$$

from 0° to 180°.

[AEB 1981]

7.   Evaluate $\sin x + 2\cos 2x$, correct to two decimal places, for values of x between 0° and 120°, at intervals of 15° beginning with $x = 0°$. Using scales of 2 cm = 15° for x and 2 cm = 0.5 for y, draw the graph of $y = \sin x + 2\cos 2x$ from $x = 0°$ to $x = 120°$.

From your graph, solve the equation $\sin x + 2\cos 2x = 1$ for values of x between 0° and 120°.

Without extending the graph, state the next positive value of x $(x > 120°)$ which is a solution of the given equation.

[O & C]

8.   (i) Solve the equation $2\tan^2 x - 3\tan x + 1 = 0$, giving all the solutions between 0° and 360°.

(ii) Draw the graph of $y = 2\sin(x + 30°)$ for values of x from 0° to 180°. Take 1 cm to 20° on the x-axis and 2 cm to 1 unit on the y-axis, and plot values for $x = 0°$, 20°, 40°,..., 180°. Hence give the values of x between 0° and 180° for which $\sin(x + 30°) = 0.6$.

[O & C]

9.   Sketch the graph of $y = \cos 3x°$ for $0 \leqslant x \leqslant 180$.

Calculate all the values of x in the interval $0 \leqslant x \leqslant 180$ for which

(a) $\cos 3x° = \sqrt{3/2}$;
(b) $\cos 3x° = -\frac{1}{2}$.

Hence write down the complete solution set of $-\frac{1}{2} \leqslant \cos 3x° \leqslant \sqrt{3/2}$ for $0 \leqslant x \leqslant 180$.

[SMP]

10.   Solve the following equations, giving all the solutions between 0° and 360°:

(i) $\tan x = -0.5$,
(ii) $\sec^2 y = 9.154$,
(iii) $6\sin^2 z - 7\sin z + 2 = 0$.

[O & C]

11.   Solve, for $-180° \leqslant x \leqslant 180°$, the following equations

(a) $3\tan x - 2 = 0$,
(b) $3\tan x - 2\cos x = 0$.

[AEB 1983]

12.   (a) Solve the equations

$$3\sin x + 4\cos y = 2,$$
$$\sin x - 2\cos y = 1,$$

giving the smallest possible positive values of x and y in degrees.

(b) Solve the equation

$$(1 + \tan x)^2 + (1 - \tan x)^2 = 4\cos^2 x,$$

giving all the solutions in the range $0° \leqslant x \leqslant 360°$.

[O & C]

13.   Find all possible values of x from 0° to 360° when

(i) $\sin^2 x = 0.75$,
(ii) $5\sin x = 3\cos x$,
(iii) $\sec 2x = 2$,
(iv) $3\sin^2 x + 2\cos x = 2$.

[O & C]

14.   Given that $\dfrac{\sin^2 A}{1 + 2\cos^2 A} = \dfrac{3}{19}$, where $90° < A < 180°$, find the value of $\dfrac{\sin A}{1 + 2\cos A}$.

[HK]

15.   Draw, on the same axes for $0° \leqslant x \leqslant 360°$, graphs of $3\cos 2x$ and of $2 + \sin x$.

Show that the values of x at the points of intersection can be found by solving:
$6s^2 + s - 1 = 0$, where s stands for $\sin x$. [You may assume that $\cos 2x = 1 - 2s^2$.]

Verify that this equation is satisfied by $s = -0.5$ and find the other possible value for s.

Hence *calculate*, correct to the nearest degree, the solutions of the equation
$3 \cos 2x = 2 + \sin x$ in the interval $0° \leqslant x \leqslant 360°$.

[SMP]

16. Show that the equation
$4 \cos x + 9 \tan x = 6 \sec x$ may be transformed into the equation $4 \sin^2 x - 9 \sin x + 2 = 0$.
Find the possible values of x between $0°$ and $360°$ satisfying the former equation.

17. Prove that

$$\frac{1 - \sin x \cos x + 2 \sin^2 x}{\cos^2 x} = 3 \tan^2 x - \tan x + 1.$$

Solve the equation

$$1 - \sin x \cos x + 2 \sin^2 x = 3 \cos^2 x,$$

giving all the values of x between $0°$ and $360°$.

[O & C]

18.

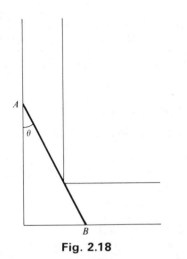

Fig. 2.18

Figure 2.18 shows two corridors, each of width 5 ft, which meet at right-angles. Show that the length of the line AB in the diagram is

$5(\sec \theta + \operatorname{cosec} \theta)$. Draw the graph of $y = 5(\sec \theta + \operatorname{cosec} \theta)$ for the values $\theta = 30°$, $35°$, $40°$, $45°$, $50°$, and $55°$. The following scales are suggested:

$$\begin{cases} \theta & 2 \, \text{cm represents } 5°. \\ y & 2 \, \text{cm represents } 1 \text{ unit.} \end{cases}$$

An attempt is made to carry a thin pole, of length 15 ft, horizontally round the corner from one corridor to the other. Use your graph to find the value of θ when the pole becomes wedged.

What is the length of the longest pole which could be carried horizontally round the corner without becoming wedged?

By how much should one end of the 15-foot pole be raised to enable it to go freely round the corner?

[O & C]

19.

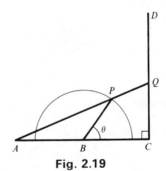

Fig. 2.19

In figure 2.19 ABC is a straight line with $AB = BC = 3$ cm; CD is perpendicular to ABC. On the semicircle with centre B and radius 2 cm is a variable point P, with angle $CBP = \theta$ radians. The line AP is produced to meet CD at Q, and $QC = y$ cm. Prove that

$$y = \frac{12 \sin \theta}{3 + 2 \cos \theta}.$$

Sketch the diagram for the case when Q is as far as possible from C.

Without using calculus, calculate the maximum value of $\dfrac{12 \sin \theta}{3 + 2 \cos \theta}$, giving to two decimal places the value of θ between 0 and π for which this occurs.

[UL]

20. The length of day measured in hours of daylight, l, is given approximately by the formula

$$l = 12 - 4.5 \cos \frac{\pi x}{6},$$

where x is the time in months since 22 December.

(i)   Write down the values of l for $x = 0, 3, 6, 9$ and 12.
(ii) Sketch the graph of l for $x = 0$ to $x = 12$.
(iii) Calculate x if $l = 16$.
(iv) The formula may be written in the form

$$l = a + b \sin \frac{\pi}{6}(x + c).$$

State a set of values for a, b and c.

[SMP]

21. Find the values of the angle x between 0 and π radians such that

(i) $\tan x = -\sqrt{3}$,
(ii) $\cos x = \cos \dfrac{7\pi}{4} - \cos \dfrac{\pi}{2}$,
(iii) $\sec 2x = -2$.

[AEB 1981]

22. Given that $\sin x = \frac{12}{13}$ and that $\frac{1}{2}\pi < x < \pi$, show that $\cos x = -\frac{5}{13}$.
Without using tables or a calculator, evaluate

(a) $\sin(x + \pi)$,
(b) $\tan(x + 2\pi)$,
(c) $\cot(\pi - x)$,
(d) $\sec(x + \frac{1}{2}\pi)$.

[AEB 1982]

23. The framework for a solar cell for a satellite is made from a length of wire bent into the shape of a sector of a circle of radius r and angle θ, as shown in figure 2.20. Write down, in terms of r and θ, expressions for (a) the length of the wire, (b) the area, A, of the sector.

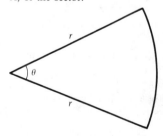

Fig. 2.20

It is decided that the wire shall be of length 3 metres. Show, by eliminating θ from your expressions (a) and (b), that

$$A = r(3 - 2r)/2.$$

Hence calculate the greatest area of the cell.

[SMP]

24. The following is a flow diagram for a calculation.

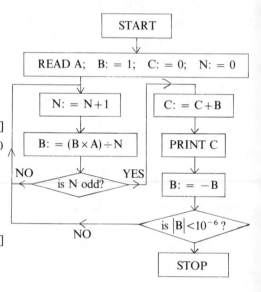

Taking A to be 0.5, calculate to 3 significant figures the first three numbers printed. Compare your results with the value of $\sin(0.5)$. (1 radian is approximately $57.3°$.)

[SMP]

EXERCISE 3X

1. $ABCD$ is a quadrilateral. P, Q, R, S are the midpoints of AB, BC, CD, DA respectively. The position vector of the point A is denoted by **a**, and the position vectors of other points are denoted similarly.

Express in terms of **a, b, c, d**:
(i) **p**; (ii) **s**; (iii) **PS**; (iv) **QR**; (v) the position vector of X, the midpoint of BD;
(vi) the position vector of Y, the midpoint of PR.

Show that if X and Y coincide then $ABCD$ is a parallelogram.

[SMP]

2. If A is the point $(2, 3)$ and B is the point $(-3, 1)$, write down **AB** as a column vector.

A half-turn about the origin followed by the translation $\begin{pmatrix} -4 \\ 9 \end{pmatrix}$ maps A to A' and B to B'. Find the coordinates of A' and B' and show that $\mathbf{A'B'} = \begin{pmatrix} 5 \\ 2 \end{pmatrix}$. Hence prove that $ABA'B'$ is a parallelogram.

Describe fully the equivalent single transformation.

[SMP]

3. $A(7, -2)$ and $C(-1, 4)$ are the ends of a diagonal of the square $ABCD$, lettered clockwise. Write down the coordinates of E, the mid-point of AC, and the x and y components of the vector **EC**. Deduce the x and y components of the vector **ED** and use them to write down the coordinates of D and of B.

Write down the gradients of the lines CD and DA and explain what connection between these numbers helps to verify your values of the co-ordinates of D.

[MEI]

4. Relative to an origin O, the points A, B, C and D have position vectors $\begin{pmatrix} 2 \\ 3 \end{pmatrix}$, $\begin{pmatrix} -2 \\ 5 \end{pmatrix}$, $\begin{pmatrix} -1 \\ 6 \end{pmatrix}$ and $\begin{pmatrix} 4 \\ 3 \end{pmatrix}$ respectively.

Calculate the position vector of P, the point on the line AC *between* A and C such that $AP : PC = 1 : 2$ and show that P is the mid-point of BD.

[AEB 1981]

5. The points A, B and C have position vectors **a**, **b** and **c** respectively referred to an origin O.

(a) Given that the point X lies on AB produced so that $AB : BX = 2 : 1$, find **x**, the position vector of X, in terms of **a** and **b**.

(b) If Y lies on BC, between B and C so that $BY : YC = 1 : 3$, find **y**, the position vector of Y, in terms of **b** and **c**.

(c) Given that Z is the mid-point of AC, show that X, Y and Z are collinear.

(d) Calculate $XY : YZ$.

[UL]

6. (i) Prove that points $A(-2, 1)$, $B(2, 3)$ and $C(8, 6)$ lie on a straight line, by a method that does not depend on accurate drawing.

(ii) Find the equation of the line **L** perpendicular to ABC through C.

(iii) Find the equation of the line **M** parallel to OB through A. (O is the origin.)

(iv) Calculate in exact fractions the coordinates of the point D at which the lines **L** and **M** intersect.

[MEI]

7. The vertices of a quadrilateral are $A(-2, 12)$, $B(5, 11)$, $C(10, -4)$ and $D(-3, 5)$. Calculate the gradients of the diagonals AC and BD and deduce a geometrical fact about these lines.

Find the equation of the line AC and show that E, the mid-point of BD, lies on it.

[MEI]

8. Plot the points $A(0, 1)$, $B(1, -1)$, $C(3, 2)$ on squared paper. By inspection of the diagram write down the coordinates of all possible fourth points, which together with A, B and C but not necessarily in that order, will form a parallelogram. (There are three such points.)

In each of the three cases calculate the equation of the diagonal of the parallelogram which passes through the new vertex. Prove that all three diagonals go through the point $(\frac{4}{3}, \frac{2}{3})$.

[MEI]

9. Two sides, AB and AD, of a parallelogram $ABCD$ have equations $7y - x + 13 = 0$ and $9x - y + 7 = 0$, respectively, and the centre of the parallelogram is the point $P(3, 3)$. Calculate the coordinates of the four vertices A, B, C and D.

[O & C]

10. The midpoint of the line joining the points $A(7, 3)$ and $B(-1, -5)$ is C. Find both values of k if the straight line joining C to the point $P(k^2, k)$ is perpendicular to AB.

[AEB 1981]

11. Prove that the line joining the points $A(-2, 3)$ and $B(4, 7)$ subtends a right angle at the point $C(-1, 8)$.

Find the co-ordinates of the point at which the line through C parallel to AB cuts the line through A parallel to the x-axis.

[MEI]

12. The coordinates of the points A, B and C are $(8, -1)$, $(1, -2)$ and $(-3, 1)$ respectively. Find

(i) the equation of the line BC,
(ii) the equation of the straight line through A perpendicular to BC,
(iii) the coordinates of the point of intersection of these lines.

[AEB 1981]

13. On squared paper (scale $1 \, \text{cm} \equiv 1 \, \text{unit}$) plot the triangle $A(7, 4)$, $B(0, 5)$, $C(9, -7)$. State the gradient of the line BC and find its equation. Find also the equation of the line through A perpendicular to BC and draw this line accurately in your diagram.

From your diagram read the coordinates of the point D where these lines meet. Verify that the coordinates of D do satisfy each of your equations, showing your working.

[MEI]

14. A triangle has vertices at the following points

$$A(-4, 9), \quad B(2, 1), \quad C(5, 7).$$

Calculate the coordinates of D, the midpoint of AB.

The line through D parallel to AC meets BC at E. Calculate the equation of the line DE and the coordinates of the point E.

[AEB 1980]

15. Sketch the triangle $A(2, 1)$, $B(1, -2)$, $C(6, \frac{1}{2})$. Find the equation of the line BC and also the equation of the line from A perpendicular to BC.

Hence calculate the coordinates of the point where these lines cut each other.

[MEI]

16. $ABCD$ is a rectangle in which the co-ordinates of A and C are $(0, 4)$ and $(11, 1)$ respectively and the gradient of the side AB is -5.

(i) Find the equations of the sides AB and BC.
(ii) Show that the coordinates of B are $(1, -1)$.
(iii) Calculate the area of the rectangle.
(iv) Find the coordinates of the point on the y-axis which is equidistant from A and D.

[JMB]

17. The line whose equation is $7y = 3x - 6$

meets the x-axis at A and the line whose equation is $3y = 18 - x$ meets the y-axis at C. The two lines intersect at the point B, and O is the origin of coordinates.

(i) Calculate the coordinates of A, C and B.
(ii) Show that OB is perpendicular to AC.
(iii) Calculate the area of triangle OBC. Hence, given that D is the point of intersection of OB and AC, show that

$$DC = \frac{9\sqrt{10}}{5}.$$

(iv) Find the coordinates of the point P such that $ABPC$ is a parallelogram.

[JMB]

18. An isosceles triangle ABC, lettered clockwise, with $AB = AC$, has area $84\frac{1}{2}$ square units. If B is the point $(14, -2)$ and C is the point $(2, 3)$, find:

(i) the coordinates of the mid-point M of BC and the length of BC;
(ii) the gradient and length of the perpendicular from A to BC;
(iii) the coordinates of A.

[MEI]

19. $ABCD$ is a parallelogram in which the coordinates of A, B and C are $(1, 2)$, $(7, -1)$ and $(-1, -2)$ respectively.

(i) Find the equations of AD and CD.
(ii) Find the coordinates of D.
(iii) Prove that $<BAC = 90°$.
(iv) Calculate the area of the parallelogram.
(v) Find the length of the perpendicular from A to BC, leaving your answer in surd form.

[JMB]

20. $A(2, -7)$, $B(6, 1)$ and $C(5, -6)$ are the vertices of a triangle. Find the equations of the perpendiculars from the vertices A and B to BC and CA respectively. Hence find the coordinates of the orthocentre of the triangle ABC. Verify that this point lies on the perpendicular from C to AB.

[O & C]

21. (i) Write down the gradient of the line U joining $A(-2, 2)$ to $B(4, 6)$ and find the equation of U.

(ii) Find the equation of the line V perpendicular to AB through the point $C(5, -2)$. Write down the coordinates of M, the mid-point of AB, and show that they satisfy the equation of the line V.

(iii) When N is the point $(6,3)$, show that the displacement vector $\mathbf{CN}$ has components $\begin{pmatrix} 1 \\ 5 \end{pmatrix}$. Find the coordinates of the point D such that the displacement vector $\mathbf{CN}$ = the displacement vector $\mathbf{ND}$.

(iv) Write down the components of the displacement vectors $\mathbf{AB}$ and $\mathbf{BD}$. Comment on a simple connection between them and what this means geometrically about the position of the point D.

[MEI]

22. In a triangle ABC, the side AB has the equation $3x - y = 3$ and the side AC has the equation $x + 2y = 15$. Calculate the coordinates of the vertex A.

If the vertex B is (h, k) and the mid-point of BC is $(4, 2)$, find

(i) the value of k in terms of h,
(ii) the coordinates of C in terms of h.

Hence find the numerical values of the co-ordinates of B and C.

[O & C]

23. O is the origin, and $\mathbf{OA}$ and $\mathbf{OB}$ are $\mathbf{a}$ and $\mathbf{b}$ respectively, where $|\mathbf{a}| = |\mathbf{b}|$. Explain why the position vector of any point on the internal bisector of the angle AOB can be given by $k(\mathbf{a} + \mathbf{b})$, for a suitable numerical value of k.

If A is the point $(3, 4)$ and B is the point $(5, 0)$, verify that $|\mathbf{OA}| = |\mathbf{OB}|$. Write down the position vector of any point on the internal bisector of the angle AOB. Calculate the position vector of the point P at which this internal bisector meets AC, where C is the point $(10, 0)$.

Show that P divides AC internally in the ratio $1:2$, i.e. $2\mathbf{AP} = \mathbf{PC}$.

[O & C]

24. Position vectors from origin O of points A, B and C are $\mathbf{OA} = \mathbf{a}$, $\mathbf{OB} = \mathbf{b}$ and $\mathbf{OC} = \mathbf{c}$. Find, in terms of $\mathbf{a}$, $\mathbf{b}$ and $\mathbf{c}$, the following vectors:

(i) $\mathbf{BC}$,
(ii) $\mathbf{BA'}$ where A' is the mid-point of BC,
(iii) $\mathbf{OA'}$,
(iv) $\mathbf{A'A}$,
(v) $\mathbf{A'G}$ where G is one-third of the way from A' to A.

Hence show that

$$\mathbf{OG} = \tfrac{1}{3}\mathbf{a} + \tfrac{1}{3}\mathbf{b} + \tfrac{1}{3}\mathbf{c}.$$

From the algebraic symmetry of this answer deduce a theorem about the point G and state this theorem clearly.

[MEI]

EXERCISE 4X

1. The function f with domain $\{x: 0 \leqslant x \leqslant 7\}$ is defined by

$$f: x \to \begin{cases} 2x & \text{for } 0 \leqslant x \leqslant 2, \\ -4 + 6x - x^2 & \text{for } 2 \leqslant x \leqslant 5, \\ 21 - 4x & \text{for } 5 \leqslant x \leqslant 7. \end{cases}$$

(a) Verify that this definition gives unique values for $f(2)$ and $f(5)$, and that there is no abrupt change of gradient at $x = 2$ or $x = 5$.

(b) Sketch the graph of $y = f(x)$.

(c) Find the derived function f ′, expressing it in a similar manner, and sketch the graph of $y = f'(x)$.

(d) Find the greatest and least values of $f(x)$ for $0 \leqslant x \leqslant 7$.

[UL]

2. Let $y = x + \dfrac{1}{x^2}$.

Find $\dfrac{dy}{dx}$ from first principles.

[HK]

3. If $y = Ax^k$, where A and k are non-zero constants, find the value(s) of k so that

$$x^2 \frac{d^2y}{dx^2} + 2x \frac{dy}{dx} - 2y = 0.$$

[HK]

4. (i) Express $(2x + 1)^3$ as a polynomial in x and, hence or otherwise, find $\dfrac{dy}{dx}$ when $y = (2x + 1)^3$.

(ii) Find the value of $\dfrac{dy}{dx}$ when $y = \dfrac{x^3 - 3x + 1}{x}$ and $x = \tfrac{1}{2}$.

(iii) A certain curve has an equation of the form $y = ax^2 + bx + c$. If the curve passes through the point $(2, -1)$ and at this *cont.*

point $\dfrac{dy}{dx} = 3$ and $\dfrac{d^2y}{dx^2} = -2$, find the

values of a, b and c.   [O & C]

5. (a) Differentiate with respect to x:

(i) $(x^2+1)\sqrt{x}$,

(ii) $\dfrac{x^2+x^9}{x^7}$.

(b) The point $(1, 5)$ lies on the curve
$y = x^3+ax^2+bx$, where a and b are
constants. The equation of the tangent to the
curve at the point $(1, 5)$ is $y = 2x+3$. Find
the values of a and b.

[O & C]

6. Calculate the coordinates of the points of
zero slope on the curve $y = x^2(x-2)$ and
sketch the curve from $x = -2$ to $x = +4$.

(There is no need to use squared paper.)

[MEI]

7. Sketch the graph of $y = x(x-2)(x-3)$
for the values of x in the interval
$-1 \leqslant x \leqslant 4$.

Find dy/dx and show that the gradient of the
graph at the point where $x = 1$ is -1. Find
the equation of the tangent to the curve at this
point.

[SMP]

8. Find the equation of the tangent to the
curve $y = x^3-3x$ at the point $(2, 2)$. Verify
that the tangent meets the curve again where
$x = -4$, and find the value of y for this point
of intersection.

[MEI]

9. (i) Show that the equation of the tangent
to the curve with equation $y = x^3+x$ at the
point where $x = 1$ is $y = 4x-2$.

(ii) Eliminate y between the tangent equation
and the equation of the curve to obtain the
equation $x^3-3x+2 = 0$. Why do you expect
$x = 1$ to be a solution of this equation?

(iii) Express x^3-3x+2 as a product of three
factors, and hence find where the tangent
meets the curve again.

[SMP]

10. If P is the point on the curve with
equation

$$y = \tfrac{1}{2}x^2+2$$

at which $x = a$, show that the equation of the

tangent at P is

$$y = ax+2-\tfrac{1}{2}a^2.$$

Find the values of a for which this tangent
passes through the origin $(0, 0)$. Hence find the
equations of the tangents from the origin to
the curve.

Illustrate your answer with a rough sketch.

[SMP]

11. Find the equation of the tangent at $(2, 1)$
to the curve $y = x^2-x-1$.

Find also the coordinates of the point on this
curve at which the normal is parallel to the
tangent at $(2, 1)$.

[MEI]

12. Find the coordinates of the points A
and B on the curve

$$y = 2x^3+x^2-x+2$$

at which the tangents are parallel to the line
$y = 3x+2$.

Calculate the equation of the normal to the
curve at the point $(1, 4)$.

[AEB 1980]

13. Sketch the curve $y = \tfrac{1}{4}x^2$ for
$-4 \leqslant x \leqslant +4$. (There is no need to use
squared paper.)

Find the equation of the tangent at P, a point
on this curve where $x = 4a$ and $y = 4a^2$.
Write down the coordinates of the point R
where this tangent meets the x-axis and of the
point S where it meets the y-axis. Find also the
equation of the line perpendicular to this
tangent through the point R. (Answers so far
include a.)

Find the coordinates of the point Q where this
line meets the y-axis and show all these points
and lines in your diagram.

Hence show that, wherever P may be on the
curve as a alters in value,   (i) Q is always the
same point,   (ii) $PR = RS$,   (iii) $PQ = QS$.

[MEI]

14. Show that the equations of the tangent
and normal at the point $P(4, 1)$ on the curve
$y = \dfrac{4}{x}$ are $4y+x-8 = 0$ and

$y-4x+15 = 0$ respectively.

The tangent at P intersects the x-axis at X and
the y-axis at Y. The normal at P intersects the
line $y = x$ at L and the line $y = -x$ at M.

Find the coordinates of the points X, Y, L and M and prove that $LYMX$ is a square.

[JMB]

15. Differentiate with respect to x,

(a) $(3x+2)^4$, (b) $2\cos 3x$, (c) $\dfrac{1}{x}+1$,

(d) $\dfrac{1}{x+1}$, (e) $\dfrac{1}{\sin x}$.

[SMP]

16. Differentiate the following functions:

(a) $f: x \to x^3 - 5x^2 - 3$;

(b) $g: x \to \dfrac{1}{x}$;

(c) $h: x \to \sin 3x$;

(d) $s: x \to \dfrac{1}{\sin 3x}$.

[SMP]

17. (a) Show that $x = 2\sin 3t$ satisfies the equation

$$\frac{d^2x}{dt^2} = -9x.$$

Hence find the values of t between 0 and 2π which give maximum values for $\dfrac{d^2x}{dt^2}$.

(b) Given that $S = 4\pi r^2$ and $\dfrac{dS}{dt} = 10$, find $\dfrac{dr}{dt}$ when $r = 2$, leaving your answer in terms of π.

[AEB 1980]

18. An aircraft P is flying horizontally at a height of $8000\,\text{m}$ on a course which has taken it directly overhead of an observer at A, at a constant speed of $250\,\text{m/s}$. When it has gone $x\,\text{m}$ past A the angle between the vertical and AP is θ (figure 4.11).

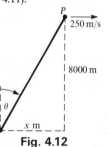

Fig. 4.12

(a) Express x in terms of θ.

(b) Given that $\dfrac{d}{d\theta}(\tan\theta) = \dfrac{1}{\cos^2\theta}$, show that

$$\frac{dx}{dt} = \frac{8000}{\cos^2\theta}\frac{d\theta}{dt}.$$

(c) Use the fact that $\dfrac{dx}{dt} = 250$ to show that

$$\frac{d\theta}{dt} = \frac{\cos^2\theta}{32}.$$

(d) Calculate the value of $d\theta/dt$ when $\theta = \frac{1}{4}\pi$.

(e) Explain why $d\theta/dt$ is greatest when the aircraft is vertically above A, and show that it is then twice the value in (d).

[SMP]

19. Find the slope of the tangent to the curve $x^3y + 2x^2y^2 - xy^3 = 14$ at the point $(1, -2)$.

[HK]

20. Find the equation of the tangent to the graph of the function

$$f: x \to x^{-2}$$

at the point where $x = 1$.

Hence calculate an estimate for $f(1 \cdot 1)$.

Show, on a sketch of the graph near $x = 1$, the error involved.

[SMP]

21. Use the method of small increments to estimate the percentage change in the volume of a right circular cone produced by

(i) a change in height of 1%, assuming no change in radius of the cone,

(ii) a change in radius of 1%, assuming no change in the height of the cone.

[AEB 1979]

22.

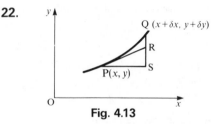

Fig. 4.13

(a) Figure 4.12 shows the points $P(x, y)$ and $Q(x+\delta x, y+\delta y)$ on a curve; PS is parallel to Ox, SRQ is parallel to Oy, and PR is   *cont.*

the tangent to the curve at P. Name the lengths in the diagram which

represent   (i) δy,   (ii) $\dfrac{dy}{dx} \delta x$,   (iii) the error

introduced by using the approximation

$$\delta y \approx \frac{dy}{dx} \delta x.$$

(b) By taking $y = \sin x$ in the approximation $\delta y \approx \dfrac{dy}{dx} \delta x$, show that, for small δx,

$$\sin(x + \delta x) - \sin x \approx \cos x \, \delta x.$$

Deduce that $\sin \left(\dfrac{\pi}{3} + \delta x \right) \approx \dfrac{\sqrt{3 + \delta x}}{2}$.

(c) Given that $\dfrac{\pi}{3} \approx 1.047$ and $\sqrt{3} \approx 1.732$,

without using tables, slide rule or calculator, estimate the value of $\sin \theta$ when $\theta = 1$ radian. Give your answer to 2 significant figures.

[UL]

23.   Prove that the maximum value of

$$23\,000 - 2400x + 90x^2 - x^3$$

is 7000. State the value of x for which it occurs and calculate the minimum value. Sketch a graph of this function for $x \geqslant 0$ and $y \geqslant 0$, labelling the coordinates of these turning points; also state the greatest and least values of the function in this region.

[SMP]

24.   (i) Find the value of $\dfrac{dy}{dx}$ when

$$y = \frac{(x+1)^3}{x^2} \quad \text{and} \quad x = \tfrac{1}{2}.$$

(ii) Find the turning points on the curve $y = x^3 + x^2 - x + 1$, and distinguish between maximum and minimum values of y.

Find the range of values of x for which $\dfrac{dy}{dx}$ is increasing.

[O & C]

25.   Find the maximum and minimum points on the graph of

$$y = 10x^6 + 24x^5 - 45x^4$$

and distinguish between them.

[SMP]

26.   (i) Expand $(x+3)^2$ and $(x+3)^3$. Hence,

or otherwise, find $\dfrac{dy}{dx}$ when   (a) $y = (x+3)^2$ and   (b) $y = (x+3)^3$.

(ii) If $Y = (x+3)^2 - (x+3)^3$, find the maximum value of Y in the range $-3 < x < -2$. On the same diagram sketch the two graphs of $y = (x+3)^2$ and $y = (x+3)^3$ between $x = -3$ and $x = -2$, indicating clearly which is which. Mark in the length corresponding to the maximum value of Y found above.

[O & C]

27.   Prove that the curve

$$y = x^3 + 2x^2 + 9x + 8$$

has neither maximum nor minimum points on it.

Calculate

(i) the value of x for which $\dfrac{d^2y}{dx^2} = 0$,

(ii) the value of $\dfrac{dy}{dx}$ for this value of x.

[AEB 1980]

28.   Find the x and y coordinates of the points on the curve $y = x^3 - 6x^2$ with zero gradient. Find also the x and y coordinates of the point where the curve has the steepest negative gradient. Sketch the curve from $x = -2$ to $+8$.

For positive values of x the curve shows the *cumulative* profit (or loss) y, in thousands of pounds, made by a trading company in the first x years of its existence.

(i)   At what time was the company losing money most rapidly?

(ii)   What was the largest value of the cumulative loss?

(iii)   After how many years did the owners recover all their losses?

(iv)   At what rate was the company making profits at the end of 8 years?

[MEI]

29.   A pastry cutter is in the shape of a sector of a circle. The perimeter of the cutter is 48 cm. Show that the area it cuts out is $24r - r^2$ cm^2, where r cm is the radius of the cutter. Hence find the greatest area which such a cutter, with the given perimeter, can have and show that for maximum area the angle of the sector is approximately $115°$.

[SMP]

30. On one right-angled corner BAF of a house an area is fenced in by a 24 metre length of fencing $BCDEF$ running parallel to the house walls as shown, so that $BC = FE = x$ metre and $AB = AF$.

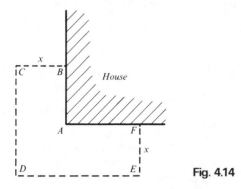

Fig. 4.14

Find the enclosed area in square metres in terms of x. Deduce the maximum value of this area and the value of x for which this occurs. Verify that it really is a maximum. [MEI]

31. The design for one page of a book consists of a rectangular printed region of area $270\,\text{cm}^2$ with margins of $2\frac{1}{2}\,\text{cm}$ above and below, and margins of $3\,\text{cm}$ on each side. Taking the width of the printed region to be $x\,\text{cm}$, show that the area, in cm^2, of the whole page is

$$300 + 5x + \frac{1620}{x}.$$

Hence find the dimensions of the page which has least area. [UL]

32. When fares went down by 10% the number of passengers increased by 20%. Calculate the percentage increase in revenue.

Suppose instead that when fares go down by $x\%$ the number of passengers increases by $4x\%$. Show that the revenue would be multiplied by $1 + 0.03x - 0.0004x^2$.

Calculate the value of x which gives maximum revenue and the percentage increase in revenue that this would bring. [SMP]

33. A cylindrical metal can, radius $r\,\text{cm}$ and height $h\,\text{cm}$, without a lid is to be made. Write down a formula in terms of r and h for the area, $A\,\text{cm}^2$, of sheet metal required.

Its capacity is to be $64\pi\,\text{cm}^3$. Write down an equation in r and h which expresses this fact.

Hence show that $A = \pi r^2 + 128\pi/r$.

Calculate the dimensions of the can if it is to require the minimum area of metal. Also state the area of metal needed.

[SMP]

34. A solid right circular cylinder of height h and radius r has a *total* external surface area of $600\,\text{cm}^2$.

Show that $h = \dfrac{300}{\pi r} - r$ and hence express the volume, V, in terms of r.

If h and r can vary, find $\dfrac{\mathrm{d}V}{\mathrm{d}r}$ and $\dfrac{\mathrm{d}^2V}{\mathrm{d}r^2}$ in terms of r. Show that V has a maximum and find the corresponding value of r in terms of π. Calculate the ratio $h:r$ in this maximum case.

[AEB 1983]

EXERCISE 5X

1. On the run prior to take-off an aircraft accelerates at $3\,\text{m/s}^2$, starting from rest.

Calculate the time it takes to reach $90\,\text{m/s}$, and the distance it has then covered.

Calculate the uniform acceleration needed to reach $90\,\text{m/s}$ from rest in a distance of $1\,\text{km}$, and the time it takes to reach this speed.

[SMP]

2. A particle travels from A to B in a straight line in $12\,\text{s}$. The particle accelerates uniformly from rest at A to a maximum speed of $16\,\text{m/s}$, travels at that speed for $6\,\text{s}$, and then retards uniformly to rest at B. The distance travelled while accelerating is twice that travelled while retarding. Sketch the velocity–time graph for the particle and calculate

(a) the distance AB,
(b) the acceleration,
(c) the retardation.

(AEB 1983]

3. A vehicle starts from rest, accelerates at $3.2\,\text{m/s}^2$ for $12\,\text{s}$ and then decelerates at $1.8\,\text{m/s}^2$ until its speed is $10\,\text{m/s}$.

Calculate the following, giving your answers corrected to two significant figures: (a) the greatest speed; (b) the time taken to decelerate; (c) the distance covered *cont.*

while accelerating;   (d) the distance covered while decelerating.

[SMP]

4. A train which is travelling at a constant speed of 36 m/s is required to slow down in order to pass through a station. It does so by decelerating uniformly at 0.2 m/s² until its speed is reduced to 12 m/s; it maintains a speed of 12 m/s for 1.8 km and then accelerates uniformly at 0.1 m/s² until it reaches its cruising speed of 36 m/s once more.

Find, in minutes, for how long the speed of the train is less than 36 m/s, and show that in this time it travels 10.44 km.

[SMP]

5. A train normally travels at a uniform speed of 40 m/s. Repairs are being carried out to 1800 m of track from *B* to *C*, and the speed of the train therefore has to be restricted to 16 m/s on this stretch. In order that the speed of the train shall be 16 m/s when it reaches *B*, the brakes are applied when the train is at a point *A*. The uniform retardation produced by the brakes is $1\frac{1}{2}$ m/s². When the train reaches *C* it accelerates uniformly so that it reaches its normal speed of 40 m/s at a point *D* where *CD* = 1344 m. Calculate

(i) the time during which the brakes are applied,

(ii) the distance *AB*,

(iii) the time during which the train accelerates,

(iv) the total time lost by the train on account of the speed restriction.

[AEB 1980]

6. An oil tanker mass 4×10^8 kg is steaming at a steady speed of 6 m s⁻¹. The total resistance is 2×10^6 N. What force is the ship's engine producing?

If the engine were to stop, what would be the deceleration of the tanker, assuming that the total resistance remained constant? How long would it take the ship to stop?

[MEI]

7. A brick of mass $\frac{1}{2}$ kg sinks when placed on the surface of the paint in a very large tin. If the resistance to motion is constant and it falls 0.3 m in 4 seconds, find its velocity at the end of this time.

Calculate also the resistance to motion in newtons.

[O & C]

8. A constant force of 35 N, always acting in the same horizontal direction, causes a particle of mass 2 kg to move over a rough horizontal plane. The particle passes two points *X* and *Y*, 4 m apart, with speeds of 5 m/s and 10 m/s respectively. The frictional resistance to motion is constant. Calculate

(i) the acceleration of the particle,

(ii) the magnitude of the frictional resistance,

(iii) the distance of the particle from *X*, 4 s after it has passed *X*.

[AEB 1981]

9. A buoy of mass 3 kg is held 5 m below the surface of the water by a vertical cable. There is an upward buoyancy force of 42 N acting on the buoy. Write down the tension in the cable (take g = 10).

Suddenly the cable breaks. Show that while in the water the buoy will accelerate at 4 m/s².

The buoy maintains this constant acceleration while it is in the water. Calculate the time taken to reach the surface and show that the velocity on emergence will be 6.3 m/s approximately.

Ignoring air resistance, calculate the height above the surface which the buoy will reach.

[SMP]

10. The descent of a cage in a mine-shaft takes place in three stages, which are uniform acceleration, followed by constant velocity and finally by uniform deceleration until the cage comes to rest. The time taken for acceleration is double that for deceleration, and the total time for the whole descent is one minute. If the depth of the mine is 600 m, and the maximum velocity attained is 12 m s⁻¹, find the time taken for each stage of the journey.

If the descent is controlled by a single cable, and the total mass of the cage and the occupants is 1750 kg, calculate the greatest tension in the cable, giving the answer in newtons.

[O & C]

11. A boat of mass 5 tonnes is being driven before the wind at a constant speed of 1 m/s. It is dragging a sea anchor, and the tension in the cable by which it is attached is 6000 N in the direction horizontally backwards. If the cable suddenly breaks, show that the boat starts to accelerate at $1.2\,\text{m/s}^2$.

If the acceleration now decreases at a constant rate and is reduced to zero in 3 seconds, sketch the time–acceleration graph.

Find the speed at which the boat will be travelling at the end of the 3 seconds.

[SMP]

12. (a) A diesel rail-car travelling between two stations which are $7\frac{1}{2}$ km apart, starts from rest at the first station and for the first kilometre it moves with uniform acceleration.

For the next 6 km the rail-car travels with uniform speed, and for the last $\frac{1}{2}$ km it is uniformly retarded before it comes to rest at the second station. In all, the journey takes 10 minutes.

(i) State the ratio of the time taken during retardation to the time taken during acceleration.

(ii) Sketch a velocity–time graph to illustrate the rail-car journey between the two stations.

(iii) Calculate the value in km/h of the maximum speed attained by the rail-car on this journey.

(iv) Calculate the time for which the rail-car was travelling with uniform speed.

(b) An oil-tanker of total mass 144 000 tonne (1 tonne = 1000 kg) reduces speed, with engines stopped, from 9 km/h, in a distance of 2 km.

(i) Calculate the magnitude of the tanker's retardation in m/s^2.

(ii) Assuming that the resistance of the water to the tanker's motion is uniform, calculate its value in kilonewtons.

[JMB]

13. (a) A buoy of mass 20 kg is held below the surface of the water by a vertical line attached to the sea-bed. If the buoyancy force is 240 N, calculate the tension in the line.

(b) The line now breaks, and so the buoy rises up to the surface. Assuming that its motion through the water causes a constant resisting force of 12 N, find the upward acceleration of the buoy.

(c) In fact, of course, the resisting force R will depend on the speed v of the buoy at any in-

stant. Assuming that the correct formula is $R = 3v^2$, find the maximum speed achieved by the buoy on its way to the surface.

14. A lift of mass 2000 kg moves up and down its shaft against a constant frictional resistance of 1200 N. The wire rope supporting the lift has a breaking strain of 29 kN.

(a) At the start of the downward journey, the lift is allowed to accelerate at $0.4\,\text{m/s}^2$ until the normal operating speed of $2.0\,\text{m/s}$ is reached. It then descends at constant speed, finally decelerating at $0.5\,\text{m/s}^2$ so as to come to rest at the foot of the shaft. The whole descent takes 16 s. Draw a velocity–time graph, and hence calculate the depth of the shaft.

(b) Calculate the tension in the wire rope during the three stages of the descent.

(c) If safety regulations require the tension in the rope never to exceed 75% of the breaking strain, calculate the maximum permissible acceleration on the way up.

15. Calculate the overall upward force B that the surrounding air must be exerting on a balloon of total mass 1 tonne, given that the balloon is descending with a constant acceleration of $0.2\,\text{m/s}^2$. At the moment when the balloon is moving down at a speed of $4.5\,\text{m/s}$ and is just 50 m above ground level, the balloonist decides to throw overboard his young companion of mass 40 kg. Assuming that B remains constant, calculate the new acceleration of the balloon, stating clearly whether it is directed upwards or downwards, and determine whether or not the balloon crashes into the ground.

16. When a construction worker attempts to lower nine stone blocks (each of mass 10 kg) from the top of a building, by means of a vertical rope passing over a pulley wheel, he finds that this load is too heavy for him. He hangs on to the rope, however, and is pulled up with an acceleration of $0.7\,\text{m/s}^2$, and of course the blocks descend with equal acceleration. By considering the blocks, show that the tension in the rope is 819 N. Then by considering the worker, and assuming that the tension in the rope is the same on both sides of the pulley, calculate the worker's *cont.*

mass. Hence determine how many blocks he could in fact just have managed to lower safely.

EXERCISE 6X

1. (i) Find the solution set for the equation

$$\begin{pmatrix} 7 & 5 \\ 5 & 3 \end{pmatrix}\begin{pmatrix} x \\ y \end{pmatrix} = \begin{pmatrix} 1 \\ 3 \end{pmatrix}.$$

(ii) If $\begin{pmatrix} a & b \\ c & d \end{pmatrix}\begin{pmatrix} 1 & -1 \\ 2 & -3 \end{pmatrix} = \begin{pmatrix} 10 & -14 \\ -1 & 2 \end{pmatrix}$,

find the values of a, b, c and d.

[O & C]

2. Solve the simultaneous equations

$$2x + 6y - 3z = 4,$$
$$x - y + z = 1,$$
$$3x + y + 2z = 7.$$

Hence write down a vector **r** satisfying

$$\begin{pmatrix} 2 & 6 & -3 \\ 1 & -1 & 1 \\ 3 & 1 & 2 \end{pmatrix} \mathbf{r} = \begin{pmatrix} 2 \\ 0.5 \\ 3.5 \end{pmatrix}.$$

[SMP]

3. Multiply together the two matrices

$$\begin{pmatrix} 1 & 3 & 2 \\ 2 & -1 & 1 \\ 3 & -2 & -1 \end{pmatrix} \begin{pmatrix} 3 & -1 & 5 \\ 5 & -7 & 3 \\ -1 & 11 & -7 \end{pmatrix}.$$

Hence, or otherwise, solve the simultaneous equations

$$3x - y + 5z = 32,$$
$$5x - 7y + 3z = -8,$$
$$x - 11y + 7z = 20.$$

[SMP]

4. (a) Find the value of a such that, for all values of t,

$$\begin{pmatrix} 2 & 2 \\ 3 & 1 \end{pmatrix}\begin{pmatrix} t \\ at \end{pmatrix} = 4\begin{pmatrix} t \\ at \end{pmatrix}.$$

What does the above equation tell you about the effect of the matrix $\begin{pmatrix} 2 & 2 \\ 3 & 1 \end{pmatrix}$ on the line $y = ax$, where a is the value found above?

(b) Find the inverse of the matrix $\begin{pmatrix} 3 & 5 \\ 1 & 2 \end{pmatrix}$.

Hence, or otherwise, find the values of a, b, c and d if

$$\begin{pmatrix} 3 & 5 \\ 1 & 2 \end{pmatrix}\begin{pmatrix} a & b \\ c & d \end{pmatrix} = \begin{pmatrix} 1 & 0 \\ 2 & 2 \end{pmatrix}.$$

[O & C]

5. Each of the following matrices, when used to premultiply column position vectors, gives a transformation in the plane. In each case **either** describe the transformation geometrically **or** illustrate it by a sketch showing the image of the unit square $OPQR$, where O is $(0, 0)$, P is $(1, 0)$, Q is $(1, 1)$ and R is $(0, 1)$.

(i) $\begin{pmatrix} 3 & 0 \\ 0 & 1 \end{pmatrix}$; (ii) $\begin{pmatrix} 0 & 0 \\ 0 & 1 \end{pmatrix}$; (iii) $\begin{pmatrix} -1 & 0 \\ 0 & 1 \end{pmatrix}$;

(iv) $\begin{pmatrix} 0 & -1 \\ -1 & 0 \end{pmatrix}$; (v) $\begin{pmatrix} 1 & 0 \\ 0 & 2 \end{pmatrix}$; (vi) $\begin{pmatrix} 1 & 0 \\ 0 & 0 \end{pmatrix}$.

Choose matrices A, B from these six satisfying:

(a) $AB = BA \neq 0$,
(b) $AB \neq BA$,
(c) $AB = 0$.

[SMP]

6. A 2×2 matrix M defines a transformation which maps

$$\begin{pmatrix} 1 \\ 0 \end{pmatrix} \rightarrow \begin{pmatrix} 0 \\ -1 \end{pmatrix} \text{ and } \begin{pmatrix} 0 \\ 1 \end{pmatrix} \rightarrow \begin{pmatrix} 1 \\ 2 \end{pmatrix}.$$

Write down M, and find M^2 and M^{-1}.

By considering two points on the line $x + y = 0$, or otherwise, find the equation of the image of the line under the transformation defined by M.

[O & C]

7. (i) If $M = \begin{pmatrix} 2 & -1 \\ 1 & 3 \end{pmatrix}$, find the values of M^2, M^3 and M^{-1}. Find x and y, given that

$$M\begin{pmatrix} x \\ y \end{pmatrix} = \begin{pmatrix} 3 \\ 5 \end{pmatrix}.$$

(ii) A transformation T is equivalent to an enlargement with centre at the origin, scale factor 2, followed by a reflection in the line $x + y = 0$. What matrix defines T? If T maps a point P onto $(6, 2)$, what are the coordinates of P?

[O & C]

8. A linear transformation T from $\mathbb{R}^2$ to $\mathbb{R}^2$ is represented by the matrix $\begin{pmatrix} 7 & 24 \\ 24 & -7 \end{pmatrix}$. Find the image of the position vector $\begin{pmatrix} 4 \\ 3 \end{pmatrix}$ under T.

Write down the position vector **p** obtained by rotating $\begin{pmatrix} 4 \\ 3 \end{pmatrix}$ through 90° anticlockwise about the origin. Find the image of **p** under *T*.

Use the information you have obtained to show that the transformation *T* consists of a reflection in an axis through the origin followed by an enlargement. Find the equation of the axis of reflection and the scale factor of the enlargement.

[UL]

9. The region *A* consists of all the points (x, y) which satisfy all the inequalities $x \geqslant 0$, $y \geqslant 0$, $5x + 2y \leqslant 10$. Shade on separate diagrams

(a) the region *A*,
(b) the image of the region *A* under the linear transformation from $\mathbb{R}^2$ to $\mathbb{R}^2$ defined by the matrix $\begin{pmatrix} -2 & 4 \\ 3 & 7 \end{pmatrix}$.

[UL]

10. *A*, *B*, *C* and *D* are the points with coordinates $(1, 1)$, $(2, 6)$, $(4, 7)$ and $(x, 2)$ respectively. Translate the quadrilateral so that *A* is mapped onto the origin *O*, and *B*, *C* and *D* are mapped onto the points *B′*, *C′* and *D′* respectively. By finding the matrix **M** which maps the triangle with vertices at $(0, 0)$, $(1, 0)$ and $(0, 1)$ onto the triangle *OB′C′*, or otherwise, find the area of triangle *ABC*.

Use a similar method to find the area of triangle *ACD* in terms of *x*.

If the area of the whole quadrilateral *ABCD* is 15 sq. units, find the value of *x*.

[O & C]

11. The triangle $A_1 B_1 C_1$ has vertices at $(2, -3)$, $(3, 0)$ and $(6, 1)$ respectively. The triangle is translated so that the point A_2, the image of A_1, is at the origin; write down the coordinates of B_2 and C_2, the images of the vertices B_1 and C_1. The triangle $A_2 B_2 C_2$ is transformed by the matrix $M = \begin{pmatrix} 1 & 2 \\ 3 & 4 \end{pmatrix}$; write down the coordinates of the corresponding image points A_3, B_3 and C_3.

The same matrix *M* is now used to transform the original triangle $A_1 B_1 C_1$ onto the triangle $A_4 B_4 C_4$. Write down the coordinates of the points A_4, B_4, C_4, and show that the triangle $A_4 B_4 C_4$ can be transformed onto the triangle $A_3 B_3 C_3$ by a translation, giving the translation in vector form.

[O & C]

12. A transformation **T** given by

$$\begin{pmatrix} x \\ y \end{pmatrix} \to \begin{pmatrix} 0 & -1 \\ -1 & 0 \end{pmatrix} \begin{pmatrix} x \\ y \end{pmatrix} + \begin{pmatrix} 4 \\ 4 \end{pmatrix}$$

is composed of two transformations. Give a full geometrical description of these two transformations.

Find the point (x, y) which is mapped by **T** onto the point $(1, 2)$.

Find two invariant points for the transformation **T**.

Give a full geometrical description of **T** as a single transformation.

[SMP]

13. The translation $\begin{pmatrix} 2 \\ 3 \end{pmatrix}$ followed by a positive quarter-turn about the origin is expressed as the mapping

$$\textbf{P:} \begin{pmatrix} x \\ y \end{pmatrix} \to \textbf{M} \begin{pmatrix} x+2 \\ y+3 \end{pmatrix}.$$

Write down the matrix **M**. Show that the image of the position vector $\begin{pmatrix} 0 \\ 0 \end{pmatrix}$ under **P** is $\begin{pmatrix} -3 \\ 2 \end{pmatrix}$ and find the images of $\begin{pmatrix} 4 \\ 1 \end{pmatrix}$ and $\begin{pmatrix} a \\ b \end{pmatrix}$.

Find the position vector of the invariant point and give a full geometrical description of the mapping **P** as a single transformation.

[SMP]

14. The point (x, y) is mapped onto the point (x', y') by the matrix **M**, where

$$\textbf{M} = \begin{pmatrix} 0 & -1 & 7 \\ 1 & 0 & 1 \\ 0 & 0 & 1 \end{pmatrix},$$

by means of the transformation

$$\begin{pmatrix} x' \\ y' \\ 1 \end{pmatrix} = \textbf{M} \begin{pmatrix} x \\ y \\ 1 \end{pmatrix}.$$

Show that the image of the point *P* (2, 1) under the transformation represented by **M** is the point (6, 3). *cont.*

Given the matrices

$$A = \begin{pmatrix} 1 & 0 & 3 \\ 0 & 1 & 4 \\ 0 & 0 & 1 \end{pmatrix}, \qquad B = \begin{pmatrix} 0 & -1 & 0 \\ 1 & 0 & 0 \\ 0 & 0 & 1 \end{pmatrix},$$

$$C = \begin{pmatrix} 1 & 0 & -3 \\ 0 & 1 & -4 \\ 0 & 0 & 1 \end{pmatrix}$$

find in the same way the image point of P under each of the transformations represented by **A**, **B** and **C**.

By considering a rectangle with OP as diagonal, or otherwise, describe geometrically the transformations effected by **A**, **B**, **C** and **M**. Verify that **M** = **ABC**.

[SMP]

15.   Referred to O as origin and Ox and Oy as coordinate axes, transformations from $\mathbb{R}^2 \to \mathbb{R}^2$ are represented by 2×2 matrices **L**, **M** and **R**, where

L represents a reflection in the line $y = 0$,

M represents a reflection in the line $x - y\sqrt{3} = 0$,

R represents an anti-clockwise rotation about O of $60°$.

(a) Find the matrices **L** and **R**.

(b) Show that

$$M = \begin{pmatrix} \dfrac{1}{2} & \dfrac{\sqrt{3}}{2} \\ \dfrac{\sqrt{3}}{2} & -\dfrac{1}{2} \end{pmatrix}.$$

(c) Show that **R** = **ML**.

(d) Show that $LMR = \begin{pmatrix} 1 & 0 \\ 0 & 1 \end{pmatrix}$.

[UL]

16.   (a) A and B are the points $(1, 0)$ and $(0, 1)$. By drawing and folding, or otherwise, write down correct to one place of decimals the coordinates of the reflections of A and B in the line $y = 2x$.

(b) Hence write down the matrix M for this reflection.

(c) Write down similarly, correct to one place of decimals, the matrix N for reflection in the line $x = -2y$.

(d) Explain why these two reflection lines are perpendicular.

(e) Hence, using the fact that the combination of reflections in two lines is equivalent to a rotation through twice the angle between the two lines, write down the matrix R for the single transformation equivalent to the combination of these two reflections in the given lines.

(f) Calculate the product of M and N and verify that it gives R correct to one place of decimals.

[SMP]

17.

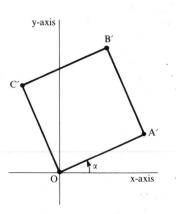

Fig. 6.4

Figure 6.4 shows the image of the unit square after a rotation of angle α about the origin.

(a) Write down the coordinates of A' and C', and hence the matrix R_α for this rotation.

(b) Write down the matrix R_β for a rotation of angle β about the origin.

(c) State the single transformation represented by the matrix product $R_\beta R_\alpha$ and complete the matrix **T** for this,

$$T = \begin{pmatrix} \cos(\alpha + \beta) & \\ & \end{pmatrix}.$$

(d) Carry out the matrix multiplication $R_\beta R_\alpha$ and show how this gives the formula for $\cos(\alpha + \beta)$.

[SMP]

EXERCISE 7X

1.   Vector **a** represents a displacement of 40 m to the north-east, vector **b** a displacement of 30 m to the south-east and vector **c** a displacement of 50 m to the south. Find, graphically, the magnitudes and the directions of the vectors equivalent to

(i) $\mathbf{a}+\mathbf{b}+\mathbf{c}$,

(ii) $\mathbf{a}-2\mathbf{b}+2\mathbf{c}$.

[AEB 1980]

2. A sailing boat on a large lake is steering due West but is also drifting towards the North. Its velocity is constant, such that in 10 minutes it travels 900 m to the West and 200 m to the North.

(a) By scale drawing, find the direction of the velocity and its magnitude in kilometres per hour.

(b) An outboard motor is now started, giving the boat an additional velocity of 3 km/h to the West. By drawing, find the magnitude and direction of the new velocity of the boat.

[SMP]

3. A particle moving initially due North with a velocity of 25 cm/s is subjected to an acceleration of 5 cm/s² in a direction 240° (S 60° W). Find, graphically or otherwise, the velocity of the particle 3 seconds later.

After what further period of time will the particle be moving instantaneously due West?

[MEI]

4. Two forces P and Q act through the point $(1, 4)$. The force P is represented in magnitude and direction by the line joining $(1, 4)$ to $(1, 9)$. The force Q is likewise represented by the line joining $(1, 4)$ to $(5, 1)$. Calculate

(i) the magnitudes of P and Q;

(ii) the magnitude of the resultant of the two forces, and the equation of its line of action.

[O & C]

5. A mass of 10 kg is to be accelerated at 5×10^{-2} m/s² in a direction 060° (N 60° E). If it is known that a constant force of 5 newtons acts in a direction due south, determine the forces acting in the directions due east, and due north, which will produce the required acceleration.

[MEI]

6. Two forces, of magnitude 6 and 8 N, act at an angle of 60° to each other, away from a given point. Calculate

(i) the magnitude of their resultant,

(ii) the angle between the resultant and the smaller force.

[AEB 1980]

7. Coplanar forces y N, 6 N, 4 N and 12 N act on a particle in the directions 0°, θ°, 120°, 210° respectively (each measured in a clockwise direction from north) and keep it in equilibrium. Write down the equations obtained by resolving the four forces in the directions north and east respectively. Hence, or otherwise, calculate the values of θ and y.

[O & C]

8. The three forces $\begin{pmatrix} 3 \\ 6 \end{pmatrix}$, $\begin{pmatrix} 5 \\ 4 \end{pmatrix}$ and $\begin{pmatrix} -4 \\ 2 \end{pmatrix}$ newton act together on a mass of 5 kg.

(i) Calculate the magnitude of the acceleration, and show that its direction is perpendicular to $\begin{pmatrix} 3 \\ -1 \end{pmatrix}$.

(ii) A fourth force, $\mathbf{P}$ newton, acting in the direction of $\begin{pmatrix} 2 \\ -5 \end{pmatrix}$, is now added. By expressing $\mathbf{P}$ as $\begin{pmatrix} 2s \\ -5s \end{pmatrix}$, find the new acceleration of the mass in terms of s.

Calculate the magnitude of $\mathbf{P}$ if this acceleration is parallel to the x-axis.

[SMP]

9. Two tugs pull the bows of a ship, one on either side, by means of horizontal cables which make angles of 35° and 25° with the line AB as shown in figure 7.14.

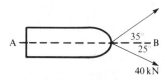

Fig. 7.14

If the tension in the cable at 25° is 40 kN, find the tension necessary in the other cable in order that the direction of the resultant pull should be along the line AB.

[MEI]

10. A mass of 18 kg is being pulled along a rough horizontal surface by a force F directed 23° above the horizontal. The total (horizontal) resisting force is 36 N.

If the mass has an acceleration of 2.8 m/s², show that $F = 94$ N approximately, and calculate the normal reaction. [Take $g = 9.8$.]

[SMP]

11. A mass of 80 kg, hanging on the end of a string, is held by a horizontal force F so that the string is inclined at $70°$ to the vertical.

(i) Draw a triangle of forces, and calculate F and the tension, T, in the string.

(ii) If the force F is suddenly removed, in which direction will the mass accelerate immediately? Draw a new diagram of forces, and calculate the new tension in the string and the acceleration of the mass.

[JMB]

12. A balloon has a mass of 5 kg and the upthrust of the air is 60 N, but it is held in still air by two light ropes each inclined at $30°$ to the vertical and at $60°$ to one another. Find the tensions in the ropes.

If a horizontal wind exerts a force of x N on the balloon and in the plane of the ropes, find the value of x if one rope just goes slack.

[O & C]

13. A man of mass 100 kg is hanging by a rope attached to a winch in a helicopter which is hovering. The helicopter begins to ascend vertically with an acceleration of $0.75 \, \text{m/s}^2$. Determine the tension in the rope in newtons.

If the rope were to be wound in at a constant rate of 1 m/s, what change would there be in the value of the tension in the rope? Comment briefly.

After a short time the helicopter ceases to rise vertically but subsequently moves horizontally with an acceleration of $0.75 \, \text{m/s}^2$. It is observed that with the winch not operating, the rope hangs at a constant angle θ to the vertical where $\tan \theta = \frac{3}{4}$. What is the tension in the rope now, and what is the horizontal force on the man due to the resistance of the air?

[MEI]

14. Figure 7.15 shows the forces acting on a tethered balloon. W is the weight; U is the upthrust. T is the tension in the cable at the point of attachment to the balloon, the cable at this point being inclined at $30°$ to the vertical. P is the force exerted by the wind, which is blowing in a horizontal direction. If the mass of the balloon is 200 kg and $P = 600$ N, calculate U and T in newtons.

If the cable breaks at the point of attachment to the balloon, state in the form $\begin{pmatrix} x \\ y \end{pmatrix}$ the re-

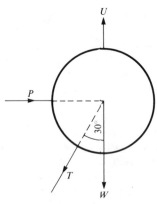

Fig. 7.15

sultant of the three forces P, U and W, and state also the vector which represents the initial acceleration of the balloon.

[O & C]

15. A mass of 3 kg on a smooth horizontal surface is pulled by forces of magnitudes P_1 and P_2 acting in the same vertical plane in directions $75°$ and $35°$ from the horizontal, as shown in figure 7.16. The mass is at rest and experiences a reaction force of 12 N from the surface.

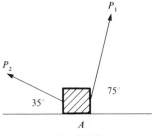

Fig. 7.16

By resolving horizontally, show that $P_2 \simeq 0.316 P_1$.

By resolving vertically, obtain a second equation and hence calculate the values of P_1 and P_2. (Take $g = 9.8$.)

[SMP]

16. A sledge of mass 8 kg is placed on a smooth plane inclined at $28°$ to the horizontal. It is pushed up the slope with a *horizontal* force of 140 N.

Show by calculation that the reaction force between the sledge and the plane is 136 N (correct to 3 significant figures), and calculate the acceleration of the sledge (take $g = 10$). Make your working clear.

[SMP]

17. The mechanism of a clockwork toy · lorry can be assumed to exert a constant propulsive force under all conditions. Starting from rest on a level table, the lorry will attain a speed of 1.2 m/s in 3 seconds. The mass of the lorry is 0.15 kg.

(a) Find the propulsive force in newtons.

(b) If the lorry is loaded with blocks of total mass 0.3 kg, find how long it will take to reach a speed of 1.2 m/s from rest.

(c) If the unloaded lorry is placed on a plank sloping up at an angle whose sine is 1/50, find how long it will take to reach the same speed.

(d) Show that the loaded lorry cannot climb this plank. [Take $g = 10 \text{m/s}^2$.]

[SMP]

18. A skier of mass 70 kg is at the top of a run which is inclined at $20°$ to the horizontal. He is already moving at 4 m/s in the direction straight down the slope. The resistances amount to a force of 95 N up the slope.

Show that his acceleration will be about 2m/s^2. [Take $g = 9.8$.]

If the slope is 77 m long and he skis straight down it, calculate how long he will take to get to the bottom and how fast he will then be travelling.

[SMP]

19. A toboggan of mass 15 kg is placed on an icy slope which is inclined to the horizontal at an angle of $18°$. It is held in position by applying a horizontal force R. [Friction and other resistances may be neglected.]

(a) Draw a diagram to show the forces acting on the toboggan.

(b) Show by calculation that the magnitude of R, correct to 2 significant figures, is 48 N. [Take $g = 9.8$.]

(c) Find the acceleration of the toboggan if the force R is now removed.

[SMP]

20. An object of mass 2 kg is on smooth level ground. A force of 8 N applied at $30°$ to the vertical causes it to accelerate at 1.5m/s^2. Show that the resistance to motion is 1 N.

If instead the ground slopes at $10°$ to the

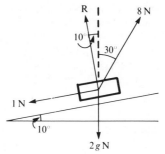

Fig. 7.17

horizontal, so that the forces are as shown in figure 7.17, verify that the force, R, of interaction between the object and the ground is about 13.6 N. Also calculate the acceleration of the object up the slope. [Take $g = 10$.]

[SMP]

EXERCISE 8X

1. Draw the graph of $y = 10^x$ for values of x between -0.4 and $+1.4$. Plot points for $x = -0.4, -0.2, 0, +0.2$, etc., and use the following scales: 10 cm per unit on the x-axis, 1 cm per unit on the y-axis.

From your graph (indicate your method clearly on the graph itself), deduce the values of the following:

(a) $\sqrt{10}$, (b) $\sqrt[3]{100}$, (c) $\log_{10} 0.8$, (d) $\log_{10} 20$.

2. Taking the same scale on the x-axis and y-axis, draw a separate sketch-graph for each of the following:

(i) $y = \log_2 x$,   (ii) $y = 2^x$, (iii) $y = \log_2(-x)$,   (iv) $y = \log_2(x+3)$.

State how the first graph, that of $y = \log_2 x$, may be transformed into each of the other three.

[SMP]

3. (a) Sketch the curves
   (i) $y = \log_e(2x+1)$,
   (ii) $y = e^{(1-2x)}$.

   (b) Solve the equation
   $$\log_{10}(x^2+1) = 1.$$

[AEB 1980]

4. Using a scale of 4 cm for one unit on both x and y axes draw the graph of $y = \log_e(2x+5)$, plotting points for $x = -2.25, -2, -1, 0, 1, 2, 3$.

Using the same scales and axes draw the graphs of $2y+3x = 3$ and $3y-2x = 3$.

Use your graphs to solve the equations

(a) $3\log_e(2x+5) = (2x+3)$,

(b) $3-\log_e\{(2x+5)^2\} = 3x$.

[AEB 1983]

5. (i) Solve the equations

(a) $9^x = \dfrac{1}{27}$, giving the exact value of x;

(b) $6^x = 100$, giving the value of x correct to three significant figures.

(ii) Draw the graph of $y = 10^x$, for the values $x = 0.6, 0.8, 1.0, 1.2$ and 1.4, using a scale of 2 cm = 0.2 units on the x-axis and 2 cm = 5 units on the y-axis.

From the graph, indicating your method on the graph paper, deduce the values of
(a) $(\sqrt[4]{10})^5$;   (b) $\log_{10}7.5$.

[O & C]

6. (i) Find x if $3^x \times 27^{3x} = 81 \times 9^{4x}$.

(ii) Evaluate to three significant figures $\sqrt[3]{0.0277}$, using logarithms and showing the details of your working.

[MEI]

7. (a) When $x = 3$ evaluate, without using a calculator,

(i) $\log_{10}(3x+1)^4$,   (ii) $(7x+4)^{-1/2}$,
(iii) $(x^2+1)^{x-3}$.

(b) Solve the equations

(i) $4^{(2x^2+4x)} = \frac{1}{8}$,
(ii) $8^x = 0.14$.

[O & C]

8. (i) Without using tables (or calculator),
(a) evaluate $27^{4/3}$,   (b) simplify and so evaluate $\log_3 225 - 2\log_3 5$.

(ii) Use tables to find x to 3 significant figures if $x^5 = 372$.

[MEI]

9. (a) Simplify

$$\frac{(x^{3/2}+x^{1/2})(x^{1/2}-x^{-1/2})}{(x^{3/2}-x^{1/2})^2}.$$

(b) Without using a calculator find the loga-

rithm of 8 to the base a

(i) when $a = 64$,
(ii) when $a = \frac{1}{4}$.

[AEB 1982]

10. (*Do not use calculator, tables or slide-rule in this question.*)

(i) Express 256 as a power of 2 and hence evaluate $(256)^{3/4}$.

(ii) State the value given to 5^0 and explain why this value is chosen.

(iii) By considering prime factors, find x and y if $8^x \times 36^y = 81^3$.

(iv) Simplify and hence evaluate $\log_5 100 - \log_5 4$.

[MEI]

11. Solve the equation $4^x - 2^x - 6 = 0$, giving your answer correct to three significant figures.
[AEB 1980]

12. Solve the following equations, correct to 2 significant figures:

(a) $x\log_{10}8 = \log_{10}9$;

(b) $8^x = 9$;

(c) $x = \dfrac{\log_2 9}{\log_2 8}$.

[SMP]

13. Solve, giving your solutions to three significant figures where appropriate,

(a) $e^{2x} - 3e^x - 4 = 0$,

(b) $\log_{10}(x+1) + \log_{10}(x-2) = 1$.

[AEB 1982]

14. Solve the following equations for x, giving your answers correct to three significant figures where appropriate,

(i) $2(3^x)+4 = 3^{x+1}$,

(ii) $e^{2x} - 4e^x + 3 = 0$,

(iii) $\log_{10}(x^2+1) - \log_{10}x^2 = 1$,

(iv) $3\log_e x = 1 + 2\log_x e$.

[AEB 1981]

15. Show that a 20% increase one week followed by a 20% decrease the next is equivalent to a 4% decrease in the fortnight.

How many decreases of 4% would be needed to halve the original value?

[SMP]

16. A population is increasing by 18% each year.

(a) After n years, by what factor will the population have been multiplied?

(b) Find how long it takes for the population to be doubled.

(c) How long ago (assuming that the law of growth has remained the same) was the population a quarter of its present size?

[SMP]

17. A colony of bacteria is observed and a reasonable estimate of its 'size' after t hours is found to be given by $a \cdot 2^{bt}$, where $a = 40$ and $b = 5$.

(a) What size was the colony initially?

(b) How long does it take to double its size?

(c) How long does it take to treble its size?

(d) What size is it after 24 minutes?

(e) At what rate per minute is its size then increasing?

(The derivative of 2^{kx} is $0.693\,k \times 2^{kx}$.)

[SMP]

18. Given that $\log_e 2 = 0.693\,147$ and $\log_e 3 = 1.098\,612$, find, without using tables (or calculator),

(i) $\log_e 12$,

(ii) $\log_e 2.25$,

(iii) $\log_e\left(\dfrac{1}{16}\right)$.

[AEB 1979]

19. (a) Given that $\log_a M = 0.5$, $\log_a N = 0.8$, $\log_a X = 1.5$, $\log_a Y = 2.0$ and $\log_b a = 0.6$, find

(i) $\log_a(MN)$,

(ii) $\log_a\left(\dfrac{X}{N}\right)$,

(iii) $\log_a(Y^3)$,

(iv) $\log_a\left(\dfrac{1}{\sqrt{N}}\right)$,

(v) $\log_b\left(\dfrac{b}{a}\right)$.

Find also the logarithms of X to the bases M, N and b.

(b) Given that $\log\left(\dfrac{x}{y}\right) = 4.5$ and $\log(x^5 y^2) = 5$, find $\log x$ and $\log y$.

[JMB]

20. (a) Express in terms of $\log N$

(i) $\log(N^4)$,

(ii) $\log\left(\dfrac{1}{N}\right)$,

(iii) $\log(\sqrt{N})$.

(b) Find the values of

(i) $\log_7 7$,

(ii) $\log_8(\sqrt{2})$,

(iii) $\log_{\sqrt{2}}(8)$.

(c) Given that $\log a^2 + \log b^2 = \log a - \log b$, prove that $ab^3 = 1$.

(d) Solve the simultaneous equations

$$x + 2y = 5,$$
$$10^x = 4^y,$$

giving your answers correct to three significant figures.

[JMB]

EXERCISE 9X

1. Three vectors $\mathbf{a}$, $\mathbf{b}$ and $\mathbf{c}$ are defined as follows:

$$\mathbf{a} = \mathbf{i} + 2\mathbf{j}, \quad \mathbf{b} = 3\mathbf{i} - \mathbf{j}, \quad \mathbf{c} = 2\mathbf{i} + 18\mathbf{j},$$

where $\mathbf{i}$ and $\mathbf{j}$ are unit vectors in different directions.

(i) Find the values of p and q such that $p\mathbf{a} + q\mathbf{b} = \mathbf{c}$.

(ii) Find the value of r such that $\mathbf{b} + r\mathbf{c}$ is parallel to $\mathbf{a}$.

[MEI]

2. Given $\mathbf{a} = \begin{pmatrix} 3 \\ 4 \end{pmatrix}$, find the vector $\mathbf{u}$ of unit magnitude which is parallel to $\mathbf{a}$.

Given

$$\mathbf{b} = \begin{pmatrix} 1 \\ -2 \end{pmatrix} \quad \text{and} \quad \mathbf{c} = \begin{pmatrix} -1 \\ 3 \end{pmatrix},$$

calculate the scalar products $\mathbf{u} \cdot \mathbf{b}$ and $\mathbf{u} \cdot \mathbf{c}$. Explain with the aid of a figure why these two quantities are opposite in sign.

[SMP]

3. $\mathbf{i}$ and $\mathbf{j}$ are unit vectors in the Ox, Oy directions respectively. Show in a diagram the displacement vector $\mathbf{a} = 3\mathbf{i} + 4\mathbf{j}$, and find its magnitude and direction. Find a displacement vector $\mathbf{b}$ of equal magnitude but in a direction at $90°$ anticlockwise to that of $\mathbf{a}$.   *cont.*

Express the displacement vector $\mathbf{c} = 24\mathbf{i} + 7\mathbf{j}$ as $p\mathbf{a} + q\mathbf{b}$ where p and q are numbers to be found. Hence calculate the magnitude of the displacement vector $\mathbf{c}$ in two different ways.

(MEI)

4. Three forces $\mathbf{P}$, $\mathbf{Q}$ and $\mathbf{R}$, act at a point such that $\mathbf{P} = \mathbf{i} + 2\mathbf{j}$, $\mathbf{Q} = -3\mathbf{i} + \mathbf{j}$, $\mathbf{R} = 9\mathbf{i} + 4\mathbf{j}$, where $\mathbf{i}$ and $\mathbf{j}$ are unit vectors in the positive x and y directions respectively. Find in terms of $\mathbf{i}$ and $\mathbf{j}$ the single force $\mathbf{S}$ which will balance these three forces and state its magnitude.

Find the value of k such that the force $\mathbf{P} + k\mathbf{Q}$ acts in the direction of y.

Find the values of a and b such that $a\mathbf{P} + b\mathbf{Q} = \mathbf{R}$.

[MEI]

5. (a) Find the scalar product of

$$\begin{pmatrix} 4.8 \\ 3.6 \end{pmatrix} \quad \text{and} \quad \begin{pmatrix} 2 \\ 3 \end{pmatrix}.$$

(b) Calculate the magnitude of $\begin{pmatrix} 4.8 \\ 3.6 \end{pmatrix}$.

(c) Hence, or otherwise, calculate the length of the orthogonal projection of $\begin{pmatrix} 2 \\ 3 \end{pmatrix}$ on the direction of $\begin{pmatrix} 4.8 \\ 3.6 \end{pmatrix}$.

(d) Calculate the angle between the two vectors.

[SMP]

6. (i) If $\mathbf{AB} = \begin{pmatrix} 1 \\ 3 \end{pmatrix}$ and $\mathbf{AC} = \begin{pmatrix} -3 \\ 4 \end{pmatrix}$, calculate the projection of $\mathbf{AB}$ on $\mathbf{AC}$ and the angle between the two vectors.

(ii) The points O, A, B and C are $(0, 0, 0)$, $(4, 4, 12)$, $(-5, 1, 5)$ and $(4, 1, 2)$ respectively. Show that $\mathbf{OA}$ is perpendicular to $\mathbf{BC}$.

[O & C]

7. (i) A is the point $(0, 0, 9)$, B is the point $(0, 12, 0)$ and C is the point $(15, 0, 0)$. Prove that angle ABC is approximately $60°$.

(ii) Find the projection of the vector

$$\begin{pmatrix} 1 \\ -2 \\ 2 \end{pmatrix} \quad \text{on the vector} \quad \begin{pmatrix} 6 \\ 2 \\ -3 \end{pmatrix}$$

and calculate the acute angle between them.

[O & C]

8. Given the three points $A(4, 5)$, $B(8, 8)$ and $C(3, 10)$,

(i) show that the scalar product

$$\mathbf{AB} \cdot \mathbf{AC} = 11;$$

(ii) calculate the lengths of AB and AC.

Hence calculate the angle CAB, to the nearest degree.

[SMP]

9. $\mathbf{i}$ and $\mathbf{j}$ are unit vectors in the Ox and Oy directions respectively. The displacement vector $\mathbf{p} = 2\mathbf{i} + 13\mathbf{j}$, and the displacement vector $\mathbf{q} = 4\mathbf{i} - 7\mathbf{j}$. Find the magnitude and direction of the displacement vector $\mathbf{p} + \mathbf{q}$.

Show the vectors $\mathbf{p}$, $\mathbf{q}$ and $\mathbf{p} + \mathbf{q}$ on an accurate diagram using a scale $2\,\text{cm} \equiv 10$ units.

Calculate the value of k such that the displacement vector $\mathbf{p} + k\mathbf{q}$ is perpendicular to the displacement vector $\mathbf{p} + \mathbf{q}$. Check that your value of k is as required by drawing the displacement vectors $k\mathbf{q}$ and $\mathbf{p} + k\mathbf{q}$ on your diagram.

[MEI]

10. Given the points $A(1, 2, 4)$, $B(5, 3, 7)$, $C(3, 7, 4)$, write down as column vectors $\mathbf{AB}$ and $\mathbf{AC}$.

Calculate (a) the scalar product $\mathbf{AB} \cdot \mathbf{AC}$; (b) the length of $\mathbf{AB}$; (c) the length of $\mathbf{AC}$.

Hence show by calculation that the angle BAC is $61.7°$ approximately.

Calculate the area of triangle ABC.

[SMP]

11. Relative to an origin O the position vectors of two points A and B are $\begin{pmatrix} 2 \\ 1 \\ -3 \end{pmatrix}$ and $\begin{pmatrix} 7 \\ -3 \\ -1 \end{pmatrix}$ respectively.

(i) Show that OA is perpendicular to AB.

(ii) Find the position vector of the point C such that $OABC$ is a rectangle.

[AEB 1979]

12. A hang-glider is at the point B above a slope OA, so that OAB is a vertical plane.

Taking x- and y-axes horizontally and vertically through O in the plane OAB, A is $(25, -10)$ and B is $(20, 12)$; the units are metres.

(i) Calculate (a) the length OB, (b) the length OA, (c) the scalar product $\mathbf{OB} \cdot \mathbf{OA}$.

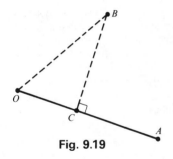

Fig. 9.19

(ii) Hence or otherwise calculate the angle *BOA*.

(iii) A girl stands at *C*, the point of the slope which is closest to *B*. Calculate the distance *OC*.

[SMP]

13. (a) Show that if $(\mathbf{a}+\mathbf{b}) \cdot (\mathbf{a}-\mathbf{b}) = 0$ then $|\mathbf{a}| = |\mathbf{b}|$.

Give a geometrical example of this fact.

(b) The diagonals *AC*, *BD* of a quadrilateral *ABCD* bisect each other and are represented by the vectors $3\mathbf{i}+2\mathbf{j}$ and $2\mathbf{i}-3\mathbf{j}$ respectively. Determine, *without scale drawing*, the shape of the quadrilateral *ABCD*.

[AEB 1982]

14. If $\mathbf{OP} = \mathbf{p}$, $\mathbf{OQ} = \mathbf{q}$, and $\mathbf{OR} = \mathbf{r}$, state in each of the following cases the geometrical meaning in relation to the points *O*, *P*, *Q*, *R* of the vector equation:

(a) $\mathbf{p}\cdot\mathbf{q} = 0$; (b) $\mathbf{p}\cdot(\mathbf{q}-\mathbf{r}) = 0$;
(c) $\mathbf{p} = \mathbf{q}+\mathbf{r}$.

[SMP]

15. A triangle has sides of 7 m and 5 m and the angle between them is $72°$. Calculate the length of the third side to 3 significant figures.

Check your answer by an accurate drawing. State the scale used and the answer given by the drawing.

[MEI]

16. A triangle *ABC*, whose largest angle is at *B*, has sides of lengths 4, 5 and 6 units.

(a) Show by calculation that the largest angle is $82.8°$, correct to 1 decimal place.

(b) The circle through the vertices *A*, *B*, *C* of the triangle has centre *O*. Using the fact that angle *AOC* is twice angle *ABC*, or otherwise, calculate the diameter of this circle.

[SMP]

17. In the triangle *PQR*, $PQ = 4$ cm, $QR = 13$ cm and $PR = 10$ cm. Calculate

(i) the size of the largest angle,

(ii) the area of the triangle, correct to three significant figures.

[AEB 1979]

18. In figure 9.20 $AB = 8$, $AD = 13$, $BD = CD = 15$, and $\angle BDC = 45°$.

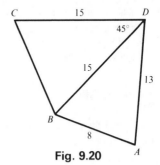

Fig. 9.20

(i) Prove by using the cosine formula that $\angle ABD = 60°$.

(ii) Calculate *BC*.

(iii) Calculate $\angle BDA$.

(iv) Calculate *AC*.

[O & C]

19. Show, by means of *sketches*, that it is possible to have two triangles *ABC* which are not congruent but in *both* of which

$AB = 15$, $BC = 12$ and angle $BAC = 40°$.

Calculate the size of angle *ACB* in each triangle.

[AEB 1980]

20. In $\triangle ABC$, $BC = 8$ cm, $AC = 5$ cm and $\angle ABC = 30°$.

(a) Calculate the two possible values of $\angle BAC$, giving your answers in degrees to one decimal place.

(b) Draw a diagram to illustrate your answers.

[UL]

21. Show that the area of the triangle *ABC* is equal to $\frac{1}{2}bc \sin A$.

Given that its area is 5.6, and that $b = 3.2$ and $c = 4.0$, calculate the two possible angles *A*.

cont.

Hence calculate the greater of the two possible lengths of the third side.

[SMP]

22. A triangle ABC has $AB = 10$ cm, angle $B = 32°$, $AC = 7$ cm. Show *by accurate drawing* that there are two differently shaped triangles which contain these measurements. Record in each case your measured values of BC, angle A and angle C.

Write down the sine formula and use the original data to *calculate* $\sin C$ and hence obtain the two possible values of angle C as accurately as you can from your tables.

In each case *calculate* angle A and BC.

[MEI]

23. In a triangle ABC, angle A is $60°$, $b = 7$, and $a = 6.3$.

Show that c, the length of side AB, satisfies the equation

$$c^2 - 7c + 9.31 = 0.$$

Calculate the possible values of c, correct to two significant figures.

One of the triangles which satisfy these data has $B = 74°$, $C = 46°$. With which of your values of c does this agree?

Justify your answer.

[SMP]

24. A sailing race is over a triangular course ABC, starting and finishing at A. The first leg of the course AB is 5 km on a bearing of $060°$ to a buoy at B. The third leg CA is 6 km with A due north of C. Find by calculation the distance to three significant figures and the bearing to the nearest degree of the second leg of the course from B to C. Support your solution with a clear sketch, marking angles and distances.

[MEI]

25. A straight path descends steadily at $12°$ from the horizontal from A to B. It then ascends steadily at $8°$ from the horizontal from B to C. $AB = 84$ m and $BC = 156$ m. By the cosine rule, or otherwise, show that the straight line distance from A to C is 237 m, correct to the nearest metre.

Use the sine rule to calculate angle CAB and hence find the angle of elevation from A to C.

[SMP]

26. From a ship at sea two points on land are sighted, a light house and a radio mast. The light house is known to be 5.4 km North-West of the radio mast. From the ship the bearings of the light house and radio mast are $259°$ and $232°$ respectively.

Calculate the distance of the ship from the light house.

[SMP]

27. Three forts A, B and C are situated in a flat desert region. A is 8 km due west of B, and C is 3 km due east of B. An oasis O is situated to the north of the line ABC and is 7 km from both A and C. Calculate

(a) the distance between O and B,

(b) the bearing of O from B.

A mine M is situated to the south of ABC. The bearing of M from A is $135°$ and the bearing of M from C is $210°$.

(c) Calculate the distance between M and B.

[UL]

28. A ship which is steaming with constant velocity is sighted on a bearing $035°$ at a range of 5 nautical miles. Half an hour later it is sighted from the same point on a bearing of $107°$ at a range of 6.2 nautical miles.

Calculate its velocity, giving its magnitude to the nearest knot and its direction to the nearest degree.

[SMP]

29. A ship moving at night on a bearing of $020°$ at 10 km/h sights the flash of a lighthouse on a bearing of $350°$. Thirty minutes later it sights it again on a bearing of $325°$. Calculate how far the ship is from the lighthouse on the second occasion, in kilometres to three significant figures.

[MEI]

30. Two forces, of 3 and 5 units, act in directions inclined at $40°$ as shown in figure 9.21.

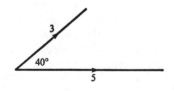

Fig. 9.21

(i) Calculate the components of the resultant (a) parallel to the larger force, (b) perpendicular to the larger force. Hence use Pythagoras' theorem to calculate the magnitude of the resultant.

(ii) Verify your last answer by making use of the cosine rule to calculate the magnitude of the resultant.

[SMP]

31. Points A and B have polar coordinates (r, α) and (r, β) respectively. O is the origin and $0 < \alpha < \beta < \pi$. By using the cosine rule in triangle AOB obtain an expression for AB^2.

Obtain another expression for this by using the cartesian coordinates of A and B, and use your two results to show that
$\cos(\beta - \alpha) = \cos \beta \cos \alpha + \sin \beta \sin \alpha$.

[SMP]

EXERCISE 10X

1. (i) Find the scalar product of the vectors

$$\mathbf{u} = \begin{pmatrix} 2 \\ 1 \\ -3 \end{pmatrix} \text{ and } \mathbf{v} = \begin{pmatrix} 4 \\ -2 \\ 1 \end{pmatrix}, \text{ and deduce}$$

the angle between them. Deduce also the projection of $\mathbf{u}$ upon $\mathbf{v}$.

(ii) If $\mathbf{O}$ is the origin and $\mathbf{OA} = \begin{pmatrix} 0 \\ 1 \end{pmatrix}$,

$\mathbf{OB} = \begin{pmatrix} 3 \\ 5 \end{pmatrix}$ and $\mathbf{OC} = \begin{pmatrix} 6 \\ -1 \end{pmatrix}$, find the

equations of AD and AL, in the form

$\begin{pmatrix} x \\ y \end{pmatrix} = \begin{pmatrix} a \\ b \end{pmatrix} + t \begin{pmatrix} c \\ d \end{pmatrix}$, where D is the mid-point

of BC and AL is perpendicular to BC.

[O & C]

2. The sides BC, CA and AB of a triangle have equations $3x - 4y = -1$, $5x + 2y = 33$ and $4x - y = 3$ respectively. Find, by calculation,

(i) the coordinates of the vertices A, B, C of the triangle;
(ii) the perpendicular distance of A from BC;
(iii) the area of the triangle.

(O & C)

3. Find the coordinates of the foot of the perpendicular from $P(-9, 6)$ to the line l, which has the equation $3y = 4x + 29$. Hence find the coordinates of Q if l is the perpendicular bisector of PQ.

If R lies on l and the gradient of the line PR is $\frac{1}{2}$, find the coordinates of R, and hence find the equation of the reflection of the line PR in l.

[O & C]

4. Write down the perpendicular distances of any point (x, y) from the lines $3x - 4y = 2$ and $5x - 12y = -18$. Write down the equations of the bisectors of the angles between the two lines, and state which one is the bisector of the acute angle.

Verify that the point $(-1, 0)$ is the centre of a circle which touches the two given lines and the y-axis.

[O & C]

5. A triangle ABC has its vertices at the points $A(-2, 8)$, $B(1, 1)$ and $C(5, 1)$. Calculate the equations of the perpendicular bisectors of the sides AB and BC.

These perpendiculars meet at the point D. Find the coordinates of D and verify that D is equidistant from A, B and C.

Calculate the equation of the circle through A, B and C.

[AEB 1983]

6. Find the centre and radius of the circle with equation $x^2 + y^2 - 8x + 24y - 9 = 0$. Find also the points of intersection of this circle and the line $x = -1$, and show that the distance between these points is 24 units.

Write down the equation of the tangent at the point $(-1, 0)$ and find the x coordinate of the point where it meets the line $y = -12$.

[O & C]

7. The equation of a circle is

$$x^2 + y^2 + 8x - 10y + 16 = 0.$$

(i) Find the radius of the circle and the co-ordinates of its centre.

(ii) Find the coordinates of the points in which the circle meets the x and y axes.

(iii) Find the equation of the tangent to the circle at the point $(-8, 8)$.

(iv) The point $(-3, 7)$ is the mid-point of a chord PQ of the circle. Find the equation of PQ.

[AEB 1981]

8. The equation of a circle is

$$x^2 + y^2 - 3x - 4 = 0.$$

Find

cont.

(i) the coordinates of its centre,
(ii) its radius,
(iii) the coordinates of the points at which it cuts the axes.

Show that the line whose equation is $3x+4y = 17$ touches the circle and find the coordinates of its point of contact.

Show also that this line and the tangent to the circle at the point $(3, -2)$ intersect at a point on the x-axis and find its coordinates.

[JMB]

9. Calculate the perpendicular distance of the point $(2, -3)$ from the line $4x-3y+c = 0$. Hence find the values of c for which $4x-3y+c = 0$ is a tangent to the circle $(x-2)^2+(y+3)^2 = 100$.

Find also the coordinates of the points of contact of the two tangents.

[O & C]

10. Find the equation of the tangent at the point $(7, 1)$ on the circle

$$x^2+y^2-6x+4y-12 = 0.$$

Verify that the point $(4, 5)$ lies on this tangent.

Write down the equation of a line with gradient m which passes through the point $(4, 5)$, and hence find the equation of the other tangent from $(4, 5)$ to the circle.

[O & C]

11. Find the equation of the circle with centre at $A(-2, 3)$ and radius 5.

Show that the point $B(1, 7)$ lies on the circle and find the equation of the tangent to the circle at B.

This tangent cuts the y-axis at the point C, the x-axis at the point D and the line $y = 3$ at the point E.

Calculate the ratio of the areas of the triangles ACE and ACD.

[AEB 1981]

12. Find the centres and radii of the circles $x^2+y^2-8x-4y-5 = 0$ and $x^2+y^2+10x+20y+25 = 0$, and deduce that the circles touch each other. If the line of centres meets the circles in the points A, B, C (in that order), find the equation of the circle which has AC as diameter. Give the answer in the same form as that of the two given circles.

[O & C]

13. A circle has its centre at the point

$C(2, 1)$ and touches the line $3x+4y-60 = 0.$

Find

(i) its radius,
(ii) its equation,
(iii) the coordinates of its point of contact, P, with the given line.

Given that the line meets the x-axis at A, show that CA is a diameter of the circle passing through C, P and A. For this second circle, find

(iv) its equation,
(v) the equation of the tangent at P.

[JMB]

14. A is the point $(1, -1)$ and B is the point $(3, 3)$.

Find

(i) the coordinates of the midpoint of AB;
(ii) the equation of the locus of points equidistant from A and B.

Show that the equation of the locus of points P such that $\angle BPA = 90°$ is

$$x^2+y^2-4x-2y = 0.$$

Hence, or otherwise, find the coordinates of the other two vertices of the square with diagonal AB.

[O & C]

15. Find the equations of the *complete* locus of a point which moves so as to be 3 units distant from the line $3x-4y+12 = 0$.

Find also the equation of the locus of a point which moves so as to be 3 units distant from the nearest point of the circle $x^2+y^2-10x+4y+25 = 0.$

Verify that the point $\left(\frac{1}{5}, -\frac{3}{5}\right)$ is 3 units distant from the given line, and also 3 units distant from the given circle.

[O & C]

16. If A is the point $(2, 4)$, O is the origin and P is the variable point (x, y), write down expressions, in terms of x and y, for the squares of the distances OP and AP.

Express the condition $AP^2 = OP^2+4$ in terms of x and y and simplify it.

Draw a sketch showing O, A and the locus of P, giving the coordinates of the points where the locus meets the axes of coordinates.

[MEI]

17. A point $P(x, y)$ moves in such a way that

$$\frac{AP}{BP} = \frac{3}{2},$$

where A and B have coordinates $(-4, -2)$ and $(1, 3)$ respectively.

(i) Find the equation of the locus of P and show that it is a circle.

(ii) Find the coordinates of its centre and show that its radius is $6\sqrt{2}$.

(iii) Find the coordinates of the points at which it intersects AB and AB produced.

(iv) Show that the tangents to the circle at these points are parallel and find their equations.

[JMB]

18. Write down the perpendicular distance of the point (h, k) from the straight line $3x - 4y = 0$. Find the equation of the locus of the point which moves so that it lies on the bisector of the acute angle between the x-axis and the straight line $3x - 4y = 0$.

Find also the equation of the locus of the point which moves so that its distance from the x-axis equals its distance from the point $(12, 1)$, simplifying your answer.

Show that the point $(15, 5)$ lies on both of these loci.

[O & C]

19. Find the position vector of the point of intersection, P, of the line with equation

$\mathbf{r} = \begin{pmatrix} 3 \\ 1 \end{pmatrix} + s \begin{pmatrix} 2 \\ 3 \end{pmatrix}$ and the line joining the points

with position vectors $\begin{pmatrix} 2 \\ 4 \end{pmatrix}$ and $\begin{pmatrix} 1 \\ 4 \end{pmatrix}$. Find the distance between P and the origin.

[AEB 1983]

20. If $\begin{pmatrix} x \\ y \end{pmatrix} = \begin{pmatrix} 2 \\ 3 \end{pmatrix} + t \begin{pmatrix} 1 \\ -2 \end{pmatrix}$ represents a given line, write down in vector form the equation of the line which is perpendicular to this line, and which passes through the point $(5, 2)$. Find the point of intersection of the two lines.

Find the equation of the line which is the reflection of the line joining $(2, 3)$ and $(5, 2)$ in

the line $\begin{pmatrix} x \\ y \end{pmatrix} = \begin{pmatrix} 2 \\ 3 \end{pmatrix} + t \begin{pmatrix} 1 \\ -2 \end{pmatrix}$.

[O & C]

21. Find the values of s and t at the point of intersection of the lines

$$\begin{pmatrix} x \\ y \end{pmatrix} = \begin{pmatrix} -2 \\ -11 \end{pmatrix} + s \begin{pmatrix} 5 \\ 12 \end{pmatrix}$$

and

$$\begin{pmatrix} x \\ y \end{pmatrix} = \begin{pmatrix} 9 \\ -7 \end{pmatrix} + t \begin{pmatrix} 3 \\ -4 \end{pmatrix}.$$

Hence calculate the coordinates of the point of intersection.

Write down unit vectors in the directions

$\begin{pmatrix} 3 \\ -4 \end{pmatrix}$ and $\begin{pmatrix} 5 \\ 12 \end{pmatrix}$. By adding these unit vectors,

or otherwise, find the equation, in column vector form, of one of the bisectors of the angles between the two lines, and simplify your answer.

[O & C]

22. Relative to an origin O the points A, B, C and H have position vectors $\mathbf{j}$, $\mathbf{i} + 2\mathbf{j}$, $4\mathbf{i} + 3\mathbf{j}$ and $-3\mathbf{i} + 10\mathbf{j}$ respectively.

Prove that

(i) AH is perpendicular to BC,

(ii) BH is perpendicular to CA.

Find the equations of AH and BC in vector form.

If AH meets CB produced at D find the position vector of D and the length of AD.

[AEB 1981]

23. The two straight lines with vector equations, relative to an origin O,

$$\mathbf{r} = \begin{pmatrix} 3 \\ 0 \end{pmatrix} + t \begin{pmatrix} 3 \\ 2 \end{pmatrix},$$

and $\mathbf{r} = \begin{pmatrix} 2 \\ 5 \end{pmatrix} + s \begin{pmatrix} -2 \\ -1 \end{pmatrix}$

meet at K. Find the position vector of K and the length OK.

[AEB 1979]

24. (a) Find the coordinates of the point of intersection of the lines

$$\mathbf{r} = \begin{pmatrix} 1 \\ 3 \end{pmatrix} + s \begin{pmatrix} -3 \\ 4 \end{pmatrix}$$

cont.

and

$$\mathbf{r} = \begin{pmatrix} -2 \\ 5 \end{pmatrix} + t\begin{pmatrix} 1 \\ -2 \end{pmatrix}.$$

(b) Find the coordinates of the points where the line $\mathbf{r} = (2+4t)\mathbf{i} + (4-2t)\mathbf{j}$ meets the circle $x^2 + y^2 = 25$.

[O & C]

EXERCISE 11X

1. The height of a solid circular cylinder is 10 cm and the radius of its base is r cm. This radius is increasing at the constant rate of 0.2 cm/s. Find in terms of π the rate of increase with respect to time, when $r = 5$,

(a) of the volume V of the cylinder,

(b) of the total surface area A of the cylinder.

Find also an expression for $\dfrac{dV}{dA}$ in terms of r.

[AEB 1982]

2. A spherical balloon is being blown up at a rate of 12 cm³/s. Express its volume V in terms of its radius r, and by differentiating find $\dfrac{dr}{dt}$ in terms of r.

Show that when the radius is 8 cm it is increasing at about 0.015 cm/s. Find the rate at which the surface area is increasing at this time.

[SMP]

3. A cube of melting ice is retaining its shape as a cube, and the length x cm of each edge is decreasing at the constant rate of 0.05 cm/s. At time t the volume of the cube is V and its surface area is S.

(i) Find the time taken for S to decrease from 600 cm² to 150 cm².

(ii) Find the value of $\dfrac{dV}{dt}$ at the instant when $x = 10$.

(iii) Show that at any instant $\dfrac{dV}{dt}$ is proportional to S.

[AEB 1981]

4. At the instant when the depth of water in a reservoir is h metres, the volume V, in m³, of the water is given by

$$V = \frac{\pi h^3}{12}.$$

If the volume of water in the reservoir is increasing at the *constant rate* of 2 m³ per minute, calculate, in terms of π, the rate at which the depth is increasing at the instant when the depth is 4 m.

Calculate the time taken for the depth to increase from 6 m to 12 m, leaving your answer in terms of π.

[AEB 1980]

5. A pile of gravel is in the form of a cone in which the base diameter is equal to six times the height. If the height is x metre and the volume is V cubic metre, show that $V = 3\pi x^3$.

The pile grows, as a result of gravel being spilt onto the highest point, but remains the same shape. Find an expression for $\dfrac{dV}{dt}$ in terms of x and $\dfrac{dx}{dt}$.

If gravel is spilt at a steady rate of 200 m³/hour, show that $\dfrac{dx}{dt} = \dfrac{7.1}{x^2}$ m/hour approximately.

Evaluate $\displaystyle\int_{10}^{12} \frac{x^2}{7.1}\, dx$ and state what physical quantity this represents.

[SMP]

6. Sketch the curve $y = (x-3)^2$ for $0 \leqslant x \leqslant 5$.

Find by integration the area enclosed between the x-axis, the line $x = 1$, and part of the curve.

[SMP]

7. Calculate the two stationary values of $f(x)$, where

$$f(x) \equiv x^3 - 3x^2 + 6.$$

Distinguish between the maximum and the minimum values of $f(x)$. Show that the graph of $f(x)$ crosses the x-axis between the points $(-2, 0)$ and $(-1, 0)$. Sketch the graph of $f(x)$ for $-2 \leqslant x \leqslant 3$. Mark on your graph the coordinates of the two stationary points.

Calculate the area of the finite region bounded by the curve, the x-axis, the y-axis and the line $x = 2$.

[UL]

8. Sketch the curve of $y = 4x(2-x)$ for values of x between -1 and $+3$. Calculate the area between the curve and the line $y = 4x$, and show the area in your figure.

[O & C]

9.

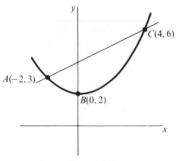

Fig. 11.8

In figure 11.8, the equation of the curve ABC is $y = 2 + \frac{1}{4}x^2$. Find the equation of the line AC.

Draw a rough sketch of the figure and shade the area for which $y > 2 + \frac{1}{4}x^2$, $x > 0$ and $y < \frac{1}{2}(x+8)$. Evaluate this area.

[MEI]

10. For the curve with equation
$$y = x^3 - x^2 - x + 1,$$

(i) find the coordinates of the points for which the value of y is a maximum or a minimum, stating which is the maximum,

(ii) show that there is only one point where the gradient of the curve is $-\frac{4}{3}$ and find the coordinates of this point,

(iii) sketch the curve for values of x from $x = -2$ to $x = 2$,

(iv) calculate the finite area bounded by the curve and the x-axis.

[AEB 1980]

11. Prove that the equation of the tangent at the point where $x = h$ on the curve $y = 2x^2 + 18$ is $y = 4hx + 18 - 2h^2$.

Hence, or otherwise, find the equations of the two tangents to the curve which pass through the origin.

Given that A and B are the points of contact of these tangents with the curve, show that the coordinates of A and B are $(-3, 36)$ and $(3, 36)$.

Calculate the area of the region bounded by the chord AB and the arc AB of the curve.

[JMB]

12. Given that $a > 1$, evaluate
$$\int_{1}^{a} (4x - x^2)\, dx.$$

Find the value of a which makes this a maximum. Using a sketch-graph, interpret this result in terms of an area.

[SMP]

13. (i) Sketch the graph of the function
$$x(x-2)(x-4)$$
plotting integer values of x for $-1 \leqslant x \leqslant 5$. State the coordinates of the points at which it crosses the x-axis.

(ii) Differentiate this function and hence show that it does not have a turning point for any integral value of x.

(iii) Integrate this function between the limits:

    (a) from 0 to 1,
    (b) from 1 to 3,
    (c) from 3 to 4.

Explain, with reference to your graph, why one of your answers is negative and also why one is zero.

[SMP]

14. (a) Calculate the area bounded by the curve $y = x^3$ and the lines $y = 0$, $x = 1$, and $x = 3$.

A parabola $y = ax^2 + bx + c$ is chosen so as to pass through three of the points, $A(1, 1)$, $B(2, 8)$, $C(3, 27)$, on the curve.

(b) Verify that $9a + 3b + c = 27$ and write down the two other equations that must be satisfied by a, b, c.

(c) Hence show that the parabola is
$$y = 6x^2 - 11x + 6.$$

(d) Calculate the area bounded by this parabola and the lines $y = 0$, $x = 1$, and $x = 3$.

[SMP]

15. The curve $y = (x-1)^3 + 10$ passes through the points $A(0, 9)$, $B(1, 10)$, $C(2, 11)$. Calculate the area bounded by the x-axis, y-axis, this curve and the line $x = 2$.

A linear approximation to this curve is made by taking the line AC. Find the equation of this line; calculate the area bounded by the axes, this line and the line $x = 2$.

Repeat this work with the tangent at   *cont.*

B as the linear approximation. Comment briefly on your results.

[SMP]

16. (a) Using a scale of 2 cm to 1 unit on each axis, sketch the graph of

$$y = 3 - \frac{5}{x^2} \quad \text{for} \quad 1 \leqslant x \leqslant 5.$$

(b) Shade the area represented by *I*, where

$$I = \int_2^4 \left(3 - \frac{5}{x^2}\right) dx.$$

(c) The rate of flow of water through a drain-pipe *t* minutes after the beginning of a storm is approximated by $100(3 - 5/t^2)$ m/min for $t \geqslant 2$.

If the drainpipe remains full and has cross-sectional area $0.2 \, \text{m}^2$, calculate the volume of water flowing through the drain during the time from $t = 2$ to $t = 4$.

[SMP]

17. (a) Integrate with respect to *x*

(i) $(2x - 3)^2$,

(ii) $\dfrac{(1 - x^2)}{x^4}$.

(b) Calculate the area enclosed between the curve $y = 3x^2 + 2$, the lines $x = 1$, $x = 3$ and the *x*-axis.

[AEB 1980]

18. Find the following integrals:

(i) $\int 6x^2 \, dx$,

(ii) $\int 2x(x^3 + 1) \, dx$,

(iii) $\int \dfrac{x^2 + x^{15}}{x^{17}} \, dx$.

Evaluate

$$\int_{-2}^2 x^2(x^2 + x + 1) \, dx.$$

[O & C]

19. (a) Integrate with respect to *x*

(i) $\dfrac{x^7 + x^4}{x^2}$,

(ii) $(x + 1)(x^3 + 1)$,

(iii) $\dfrac{1}{x^{3/2}}$.

(b) Evaluate $\displaystyle\int_{-1}^3 (3x^2 + 4x) \, dx$.

[O & C]

20. (a) Integrate with respect to *x*

(i) $\left(x + \dfrac{1}{x}\right)^2$,

(ii) $\sqrt{(3x^3)}$.

(b) Evaluate $\displaystyle\int_{-5}^{-2} \dfrac{3}{x^3} \, dx$.

[AEB 1980]

21. (a) Integrate with respect to *x*

(i) $(x^2 - 3)^2$,

(ii) $\dfrac{x + x^5}{x^3}$.

(b) Evaluate

(i) $\displaystyle\int_{-2}^2 x(x^2 - 1) \, dx$,

(ii) $\displaystyle\int_4^9 \dfrac{dx}{\sqrt{x}}$.

[O & C]

22. (i) Find the equation of the tangent to the curve $y = (2x + 1)^2$ at the point $(2, 25)$.

(ii) Evaluate $\displaystyle\int_1^4 \dfrac{x - 1}{\sqrt{x}} \, dx$.

[MEI]

23. (a) The gradient of a curve at the point (x, y) is given by $\dfrac{dy}{dx} = 3x^2 + 2x - 5$. If the curve passes through the point $(2, 4)$, find its equation.

(b) Evaluate

(i) $\displaystyle\int_{-1}^2 x^2(x - 1) \, dx$,

(ii) $\displaystyle\int_1^2 \left(x^2 - \dfrac{1}{x}\right)^2 dx$.

[O & C]

24. At any point (x, y) on a certain curve,

$$\frac{dy}{dx} = (3x - 2)(x + 2).$$

Given that it passes through $(-1, 1)$ find the equation of the curve.

Find, and distinguish between, the turning points of the curve.

[AEB 1982]

25. The gradient of a curve at the point (x, y) is given by $\dfrac{dy}{dx} = 3x^2 - 12$. If the curve passes through the point $(1, 0)$, find its equation.

Find the equations of the tangents which are parallel to the x-axis.

Find also the coordinates of the point at which the gradient has a minimum value.

[O & C]

26. Find a formula for y in terms of x if

$$\frac{dy}{dx} = \frac{x^2 - 1}{\sqrt{x}}$$

and $y = 0$ when $x = 1$.

Calculate y when $x = 4$.

[MEI]

27. Obtain an expression for V given that

$$\frac{dV}{dx} = (2x^2 - 3)\left(3 + \frac{1}{x^2}\right).$$

If $V = 10$ when $x = 1$, find the value of V when $x = 3$.

[MEI]

28. (i) Do the following integrations:

(a) $\int (x + 3)\,dx$;

(b) $\int 3x\,dx$;

(c) $\int x^3\,dx$.

(ii) Evaluate $\displaystyle\int_{\pi/4}^{3\pi/4} \cos 2x\,dx$ and illustrate on a sketch graph the region whose area this represents.

[SMP]

29. Given that

$$\frac{dy}{dx} = 3\sin\left(2x + \frac{\pi}{3}\right) + \cos\left(\frac{x}{2}\right) \text{ and that}$$

$y = -1$ when $x = 0$ find the value of y when $x = \dfrac{\pi}{2}$.

[AEB 1979]

30. (a) (i) Differentiate, with respect to x, the function

$$f : x \to (x^2 - 5)^3.$$

(ii) Make use of the chain rule to show that the derived function of

$$g : x \to \frac{1}{\cos^2 x}$$

is

$$g' : x \to k\sin x \cos^{-3}x,$$

and state the value of k.

(b) Using the results in (a), or otherwise, find

(i) $\int x(x^2 - 5)^2\,dx$;

(ii) $\displaystyle\int_0^{\pi/3} \frac{\tan x}{\cos^2 x}\,dx.$

[SMP]

EXERCISE 12X

1. A body is projected from O vertically upwards with an initial speed of $70\,\mathrm{m\,s^{-1}}$. If it reaches a point A after t seconds and a point B one second later, B being $21\,\mathrm{m}$ higher than A, find

(i) expressions for OA and OB in terms of t;

(ii) the value of t;

(iii) how much higher than B the body travels before coming momentarily to rest.

[O & C]

2. A skier is sliding out of control down a straight, steady slope and is accelerating uniformly at $1.5\,\mathrm{m/s^2}$.

(i) While he covers a particular stretch of $25\,\mathrm{m}$ his speed is doubled. Find by calculation how fast he was going at the end of the $25\,\mathrm{m}$.

(ii) If he started from rest (with the same acceleration), calculate

(a) the time he would take to cover $25\,\mathrm{m}$,

(b) the speed he would have attained in that time.

[SMP]

3. Two small pebbles, A and B, are dropped simultaneously from a tower, A from the top of the tower and B from a window $5\,\mathrm{m}$ vertically below the top. The pebbles fall freely. One pebble reaches the foot of the tower $0.2\,\mathrm{s}$ before the other. Calculate

(i) the time taken by pebble A to reach the foot of the tower,

(ii) the speed with which each of the pebbles strikes the ground at the foot of the tower.

[AEB 1981]

4. Two model monorail cars, A and B, run on parallel tracks. Car A starts from rest, with constant acceleration $1.2\,\mathrm{m/s^2}$, when car B is $2.4\,\mathrm{m}$ behind and travelling at $5\,\mathrm{m/s}$ with constant acceleration $0.4\,\mathrm{m/s^2}$.

Show that B will overtake A $0.5\,\mathrm{s}$ later, and find how long it will take for A to   *cont.*

catch up with *B* again. Calculate their speeds at both these times, and the distance travelled during the interval between them.

[SMP]

5. A ball *A* is thrown vertically upwards at 25 m/s from a point *P*. Three seconds later a second ball *B* is also thrown vertically upwards from the point *P* at 25 m/s. Calculate

(i) how long *A* has been in motion when the balls meet,

(ii) the height above *P* at which *A* and *B* meet.

[AEB 1979]

6. A particle *A* is constrained to move in a straight line. It starts from rest at *X* and accelerates at 2 m/s^2 until it reaches speed *V*. It then travels with constant speed *V* for 60 s before decelerating at 1 m/s^2 to come to rest at *Y*. The total time for the motion is 105 s. Find the distance *XY*.

A particle *B* starts from *X*, at time $t = 0$, and moves along the same straight line towards *Y*, with speed $(2t + 10)$ m/s, where *t* is the time in s. Calculate the time taken by *B* to reach *Y* from *X*.

[UL]

7. (i) The height above the ground of a model aeroplane *t* minutes after take-off is given in metres by

$$h = 20t^4 - 80t^3 + 80t^2$$

for values of *t* from 0 to 2.

(a) What is its greatest height?

(b) When is its upward velocity greatest?

(c) What is its downward velocity when it reaches the ground again?

(ii) Evaluate $\displaystyle\int_{-1}^{2} x^2(x+3)\,dx$.

[O & C]

8. Particles *A* and *B* move in the same straight line. After *t* seconds the displacements in metres of *A* and *B* from a fixed point *O* on the line are given by $x = t^3 - 4t^2 + 4t + 20$ and $x = \frac{5}{2}t^2 - 15$, respectively.

Calculate

(a) the distance between *A* and *B* at time $t = 2$,

(b) the velocity of *A* relative to *B* at time $t = 1$,

(c) the times at which the velocities of *A* and *B* are equal,

(d) the accelerations of *A* and *B* at time $t = 4$,

(e) the total distance travelled by *A* in the first two seconds.

[AEB 1983]

9. The velocity of an object *t* second after leaving a point *A* is given by

$$v = 12 + 4t - t^2 \text{ m s}^{-1}.$$

Find

(i) the acceleration of the object when the velocity is zero;

(ii) the distance of the object from *A* when the acceleration is zero.

[MEI]

10. The forward speed, *v* m/s, of a particle travelling in a straight line is given after *t* second by $v = 16 - 3t^2$.

(a) How far does it move in the first second?

(b) After how many seconds does it start to move backwards?

(c) Show that it is back at its starting point after 4 seconds.

(d) What total distance (forwards and backwards) does it travel in these 4 seconds?

[SMP]

11. Figure 12.15 shows two particles, *P* and *Q*, which are moving in the direction shown along a straight line passing through a fixed point *O*. At time *t* seconds after *P* passes through *O*, the velocities of *P* and *Q* are $(3+t) \text{ m s}^{-1}$ and $(5-t^2) \text{ m s}^{-1}$ respectively. When $t = 0$, *P* is at *O* and $OQ = 2$ m. At what time are *P* and *Q* moving with the same velocity, and what is the distance *PQ* at this time?

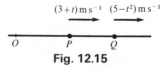

Fig. 12.15

Find, to two decimal places, the time when the distance *PQ* is again equal to 2 m (*Q* still being to the right of *P*).

[O & C]

12. Two spots of light start from rest at the same instant from *O* and move along a straight line so that their velocities, *t* second after leaving *O*, are given by $v = t(4-t) \text{ m s}^{-1}$ and $v = t(t-2) \text{ m s}^{-1}$.

After how many seconds are the spots of light moving with the same velocity, and how far are they then apart?

Show that the two spots of light pass each other, moving in opposite directions, $4\frac{1}{2}$ seconds after leaving O, and find how far from O they are at this instant.

On the same axes, draw a sketch of the displacement-time function for each spot of light for $0 \leqslant t \leqslant 6$.

                               [MEI]

13. The velocity of a particle moving in a straight line is given at time t by:
$$v = 3 \cos \pi t.$$

(a) What is its initial speed?

(b) Write down the acceleration at time t.

(c) When does it first stop? Show that its acceleration is then of magnitude 3π.

(d) State its displacement from the initial position at time t, and find after how long it first returns to its starting point.

(e) What is its greatest displacement from the initial position?

                               [SMP]

14. In the first 20 seconds of its motion down a runway, an aircraft is subject to an acceleration given by $(10 - \frac{1}{2}t) \text{ m/s}^2$. Find its velocity at the end of this time, and how far it has travelled, to the nearest metre.

                               [MEI]

15. A particle starts from rest at a point A and moves in a straight line. Ten seconds later the particle comes to rest at a point B. Between A and B the acceleration of the particle in m/s^2 is $(k - 3t)$, where k is a constant and t is the time in seconds from the start of the motion. Show that $k = 15$.

(i) Calculate the maximum speed of the particle during its motion from A to B.

(ii) Calculate the length of AB.

(iii) Calculate the distance travelled by the particle while its acceleration is positive.

(iv) Sketch a graph showing the relation between acceleration and time for $0 \leqslant t \leqslant 10$.

(v) Sketch a graph showing the relation between velocity and time for $0 \leqslant t \leqslant 10$.

                               [JMB]

16. A mass of 3 kg has position vector $\mathbf{r} = (3t^2 + 2t)\mathbf{i} - 4t^2\mathbf{j}$, where r is measured in metres and t is the time in seconds.

Find its velocity and acceleration vectors in terms of t.

Show that it is subject to a force of magnitude 30 N, and find the direction of the force.

                               [SMP]

17. Two particles A and B are moving in horizontal straight lines in the plane of the co-ordinate axes Ox and Oy, the units of distance and time being the metre and the second respectively. At time t seconds, A has position vector $t^2\mathbf{i} + 2\mathbf{j}$ and B has position vector $t(3\mathbf{i} - 4\mathbf{j})$.

(a) Calculate the distance between A and B when $t = 3$.

(b) Show that the velocity of B is constant and calculate its magnitude and direction.

(c) Calculate the acceleration of A.

(d) Find the magnitude and the direction of the velocity of B relative to A when $t = 2$.

                               [UL]

18. An object has initial velocity vector $\mathbf{u} = 24\mathbf{i} + 40\mathbf{j}$, and is subject to a constant acceleration vector $\mathbf{a} = 2\mathbf{i} - 10\mathbf{j}$, where $\mathbf{i}$ and $\mathbf{j}$ are unit vectors in the Ox and Oy directions respectively.

Find the velocity vector $\mathbf{v}$ of the object after (a) 2 seconds, (b) t second.

In what direction, with respect to the positive Ox direction, is the object initially moving?

At what times will the object be moving in a direction which is at $45°$ on either side of the positive Ox axis? At what time will the object be moving at right angles to its initial direction of motion?   [MEI]

19. Wonderwoman leaps from a skyscraper. Until she lands her velocity t seconds after she leaps is given in m/s by: $\mathbf{v} = 30\mathbf{i} + (20 - 10t)\mathbf{j}$. The origin is at the base of the building and the axes are horizontal and vertical.

(a) Find the speed with which she leaps.

(b) State the acceleration at time t and what this suggests about her powers of levitation.

(c) She lands on level ground 7 seconds after she leaps. Give her displacement at time t and the height from which she leaps.

                               cont.

(d) Show that she rises 20 metres before starting to descend.

(e) Calculate how far from the building she lands and the angle at which she hits the ground.

[SMP]

20. A particle P has a velocity at time t seconds represented by the vector $\begin{pmatrix} 2t \\ 3 \\ t^2 \end{pmatrix}$, where the units are in m s^{-1}.

If it starts from the point $(0, 0, 2)$, find, giving your answers as vectors,

(i) its position vector when $t = 1$;
(ii) its velocity when $t = 2$;
(iii) its acceleration when $t = 3$;
(iv) the change in acceleration between $t = 3$ and $t = 4$.

[O & C]

21. The acceleration of a particle P is constant and is represented by the vector $\begin{pmatrix} -10 \\ 0 \end{pmatrix}$, where the units are m s^{-2}. If, when $t = 0$, its velocity in m s^{-1} is represented by $\begin{pmatrix} 2 \\ 3 \end{pmatrix}$ and its position vector is $\begin{pmatrix} 0 \\ 5 \end{pmatrix}$, calculate its velocity and position vectors at time t. Deduce the greatest value of the x coordinate of the particle in the ensuing motion, and calculate the coordinates of the point where it crosses the y-axis again.

What angle does the direction of motion make with the x-axis when $t = 1$?

[O & C]

22. A charged particle, of mass 5×10^{-6} kg, is moving across a rectangular grid of centimetre squares under a constant force of $\begin{pmatrix} 10^{-5} \\ -10^{-5} \end{pmatrix}$ newtons maintained by deflector plates. It is observed at the point $(3, 3)$ to be travelling with velocity $\begin{pmatrix} -1 \\ 2 \end{pmatrix}$ m/s. What is its velocity t seconds later?

Show that it passes through the point $(9, 0)$, and state the value of t for which this occurs.

[SMP]

23. A block of mass 1.5 kg rests on a smooth horizontal surface. Horizontal forces represented by the vectors $\begin{pmatrix} 2 \\ 4 \end{pmatrix}$, $\begin{pmatrix} -1 \\ 7 \end{pmatrix}$ and $\begin{pmatrix} 5 \\ y \end{pmatrix}$ act on the block (the units are in newtons). Under the action of these forces the block moves parallel to the x-axis. Find y and hence calculate the acceleration of the block.

If a further force $\begin{pmatrix} 3 + 3t \\ 4.5t \end{pmatrix}$, which varies with time t seconds, also acts on the block as well as the previous forces, find the acceleration of the block, giving the answer in vector form in terms of t.

If the block starts from rest at the origin, find the position vector of the block after one second.

[O & C]

24. A stone is thrown with velocity $\begin{pmatrix} 10 \\ 20 \end{pmatrix}$ m/s from the top of a 300 m cliff. [The x-axis is taken horizontally outwards from the cliff, and the y-axis vertically upwards.]

Calculate its velocity and position 3 seconds later, and indicate your results clearly on a sketch.

[Take $g = 9.8$.]

[SMP]

25. A golf ball landed at a distance of 75 m from where it was struck, at the same horizontal level. The greatest height reached by the ball in its flight was 5 m. Calculate the horizontal and vertical components of the velocity with which the ball left the club head.

[AEB 1981]

26. A stone was thrown up at 60° from the horizontal at a building 36 metres away and broke a window 3 seconds later.

(a) State the initial horizontal speed and show that the initial vertical speed was approximately 20.8 m/s.

(b) Calculate the height of the window above the point from which the stone was thrown. (Take g to be 10.)

(c) State with reason whether the stone was rising or falling when it hit the window.

[SMP]

27. A ball is thrown with velocity 20 m/s at an angle of 60° to the horizontal. The gravitational attraction of the earth gives the ball a constant acceleration of 9.8 m/s² vertically downward. All other forces are negligible. Find by drawing or by calculation

(a) its speed after 2 seconds,

(b) its displacement after 3 seconds,

(c) the direction in which it is travelling after 4 seconds,

(d) when it is travelling horizontally.

[SMP]

28.   A particle is projected with speed V m/s from a point on a horizontal plane and moves freely under gravity. Show that, for the maximum horizontal range R m, the angle of projection is 45° with the horizontal. Find R in terms of V and g.

A shell is fired from a gun with angle of elevation α and initial speed V m/s and moves freely under gravity. The shell passes through a point whose horizontal and vertical distances from the point of projection are $R/2$ m and $R/4$ m respectively. Show that one possible value of $\tan \alpha$ is 3, and find the other possible value of $\tan \alpha$.

[UL]

29.   Figure 12.16 shows the trajectory of a body projected with a velocity of $14\,\mathrm{m\,s^{-1}}$, inclined at 30° to the horizontal, from a point A on a hillside.

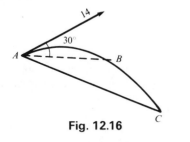

Fig. 12.16

(i)   Find the time taken to reach the point B, which is on the same level as A.

(ii)   If the body is in the air for a total of 2 s before reaching the ground at C, find the vertical depth of C below A.

(iii)   Find the vertical component of the velocity when the body is at C.

[O & C]

30.   A ball is projected upwards at an angle of 60° to the horizontal from the top of a vertical cliff. After 8 seconds the ball strikes the

sea at a horizontal distance of 120 metres from the point of projection. Calculate

(i)   the speed of projection,

(ii)   the vertical height to which the ball rises above the cliff top,

(iii)   the time taken by the ball to reach its greatest height,

(iv)   the height of the cliff above sea-level.

[AEB 1979]

31.   A ball is projected from a height of 0.9 m above the ground, presumed level, with a velocity of $25\,\mathrm{m\,s^{-1}}$ at an angle θ to the horizontal, where $\tan \theta = \frac{7}{24}$. Find at what times after projection the ball reaches a height of 3 m above the ground.

If the ball is caught by a fieldsman 32 m horizontally from the point of projection, at what height above the ground does he make the catch?

[O & C]

32.   A small stone of mass 125 g is attached to one end of a light inextensible string, $1\frac{1}{2}$ m in length. The other end of the string is fixed at a point on the surface of a smooth horizontal table. The stone travels in a circle on the table at a constant speed of 12 m/s with the string taut. Calculate the tension in the string.

If the string would break were the tension to exceed $33\frac{1}{3}$ N, calculate the maximum possible speed of the stone.

[AEB 1980]

33.   A particle of mass 600 g is attached to one end of a light inextensible string of length 150 cm. The other end of the string is attached to a fixed point O at a vertical height of 75 cm above a smooth horizontal table. With the string taut, the particle moves steadily on the table, describing a circle with its centre at the point vertically below O. The speed of the particle in the circle is 3 m/s. Calculate

(a)   the tension in the string,

(b)   the force exerted on the table by the particle.

[AEB 1982]

34. A is travelling with velocity $\begin{pmatrix} 2 \\ -4 \end{pmatrix}$ m/s and B with velocity $\begin{pmatrix} 7 \\ 5 \end{pmatrix}$ m/s. Calculate the velocity and the speed with which B is approaching A.   *cont.*

When A is at the point $(9, 10)$, B is at the point $(-3, 1)$. Show that they will never meet.

[SMP]

35. A ship Y is 6 km due south of another ship X. Ship X is steaming due east at 15 km/h and ship Y is steaming due north at 10 km/h. Find graphically

(i) the magnitude and direction of the velocity of X relative to Y,

(ii) the period of time during which X is visible from Y, if the maximum visibility is $5\frac{1}{2}$ km.

[AEB 1981]

36. A bee which flies through the air at 6 m/s is aiming to reach a tree 600 m due South of the hive. It happens that the sun is also due South, so the bee wishes to move directly towards the sun; but there is a wind blowing in the direction 052° (that is, approximately from the South-West) at 2.5 m/s.

Sketch a triangle of velocities, showing the resultant velocity of the bee in the direction due South, and mark the known values on your diagram.

By calculation using the sine rule, show that the bee must aim in a direction 19.2° to the right of the sun.

Calculate how long the bee will take to reach the tree.

[SMP]

37. On a windy day, rain is falling at 7 m/s at an angle of 28° from the vertical, and I am walking along a horizontal road at 1.8 m/s straight into the rain.

Show, by scale drawing or calculation, that if the rain is to land directly onto my umbrella then I must hold it at an angle of about 39.5° from the vertical. Find the speed at which the rain is then striking the umbrella.

Find also at what speed I must walk straight away from the rain so that the best way to hold the umbrella is straight up (that is, so that the rain's velocity relative to me is vertically downwards).

[SMP]

38. Two men, each of whom is in a rowing boat and rows at a speed of 1.6 m/s through the water, are to cross to the far bank of a straight stretch of river, 48 m wide, which flows at 1.2 m/s. They start from the same point at the same time. One, by heading sufficiently upstream, travels straight across the river to a point A immediately opposite their starting point. The other heads straight across the current and so lands downstream, at B.

Show, by calculation that the first takes about 45 seconds to cross to A, and calculate how far downstream the second lands (i.e. the distance AB).

The second now immediately runs up the far bank from B to A and reaches A just as his companion is landing. Calculate his running speed.

[SMP]

39. A man wishes to cross a river, travelling as directly across as possible, in a motorboat which travels at a steady speed of 4 m/s. By calculation or drawing,

(a) find at what angle to the bank, to the nearest degree, he should head if the tide is flowing at 3 m/s;

(b) show, with reasons, that if the tide is flowing at 5 m/s the best he can do is to head at an angle of about 37° to the bank.

Verify that it will take him about 10% · longer to cross in case (b) than in case (a), and calculate how many metres downstream he will land if the banks are 1.2 km apart.

[SMP]

40. At a given instant, two ships S and T are 10 km apart, with T south west of S. Ship T is steaming at 20 km/h on a course of 290°, while S is steaming due west at 15 km/h. Assuming that the ships continue to steam at these speeds and on these courses, find *graphically*

(a) the magnitude and direction of the velocity of T relative to S,

(b) the distance between the two ships when they are closest together.

Instead of steaming on a course of 290°, the captain of T decides to change course immediately in order to intercept S, whose speed and course are unaltered. Assuming that T continues to steam steadily at the same speed as before, up to the instant at which it meets S, find *graphically*

(c) the new course (assumed constant) on which T must steam,

(d) the time which has elapsed when the ships meet.

[AEB 1982]

41. A yacht in distress is drifting at 10 km/h on a course 30° West of North and is 20 km due East of a lifeboat whose maximum speed through the water is 40 km/h.

(i) Show that the bearing on which the lifeboat must travel in order to reach the yacht as soon as possible is $\alpha°$ East of North where $\cos \alpha = \dfrac{\sqrt{3}}{8}$.

(ii) Calculate the speed of the lifeboat relative to the yacht.

(iii) Calculate the time taken for the lifeboat to reach the yacht, giving your answer correct to the nearest minute.

[JMB]

EXERCISE 13X

1. The following table shows the distribution by size and by colour of a batch of 500 dresses of similar design.

COLOR	SIZE			
	12	*14*	*16*	*18*
Green	23	45	39	23
Blue	49	102	73	56
Pink	18	23	28	21

A dress is selected at random from the batch. Determine the probability that it is

(a) blue,
(b) either size *12* or size *16*.

If two dresses are selected at random, without replacement, *from the 100 size 18 dresses*, determine the probability that

(c) both are blue,
(d) one is green and one is pink.

[AEB 1983]

2. Five cards are numbered 1 to 5 respectively. Two cards are to be drawn at random without replacement. Make a list of the possible outcomes.

Find the probability that

(i) the sum of the numbers drawn will be less than 6,

(ii) the larger of the numbers drawn will be 3,

(iii) neither of the cards numbered 1 and 5 will be drawn.

Let A denote the event 'the number 1 is drawn' and let B denote the event 'the number 5 is drawn'. Find the values of $P(A \cap B)$, $P(A \cup B)$ and $P(A \mid B)$.

[AEB 1981]

3. Four men agree to meet at the *King's Head* public house in a certain town, not realizing that there are four public houses with this name in the town. If each man selects at random which *King's Head* he goes to, what is the probability that

(a) the four men all go to the same *King's Head*;

(b) the four men each go to a different *King's Head*;

(c) no man finds himself at a *King's Head* on his own?

[MEI]

4. Two unbiased six-sided dice are thrown. The greater of the numbers showing (or either if they are the same) is recorded as the score for that throw. Calculate the probability of a score of

(i) 1,
(ii) 2,
(iii) 6,
(iv) 2, followed by a score of 6 on the next throw.

[AEB 1980]

5. What is the probability of scoring a total of 4 when two dice are thrown? What is the probability that a total of 4 will be scored on each of two successive throws of two dice?

Two dice are thrown and the total scored is recorded. The two dice are thrown again. What is the probability that the second throw will give the same total score as the first throw?

[MEI]

6. Two people each choose a number at random *between* 0 and 10. Call these numbers x and y.

(a) If x and y are *whole* numbers, what is the probability that $x + y \leqslant 5$? *cont.*

(b) If x and y are any real numbers, we can model the situation by sticking a pin at random in the square $(0, 0)$, $(10, 0)$, $(10, 10)$, $(0, 10)$ and taking (x, y) as the co-ordinates of the pin-point. The probability of sticking a pin in any region may be taken to be proportional to the area of that region. What is now the probability that $x + y \leqslant 5$? What is the probability that $x^2 + y^2 \leqslant 25$?

What is the probability that $x + y > 5$ and also $x^2 + y^2 \leqslant 25$?

[SMP]

7. A bag contains just five balls numbered 1, 2, 3, 4 and 5. In a certain game a player's turn consists of drawing balls from the bag one at a time with replacement. Whenever the player draws the ball numbered 5, it is replaced in the bag and he draws another ball. The player's turn ends when he draws one of the balls numbered 1, 2, 3 or 4. The player is given a score equal to the sum of the numbers on all the balls drawn during his turn.

(a) Find the probability that, in one turn, a player will score
   (i) 4.   (ii) 8,   (iii) 25,   (iv) 26.

(b) Find the probability that, in one turn, a player will make exactly
   (i) two draws from the bag,   (ii) three draws from the bag.

(c) Find an expression for the probability that, in one turn, a player will make more than n draws from the bag.

[UL]

8. A biassed coin is such that in one throw the probability of Heads is p and the probability of Tails is $1 - p$. Draw a tree diagram for two throws of the coin.

If the probability of obtaining exactly one Head in two throws is 0.32, show that p must satisfy the equation $25p^2 - 25p + 4 = 0$.

Solve this equation to find p.

[SMP]

9. The probability of a fine day being followed by a fine day is $\frac{2}{3}$, and the probability of a wet day being followed by a wet day is $\frac{1}{2}$ (you may assume that any day is either wet or fine). If a certain Monday is fine, find by drawing a tree-diagram, or otherwise, whether the chance of fine weather is better if a picnic is arranged for   (a) Wednesday, or
(b) Thursday, of the same week.

Find also the probability that both Wednesday and Thursday will be fine.

[O & C]

10. If I roll a red die followed by a green die, what is the probability that the red die will have an even number on it?

(i) (a) Give the probability that my total score will be 9.

   (b) If the red die does come up with an even number, show, by enumerating all the possible situations, that I am no less likely to get a final total of 9.

   (c) If my total score turns out to be 9, find the probability that the red die came up with an even number.

(ii) Answer the same three questions as for part (i), but for a total of 8 instead of 9.

Hence confirm that scoring 9 is independent of whether the red score is even or odd (i.e. the probability of scoring 9 is unaltered), but that scoring 8 is not.

[SMP]

11. John and Peter each have two pennies. John tosses each of his coins once and gives to Peter those which fall heads. Peter now tosses once each of the coins in his possession, giving to John those which fall heads. Using a probability tree, or otherwise, determine the probability that:

(a) Peter now has all the coins.

(b) John now has all the coins.

(c) John and Peter each now have two coins.

[MEI]

12. In a game each player in turn throws two fair dice and scores the sum of the numbers uppermost. Every time a player throws a double (obtaining the same number on each die), he has a further throw of the two dice and adds the sum of the new numbers uppermost to his previous score. If his second throw is also a double, he keeps throwing until he fails to throw a double and his total score is increased accordingly. Find, to three significant figures, the probability that a player in one turn scores a final total of exactly

(i) 4,   (ii) 6,   (iii) 8.

[AEB 1981]

13. A bag contains 5 white balls and 4 red balls. One ball is chosen at random from the bag and hidden.

(a) Find the probability that the hidden ball is red.

(b) A second ball is chosen at random from the eight remaining in the bag. This second ball is red. In the light of this extra information, find now the probability that the hidden ball is red.

(c) The second ball chosen is replaced. A further ball is now chosen at random from the eight in the bag. This ball is also red. Find now the probability that the hidden ball is red.

[UL]

14.   On average I get up early three days out of ten and get up late one day in ten. I forget something on two out of every five days on which I am late and on one-third of the days when I am early. I do not forget anything on the days when I get up on time. Draw a tree diagram showing all this information.

  (i) State the probability that I am:
   (a) early and forgetful;
   (b) late and forgetful;
   (c) punctual and forgetful.

 (ii) Hence calculate:
   (a) the probability of my not forgetting anything;
   (b) the probability that, if I have forgotten something, I got up late.

(iii) Nevertheless confirm that for 80 per cent of the time I am neither forgetful nor late.

[SMP]

15.   Three independent tests are carried out to test for the presence of a particular virus infection in an animal. Test A has a probability of $\frac{2}{3}$ of proving positive if the virus is present, and a probability of $\frac{1}{6}$ of proving positive if the virus is not present. The equivalent probabilities for tests B and C are as set out in the table.

	Virus present	Virus not present
Test B positive	$\frac{4}{5}$	$\frac{1}{8}$
Test C positive	$\frac{3}{4}$	$\frac{1}{5}$

The tests are carried out in the order A, B, C.

What is the probability that two tests will prove positive and one test negative on an infected animal?

A minimum of two positive tests is taken as a criterion for deducing the presence of the virus.

Using tree diagrams or otherwise, find the probability that

(a) the criterion will not be satisfied after all three tests have been carried out on an infected animal;

(b) the criterion will be satisfied after all three tests have been carried out on an uninfected animal.

(Give your answers as exact fractions reduced to their lowest terms.)

[MEI]

16.   The probability that a colony of bees will survive a particularly hard winter is 0.35. If I have four colonies what is the probability that exactly one of these colonies will survive? I have a friend who has twice as many colonies (eight). Write down an expression for the probability that exactly one of his colonies will survive. Is the probability greater or less than in my case?

[SMP]

17.   In a large batch of eggs, one in ten is found to be bad. What is the probability that in twelve eggs there will be

  (i) no bad egg?
 (ii) exactly one bad egg?
(iii) more than one bad egg?

(Give your answers correct to 3 significant figures.)

[O & C]

18.   Given that 10% of a population is left-handed and that five people are selected at random,

  (i) show that the probability that none of the five is left-handed is 0.590 49,

 (ii) show that the probability that two and only two of the five are left-handed is less than 0.08,

(iii) find, correct to three places of decimals, the probability that no more than two of the five are left-handed.

[AEB 1980]

19.   In a large batch of manufactured drinking glasses, 25% are considered to be substandard and are labelled 'seconds'.

Find the probability that a random sample of 4 glasses drawn from the batch contains

(a) not more than one 'second',

(b) exactly two 'seconds'.   *cont.*

A wholesaler will accept a batch if either
(i) a sample of 4 glasses contains not more
than one 'second', or (ii) a first sample
contains exactly two 'seconds' but a further
sample of 4 glasses contains no 'seconds'. Calculate the probability that the wholesaler will
accept a batch.

(Give all your answers correct to 3 significant
figures.)

[MEI]

20. When a Molaris Missile is fired the
probability that it will detonate is 0.8.

(i) If four are fired, give the probability that
the number that detonate is (a) more than
3, (b) exactly 3, (c) at least 3.

(ii) What would these three probabilities be if
one of the four fired is in fact a Canine Missile
whose probability of detonation is only 0.4?

(iii) State how many Molaris Missiles must be
fired to be sure of a detonation with
certainty (a) 99%, (b) 100%.

[SMP]

21. A laboratory uses mice for experimental
purposes. The mice are either black or white,
and are selected at random from a large number of mice of which twice as many are white
as are black.

If four mice are selected at random for a certain experiment, what is the probability that
they are all white?

If five mice are selected at random, what is the
probability that the selection will contain more
white mice than black mice?

If six mice are selected at random, what is the
probability that at least two of the mice will be
white?

[MEI]

22. A team of ten children representing a
junior school is found to contain 3 boys and 7
girls, and it is suggested that this is evidence
that girls are more likely to be chosen.

Assuming that boys and girls are equally likely
to be chosen:

(a) show that the probability that a party of
ten will contain exactly 3 boys is approximately 0.117;

(b) calculate the probability that a party of ten
will contain 3 or fewer boys.

Use your answers to comment on the sugges-
tion in the first paragraph.

[SMP]

23. The probability that one particular
player out of three obtains the 'best' hand
when cards are dealt for a game is $\frac{1}{3}$. If six
games are played, what is the probability that
he will obtain the 'best' hand less than three
times?

If this player is dealt the 'best' hand, the
probability that he wins that game is $\frac{3}{5}$. What
is the probability that he is dealt the 'best'
hand and wins? What is the probability that in
exactly three games out of six he is both dealt
the 'best' hand and wins? What is the probability that in at least two games out of three
he is both dealt the 'best' hand and loses?

[MEI]

24. At one packing station it is found that
20% of the eggs are brown rather than white
and that 30% are large, the rest being standard. Size and colour are independent.

(i) Give the probability of an egg being
(a) large and white, (b) standard or brown.

(ii) They are sorted by size, but not colour,
and put in boxes of six eggs.
 (a) Show that the probability that a box of
   standard eggs will contain no brown ones
   is about 0.26.
 (b) Find the probability that a box of large
   eggs will contain some brown ones.

(iii) They are finally dispatched in packets of
ten boxes of the same-sized eggs.
 (a) Find the probability that a packet of
   boxes of standard eggs will contain exactly four boxes without any brown eggs.
 (b) Show that about half the packets of boxes
   of large eggs contain at least eight boxes
   with some brown eggs.

[SMP]

25. A company has ten telephone lines. At
any instant the probability that any particular
line is engaged is 1/5. State the expected
number of free telephone lines. Calculate for
any instant, correct to two significant figures,
the probability that

(i) all the lines are engaged,
(ii) at least one line is free,
(iii) exactly two lines are free.

[AEB 1980]

26. In a multiple-choice test there are 30

questions. For each question a candidate must choose one of five responses *A*, *B*, *C*, *D* or *E*, only one of which is correct. An ill-prepared candidate decides to answer all the questions at random.

Given that one mark is awarded for a correct answer and zero for an incorrect answer, state the candidate's expected score.

If P(*r*) denotes the probability that the candidate scores *r* marks, show that

(i) P(0) is approximately 0.0012,

(ii) $P(1) = \dfrac{30}{4} \times P(0)$,

(iii) $P(2) = \dfrac{29}{8} \times P(1)$.

Obtain P(3) in terms of P(2) and show that the candidate's most probable score is 6.

[AEB 1981]

27. A man is being taken for a walk by his dog. His house is at the corner *D* of a square *ABCD* of side 100 m. On leaving the house, the dog is equally likely to go along *DA* or *DC*. When they reach a corner, the probability that the dog continues round the square is $\frac{2}{3}$, and the probability that the dog turns back is $\frac{1}{3}$. Once the dog has turned back, they go home without any further reversal of direction. The walk stops when they reach the house again.

(a) Calculate the probability that they will go as far as *A* and then turn back.

(b) Calculate the expected length of the walk.

[UL]

28. A series of prototype aeroplanes is to be developed by an aircraft company. Prototypes are to be made until one satisfies the design and operational specifications, but if after four prototypes are made none has proved satisfactory then the project is to be abandoned. At each stage in the programme the probability of producing a satisfactory prototype is estimated to be 0.6. The initial cost of the first prototype is estimated to be £30 million, and each subsequent prototype if necessary is estimated to cost £20 million. A successful prototype is estimated to be worth £120 million. What is the expected profit to the aircraft company?

(Give your answer to 3 significant figures.)

[MEI]

29. A certain gambling machine costs 5 p to play. The machine pays out 20 p if more than four balls out of a total of six come to rest in their correct positions. The independent probabilities of balls coming to rest in their correct positions are each 0.6.

What is the probability of the machine paying out on any particular play of the machine? Give your answer to 3 significant figures.

What is the expected profit which will be made by the machine after it has been played one hundred times? Give your answer to the nearest penny.

[MEI]

30. To investigate whether a person has a certain disease, two tests *A* and *B* are used independently. The result of each test is either positive or negative. For a person who has the disease, the probability that test *A* gives a positive result is $\frac{3}{4}$, and the probability that test *B* gives a positive result is $\frac{2}{3}$.

The procedure is to give test *A*, then test *B*. If both tests are positive, presence of the disease is diagnosed. If both tests are negative, absence of the disease is diagnosed. If one test is positive and the other is negative, the diagnosis is decided by applying test *A* again. A positive or negative result in this third test is taken to indicate presence or absence of the disease respectively.

(a) Leaving your answer as a fraction, find the probability that the diagnosis is 'absence of disease' when the person has the disease.

(b) Test *A* costs £21 and test *B* costs £15. Find the expected cost of applying this testing procedure to a person who has the disease.

[UL]

31. A traditional game played between two players requires each, at the same time, to show either one or two fingers. Bill and Ben agree to the following stakes before they start to play. If they both show two fingers or if they both show one finger, then Ben will pay Bill 2 p. If Bill shows one finger and Ben shows two fingers, then Bill will pay Ben 3 p. If Bill shows two fingers and Ben shows one finger, then Bill will pay Ben 1 p. If both players are equally likely to show either one or two fingers, explain carefully why, in the long run, neither player can expect to make a profit.

Ben continues to be equally likely   *cont.*

to show either one or two fingers. How should Bill play to hope to make the most profit, and what would he expect his profit to be after 20 games?

If Ben realises Bill's plan, and Bill continues to play according to his plan, what should Ben do to counter it? In a further 20 games who would now hope to make a profit, and what would he expect his profit to be?

[MEI]

32.

	$Y = 0$	$Y = 1$	$Y = 2$
$X = 1$	$\dfrac{1}{12}$	$\dfrac{1}{6}$	$\dfrac{1}{12}$
$X = 2$	$\dfrac{1}{6}$	$\dfrac{1}{3}$	$\dfrac{1}{6}$

The above table gives the joint probability distribution of two random variables X and Y. Calculate

(a) $P(Y = 1)$,
(b) $P(XY = 2)$,
(c) $E(X+Y)$.

[UL]

33. A concert pianist has prepared seven different pieces of music for a recital, three of which are modern and four are classical. Calculate the number of different orders in which she can play the seven pieces when

(a) there are no restrictions,

(b) the recital must start and end with classical pieces,

(c) classical and modern pieces must alternate throughout the recital.

[AEB 1982]

34. A club contains 12 boys and 8 girls. A committee of 3 is to be chosen. In how many ways can the committee be chosen if:

 (i) it is to contain 2 boys and 1 girl;
 (ii) it is to contain 2 girls and 1 boy;
(iii) it is to contain at least 1 girl and 1 boy?

[MEI]

35. (i) Find how many arrangements can be made using all the letters of the word ANAGRAM. In how many of these will no two consonants be adjacent?

(ii) How many different doubles matches are possible if five players A, B, C, D, E meet at a tennis club and draw lots to decide both

(a) who shall sit out, and

(b) how the other four shall split into two pairs?

[O & C]

36. Six men enter a room in which eight chairs are arranged in a straight line. If the men take seats at random, in how many different ways may they be seated?

Calculate the probability that two particular men will be seated in adjoining chairs.

[MEI]

37. In a game of poker a hand of five cards is to be dealt at random to a player from a normal pack of 52 cards.

(a) Show that the probability that the player will receive a hand containing all black cards is $\dfrac{_{26}C_5}{_{52}C_5}$.

Leaving your answers in a similar form, calculate the probability that the player will receive a hand containing

(b) exactly four black cards,

(c) all four aces,

(d) exactly three kings.

[UL]

38. An art gallery is offered a choice of 6 pictures by artist A, 7 by artist B and 8 by artist C. It is decided to exhibit 12 of these pictures including exactly 3 of the pictures by A. Find the number of different selections which are possible given that the exhibition must also include

 (i) exactly 5 of the pictures by B,
 (ii) at least 5 of the pictures by B.

A definite selection of 3 by A, 5 by B and 4 by C is made and these 12 pictures are displayed in the gallery.

(iii) A man then visits the exhibition to buy 7 of these 12 pictures. Find the number of different selections available to him.

(iv) After some thought, the man decides to limit his choice to any 2 of the exhibited pictures by A, any 2 by B and any 3 by C. Find the number of different selections which are now possible.

(v) After the man has chosen 2 pictures by A, 2 by B and 3 by C, his wife decides to arrange them in a line on one wall of their home so that the pictures by C occupy the second, fourth and sixth positions in the line. Find the number of different arrangements which are possible.

[JMB]

EXERCISE 14X

1. A hot-air balloon is rising vertically with an acceleration of $0.2\,\mathrm{m\,s^{-2}}$. A man, mass $80\,\mathrm{kg}$, stands in the cage of the balloon carrying in his hand a telescope which, to him, appears to weigh $15\,\mathrm{N}$. Calculate the force that the floor of the cage exerts on the man, and the mass of the telescope.

[MEI]

2. A tug is towing two barges along a canal and slowing down at $0.015\,\mathrm{m/s^2}$. The mass of each barge is 12 tonnes, and of the tug 8 tonnes.

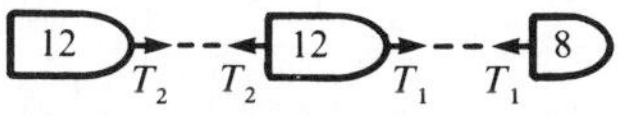

$$\boxed{12}\!\!\succ\!\cdots\!\prec\!\boxed{12}\!\!\succ\!\cdots\!\prec\!\boxed{8}$$
$$\quad\; T_2 \quad T_2 \qquad\quad T_1 \quad T_1$$

Fig. 14.19

Each of the barges and the tug experiences the same resistance from the water, R, and the engines give a forward force of $120\,\mathrm{N}$ on the tug.

Show that the tension T_1 in the first cable is double the tension T_2 in the second cable.

Calculate the values of T_1 and R.

[SMP]

3. A heavy goods lorry mass 9 tonnes tows a trailer mass 6 tonnes. Assuming that the total resistance to the lorry is $8000\,\mathrm{N}$, and to the trailer is $2000\,\mathrm{N}$, calculate what force must be produced by the engine of the lorry to produce a constant acceleration taking the lorry and trailer from rest to a speed of $10\,\mathrm{m\,s^{-1}}$ on a horizontal road in 15 seconds. What will be the tension in the tow-bar while the lorry and trailer are accelerating? Assuming that the resistances to the lorry and the trailer are as before, what will be the retardation of the lorry and the trailer and what will be the thrust in the tow-bar if the engine is now put out of gear?

[MEI]

4. A motor-boat tows a water-skier by means of a horizontal, inextensible rope. When the boat and the skier are moving with a constant velocity the engine of the boat is producing a forward force of $60\,\mathrm{N}$. The mass of the motor-boat and its occupant is $500\,\mathrm{kg}$, and that of the skier $80\,\mathrm{kg}$. What is the total resistance to motion on the boat and the skier?

If these resistances are assumed to remain constant, and are divided between the boat and the skier in the ratio $5:1$ respectively, calculate the acceleration of the boat and the skier and the tension in the rope when the forward force provided by the engine of the boat is increased to $1800\,\mathrm{N}$.

If the rope suddenly snaps, by how much will the acceleration of the boat increase?

[MEI]

5. A 2-tonne car, towing a caravan of mass 0.8 tonne, starts from rest along a level road. The tractive force of the car is kept at $6000\,\mathrm{N}$ and the total resistances to motion on each object may be taken to be $150\,\mathrm{N/tonne}$.

(a) By considering the combined mass of 2.8 tonne, calculate the car's acceleration.

(b) Hence, by considering just the caravan, show that the tension in the coupling is about $1700\,\mathrm{N}$.

The car now starts to climb a hill of slope $20°$. (Take $g = 9.8$.)

(c) Calculate the car's acceleration up the hill and confirm that it is losing speed.

(d) Calculate the tension in the coupling.

When the car stops on the hill the driver puts on the car's brakes only and parks where it stopped.

(e) Calculate the tension in the coupling.

(f) If in fact the coupling would only stand a force of $2500\,\mathrm{N}$, find when it would break.

[SMP]

6. Figure 14.20 shows the cross-section of a wedge of mass $5\,\mathrm{kg}$ whose surfaces are smooth, and on which is placed a mass of $5\,\mathrm{kg}$. *cont.*

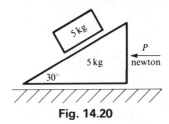

Fig. 14.20

The wedge itself is resting on a smooth horizontal surface.

The wedge is held still by a horizontal force *P* newton, and the mass is released from rest. Draw a diagram which clearly shows the forces acting on the mass, and calculate its acceleration down the slope.

Draw a second diagram which clearly shows the forces acting on the wedge, and hence calculate the magnitude of *P*.

[MEI]

7.   Masses of 1 kg and 2 kg are attached to the ends of a long light string which passes over a light pulley supported by a frictionless horizontal axis. If the tension in the string is *T* newtons, write down the equation of motion of each mass, and hence find

(i)   the tension in the string,
(ii) the time taken for the heavier mass to fall from rest a distance of 1.5 m.

[O & C]

8.   A small block *A* of mass 1.1 kg rests on a smooth horizontal table. It is attached by a light string passing over a smooth pulley at *P* to another small block *B* of mass 0.5 kg which hangs freely over the edge of the table, as shown in figure 14.21. Write down an equation of motion for each of the blocks *A* and *B*, denoting the tension in the string by *T*, and the acceleration of the block *A* towards the edge of the table by *a*. Deduce the values of *T* and *a*.

What mass would have to be added to the block *B* in order to double the acceleration?

[O & C]

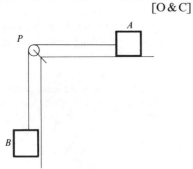

Fig. 14.21

9.   Figure 14.22 shows a light inextensible string *ABCDE*, with *AB = DE* and *BC = CD*. The ends *A* and *E* of the string are

fixed at the same horizontal level. A particle of mass 200 g is suspended from *C* and particles each of mass 50 g are suspended from *B* and *D*. In the position of equilibrium the string hangs symmetrically, with *BC* and *CD* each making an angle of 30° with the horizontal, while *AB* and *DE* each make an angle *θ* with the horizontal.

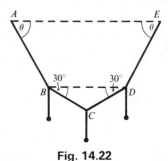

Fig. 14.22

Calculate

(a) the tension in *BC*, in newtons,
(b) the angle *θ*.

[AEB 1982]

10.   A particle of mass 0.1 kg rests on a rough horizontal plane. A force of 0.8 N acts horizontally on the particle and after 2 seconds the particle has a velocity of 8 m s⁻¹. Find the acceleration of the particle and the coefficient of friction.

The same horizontal force would just support the particle on a smooth plane inclined at an angle *x*° to the horizontal. Find *x*.

[O & C]

11.   A body of mass 2 kg rests on a rough horizontal plane and the coefficient of friction between the body and the plane is $\frac{1}{4}$. A horizontal force of 18 N is applied to the body for 4 s and is then removed. Calculate

(i)   the initial acceleration of the body,
(ii)   the speed acquired by the body in the first 4 s of its motion,
(iii) the retardation of the body after the horizontal force has ceased to act,
(iv)   the total distance travelled by the body.

[AEB 1979]

12.   A small box of mass 1 kg slides down a rough plane inclined at 40° to the horizontal with an acceleration of 2 m s⁻². Calculate the coefficient of friction.

What is the smallest force normal to the plane which would need to be applied to the box to prevent the box slipping?

[O & C]

13. A body of mass 2 kg resting on a rough plane is on the point of slipping down the plane when this is inclined at 25° to the horizontal. What is the coefficient of friction between the body and the plane?

When the inclination of the plane is increased to 45°, an additional force is applied to the body in the direction of the line of greatest slope of the plane in order to prevent the body from sliding down. Find the least possible magnitude of this force in newtons.

[O & C]

14. Two particles of mass 0.2 kg and 0.3 kg are connected by a light inextensible string. The particle of mass 0.2 kg is held at rest on a rough horizontal table, the string passes over a smooth pulley at the edge of the table, and the 0.3 kg mass hangs vertically below the pulley. The particles are released and begin to move with an acceleration of 5 m/s². Calculate

(a) the tension in the string,

(b) the coefficient of friction between the 0.2 kg mass and the table.

[AEB 1983]

15. A particle P, of mass 0.2 kg, rests on a plane inclined at 30° to the horizontal, and the forces acting on P are shown in figure 14.23.

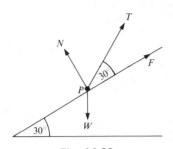

Fig. 14.23

They consist of

(i) W, the weight of P;

(ii) the normal reaction N between the plane and the particle;

(iii) the frictional force F;

(iv) the tension T in a string which is attached to P and which makes an angle of 30° with the line of greatest slope of the plane.

If the force F has a magnitude of 0.5 N, calculate

(a) the magnitude of T;

(b) the least possible value of the coefficient of friction between P and the plane.

[O & C]

16. A car, of mass 700 kg, travels on level ground along an arc of a circle of radius 28 m. Calculate the frictional force between the car and the road, acting towards the centre of the circle, when the car is travelling at 10 m/s.

If the coefficient of friction between the car and the road is 0.7, calculate the greatest speed at which the car can travel round this circle.

[AEB 1980]

17. A right circular cylinder of radius 50 cm rotates steadily at $\dfrac{5}{2\pi}$ revolutions per second about its axis, which is fixed in a vertical position. A particle of mass 2 kg is in contact with the inner surface of the cylinder, at rest relative to the cylinder but on the point of slipping down. Calculate the coefficient of friction between the particle and the cylinder wall.

[AEB 1981]

18. A railway engine of mass 5300 kg, moving on horizontal rails at 0.4 m/s, strikes the buffers in a siding and is brought to rest from this speed in 0.2 s. Calculate

(a) the impulse, in N s, of the force exerted by the buffers on the engine in bringing the engine to rest,

(b) the magnitude, in N, of this force, assuming it to be constant.

[UL]

19. A small ball of mass 500 g fell freely from a height of 1.25 m on to a horizontal floor and rose to a height of 0.2 m after the impact. The ball was in contact with the floor for 0.005 s. Calculate

(i) the speed, in m/s, with which the ball struck the floor,

(ii) the speed, in m/s, with which the ball rebounded from the floor,

(iii) the change in momentum of the ball caused by the impact, *cont.*

(iv) the mean force, in newtons, exerted by the floor on the ball.

[AEB 1981]

20. The police are firing a water cannon straight at a flat shield held vertically by a rioter. During a period of $10\,$s, the shield is struck by $300\,$kg of water moving horizontally at $25\,\mathrm{m\,s}^{-1}$. Assuming that the rioter stands his ground, and that the water does not rebound from the shield, calculate the water's total loss of horizontal momentum and hence the impulse between it and the shield. Deduce the force exerted by the water on the shield.

21. Two people, each with a suitcase of mass $20\,$kg, are standing on a stationary trolley which is free to run forwards on horizontal ground.

The total mass of the trolley and the people, not including the suitcase, is $180\,$kg.

(a) If one person throws his suitcase backwards with an impulse of $100\,$N-s, calculate the velocity given to the trolley. If the second person now throws his suitcase backwards with the same impulse, show that it will have a velocity of $4.5\,$m/s, and calculate the final velocity of the trolley.

(b) If, starting from rest, they throw their suitcases backwards simultaneously, each with an impulse of $100\,$N-s, calculate the subsequent velocity of the trolley.

[SMP]

22. A force P, magnitude $5\,$N, direction $090°$, acts on a mass of $2\,$kg initially at rest. What is the momentum of the mass after 6 seconds? Hence determine the velocity of the mass at that instant.

An *additional* force Q, magnitude $30\,$N, direction $180°$, acts on the mass during the next 4 seconds. What is the magnitude of the velocity of the mass at the end of the 10-second period?

[MEI]

23. A ball of mass $0.8\,$kg, travelling at $6\,$m/s, is struck by a bat so that it returns back the way it came at $2\,$m/s.

(i) Calculate the impulse applied to the ball by the bat.

(ii) If the same magnitude of impulse had been applied instead at right angles to the initial direction of travel of the ball, show that the

final speed of the ball would have been $10\,$m/s. Also calculate the angle through which the ball would have been deflected.

(iii) Calculate the direction in which an impulse of this same magnitude would have to be applied so as to deflect the ball through $90°$.

[SMP]

24. An electron, mass $9 \times 10^{-31}\,$kg, is moving with a velocity of $6 \times 10^{6}\,\mathrm{m\,s}^{-1}$. A force $2.4 \times 10^{-15}\,$N acts at right angles to the initial direction of motion of the electron for 3×10^{-9} seconds. Calculate the magnitude of the velocity of the electron at the end of this period of time, and the angle through which the direction of the velocity of the electron has turned.

If, instead, the electron is to have a final velocity unchanged in magnitude but at right angles to its original velocity, in what direction and for how long should the constant force of $2.4 \times 10^{-15}\,$N be applied?

[MEI]

25. A mass of $2\,$kg moving with velocity $\begin{pmatrix} 3 \\ 5 \end{pmatrix}\,$m/s collides and combines with a mass of $3\,$kg moving with velocity $\begin{pmatrix} 1 \\ -2 \end{pmatrix}\,$m/s.

Calculate the velocity of the single mass so formed.

Find also the impulse which each mass has received.

[SMP]

26. A car of mass 1 tonne, travelling at $100\,$km/h, strikes at right angles a lorry of mass 3 tonnes, travelling at $60\,$km/h and becomes embedded in the lorry. What is their common velocity immediately after impact?

[SMP]

27. The x and y axes lie in a given horizontal plane, and particles P and Q are projected in this plane from the points $(-4, -2)$ and $(0, -3)$ respectively. The particle P has constant velocity $\begin{pmatrix} 12 \\ 5 \end{pmatrix}$, and Q has constant velocity $\begin{pmatrix} 8 \\ 6 \end{pmatrix}$. Write down in vector form the equations of the paths described by P and Q, and determine the point of intersection of these paths.

If the particles are projected at the same instant, verify that they collide. Given that the masses of the particles are equal and that they stick together on contact, find the vector equation of the path followed by the combined particles after the impact.

[O & C]

28. A mass of 3 kg moving with velocity $\begin{pmatrix} 3 \\ 2 \\ -2 \end{pmatrix}$ m/s collides with a mass of 5 kg moving with velocity $\begin{pmatrix} -1 \\ 2 \\ 6 \end{pmatrix}$ m/s. After the collision they each have the same velocity. Find this velocity and also the impulse which each receives as a result of the collision.

[SMP]

29. A space capsule of mass 1050 kg is travelling at $400\,\mathrm{m\,s}^{-1}$ when a rocket of mass 50 kg is fired from the capsule forward at an angle of $39°$ with the direction of flight so that it has a speed of $500\,\mathrm{m\,s}^{-1}$, thereby reducing the mass of the capsule by 50 kg and changing the direction of its flight. By considering the conservation of momentum, calculate the new speed of the capsule after firing the rocket, and the change in the direction of its flight.

[O & C]

EXERCISE 15X

1. If $2x + 3y = 5$, express $x^2 + 3xy - 9y^2$ in terms of x, and simplify the result.

Solve the simultaneous equations

$$2x + 3y = 5$$

and

$$x^2 + 3xy - 9y^2 = \frac{5}{4}.$$

[O & C]

2. Solve the simultaneous equations

$$y = x + 3 \quad \text{and} \quad 4y = x^2.$$

Illustrate accurately on one graph the three inequalities $y \leqslant x + 3$, $x \geqslant 2$, $y \geqslant \frac{1}{4}x^2$ by drawing suitable boundaries and shading areas that are excluded. (Mark axes from -4 to 6 in x and -2 to 10 in y. Unit: centimetre.)

[MEI]

3. (i) Verify that the values of x and y satisfying the simultaneous equations $x - \dfrac{3}{y} = 3$

and $3x + \dfrac{6}{y} = 4$ also satisfy the equation $x^2 - xy - y^2 = 1$.

(ii) Solve completely the simultaneous equations

$$p + 3q = 1,$$
$$p^2 + 2pq + q^2 = 25.$$

[O & C]

4. Calculate the coordinates of the points of intersection of the straight line $x - y = 3$ and the curve $x^2 - 3xy + y^2 + 19 = 0$.

[AEB 1983]

5. (i) Find the values of $3x + 2y$ and $3x^2 - xy - 2y^2$ when $x = 2$ and $y = -3$.

(ii) Solve the simultaneous equations

$$3x + 2y = 1,$$
$$3x^2 - xy - 2y^2 = -3.$$

[O & C]

6. (a) Find the equation of the line L which has gradient m and which passes through $(1, 8)$.

(b) Find the quadratic equation whose roots are the x-coordinates of the points where L meets the curve

$$y = x(5 - x).$$

(c) Write down the condition for this quadratic equation to have coincident roots, and hence find the values of m for which L is a tangent to the curve.

(d) Find the coordinates of the points where these tangents touch the curve.

(e) Draw a diagram showing the curve and these tangents.

[UL]

7. The equations of the line L and the curve C are $y = x - 9$ and $y = x^2 - kx$ respectively, where k is a constant.

(a) Form a quadratic equation whose roots are the x-coordinates of the points of intersection of L and C.

(b) Hence, by requiring the equation of (a) to have two equal roots, or otherwise, find the two values of k for which L is a tangent to C. For each of these values of k find the coordinates of the point where L touches C.

(c) Draw a sketch showing L and the two curves C which touch L.

[UL]

8. If $f(x)$ denotes the polynomial $2x^3 - 3x^2 - 8x - 3$, find the remainders when $f(x)$ is divided by (i) $x - 1$, (ii) $x + 3$, and (iii) $2x + 1$. Deduce which of $(x - 1)$, $(x + 3)$, and $(2x + 1)$ is a factor of $f(x)$, and find its remaining factors.

[O & C]

9. Find the remainder when $x^3 - 7x + 6$ is divided by

(i) $x + 2$,
(ii) $x - 3$.

Show that $x - 2$ is a factor of $x^3 - 7x + 6$ and find the other factors.

[AEB 1981]

10. (i) Divide $2x^3 + 9x^2 + 4x - 15$ by $x + 3$, and deduce three factors of $2x^3 + 9x^2 + 4x - 15$.

(ii) If $y + k$ is a factor of $3y^3 + 8y^2 + 3y - 2$, find the possible integral values of k.

[O & C]

11. Show that $x + 4$ is a factor of $4x^3 - 57x + 28$ and hence factorize the expression completely.

Find the ranges of values of x for which $4x^3 - 57x + 28 > 0$.

[AEB 1979]

12. (i) Factorise $7x^2 - 3xy - 22y^2$.

If $7x^2 - 3xy - 22y^2 = 0$ and $x \neq 2y$, find x in terms of y.

(ii) Factorise the expression $x^3 - 4x^2 + x + 6$.

[O & C]

13. When $2x^3 - x^2 - 13x + k$ is divided by $x - 2$ the remainder is -20. Show that $k = -6$.

Show that $2x^3 - x^2 - 13x - 6$ is divisible by $2x + 1$, and find the roots of the equation

$$2x^3 - x^2 - 13x - 6 = 0.$$

[AEB 1982]

14. If $f(x) = x^3 - 7x + 6$, find $f(1)$ and $f(2)$, and hence factorize the expression $x^3 - 7x + 6$.

Given that the equation $x^3 + x^2 + ax + 3 = 0$, where a is an integer, has two solutions in common with the equation $x^3 - 7x + 6 = 0$, find these two solutions and the value of a.

[O & C]

15. (i) Write down one factor of the expression

$$(x + 4)(2x^2 + 5x + 5) - (x + 4)(x + 1)(x - 1).$$

By factorising, or otherwise, show that $(x + 3)$ is also a factor, and find the third factor.

Find the coefficient of x^2 in the expression.

(ii) $\dfrac{3x^2 - x + 5}{x - 1}$ may be expressed in the form

$$ax + b + \frac{r}{x - 1}.$$

Show that $b = 2$ and find the values of a and r.

[SMP]

16. (i) If the expression $3x^3 - 11x^2 + 8x + k$ is divisible by $3x + 1$, find the value of k. With this value of k, factorise the expression and show that there is a repeated factor.

(ii) The expression $x^3 + ax^2 + bx$ leaves a remainder -12 when it is divided by $x + 2$ or $x - 2$. Find the values of a and b.

With these values of a and b,

(a) find the remainder when the expression is divided by $x - 1$;

(b) show that $x - 4$ is a factor.

[O & C]

17. (i) Multiply $x^2 + 3x - 5$ by $2x^2 - x + 4$.

(ii) Find values of p, q, r, s such that

$$(2x + 3)(px^3 + qx^2 + rx + s)$$
$$= 2x^4 + 13x^3 + 7x^2 + 18$$

for all values of x.

(iii) Simplify $(x + 1)(3x^2 + 2x - 5) - (x + 1)(2x^2 + x + 1)$ as the product of three factors.

[SMP]

18. Show that 4 is a solution of the equation

$$6x^3 - 23x^2 - 6x + 8 = 0$$

and find the other two solutions of this equation.

Hence solve the equations

(a) $6 \times 2^{3y} - 23 \times 2^{2y} - 6 \times 2^y + 8 = 0$,

(b) $6 \sin^3 z° - 23 \sin^2 z° - 6 \sin z° + 8 = 0$, where $0 \leqslant z \leqslant 360$, giving your answers to the nearest integer.

[UL]

19. Expand $(3 - 2x)^5$ and work out the terms. Show how you can check your answer by putting $x = 1$.

[MEI]

20. Obtain the binomial expansion of $(1+2x)^7$ in ascending powers of x, as far as the term in x^3.

If $(1+2x)^7(a+bx+cx^2)$, where a, b, c are constants, is expanded in ascending powers of x, the first three terms are $1+11x+44x^2$. Calculate the values of a, b and c.

[AEB 1980]

21. (i) Expand $(2+y)^5$ and work out the coefficients.

(ii) Deduce the value of $(2.01)^5$ *exactly* in decimal form.

(iii) What is the percentage error to one significant figure if only the first two terms of the expansion are used?

[MEI]

22. Expand $(2+x)^6$ and work out the coefficients. Use the expansion to evaluate $(2.01)^6$ to five significant figures *without using tables, slide rules or calculators*. Make the method clear and point out which terms are relevant.

Use the original expansion to evaluate $(1.99)^6$ to five significant figures.

[MEI]

23. (a) In the expansion by the binomial theorem of $\left(x^2+\dfrac{1}{x}\right)^6$ in descending powers of x, state and simplify (i) the first two terms, (ii) the last two terms, (iii) the term independent of x.

(b) Expand $(1+x)^4$ using the binomial theorem.

By taking the first two terms of the expansion, show that $x = 0.03$ is an approximate solution of the equation $(1+x)^4 = 1.12$. Find a more accurate approximation by taking the first three terms and solving the resulting equation.

[O & C]

24. (i) The equation
$$4x^3 - 3x^2 - 10x - 49 = 0$$
has a root which is approximately 3. By substituting $x = 3+h$ and neglecting squares and higher powers of h, find a closer approximation to the value of the root.

(ii) In the expansion of $(1-2ax)^{15}$ in powers of x the coefficient of x^2 is $\frac{28}{15}$. If a is positive find its value and the resulting coefficient of x^3.

[MEI]

25. Using the binomial theorem or otherwise, show that $(x+2)^5-(x-2)^5 = 4(5x^4+40x^2+16)$, and obtain a similar result for $(x+2)^5+(x-2)^5$.

By choosing a suitable value for x, find the exact values of 102^5-98^5 and 102^5+98^5, and hence the exact values of 102^5 and 98^5.

26. Write down the binomial expansion for $(1-x)^{25}$ in ascending powers of x as far as the term containing x^3, giving the numerical value of each coefficient.

Showing all your working, use this expansion to obtain

(a) the value of $(0.999)^{25}$ correct to 6 decimal places,

(b) the expansion of $(1-y-3y^2)^{25}$ in ascending powers of y as far as the term containing y^3.

[UL]

27. Write down and simplify the complete expansion of $(1+x)^8$ in ascending powers of x. Find the first term whose value is less than 0.000001 (a) if $x = 0.001$, and (b) if $x = 0.005$. Hence evaluate 1.001^8 and 1.005^8 correct to 6 decimal places.

Using just the first two terms of the expansion, obtain an approximate solution to the equation $(1+x)^8 = 1.008$. Then improve your approximation by using the first three terms of the expansion and solving the resultant quadratic equation.

28. The volume of a cube is given by the formula $V = a^3$. If a is increased by $p\%$, where p is quite small, show by means of the binomial theorem that V is increased by approximately $3p\%$.

Demonstrate that if $p = 2$ then this approximation is in error by less than 2% of the correct result.

29. The binomial theorem states that if n is a positive integer then
$$(1+x)^n = 1+nx+n(n-1)x^2/2!$$
$$+n(n-1)(n-2)x^3/3! \text{ etc.}$$

Show that if you let n equal -1 and simplify appropriately you obtain the statement
$(1+x)^{-1} = 1-x+x^2-x^3$ etc.   *cont.*

Check the validity of this statement by setting $x = 0.1$, and then evaluating (a) the left-hand side of the equation, (b) the sum of the first six terms of the right-hand side.

30. In the expansion of $(1-4x)^k$ in a series of ascending powers of x, assuming the expansion is valid, the coefficient of x^2 is 6. Find the two possible values of k.

For the negative value of k, find the coefficients of x^3 and x^4 in the expansion.

[AEB 1981]

31. Assuming that the value of x is such as to make the expansion valid, find the first four terms in the expansion of $(1-2x)^{3/2}$ in a series of ascending powers of x, simplifying the coefficients.

In the expansion of

$$(1+ax+bx^2)(1-2x)^{3/2}$$

as a series of ascending powers of x, the coefficients of x and x^2 are zero. Find the values of the constants a and b.

[AEB 1982]

32. Show that $\dfrac{3}{(1+x-2x^2)}$ can be expressed

as $\dfrac{1}{(1-x)} + \dfrac{2}{(1+2x)}$.

Hence or otherwise expand $(1+x-2x^2)^{-1}$ as far as the term in x^4, the values of x being such as to make the expansion valid.

(a) By putting $x = -0.02$, use your expansion to evaluate, correct to seven decimal places, $(0.9792)^{-1}$,

(b) by giving x a suitable value, use your expansion to evaluate $(1.0098)^{-1}$, to seven decimal places.

[AEB 1982]

33. Given that

$$\frac{x^2-2x+10}{(2+x)(1-x)^2} \equiv \frac{A}{2+x} + \frac{B}{1-x} + \frac{C}{(1-x)^2},$$

find the constants A, B and C.

Hence, or otherwise, expand

$$\frac{x^2-2x+10}{(2+x)(1-x)^2}$$

in ascending powers of x up to and including the term in x^3.

[UL]

EXERCISE 16X

1. A tripod consists of three straight rods, each 2 metres long, hinged together at the top point V. The feet A, B, C are placed on horizontal ground at the corners of an equilateral triangle. Draw a diagram of the tripod and mark in it the point G on the ground vertically below V. Each leg of the tripod makes an angle of $60°$ with the ground; mark one of these angles clearly in your diagram.

(i) Find the distance between two of the feet of the tripod.

(ii) Find the angle between two of the legs of the tripod.

(iii) Add lines as necessary to your diagram so that you can mark clearly in it the angle θ between the plane VAB and the ground. Calculate this angle.

[MEI]

2. The points $A(1,2)$, $B(8,3)$, $C(6,7)$ lie in a horizontal plane. Prove that the triangle ABC is isosceles. The lines AD, BE, CF are drawn in a vertical direction on the same side of the plane ABC. The lengths of AD, BE, CF are 3 units, 5 units and 5 units respectively. Prove that the lines DE, DF are equally inclined to the horizontal, and calculate the angle of inclination.

Calculate also the angle of inclination of the plane DEF to the horizontal.

[O & C]

3. The steepest line up a uniformly sloping plane hill-side goes due north and rises 10 m vertically for every 50 m up the slope. Going diagonally across this hill-side in a direction to the East of North, a road is to be built to rise 1 m for each 10 m up the road.

Calculate the angle to the lines of steepest slope at which it must be built.

Calculate also the map bearing of this road, noting that a map represents the projection of the road on to a horizontal plane. Support your solution with a clear diagram.

[MEI]

4. A straight stick of length 4 metres is placed inside a rectangular shed with internal length 3 metres, width 2 metres and height 2.5 metres. One end A of the stick is placed in a bottom corner of the shed and the other end B falls until the stick makes the smallest possible angle with the floor. Draw a diagram showing the position *AB* and calculate this angle.

B is now moved along the shorter wall into a position *C* so that the stick makes the greatest possible angle with the floor, *A* remaining still. Show the position *AC* in your diagram and calculate its angle with the floor. Find also the angle between the vertical plane through *AC* and the plane of one of the longer walls.

[MEI]

5. A stone pyramid has a horizontal square base *ABCD* of side 12 metres and its vertex *V* is 8 metres directly above the mid-point *E* of *AB*. Reproduce a sketch of figure 16.14, mark in it clearly the following angles and calculate them:

(i) the angle of slope to the horizontal of the edge *VC*,

(ii) the angle between planes *VAB* and *VCD*.

[MEI]

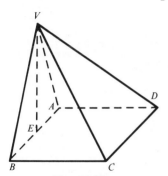

Fig. 16.14

6. A solid pyramid has a horizontal square base *ABCD* of side 4 metres. Its vertex *V* is 3 metres vertically above the corner *A*. Calculate the angle *VCB* and the length of the perpendicular *BX* from *B* to the line *VC*.

An intelligent insect wishes to walk on the surface of the pyramid from *B* to *D* by the shortest possible route. He cannot burrow underneath the pyramid along the direct line *BD*. Which way should he go and how far is it?

What is the angle between the planes *VBC* and *VDC* to the nearest degree?

Support your work with a clear diagram.

[MEI]

7. A pyramid has a horizontal square base *ABCD* of side 10 m. The vertex *V* is 4 m verti-

cally above the middle point *M* of the square base.

(i) Calculate the length of *VA* to three significant figures.

(ii) Calculate the angle *VAB* in degrees to one decimal place.

The line *BZ* is drawn in the plane *VAB* from *B* perpendicular to *VA* to meet *VA* at *Z*. *DZ* is joined. Note that, by symmetry, *DZ* is perpendicular to *VA* and equal in length to *BZ*.

(iii) Calculate the length of *BZ* to three significant figures.

(iv) State in letters the angle between the planes *VBA* and *VDA* and calculate this angle to the nearest degree.

Support your solution with a clear diagram.

[MEI]

8. Given that α and β are acute angles so that $\sin \alpha = \dfrac{1}{\sqrt{10}}$ and $\sin \beta = \dfrac{1}{\sqrt{5}}$, prove, *without using tables, slide rule or calculator*, that

$$\sin(\alpha + \beta) = \frac{1}{\sqrt{2}}.$$

[UL]

9. (i) On the same diagram, sketch the graphs of $y = 3 \cos x$ and $y = 2 \sin 2x$ in the interval $0° \leqslant x \leqslant 360°$.

(ii) By using the formula for $\sin 2x$, solve by calculation the equation $2 \sin 2x = 3 \cos x$ in the same interval.

(iii) Solve the inequality $2 \sin 2x \geqslant 3 \cos x$ in this interval.

[SMP]

10. State the expansion of $\cos(A + B)$ and use it to express $\cos 2x$ in terms of $\cos x$.

Find to the nearest degree all the values of the angle *x* between $0°$ and $360°$ such that

$$5 \cos 2x + 3 \cos x + 1 = 0.$$

[AEB 1981]

11. (a) Without using tables, write down expressions for $\sin \frac{1}{6}\pi$ and $\cos \frac{1}{6}\pi$.

(b) It is known that if θ is small (θ in radians), then $\sin \theta \simeq \theta$ and $\cos \theta \simeq 1$.

Make use of the identity

$$\sin(A + B) = \sin A \cos B + \cos A \sin B$$

cont.

to show that, even if we have no trigono-metrical tables, we can calculate that $\sin 31°$ is about 0.515.

[If necessary, take the values of π and $\sqrt{3}$ to be 3.14 and 1.73 respectively.]

[SMP]

12. Prove that, for all angles x,

$$\sin(x+30°) - \sin(x-30°) = \cos x.$$

Obtain the corresponding result for $\cos(x-30°) - \cos(x+30°)$.

Using the above results solve the following equations, for $0° \leqslant x \leqslant 360°$.

(i) $\sin(x+30°) - \sin(x-30°) = -\dfrac{1}{2}$,

(ii) $\sin(x+30°) - \sin(x-30°)$
$= 2\{\cos(x-30°) - \cos(x+30°)\}$,

(iii) $\{\sin(x+30°) - \sin(x-30°)\}^2$
$= 2\{\cos(x-30°) - \cos(x+30°)\} + 1$.

[AEB 1980]

13. After t seconds the extension of a piston is given by $x = \sin 3t$ and of its crankshaft by $x = \sin^2 t$.

(a) Sketch these two curves on the same axes for $0 \leqslant t \leqslant 2\pi$.

(b) Prove that $\sin(t+2t) = 3\sin t - 4\sin^3 t$.

(c) Hence verify that the extension of the piston is the same as that of the crankshaft when $S(S+1)(4S-3) = 0$, where $S = \sin t$.

(d) Calculate, corrected to 3 significant figures, all the times in the first five seconds when the extensions are the same.

(e) Hence find the percentage of the time in each cycle for which the piston is more extended than the crankshaft.

[SMP]

14. (a) A and B are acute angles such that

$$\sin A = \frac{2}{3} \quad \text{and} \quad \tan B = \frac{3}{4}.$$

Without using tables or calculators, find the value of

(i) $\sin(A+B)$,
(ii) $\cos(A+B)$,

leaving your answers in surd form.

Hence state, with a brief reason, whether angle $A+B$ is acute or obtuse.

(b) Show that, for all values of θ,

$$\frac{\cot^2\theta}{1+\cot^2\theta} = \cos^2\theta.$$

Hence, or otherwise, find the solutions in the range $-180° \leqslant \theta \leqslant 180°$ of the equation

$$\frac{\cot^2\theta}{1+\cot^2\theta} = 2\cos 2\theta.$$

[JMB]

15. **Tables, slide rules and calculators are NOT to be used in this question.**

(a) Starting with the formulae for $\sin(A-B)$ and $\cos(A-B)$ prove that

$$\tan(A-B) = \frac{\tan A - \tan B}{1 + \tan A \tan B}.$$

(b) State the values of $\tan\dfrac{\pi}{4}$ and $\tan\dfrac{\pi}{6}$ and hence prove that

$$\tan\frac{\pi}{12} = \frac{\sqrt{3}-1}{\sqrt{3}+1}.$$

(c) Given that $\sin\left(\theta - \dfrac{\pi}{12}\right) = 2\cos\left(\theta + \dfrac{\pi}{12}\right)$, prove that

$$\tan\theta = \frac{3\sqrt{3}+1}{3\sqrt{3}-1}.$$

[UL]

16. (i) Given that $\tan 2x = \frac{3}{4}$, use the formula

$$\tan(A+B) = \frac{\tan A + \tan B}{1 - \tan A \tan B}$$

to show that $\tan 4x = \frac{24}{7}$.

(ii) If $t = \tan x$, show that $3t^2 + 8t - 3 = 0$.

(iii) Show that one possible value of $\tan x$ is $\frac{1}{3}$, and find the other possible value.

[SMP]

17. Express $\sin 2x$ and $\cos 2x$ in terms of $\sin x$ and $\cos x$.

(a) Show that

$$\tan 2x = \frac{2\tan x}{1 - \tan^2 x}.$$

Find the values of x between $-\dfrac{\pi}{2}$ and $\dfrac{\pi}{2}$ for which

(i) $\tan 2x = \cot x$,
(ii) $\tan 2x = 3\tan x$.

(b) Show that

$$\sin 2x = \frac{2 \tan x}{1 + \tan^2 x}.$$

Hence find the possible values of $\tan x$ given that $\sin 2x = \dfrac{7}{25}$.

[AEB 1982]

18. $3 \cos \theta + 4 \sin \theta$ may be written in the form $r \cos (\theta - \alpha)$.

(a) Calculate the value of r and show that one value of α is approximately $53.1°$.

(b) Hence show that one solution of $3 \cos \theta + 4 \sin \theta = 2$ is approximately $120°$.

(c) State all the other solutions for $0° \leqslant \theta \leqslant 500°$.

(d) Hence give the values of θ less than $500°$ for which $3 \cos \theta + 4 \sin \theta > 2$.

[SMP]

19. (i) Solve, for $0 \leqslant \theta \leqslant 2\pi$, the equation

$$6 \sin^2 \theta + \cos \theta - 5 = 0.$$

(ii) Given that

$$5 \cos \theta° - 12 \sin \theta° \equiv R \cos (\theta° + \alpha°),$$

where $R > 0$ and $0 < \alpha < 90$, calculate

(a) the value of R,

(b) the value of α to 1 decimal place.

Hence solve, for $0 \leqslant \theta \leqslant 360$, the equation

$$5 \cos \theta° - 12 \sin \theta° = 6\tfrac{1}{2}.$$

[UL]

20. Sketch the graphs of $y = \sin x$ and $y = \sin (x + 30°)$ for the interval $0° \leqslant x \leqslant 360°$, and use the latter to illustrate the solutions to the equation $\sin (x + 30°) = 0.6$ in this interval.

For all x, $\sin (x + 30°) = \dfrac{\sqrt{3}}{2} \sin x + b \cos x$.

State the value of b.

Hence solve the equation

$$\sqrt{3} \sin x + \cos x = 1.2$$

in the interval $0° \leqslant x \leqslant 360°$.

[SMP]

21. (a) Express $1.2 \cos x + 1.6 \sin x$ in the form $R \cos (x - \alpha)$, where R is a positive constant and $0° < \alpha < 90°$. Hence, or otherwise,

(i) find the maximum and minimum values of $1.2 \cos x + 1.6 \sin x$,

(ii) solve the equation $1.2 \cos x + 1.6 \sin x = 1.5$, giving the values of x between $0°$ and $180°$.

(b) Prove that, for all values of x,

$$\sin (x + 30°) - \sin (x - 30°) = \cos x.$$

(c) Solve the equation $\sin 4\theta + \sin 2\theta = \cos \theta$, giving the values of θ in the range $0° < \theta < 360°$.

[JMB]

22. (a) Without using tables or calculators, show that $\cos 83° + \cos 37° = \cos 23°$.

(b) Solve the equation $\sin 5x + \sin 3x = \cos x$ giving the solutions in the range $0° \leqslant x \leqslant 180°$.

(c) A rod AB of length $2\,\mathrm{m}$ is rigidly attached at B to another rod BC of length $1.5\,\mathrm{m}$ so that $\angle ABC$ is a right-angle. The resulting L-shaped figure is free to rotate about B in a vertical plane. Given that AB makes a variable angle θ with the horizontal and that A is above and C is below the horizontal through B, express in terms of θ the vertical height of A above C.

Find the values of θ for which this vertical height is $2.2\,\mathrm{m}$.

[JMB]

23. For the curve $y = \sin^2 x$ show, by differentiation, that the gradient when $x = \pi/4$ is 1 and state the gradient when $x = \pi$. Sketch the curve for $0 \leqslant x \leqslant 2\pi$.

Given that $\cos (A + B) = \cos A \cos B - \sin A \sin B$ and that $\sin^2 A + \cos^2 A = 1$, by writing $A = B = x$, prove that $\sin^2 x = [1 - \cos 2x]/2$. Differentiate the right-hand side of this expression and hence verify your gradients above. Also use this expression to show that $\displaystyle\int_0^\pi \sin^2 x \, dx = \pi/2$ and indicate the significance of this result in relation to your sketch graph.

[SMP]

24. Starting with the formula for $\cos (A + B)$, prove that

(a) $\cos 2x \equiv 2 \cos^2 x - 1$,

(b) $\cos 3x \equiv 4 \cos^3 x - 3 \cos x$.

Use these results to evaluate

$$\int_0^{\pi/4} \frac{\cos 3x}{\cos x} \, dx.$$

[UL]

EXERCISE 17X

1. Sketch the curve $y = 4 - x^2$ in the interval $-3 \leqslant x \leqslant +3$. Shade the area enclosed between the x-axis and the curve.

Calculate the volume swept out when this area is rotated through $360°$ about the x-axis. (Unit: centimetre.)

[MEI]

2. Sketch the curve $y = (x-3)^2$ between the values $x = 0$ and $x = 3$. Find the area between this portion of the curve and the axes of x and y.

If this area is revolved through 2π radians about the x-axis, find the volume of this solid of revolution.

[You may assume that

$$\int (x-a)^n \, dx = \frac{(x-a)^{n+1}}{n+1} + C,$$

for positive n.]

[O & C]

3. Sketch the curve

$$y^2 = 1 - 2x.$$

Calculate the area enclosed by this curve and the *y-axis*.

Leaving your answers in terms of π, calculate the volume of the solid formed by rotating this area completely about

(i) the x-axis,
(ii) the y-axis.

[AEB 1980]

4. A rugby football can be generated, approximately, by rotating the curve $y^2 = 100 - 400x^2/625$ about the x-axis through $360°$, where both scales are in centimetres. Sketch the part of the curve that lies in the positive quadrant, and find the volume of the whole ball in cubic centimetres.

5. Sketch the graph of $y = x^2$.

Calculate the area of the region between this curve and the x-axis for which $1 \leqslant x \leqslant 3$. Also calculate the volume of the solid generated by rotating this region through $360°$ about the *y-axis*.

[SMP]

6. On squared paper draw the curve $y = \dfrac{9}{x^2}$

for $1 \leqslant x \leqslant 6$ and the lines $y = 9$ and $x = 6$. (Units: centimetres.) Shade the area containing those points whose coordinates obey the inequalities $y < \dfrac{9}{x^2}$, $0 < y < 9$ and $0 < x < 6$. Calculate the shaded area.

Calculate also the volume created when the shaded area is rotated through $360°$ about the x-axis. Give this answer as a multiple of π.

[MEI]

7. Verify that the curve $y = x^3 - 12x^2 + 20x$ crosses the axis $y = 0$ at $x = 0$ and $x = 10$, and find where it crosses in between. Sketch, without any plotting, the shape of this curve.

Calculate the total area of paint needed to cover the areas enclosed by the curve and the line $y = 0$. This portion of the curve, for $0 \leqslant x \leqslant 10$, is rotated through $360°$ about the line $y = 0$. Write down in terms of x a definite integral which represents this volume. [You are not required to simplify or evaluate this integral.]

[SMP]

8. Using the same axes, sketch the curve $y = x^2 + 1$ and the straight line $y = 2x + 1$. Calculate the coordinates of their points of intersection and the volume obtained when the area bounded by the two graphs is rotated through $360°$ about the x-axis, leaving your answer as a multiple of π.

[O & C]

9. The points $P(3, 2)$ and $Q(0, 1)$ lie on the curve $y^2 = x + 1$. Calculate the volume of the solid generated when the region bounded by the lines $y = 0$, $x = 0$, $x = 3$ and the arc PQ of the curve is rotated completely about the x-axis. Give your answer as a multiple of π.

S is the region bounded by the lines $y = 1$, $x = 3$ and the arc PQ of the curve. Show that when S is rotated completely about the x-axis the volume of the solid generated is $\dfrac{9\pi}{2}$.

When S is rotated completely about the line $x = 3$ show that the volume of the solid generated is

$$\pi \int_1^2 (4 - y^2)^2 \, dy.$$

Calculate this volume in terms of π.

[JMB]

10. Show that
$\sin x - \cos x = \sqrt{2} \sin(x - \pi/4)$.
Find the greatest and least values of
$(\sin x - \cos x)$.

Sketch the curve $y = \sin x - \cos x$ for values of x in the interval $0 \leqslant x \leqslant 2\pi$.

The region bounded by the x-axis and the arc of this curve for which $\pi/4 \leqslant x \leqslant 5\pi/4$ is rotated completely about the x-axis. Find the volume of the solid of revolution swept out, leaving your answer in terms of π.

[AEB 1981]

11. The combustion chamber of a jet engine is in the form of the surface formed by revolving the part of the curve

$$y = \frac{x}{10} + \frac{2}{5x}$$

from $x = 1$ to $x = 4$ about the x-axis, the units being metres. Find the volume of the chamber, leaving π in the answer.

An approximate formula for the volumes of bodies of this shape is

$\frac{1}{6}$ length $\times$ (sum of two end areas

$+ 4 \times$ area of mid-section),

where the mid-section is half way between the two ends. Use this to calculate the volume again. What is the percentage error in using this formula?

[SMP]

12. (i) The portion of the curve $y^2 = 4 - \frac{1}{4}x^2$ which lies in the first quadrant (the values of both x and y are positive) is rotated through 4 right-angles about the x-axis. Find the volume generated, leaving the answer as a multiple of π.

(ii) Using the trapezoidal rule, or other appropriate method, find the *approximate* area bounded by the portion of the curve $y = \sqrt{(4 - \frac{1}{4}x^2)}$ which lies in the first quadrant and by the lines $x = 0$ and $y = 0$. [Use the ordinates at $x = 0, 1, 2, 3$ and 4.]

[MEI]

13. Copy and complete the following table, giving values of 3^x to 3 decimal places:

x	0	0.1	0.2	0.3	0.4
3^x	1				

Sketch the curve $y = 3^x$ for values of x from 0 to 0.4 and estimate the value of $\int_0^{0.4} 3^x \, dx$,

using Simpson's rule with four strips, or another suitable method.

[O & C]

14. Evaluate $\sqrt{(16 - x^2)}$ for the values $x = 0, 1, 2, 3$ and 4. Using Simpson's rule or another suitable method, find an approximate value for the area bounded by the curve $y = \sqrt{(16 - x^2)}$ between $x = 0$ and $x = 4$, and the positive coordinate axes.

If this result is used to deduce the area of a circle of radius 4 units, find the percentage error in the result obtained.

[O & C]

15. The depth y metres of a stream 10 metres wide at a point x metres from one particular side is given by the formula

$$y = \sqrt{(x - \tfrac{1}{100}x^3)}.$$

Work out and record the depth at 2, 4, 6 and 8 metres from that side.

If the stream flows at 50 metres a minute write down a formula (including an integral) for the number of cubic metres of water passing per minute.

Use an approximate method of integration to estimate to two significant figures how much this is.

[MEI]

16. Soundings are taken across a river with the following results:

Distance from left bank (m)	0	2	4	6	8
Depth of water (m)	0	0.8	1.0	1.4	1.8

Distance from left bank (m)	10	12	14	16
Depth of water (m)	2.4	1.8	0.6	0

State a rule for finding an approximate value for the area of cross-section of the water and, using this rule, estimate the area in question.

Readings are also taken to find the rate of flow of the river and the average value is found to be $0.8 \, \text{m s}^{-1}$. Make an estimate of the weight of water carried downstream in tonnes per hour.

[$1 \, \text{m}^3$ of water weighs 1 tonne.]

[O & C]

17. y is a function of x which takes the following values (unit: centimetre):

x	0	2	4	6	8	10	12
y	2	4	5	4	1.6	0.4	0

Sketch the graph of y against x.

(i) Write down an integral in terms of x and y for the area bounded by the curve and the x and y axes. Estimate this area to the nearest cm², explaining your method.

(ii) Consider the solid shape created by rotating this area about the x-axis through 360°. Write down an integral in terms of x and y for this volume. Estimate this volume to the nearest cm³, showing your working.

[MEI]

18. Mark out axes on graph paper from -6 to $+6$ in x and 0 to 12 in y. (Units: centimetres.) Plot the following points: $(2,0)$, $(5,2)$, $(6,4)$, $(5,6)$, $(4,8)$, $(4,10)$, $(5,12)$. Draw as smooth a curve as you can through these points. Shade the area between the curve and the y-axis in the interval $0 \leqslant y \leqslant 12$.

When this area is rotated round the y-axis through 360° it traces out a new design of jam-jar. Sketch the jam-jar and write down an integral for the volume it will contain when full, regarding x as a function of y.

Use an approximate method to evaluate this integral, giving an answer in cm³, first as a multiple of π and then worked out to three significant figures.

[MEI]

19. Draw the graph of $y = \sin x$ for $0 \leqslant x \leqslant \pi$, plotting points with x-coordinates at intervals of $\pi/6$, and labelling them O, A, B, C, D, E, F successively.

Calculate the area of the polygon $OABCDEF$ by dividing it into strips parallel to the y-axis, or otherwise. Hence give an approximation to

$$\int_0^{\pi/2} \sin x \, dx.$$

[SMP]

20. Functions f and g are given as

$$f : t \to t^2 + 3t - 5 \quad \text{and} \quad g : x \to x + 2.$$

If the function h is given as
$$h : x \to (x^2 + 3x - 5)(x + 2),$$

(a) multiply this out, to obtain $h(x)$ as a single polynomial;

(b) find $h'(x)$ and verify that $h'(2) = 33$;

(c) write down the derived functions f′ and g′;

(d) verify that $h'(2) = f'(2) . g(2) + f(2) . g'(2)$.

[SMP]

21. Show that the gradient of the curve
$$y = \frac{2x}{x^2 + 1}$$ is positive for $-1 < x < 1$. Find the coordinates of the turning points on the curve.

[AEB 1982]

22. Differentiate with respect to x

(i) $x^2 \cos(3x)$,

(ii) $\dfrac{x-1}{x+1}$,

(iii) $\tan^3(2x)$.

[AEB 1981]

23. Given that $y = x^2 e^x$, show that
$$\frac{dy}{dx} = x(x+2) e^x.$$ Find the coordinates of the points of zero slope on the curve $y = x^2 e^x$. In each case state with a reason whether the point is a maximum or minimum point.

Prove that the tangent to this curve at the point where $x = -1$ passes through the origin.

[UL]

24. Sketch the curve $y = \tan x$ for values of x between $-\dfrac{\pi}{2}$ and $\dfrac{\pi}{2}$. Show that the gradient of the curve at the point given by $x = \dfrac{\pi}{4}$ is 2. Use the method of small increments to show that

$$\tan\left(\frac{\pi}{4} + \frac{\pi}{180}\right) \approx 1 + \frac{\pi}{90}.$$

[AEB 1982]

25. (a) Differentiate with respect to x

(i) $x \cos x$,

(ii) $(2x+3)^4$,

(iii) $\dfrac{(\sin x)}{x}$.

(b) Integrate with respect to x

(i) $\sin 4x$,

(ii) $\dfrac{e^{2x} + 1}{e^{2x}}$,

(iii) $\dfrac{1}{2x+1}$.

[AEB 1982]

26. Given that $y = \log_e \cos x$, find $\dfrac{dy}{dx}$.

Hence find $\int \tan x \, dx$.

Using the same axes and scales, sketch the curves $y = \tan x$ and $y = \sin 2x$ in the range $0 \leqslant x < \dfrac{\pi}{2}$, verifying that the curves intersect at $x = \dfrac{\pi}{4}$.

Calculate the area enclosed between the two curves in this range, giving your answer correct to three significant figures.

[AEB 1979]

27. Evaluate the following integrals, giving your answers correct to three decimal places.

(i) $\displaystyle\int_0^1 \dfrac{1}{(2x+1)^2} \, dx$,

(ii) $\displaystyle\int_0^3 \dfrac{1}{(2x+3)} \, dx$,

(iii) $\displaystyle\int_0^1 e^{2x-1} \, dx$.

[AEB 1981]

28. (a) Differentiate with respect to x

(i) $(2x+5)^4$,

(ii) $x^4 \sin 3x$,

(iii) $\dfrac{x}{x^2+2}$.

(b) Find the equation of the tangent to the curve $y = \sin^2 x$ at the point where $x = \dfrac{\pi}{3}$.

For values of x in the range $0 \leqslant x \leqslant 2\pi$

(i) find the coordinates of the turning points, determining which are maximum points and which are minimum points,

(ii) sketch the curve,

(iii) find the total area of the regions bounded by the curve and the x-axis.

[JMB]

29. Sketch the curve $xy = 10$ for positive values of x.

Calculate to one decimal place the area of the

region given by the inequalities $1 \leqslant x \leqslant 5$ and $0 \leqslant y \leqslant \dfrac{10}{x}$.

Find in terms of π the volume swept out when this region is rotated completely

(a) about the x-axis,

(b) about the y-axis.

[AEB 1982]

30. Given that $y = e^{2x}(a \cos x + b \sin x)$ where a and b are constants, find $\dfrac{dy}{dx}$.

Find the values of a and b for which $\dfrac{dy}{dx} = e^{2x} \cos x$.

Use your result to find $\int e^{2x} \cos x \, dx$.

[AEB 1981]

EXERCISE 18X

1. A cricket ball and a golf ball are of mass 160 g and 50 g respectively. They are projected with equal kinetic energies, the cricket ball having a speed of 30 m/s. Calculate

(i) the kinetic energy of the cricket ball, stating the units of your answer,

(ii) the speed of projection of the golf ball,

(iii) the initial impulse given to the golf ball, stating the units of your answer.

[AEB 1979]

2. A boat of mass 600 kg, initially at rest, slides a distance of 20 metres down a slipway inclined at 13° to the horizontal. The frictional force opposing motion is equal to the weight of 60 kg. Find

(i) the kinetic energy of the boat at the bottom of the slipway, using the kilogram as the unit of mass, and the metre per second as the unit of velocity;

(ii) the velocity of the boat at this moment expressed in metres per second.

[MEI]

3. A boy on a sledge slides down a hill of variable gradient. In so doing he travels a distance of 168 m, measured along the surface of the track, and descends a vertical distance of 30 m. The combined mass of the boy and the sledge is 80 kg. If the initial speed is $2\,\mathrm{m\,s^{-1}}$ and the final speed is $16\,\mathrm{m\,s^{-1}}$, find in the same units

cont.

(i) the increase in the kinetic energy of the combined mass of boy and sledge,

(ii) the work done by gravity.

Hence find the average resistance to motion (defined as the work done against the resisting forces divided by the distance travelled).

[O & C]

4. Near the surface of a particular planet, the acceleration of a falling body is one-fifth of its value near the surface of the earth. If a body of mass 250 g is projected vertically at 16 m/s from the surface of this planet, calculate

(i) the height, above the surface of the planet, to which the body ascends,

(ii) the time which elapses before the body strikes the planet,

(iii) the potential energy gained by the body in ascending to its highest point.

(AEB 1980)

5. Figure 18.13 shows a block *P*, of mass 0.6 kg, resting on the smooth surface of a horizontal table. Inextensible light strings connect *P* to blocks *A* and *B* which hang freely over light smooth pulleys placed at opposite parallel edges of the table. The masses of *A* and *B* are 0.3 kg and 0.5 kg respectively and all portions of the strings are taut and perpendicular to their respective edges of the table. The system is released from rest. Calculate

(a) the common magnitude of the accelerations, in m/s², of the blocks,

(b) the tensions, in N, in the strings.

Given that no block reaches a pulley, find the loss in potential energy of this system during the first second of its motion.

[UL]

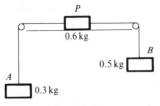

Fig. 18.13

6. A bullet of mass 50 g, moving horizontally, strikes a stationary target at 486 m/s and becomes embedded in it. The target is of mass 4 kg and is free to move. Calculate, ignoring

the time taken by the bullet to become embedded in the target,

(i) the speed at which the target and the embedded bullet move initially,

(ii) the impulse imparted to the target by the bullet,

(iii) the kinetic energy lost in the impact.

[AEB 1980]

7. A railway truck of mass 12 tonnes travelling freely at 10 m/s strikes another truck of mass 8 tonnes which is travelling freely at 5 m/s along the same straight line in the same direction. After the impact the trucks move on together. Calculate

(i) the common speed of the trucks after impact,

(ii) the loss of kinetic energy, in joules, due to the impact,

(iii) the impulse imparted to each truck by the impact, stating the units of your answer.

[AEB 1980]

8. A bullet of mass 120 g is fired horizontally with velocity 80 m s⁻¹ into a block of wood of mass 3 kg which rests on a smooth horizontal plane, and after the bullet has penetrated the block they both move on with a common velocity. Find this common velocity and the loss of kinetic energy of the system.

If the mean resistance to the bullet when penetrating the block is 1920 N, find how far the bullet penetrates into the block.

[O & C]

9. Three particles *A*, *B* and *C* are of mass 20 g, 30 g and 50 g respectively. They lie in a straight line on a smooth horizontal table, with *B* between *A* and *C*. Two light inextensible strings connect *B* to *A* and *B* to *C*. Initially the strings are slack. The particle *A* is projected along the table with velocity 4 m/s in the direction *CA*. Calculate

(a) the speed with which *A* and *B* move immediately after the string connecting them becomes taut.

(b) when *C* is also jerked into motion, the total kinetic energy lost in the tightening of the two strings.

[AEB 1982]

10. In a fairground, a 'Dodgem' car of mass 5*m* kg travelling at (*u* + 1) m s⁻¹ collides with another of mass $4m$ kg which is travelling at u m s^{-1} in the same direction and along the same straight line. After the impact both cars are still travelling in the same direction but with speeds v and $(v+\frac{1}{2})$ m s^{-1} respectively. Prove that $v = u + \frac{1}{3}$.

Verify that the loss of kinetic energy which takes place at the impact is independent of the value of u.

[O & C]

11. A lump of metal, of mass 300 kg, is used as a sledge-hammer to drive vertically a pile, of mass 540 kg, into horizontal ground. The hammer is released from rest at height 2.5 m above the pile and falls freely under gravity. The hammer strikes the pile directly and does not rebound.

(a) Show that the common speed of the hammer and pile at the instant immediately following impact is 2.5 m/s.

(b) Calculate, in N s, the impulse of the force exerted by the hammer on the pile due to the impact.

(c) Calculate, in J, the total kinetic energy lost due to the impact.

[UL]

12. A pile driver of mass 4.5 tonnes is allowed to fall from a height of 1.25 m on to a pile of mass 1.5 tonnes. The driver does not rebound. The ground resists penetration by the pile with a force which may be assumed to be constant. As a result of the blow the pile is driven 12.5 cm into the ground. Calculate

(i) the speed, in m/s, with which the driver strikes the pile,

(ii) the speed, in m/s, with which the driver and the pile begin to move after the impact,

(iii) the retardation, in m/s^2, of the driver and the pile during penetration,

(iv) the force, in kN, with which the ground resists the penetration by the pile.

[AEB 1981]

13. A smooth thin wire, in the form of a circle centre C and radius 40 cm, is fixed in a vertical plane. Two small beads P and Q, of mass 15 g and 10 g respectively, are threaded on the wire and are initially in equilibrium with P at the highest point of the wire and Q at the lowest point. The bead P is slightly disturbed,

slides down the wire, and collides with Q. Immediately after the collision P moves with a speed of 2 m/s in the same direction as before. Calculate

(a) the speed with which P strikes Q,

(b) the speed with which Q moves immediately after its collision with P,

(c) the angle CQ makes with the upward vertical when Q is at its greatest height after the collision.

[AEB 1982]

14. Two particles of mass 600 g and 400 g are attached to the ends of a long light inextensible string which passes over a smooth fixed pulley. The system is released from rest with the particles hanging vertically. When it has been in motion for 3 s, the heavier particle strikes a fixed inelastic horizontal platform and the lighter particle is then at a point P. Calculate

(i) the acceleration of the particles during the first 3 s of the motion,

(ii) the velocities of the particles just before the platform is struck,

(iii) the height above P to which the lighter particle rises,

(iv) the velocity with which the heavier particle is jerked into motion, stating clearly the reason for your answer.

[AEB 1980]

15. A train of mass 400 tonnes travels at 20 m/s on a horizontal track against a resistance of 60 newtons/tonne. Calculate the power the engine is developing.

If the power is suddenly increased to 640 kW, calculate the initial acceleration of the train.

[AEB 1980]

16. At a mine an engine raises coal of mass 1200 kg from a vertical depth of 400 m. The coal starts from rest and ends at rest and the time required to complete this operation is 210 s. Calculate, in kW, the average rate of working by the engine which raises this coal.

[UL]

17. A vehicle of mass 1.8 tonnes, travelling on a straight level road, accelerates uniformly from 18 km/h to 54 km/h in 12 s. The tractive force exerted by the engine of the vehicle is constant. The total resistance to the motion of the vehicle is constant and equal to   *cont.*

3 kN. Calculate, stating the units in each case,

(i) the tractive force exerted by the engine,

(ii) the power being developed by the engine at the end of the 12 second interval,

(iii) the kinetic energy gained by the vehicle.

[AEB 1981]

18. A passenger train of length 96 m travelling on a level track has a speed of 5 m/s and a uniform acceleration of $\frac{2}{3}$ m/s^2 at the instant it begins to pass a goods train of length 126 m travelling on a parallel track in the opposite direction with a uniform speed of 30 m/s.

Calculate

(i) the speed of the passenger train relative to the goods train at the instant the two trains begin to pass each other,

(ii) the time taken for the trains to pass each other completely,

(iii) the time which elapses from the instant the trains begin to pass each other until the instant the speed of each train is the same.

The total mass of the passenger train is 240 tonne (1 tonne = 1000 kg) and the frictional resistance to its motion is 50 newtons per tonne. Calculate the power developed by the engine of this train at the instant its speed is 5 m/s and its uniform acceleration is $\frac{2}{3}$ m/s^2.

[JMB]

19. A pump raises $2\frac{1}{4}$ tonnes of water from a depth of 18 m to ground level in $1\frac{1}{2}$ minutes and discharges it horizontally at a speed of 8 m/s. Calculate, in kW, the power at which the pump is working.

The water, still travelling horizontally at 8 m/s, strikes a vertical wall and does not rebound. Calculate the mean force exerted by the water on the wall.

[AEB 1982]

20. Define the unit of work called a joule.

A car of mass 1200 kg is travelling up a hill inclined at an angle θ to the horizontal, where $\sin \theta = \frac{1}{15}$, at a uniform speed of 45 km h^{-1}. If the frictional resistance to motion is 416 N, calculate the rate at which the car's engine is working in kilowatts, given that 1 watt = 1 joule per second.

[O & C]

21. The combined mass of a cyclist and his machine is 64 kg. When he freewheels down an incline of 1 in 128 his speed is constant. Calculate, in newtons, the resistance R to his motion.

Assuming that he experiences the same resistance R, calculate the power necessary for him to cycle up an incline of 1 in 100 at a steady speed of 3 m/s. State the units in which you give your answer.

[AEB 1982]

22. The non-gravitational resistances to the motion of a car of mass 600 kg are constant and total 180 N.

The car is moving along a straight horizontal road with the engine working at 4.5 kW.

(a) Given that at a particular instant the speed of the car is 20 m/s, find the acceleration, in m/s^2, of the car at this instant.

(b) Find the greatest steady speed, in m/s, which the car could attain under these conditions.

The car moves up a hill which is inclined at an angle θ to the horizontal, where $\sin \theta = 1/20$.

(c) Given that the engine is working at 11 kW, find, in m/s to 1 decimal place, the greatest steady speed which the car could attain up this hill.

[UL]

23. A train of mass 300 tonne (1 tonne = 1000 kg) is found to run down a uniform slope at constant speed with the power shut off. The slope is inclined at an angle α to the horizontal, where $\sin \alpha = \frac{1}{200}$.

Show that the magnitude of the total resistances to the train's motion is 14.7 kN.

Assuming the total resistance to the motion of this train remains the same, calculate the power needed to move the train up the same slope at a constant speed of 40 km/h.

The engine pulling this train works at a rate of 250 kW when the train is travelling along a straight level track against a total resistance of 12 kN. Calculate the train's acceleration, in m/s^2, at the instant its speed is 20 km/h.

[JMB]

EXERCISE 19X

1. The functions f and g are defined by

$$f: x \to 4x+3,$$

$$g: x \to 5x-k,$$

where $x \in \mathbb{R}$ and k is a constant.

(a) Find the value of k for which $fg = gf$.

(b) Prove that $fff: x \to 64x+63$.

[UL]

2. The functions f and g are defined by

$$f: x \to \frac{1}{2+x}, \text{ where } x \geqslant 0,$$

$$g: x \to 3-x, \text{ where } x \geqslant 0.$$

State the range of each function.

Define in a similar way the functions fg and gf, including a clear description of the domain in each case.

Find, to three significant figures, all the values of x for which $fg(x) = gf(x)$.

[UL]

3. The functions f and g are defined as follows:

$$f: x \to x^2 \quad \text{and} \quad g: x \to x+3.$$

(i) Show that $gf(5) = 28$, and write down expressions for the following: (a) $gf(x)$; (b) $fg(x)$.

(ii) If the domain is the set of real numbers, state the range of gf.

(iii) Say whether the inverse of gf is a function, and justify your answer.

[SMP]

4. The function f is defined by

$$f: x \to \frac{1}{2-x},$$

where $x \in \mathbb{R}$ and $x \neq 2$.

(a) Define in a similar way the inverse function f^{-1} and state its domain.

(b) Evaluate (i) $ff(3)$, (ii) $f^{-1}(3)$.

[UL]

5. Find the gradient of the curve $y = \log_e x$ at the point (e, 1). Show that the tangent to the curve at (e, 1) passes through the origin.

By means of a sketch, find the range of values of the constant k such that the equation $\log_e x = kx$ has two real roots.

Draw the graph of $y = \log_e x$ in the range $1 \leq x \leq 2$, using values of x at intervals of

0.1. Take 2 cm to represent 0.2 on the x-axis and 0.1 on the y-axis. By drawing a suitable straight line, estimate from your graph the smaller root of the equation $\log_e x = 0.3x$.

[AEB 1980]

6. Copy and complete the following table for

$$y = 2\sin 2x°.$$

x	0	15	30	45	60	75	90
y	0						0

Draw the graph of $2\sin 2x°$ for $0 \leqslant x \leqslant 90$. Using the same axes, draw the graph of

$$\tfrac{1}{2}e^{\sin 2x°}$$

for $0 \leqslant x \leqslant 90$ and hence obtain approximate solutions of the equation

$$\tfrac{1}{2}e^{\sin 2x°} = 2\sin 2x°.$$

[UL]

7. The function f is defined by

$$f: x \to \frac{x-3}{2x+3}, \text{ where } x \in \mathbb{R} \text{ and } x \neq -\frac{3}{2}.$$

On the same diagram sketch the graph of f and its asymptotes.

Write on your sketch

(a) the coordinates of the points where the curve intersects the coordinate axes,

(b) the equations of the asymptotes.

[UL]

8. (a) Find the range of values of x for which $4x^2 - 12x + 5 < 0$.

(b) Find the ranges of values of x such that

$$x > \frac{2}{x-1}.$$

[AEB 1982]

9. The curve $y = \frac{2x+3}{x-1}$ has asymptotes parallel to the coordinate axes. State the equations of these asymptotes.

Draw a sketch of this curve, showing the asymptotes and giving the coordinates of the points where the curve meets the axes. Solve the inequalities

(a) $2x+3 \leqslant 3(x-1)$, (b) $\frac{2x+3}{x-1} \leqslant 3$.

[UL]

10.   Sketch the curve

$$y = 2x + \frac{1}{x-3}$$

for $-5 \leqslant x < 3$ and $3 < x \leqslant 5$.

What line or lines does the curve approach when x is   (a) a very large positive number, (b) a very large negative number?

[SMP]

11.   An inspector counted the following numbers y of small sweets contained in five jars of exactly similar shape but of different heights x cm.

x	10	12	15	18	20
y	512	885	1728	2784	4098

Write down a formula for y in terms of a suitable power of x which you would theoretically expect these figures to obey. State what quantities should be plotted along the axes of a graph to test the given figures in this formula. By doing this accurately on squared paper, show that most of them do obey such a law.

Which bottle would the inspector reject because it has not been correctly filled? How many sweets, to two significant figures, should there have been in this bottle?

[MEI]

12.   It is expected that results of an experiment will obey a formula of the type

$$y = \frac{A}{x} + B$$ but it is possible that not all the

readings are accurate. Explain what should be done to check whether most of the readings do obey such a law and, if so, to find any that are inaccurate.

Carry out this procedure for the following set of readings and find the constants A and B.

x	3	4	5	6	7	8	9
y	7.4	6.2	5.1	5.0	4.65	4.4	4.2

Assuming that the values of x are correct, state which value of y appears to be inaccurate and give a more accurate value.

[MEI]

13.   In an experiment, the distance D cm travelled by a particle is measured after time T seconds with the following results:

T	2	4	6	8	10
D	14	22	32	52	72

By drawing a suitable straight line graph, show that D and T could be connected by a relation of the form $D = a + bT^2$.

From your graph find approximate values for a and b and estimate

(i) the value of D when $T = 7$,
(ii) the value of T when $D = 30$.

[AEB 1979]

14.   The following readings are expected to obey a formula of the type $y = Ax^2 + Bx$ where constants A and B are to be found.

x	2.7	4	6.9	8.5	10
y	77	136	318	450	592

By dividing each term of the proposed formula by x, or otherwise, explain a practical method of checking that the readings do satisfy such a formula and of finding A and B.

Carry your method through to a detailed solution. State clearly the values obtained for A and B, rewrite the formula and forecast the value of y when $x = 12$.

[MEI]

15.   An experiment gave the following corresponding values of x and y

x	0.2	0.3	0.4	0.5	0.6
y	1.4	1.8	2.0	2.1	2.2

Calculate, correct to one decimal place, the corresponding values of $\frac{1}{x}$ and y^2 and by drawing a suitable straight line graph show that x and y could be connected by a relationship of the form

$$y^2 = \frac{a}{x} + b,$$ where a and b are constants.

From your graph find approximate values of a and b and estimate

(i) the value of y when $x = 1.5$,
(ii) the value of x when $y = 1.5$.

[AEB 1980]

16.   All but one of the following pairs of readings satisfy, to 3 significant figures, a formula of the type $y = Ax^B$.

x	1.51	2.13	3.50	4.62	5.07	7.21
y	2.09	2.75	4.09	5.10	6.21	7.28

Find the values of A and B, explaining your method.

If the values of x are correct, state which value of y appears to be wrong and estimate what the value should be.

[MEI]

17.   The number of cells in a bacterial culture is expected to obey a law of the type $N = A \times B^t$, where N is the number of thousands of cells at time t hour from the start. A and B are constants which the experimenter hopes to find.

He makes the following estimates of the number of thousands of cells N at the times t indicated in the table:

t	0.5	2	4.2	6
N	235	567	2070	5952

By taking logarithms of the proposed formula, explain how a graph can be used to verify that there is a formula of the required type which closely fits the given values. Find A and B and rewrite the formula with your values of A and B in it.

Estimate to two significant figures how many cells were present when $t = 0$ and how many there will be when $t = 24$ if the same law continues to be obeyed.

[MEI]

18.   (i) Solve for x and y the equations

$$3x - y = 2,$$
$$3xy - 7x^2 = 20.$$

(ii) Show on a diagram of the cartesian plane the region defined by the following inequalities:

$$y \geqslant 6,$$
$$5y - 12x - 18 \leqslant 0,$$
$$3y + 4x - 78 \leqslant 0.$$

Calculate the perimeter of the region.

[UL]

19.   Given that

$$2x - 3y + 5 < 0,$$

and

$$3x + y - 3 \leqslant 0,$$

find, if possible, inequality restrictions for x and y separately. Illustrate your answer with a sketch graph.

[SMP]

20.   A small transport firm plans to buy x minibuses which can carry 10 passengers and cost £4000 each, and y coaches which can carry 40 passengers and cost £10 000 each. It has already accepted a contract to carry 180 people simultaneously on a regular weekly journey; it cannot afford to spend more than £56 000; it has already agreed to buy at least 2 minibuses.

Form three inequalities for x and y and draw accurately on graph paper suitable graphs of y against x, shading areas that the inequalities do *not* allow. (Scale 1 cm $\equiv$ 1 unit.)

List the different ways in which the firm can satisfy requirements, giving the total cost and passenger capacity in each case. Work out the cost per passenger seat in each case and so find which gives the firm best value for money on this basis.

[MEI]

21.   Calculate numbers

(i) x and y such that $\frac{3}{4}$, x, y, $-\frac{1}{4}$, ... are in arithmetic progression,

(ii) p and q such that $\frac{3}{4}$, p, q, $-\frac{2}{9}$, ... are in geometric progression.

[AEB 1980]

22.   Find the sum of the numbers divisible by 3 which lie between 1 and 100. Find also the sum of the numbers from 1 to 100 inclusive which are *not* divisible by 3.

[MEI]

23.   The sum of the first n terms of an arithmetic progression is given by $\frac{1}{2}n(3n+5)$. By giving n suitable values, or otherwise, find the first term, the common difference and the twentieth term.

[AEB 1983]

24.   (a) The first and last terms of an arithmetic progression are -2 and 73 respectively, and the sum of all the terms is 923. Calculate the number of terms and the common difference of the progression.

(b) The three positive numbers $x-2$, x, $2x-3$ are successive terms of a geometric progression. Calculate the value of x.

Given that x is the second term of the progression, calculate the value of the seventh term.

[JMB]

25.   (i) The first term of an arithmetic progression is 2 and the common difference is 3. Find the sum to n terms of this progression.

cont.

Find the value of n for which the sum of the progression is 610.

Find, also, the least value of n for which the sum exceeds 1000.

(ii) Find $S_n = \sum_{r=0}^{n-1} 3^r$.

Find also the least value of n such that $S_n > 10\,000$.

[UL]

26. (a) Find the sums to infinity of the geometric progressions with third term $\frac{4}{3}$ and seventh term $\frac{64}{243}$.

(b) If $S = 1 + 2x + 3x^2 + 4x^3 + \ldots nx^{n-1} + \ldots$ and $-1 < x < 1$ find, in ascending powers of x, the first five terms of

(i) xS,

(ii) $S - xS$.

Hence find an expression for the sum to infinity of S.

[AEB 1982]

27. Pascal's triangle, in which each number is the sum of the two diagonally above it, starts as follows:

$$
\begin{array}{ccccccc}
 & & & 1 & & 1 & \\
 & & 1 & & 2 & & 1 \\
 & 1 & & 3 & & 3 & & 1 \\
1 & & 4 & & 6 & & 4 & & 1
\end{array}
$$

so that in the first four rows there are altogether 14 numbers. Find a formula for the number of numbers in the first n rows. Check your answer by putting $n = 4$.

In which row is the 500th number used and how many numbers have been used by the end of that row?

[MEI]

28. You double your savings every week, starting with one pound. After how many weeks will you first have saved more than one million pounds?

By using a binary representation find the sum of the first 52 terms of the series $1 + 2 + 4 + 8 + \ldots$ in the form $2^a - 1$, where a is an integer.

A friend saves £1 the first week, a further £2 the second week, and in each successive week he adds to his savings double the amount that he added the previous week. How many weeks less would he take to save one million pounds than it takes you?

[SMP]

29. A boy's trustees have altogether £690 to provide a cash present on his birthday each year from his fifth to nineteenth birthday inclusive and they decide that the present will increase by £5 each year. How much should the present be on his fifth birthday?

If alternatively they decide that the present shall be 20% more each year than it was the year before, how much then should the first present be, to the nearest new penny?

[MEI]

30. A man of mass 110 kg starts a strict diet in order to lose weight. In the first week his mass is reduced by 4 kg, and then the loss of mass in any one week is two thirds of the loss of mass in the week before. Write down an expression for the loss of mass in the Nth week.

Find his mass, in kg to two decimal places, after six weeks on the diet.

Prove that, however long he keeps to this diet, his mass will always be greater than 98 kg.

[UL]

31. Show that a sum of money £P invested in a savings account at 5% per annum, compound interest, is multiplied by a factor 1.05 each year. Deduce the formula for the final amount after n years.

A man invests £P on 1 January each year for 20 years. Interest is added at the rate of 5% per annum and there are no withdrawals. Without doing any detailed arithmetic, write down the first three terms and the last term of a series, the sum of which gives the final amount saved when he has just made the 20th investment.

Identify the type of series involved, state a formula you intend to use for its sum and so work out the total amount saved if $P = 100$, giving the answer to two significant figures.

[MEI]

32. Ten people, one of them called Fred, are going on a canal holiday. Each day one of them will be chosen at random to be cook for that day.

(a) Write down an expression for the probability that Fred will be cook for the first time on the kth day.

(b) Give as a geometric series the probability that Fred will be cook for the first time on some day during the first n days.

(c) Show that the sum of the series in (b) is $1-(0.9)^n$. Give a probability argument which produces this answer directly, without using a geometric series.

(d) Find the least integer value of n for which

$$1-(0.9)^n > 0.5.$$

[UL]

33. On 1st January 1984 my bank agrees to lend me £10 000 on condition that I pay back a fixed sum £F on each subsequent 1st January until the loan is completely repaid. The bank charges interest on the amount outstanding, however, at a rate of 12% per annum. Thus the interest for 1984 is 12% of £10 000, but I repay the sum of £F, and therefore the amount owing at the start of 1985 is £$(11 200-F)$.

(a) What would happen if F equalled 1200?

(b) If $F = 2000$, when will the loan be finally repaid?

(c) If the loan is to be repaid in full by 1st January 1989, i.e. within five years, what is the minimum possible value of F?

34. (a) Find the sum (S_r) of the arithmetic series

$$1+3+5+\ldots+(2r-1).$$

Prove by induction, or otherwise, that the sum of the series

$$S_1+S_2+S_3+\ldots+S_n$$

is

$$\frac{1}{6}n(n+1)(2n+1).$$

(b) For all positive integral values of n the sum of the first n terms of a series is $n(n+1)(n+2)$. Find the nth term in its simplest form.

(c) Prove by induction, or otherwise, that, for all positive integral values of n, $10^n+3(4^{n+2})+5$ is divisible by 9.

[JMB]

35. (a) For all positive integral values of n, the sum of the first n terms of a series is $3n^2+2n$. Find the nth term in its simplest form.

(b) Show that, for all positive integral values of n, 7^n+2^{2n+1} is divisible by 3.

(c) Prove, by induction or otherwise, that

$$(1)(4)(7)+(2)(5)(8)+\ldots+n(n+3)(n+6)$$

$$=\frac{1}{4}n(n+1)(n+6)(n+7).$$

[JMB]

36. (a) For all positive integral values of n, the sum of the first n terms of a series is $2n^2(n+1)^2$. Find the nth term in its simplest form.

(b) Prove by induction, or otherwise, that

$$\frac{1}{(3)(4)}+\frac{1}{(4)(5)}+\ldots+\frac{1}{(n+2)(n+3)}=\frac{n}{3(n+3)}.$$

(c) Show that $5^{2n+2}+24n-25$ is a multiple of 48 for all positive integral values of n.

[JMB]

37. $z = 3+2j$ and $w = 5+j$.

(i) Calculate zw in the form $a+bj$, where a and b are real.

(ii) On an Argand diagram, mark and label points corresponding to z, w and zw.

(iii) Measure $\arg z$, $\arg w$, $\arg zw$ and, using these values, find

$$\arg z+\arg w-\arg zw.$$

Comment on the result.

[SMP]

38. Multiply (a) $4+3j$ by $2+j$;

(b) $2-j$ by $2+j$.

(c) Hence express $\dfrac{4+3j}{2-j}$ in the form $a+bj$.

On an Argand diagram drawn on squared paper, mark and label the points corresponding to the three numbers $4+3j$, $2+j$ and $2-j$, and the points corresponding to your three answers.

[SMP]

39. Express the complex number

$$\left(\frac{1+2i}{1-i}\right)^2$$

in the form $(a+bi)$, where a and b are real numbers and $i^2 = -1$.

[HK]

40. Show that $1+j$ is a square root of $2j$. What is the other square root?

Evaluate $(1-j)^2$.   *cont.*

Find all the fourth roots of -4 and show them on a diagram of the complex number plane.

[SMP]

41. (a) Write down a cube root of 8.

(b) If

$$\alpha = \frac{-1 + j\sqrt{3}}{2},$$

calculate β where $\beta = \alpha^2$.

(c) Verify that $\alpha^3 = 1$, and hence write down a second cube root of 8.

(d) Write down the value of α^6.

(e) Write down the value of β^3, and hence write down a third cube root of 8.

[SMP]

42. Show that $2 - j$ is one root of $x^2 - 4x + 5 = 0$.

What is the other root?

Express $x^2 - 4x + 5$ as the product of two linear factors.

If $y = 1/(2 - j)$, express y in the form $a + bj$ and find the value of $1 - 4y + 5y^2$.

[SMP]

43. $f(X) = \cos X + j \sin X$, where $j^2 = -1$.

Multiply $f(X)$ by $f(Y)$ and use the addition formulae to verify that $f(X) \cdot f(Y) = f(X + Y)$. Hence show that $[f(X)]^2 = \cos 2X + j \sin 2X$ and write down a similar result for $[f(X)]^4$.

Write down the expansion of $(a + b)^4$.

Hence show that
$\cos 4X = \cos^4 X - 6\cos^2 X \sin^2 X + \sin^4 X$ and write down the corresponding expression for $\sin 4X$.

[SMP]

EXERCISE 20X

1. A uniform rod AE, of length 80 cm and mass 2 kg, rests horizontally on two smooth supports placed at B and D where $AB = 10$ cm and $DE = 20$ cm. Calculate the thrusts on the supports at B and D.

When a load of mass M kg is attached to the rod at the point A, the rod still rests horizontally and the thrust on the support at D is found to be zero. When the load of mass M kg is attached to the rod at a point x cm from E, the rod still rests horizontally and the thrust on the support at B is now found to be zero. Calculate the numerical values of M and x.

[AEB 1980]

2. A uniform straight plank AB, of mass 12 kg and length 2 m, rests horizontally on two supports, one at C and the other at D, where $AC = CD = 0.6$ m. A particle P of mass X kg is hung from B and the plank is on the point of tilting.

(a) Find the value of X.

The particle P is removed from B and hung from A.

(b) Find, in N, the magnitude of the force exerted on the plank at each support.

[UL]

3. A uniform rod AB, of length 16 cm and mass 80 g, has a particle of mass 120 g attached to it at a point P. The rod rests horizontally on two smooth supports placed at C and D where $AC = DB = 5$ cm. If the force exerted by the support at D is three times that exerted by the support at C, calculate the distance of the point P from the end B of the rod.

[AEB 1979]

4. A thin non-uniform beam AB, of length 6 m and mass 50 kg, is in equilibrium resting horizontally on two smooth supports which are respectively 2 m and 3.5 m from A. The thrusts on the two supports are equal. Find the position of the centre of gravity of the beam.

The original supports are removed and a load of 10 kg is attached to the beam at B. The loaded beam rests horizontally on two new smooth supports at A and C, where C is a point on the beam 1 m from B. Calculate the thrusts on each of the new supports.

[AEB 1981]

5. A uniform rod AB of mass M and length $6a$ rests horizontally between two smooth pegs X and Y, X below and Y above the rod with $AX = 4a$ and $YB = a$. A particle of mass $3M$ is hung from A.

(a) A vertical force P acts downwards at B.

  (i) Draw a clear diagram showing all the external forces acting on the rod.

  (ii) Calculate the greatest possible value of P if equilibrium is not to be broken.

(b) The force P is replaced by a vertical force Q acting upwards at B. The peg Y will break if the force on it exceeds $15Mg$.

  (i) Draw a clear diagram showing all the external forces acting on the rod.

(ii) Calculate the greatest possible value of **Q** if equilibrium is not to be broken.

[AEB 1983]

6. The sides AB and AD of a thin uniform rectangular plate $ABCD$ are of length 16 cm and 12 cm respectively. Points X and Y are taken on the diagonal AC so that $AX = CY = 5$ cm. Two circular holes are cut out of the plate, one with centre X and area 20 cm^2 and the other with centre Y and area 22 cm^2. Calculate the distances of the centre of mass of the remaining plate from each of the sides AB and AD.

[AEB 1982]

7. A can in the form of a circular cylinder, without a lid, is made of thin metal sheeting of uniform thickness and with a mass per unit area of 1 g/cm^2. The radius of the can is 10 cm and its height is 20 cm. The can is placed with its base on a horizontal plane and is half-filled with a liquid of density 1.5 g/cm^3. Calculate the height of the centre of gravity of the can together with the liquid, above the base of the can.

[AEB 1981]

8. A thin uniform wire, of length 40 cm, is bent to form the sides of a right-angled triangle ABC in which $AB = 8$ cm, $BC = 15$ cm and $CA = 17$ cm.

(a) Show that the centre of mass of the triangular wire is at a distance 6 cm from AB and at a distance 2.5 cm from BC.

The vertex B is smoothly hinged to a fixed point so that the triangular wire can rotate freely in a vertical plane about B.

(b) Find, to the nearest degree, the acute angle made by BC with the vertical when the wire rests in equilibrium.

(c) Given that 1 cm of the wire is of mass 0.005 kg, find, in N m, the magnitude of the couple, applied to the wire, which would be required to keep the triangular wire at rest with BC horizontal.

[UL]

9. A uniform rectangular lamina $ABCD$, with sides $AB = 2a$ and $BC = 5a$, is of mass $4M$. Particles of masses $2M$, M and $3M$ are attached at A, B and C respectively. Calculate the distance of the centre of mass of the loaded lamina from

(a) AB,

(b) AD.

The loaded lamina is now hung from A. Find the tangent of the angle AD makes with the downward vertical.

[AEB 1983]

10. A uniform lamina $ABCEF$ is obtained from a rectangle $ABCD$, with $AB = CD = 8$ cm and $BC = AD = 6$ cm, by removing the $\triangle EDF$, where E, F lie on CD, AD respectively, with $CE = 2$ cm and $AF = 3$ cm.

(a) Find the distances of the centre of mass of the lamina $ABCEF$ from AB and AD.

(b) The lamina is suspended freely from F and hangs in equilibrium under gravity. Find the angle which AF makes with the vertical.

[UL]

11. A uniform lamina of mass M is in the shape of a circular disc, centre O. Two points A and B on the circumference of the disc are such that the angle AOB is a right angle. A particle of mass kM is attached to the disc at B. When the loaded disc is in equilibrium suspended freely from A, AO is inclined to the downward vertical at an angle α, where $\tan \alpha = 0.4$. Calculate the value of k.

[AEB 1982]

12. A uniform square sheet of cardboard $ABCD$ of side 6 cm has cut from it an isosceles triangle BEC, in which $BE = CE$, in such a way that the centre of gravity of the remainder is at E.

Show that the distance E from AD is $3(\sqrt{3} - 1)$ cm.

The portion $ABECD$ is freely suspended from B and hangs in equilibrium. Calculate, correct to the nearest degree, the angle which the side BA makes with the vertical.

[JMB]

13. Two parallel forces of 15 N and 25 N act at a distance apart of 16 cm. Calculate the magnitude, direction and the position of the line of action of the equivalent resultant force, if the given forces act

(i) the same direction,

(ii) in opposite directions.

[AEB 1979]

14. Three forces are represented by the vectors $-2\mathbf{i} - 3\mathbf{j}$, $3\mathbf{i} + 4\mathbf{j}$ and $-\mathbf{i} - \mathbf{j}$. The forces act

cont.

at the points $(2, 0)$, $(0, 3)$ and $(1, 1)$ respectively. Show that the three forces combine to form a couple, and find the magnitude of the couple.

[AEB 1981]

15. Three forces are represented by the vectors $3\mathbf{i} + 2\mathbf{j}$, $2\mathbf{i} - 2\mathbf{j}$ and $-2\mathbf{i} - 5\mathbf{j}$. They act at the points $(4, 1)$, $(1, 1)$ and $(-2, -1)$ respectively. Calculate

(a) the magnitude of the resultant of the three forces,

(b) the coordinates of the point in which the line of action of the resultant cuts the x-axis.

[AEB 1982]

16. In the rectangle $ABCD$ the sides AB and BC are of length 48 cm and 20 cm respectively. Forces of 1, 4, 3, 2 and 6.5 N act along BA, BC, DC, DA and BD respectively, in the directions indicated by the order of the letters. Calculate the magnitude of the resultant of this system of forces.

When a single force, acting through the point D, is added to the given system, the resultant of the six forces is a couple. Calculate the moment and the sense of this couple.

[AEB 1982]

17. A thin uniform rod AB, of length 3 m, is lying on rough horizontal ground. A light inextensible string is attached to the end B of the rod, and passes over a peg which is situated at a point 4 m vertically above the end A. A tension of 25 N in this string just begins to lift the end B of the rod, with the end A on the point of slipping. Calculate

(a) the mass of the rod,

(b) the coefficient of friction between the rod and the ground.

[AEB 1982]

18. A uniform rod AB has the end A smoothly hinged to a fixed point and the end B resting against a smooth vertical wall. The rod rests in equilibrium at an angle θ to the vertical, where $\tan \theta = \frac{1}{3}$. The vertical plane containing the rod is perpendicular to the wall. Given that the mass and the length of the rod are M and $2l$ respectively, find

(a) the reaction of the wall on the rod,

(b) the magnitude and direction of the force exerted by the hinge on the rod.

[UL]

19. The centre of mass of a non-uniform rod AB, of length $3a$ and weight $2W$, is at the point G, where $AG = a$. The rod is placed in

limiting equilibrium with the end A on rough horizontal ground and the end B against a smooth vertical wall. The vertical plane containing AB is perpendicular to the wall. The coefficient of friction between the rod and the ground is $\frac{1}{2}$.

(a) Sketch a diagram showing all the forces acting on the rod.

(b) Calculate, to the nearest degree, the angle made by AB with the horizontal.

Find, in terms of W, the magnitude of the greatest horizontal force, acting directly towards the wall, which could be applied to the rod at A without disturbing the equilibrium.

[UL]

20. A uniform ladder of mass 50 kg and length 8 m rests with its upper end against a smooth vertical wall and its lower end on rough horizontal ground. The ladder is in a vertical plane perpendicular to the wall and is inclined at $60°$ to the horizontal. The coefficient of friction at the lower end of the ladder is $\dfrac{\sqrt{3}}{4}$. Draw a diagram showing all the external forces acting on the ladder and calculate

(i) how far up the ladder a man of mass 100 kg would be if the ladder is on the point of slipping,

(ii) the smallest mass that must be placed on the lower end of the ladder, so that the man may stand at the top of the ladder without it slipping.

[AEB 1980]

21. A rough plane is inclined at $60°$ to the horizontal. A uniform sphere of mass 10 kg is placed on the plane, as in figure 20.28, and is held in equilibrium by a force X acting at the highest point of the sphere. The force X is horizontal and in the same vertical plane as a line of greatest slope of the inclined plane.

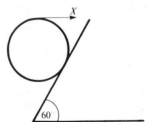

Fig. 20.28

Draw a diagram showing all the forces acting on the sphere and find the magnitude of X.

[AEB 1981]

SELECTED ANSWERS

Note For the sake of convenience, more figures are often given in numerical answers than are strictly justified.

EXERCISE 1S

1. $2, -1$
3. $0.4, -2.4$
5. $2x^2 + 3x - 20$
7. $6x^2 - 7x - 24$
9. $x^3 + x^2 - 12x$
11. $+8, -3$
13. $-7/2, -1/3$
15. ± 1
17. 25
19. $1/4$
21. $(x-6)(x+1)$
23. $(2x-1)(x-2)$
25. $(4x+5)(x+2)$
27. $(3x-2)(x+4)$
29. $-2, 3/5$
31. $1/2, 4/3$
33. $3/2, -5$
35. $1.236, -3.236$
37. $-0.219, -2.281$
39. $1.131, -0.531$
41. $3, -5$
43. $-4/5, 1/5$
45. $2, 20$
47. $6, 8$
49. (a) $x^2 - 15x - 25 = 0$
    (b) $x^2 + x - 3 = 0$
51. (a) $x^2 + x - 10 = 0$
    (b) $5x^2 - 11x + 4 = 0$
53. ± 3
55. $-2, +10$
57. 2209, yes
59. 57, no
61. $x = -3, (-3, -17)$
63. $x = 2, (2, 11)$
65. $x \leqslant -3$ or $x \geqslant +7$
67. $\frac{1}{2} \leqslant x \leqslant 4$

EXERCISE 2S

1. $(2.57, 3.06)$
3. $(2.18, 7.30)$
5. $(0, 4)$
7. $(-5, 0)$
9. $(-4.40, 1.24)$

11. $(0.0105, -0.0242)$
13. $41.4°, 2.65$
15. $24.4°, 5.21$
17. $21.5, 54.1°$
19. $-\cos 37°$
21. $-\sin 63°$
23. $+\cos 44°$
25. $-\sin 39°$
27. $-\cos 67°$
29. $+\sin 68°$
31. $+\cos 73°$
33. $+\sin 16°$
35. $-\cos 3°$
37. $+\sin 53°$
39. $147.5°, 212.5°$
41. $48.0°, 132.0°$
43. $36.5°, 323.5°$
45. $201.5°, 338.5°$
47. $74.5°, 285.5°$
49. $234.5°, 305.5°$
51. $-\tan 43°$
53. $+\tan 57°$
55. $-\tan 63°$
57. $+\tan 53°$
59. $36.2°, 216.2°$
61. $118.5°, 298.5°$
63. $127.3°, 307.3°$
65. $106.0°, 254.0°$
69. $\begin{pmatrix} +3.63 \\ +1.69 \end{pmatrix}$
71. $\begin{pmatrix} -5.40 \\ +5.20 \end{pmatrix}$
73. $\begin{pmatrix} -0.348 \\ -0.255 \end{pmatrix}$
75. $\begin{pmatrix} +119 \\ -247 \end{pmatrix}$
77. $[7.81, 50.2°]$
79. $[4, -53.1°]$
81. $[821, 151.9°]$
83. $[0.0661, -100.5°]$
85. $3, 3\sqrt{3}, 3\sqrt{6}, 3(1 + \sqrt{3})$
87. $40\sqrt{3} - 24$
89. $3, 2\sqrt{2}$
91. $-\sqrt{3}$

105. 54.7°, 125.3°, 234.7°, 305.3°
107. 30°, 150°, 270°
109. 30°, 150°, 210°, 330°
111. 45°, 135°, 225°, 315°
113. 30°, 150°, 270°
115. 53.1°, 153.4°, 233.1°, 333.4°
117. $s = 12$, $A = 48$
119. $\theta = 1.2$, $A = 1500$
121. $\theta = 2.5$, $s = 10$
123. 2 cm
125. $\pi/3$, $5\pi/3$
127. $3\pi/8$, $7\pi/8$, $11\pi/8$, $15\pi/8$
129. 1.266, 1.671, 4.612, 5.017
131. 0, 1.895

EXERCISE 3S

1. $\begin{pmatrix} +1 \\ -1 \end{pmatrix}$, $\sqrt{2}$, -1

3. $\begin{pmatrix} +12 \\ -12 \end{pmatrix}$, $12\sqrt{2}$, -1

5. $\begin{pmatrix} -2.0 \\ +2.2 \end{pmatrix}$, 2.97, -1.1

7. $\begin{pmatrix} +4/5 \\ +3/5 \end{pmatrix}$, $\pm\begin{pmatrix} +3/5 \\ -4/5 \end{pmatrix}$

9. $\begin{pmatrix} +0.28 \\ +0.96 \end{pmatrix}$, $\pm\begin{pmatrix} +0.96 \\ -0.28 \end{pmatrix}$

11. $\begin{pmatrix} +3/\sqrt{10} \\ -1/\sqrt{10} \end{pmatrix}$, $\pm\begin{pmatrix} +1/\sqrt{10} \\ +3/\sqrt{10} \end{pmatrix}$

13. $\begin{pmatrix} -0.96 \\ +0.28 \end{pmatrix}$, $\pm\begin{pmatrix} +0.28 \\ +0.96 \end{pmatrix}$

15. $\begin{pmatrix} +21/29 \\ +20/29 \end{pmatrix}$, $\pm\begin{pmatrix} -20/29 \\ +21/29 \end{pmatrix}$

17. $\begin{pmatrix} -35/37 \\ +12/37 \end{pmatrix}$, $\pm\begin{pmatrix} +12/37 \\ +35/37 \end{pmatrix}$

19. $-1/3$
21. $-2/3$
23. $+1/4$
25. $+4/5$
27. $-10/7$
29. 0
31. $5x - y = 6$
33. $2x + y + 7 = 0$
35. $x + 3y = 17$
37. $2x - y + 1 = 0$
39. $2x - 5y + 24 = 0$
41. $7x - 6y + 42 = 0$
43. $x - y + 1 = 0$
45. $x = 11$
47. $y = -3$
49. $+2$

51. $-3/7$
53. $+1/11$
55. $+5/7$
57. $+4/7$
59. $-3/2$
61. $3x + 4y = 13$, $4x - 3y + 41 = 0$
63. $4x + 7y = 0$, $7x - 4y = 0$
65. $2x + 3y = 19$, $3x - 2y + 4 = 0$
67. $(2, 3)$
69. $(34/3, 8)$
71. $(-4, 4)$
73. $\dfrac{2\mathbf{b} + 1\mathbf{c}}{3}$, $\dfrac{1\mathbf{c} + 2\mathbf{a}}{3}$, $\dfrac{2\mathbf{a} + 3\mathbf{b}}{5}$
75. $(1, 2)$
77. $(1, 11/3)$
79. $(-1/3, 7)$

EXERCISE 4S

1. $+3$
3. $-1/3$
5. -1
7. -14
9. $+10$
11. ± 12
13. ± 3
15. $(0, 0)$, 0; $(3, 18)$, $+12$
17. $(1, 6)$, $+2$; $(5, 30)$, $+10$
19. $2x - 2$
21. $2x + 2$
23. $8x^3 + 7$
25. $-3/x^2$
27. $4 - 1/x^2$
29. $+12$, $y = 12x - 20$
31. $+3$, $y = 3x - 3$
33. -4, $y + 4x = 9$, $4y - x = 2$
35. $+1$, $y - x = 8$, $y + x = 12$
37. $-3\sin x + 4\cos x$
39. $6t^5$
41. $6(3t + 2)$
43. $5a(ax + b)^4$
45. $3(1 - 2x)(3 + x - x^2)^2$
47. 3, $y = 3x - 4$
49. $-1/2$, $2y + x = 3$
51. 3.13, 3.130801
53. 1 004 002 000, 1 004 005 002
55. 6%
57. Increasing for $x < 1.5$
59. Increasing for $-1 < x < +1$
61. $t < 7.5$
63. Max at $(+2, +16)$, min at $(-2, -16)$
65. Min at $(-3, -6)$
67. 10, $10 \times 10 \times 5$ cm
69. 20

71. P.I. at $(0, 0)$
73. Max at $(-2, 32)$, min at $(2, 0)$, P.I. at $(0, 16)$

EXERCISE 5S

1. $+4$
3. -4
5. $+4$
7. $+3.0$
9. $+3.5$
11. 0.3
13. $66\,\text{m}$
15. $192\,\text{m}$
17. $2.5\,\text{m/s}^2$
19. $750\,\text{N}$
21. $20\,\text{kg}$
23. $0.5\,\text{N}$
25. $375\,\text{N}$
27. $66.7\,\text{kg}$
29. $5.33\,\text{m/s}$
31. $29.4, 5.39, 1.96, 4900\,\text{N}$
33. $3.06, 102, 0.0102\,\text{kg}$
35. $19.6, 25.6, 13.6\,\text{N}$
37. $2.3\,\text{m/s}^2$ down, 0.2 up, 2.7 up
39. $39\,200\,\text{kN}, 0.98\,\text{m/s}^2$
41. $8800\,\text{N}, 25\,\text{s}$ later

EXERCISE 6S

1. $\begin{pmatrix} +5 & -2 \\ +1 & +6 \end{pmatrix}$
3. $\begin{pmatrix} -3 & -1 \\ +4 & +4 \end{pmatrix}$
5. $\begin{pmatrix} 0 \\ 5 \end{pmatrix}$
7. 0
9. $1 \times 2 \leftrightarrow 1 \times 2$
11. $\begin{pmatrix} 0 & 0 & -1 & -1 \\ 0 & +1 & 0 & +1 \end{pmatrix}$
13. $2, \begin{pmatrix} +0.5 & +0.5 \\ -0.5 & +0.5 \end{pmatrix}$
15. $2, \begin{pmatrix} +1.5 & -0.5 \\ -2.0 & +1.0 \end{pmatrix}$
17. $-1, \begin{pmatrix} -7 & -5 \\ +4 & +3 \end{pmatrix}$
19. $-1, \begin{pmatrix} 0 & +1 \\ +1 & -2 \end{pmatrix}$
21. 2-way stretch, scale factors 2 and 3
23. Enlargement scale factor $+5$ and rotation of $-53.1°$

25. Shear, axis $x = 0$ and scale factor 3
27. Enlargement scale factor -2 and shear with axis $y = 0$
29. Reflection in $x = 0$ and then rotation of $+90°$ equals reflection in $x + y = 0$
31. Half-turn twice = identity
33. $\begin{pmatrix} -11 & +5 \\ -13 & +5 \end{pmatrix}$
35. 4

EXERCISE 7S

1. $[3.61, 73.9°]$
3. $[6.40, 91.3°]$
5. As in 1
7. As in 3
9. $6.65, 44.9°$
11. $1.04, -145.2°$
13. As in 11
15. 20.4 knots in direction $123.7°$
17. As in 15
19. $225 \pm 19.5°$
21. $3.83\,\text{m/s}^2$
23. $19.5°, 52.0\,\text{N}, 17.3\,\text{N}$
25. As in 23
27. $43.4°, 61.0°, 17.7\,\text{N}, 13.9\,\text{N}$
29. $0.878\,\text{kg}$
31. (a) $0.4\,\text{m/s}^2, 1960\,\text{N}$
    (b) $0.306\,\text{m/s}^2, 1910\,\text{N}$
    (c) $0.3\,\text{m/s}^2, 1960\,\text{N}$
    (d) $0.206\,\text{m/s}^2, 1910\,\text{N}$
33. (a) $1960, 50$
    (b) $1910, 15.5$
35. (a) $28.1\,\text{N}, 40.1\,\text{N}$
    (b) $1.62\,\text{m/s}^2$
37. $34.2\,\text{N}, 80.3\,\text{N}$
39. $1.8°$
41. $387\,\text{N}, 0.138\,\text{m/s}^2, 0.236\,\text{m/s}^2$

EXERCISE 8S

1. $6\sqrt{2}$
3. $2/3$
5. 9
7. $20\sqrt{2}$
9. $2\sqrt{2}$
11. $30 - 18\sqrt{3}$
13. $28 + 16\sqrt{3}$
15. $19\sqrt{6}$
17. 4
19. 1000
21. $243/32$
23. $343/8$
25. $10/13$

27. 0.0001
29. $15qr$
31. $2a^3b^{-1}$
33. 2^{2t+9}
35. 3^{2n}
37. 1000
39. -1
41. 0, 1
43. 4
45. $(1-3x)\div(2\sqrt{x})$, $1/3$
47. $(x-1)\div(2x\sqrt{x})$, 1
49. $\sqrt{3}-\sqrt{2}$
51. $x=27$, $y=18$
53. 2.08
55. 1.19
57. $31.1°$
59. 1.4037
61. $-0.172\,16$
63. 15.93
65. 1.5
67. 12.75 years
69. 2
71. 4
73. $2\log 2+3\log 3$
75. 1.0792, -0.1249, 1.0054
77. 3/2
79. 1, 10
81. $2/t$
83. 316.2, 2, -1

EXERCISE 9S

1. $2\mathbf{a}+\mathbf{b}$
3. $3\mathbf{a}-2\mathbf{b}$
5. $(31\mathbf{a}+13\mathbf{b})/7$
7. 11.5
9. -6.90
11. -0.200
13. 2.30
15. -1.99
17. -0.387
19. 7, 3.13
21. 73, 10.3
23. -16, -2.83
25. 12, 3
27. 40, 8, 6
29. 1.6, 3.8, 19
31. $45°$ (exactly)
33. $97.1°$
35. $79.7°$
37. $38.2°$
39. $95.6°$
43. 4.08
45. 0.182

47. $61.9°$
49. $93.4°$
51. $37.6°$
53. 5.53
55. 8.46
57. $42.0°$
59. $66.6°$
61. $14.1°$
63. 10.2
65. 35 200
67. 11.17, $61.9°$, $38.1°$
69. $78.46°$, 5.29

EXERCISE 10S

1. $(6,15)$
3. $(20,10)$
5. $(1,1)$, $(7,-7)$
7. 15, $(-7,8)$, $(9,-4)$
9. $\begin{pmatrix}-7\\1\end{pmatrix}$, $\begin{pmatrix}1\\-2\end{pmatrix}$, $\begin{pmatrix}2\\1\end{pmatrix}$, $\begin{pmatrix}1\\3\end{pmatrix}$, $\begin{pmatrix}-2\\5\end{pmatrix}$, $\begin{pmatrix}6\\19\end{pmatrix}$
11. 13/5
13. (a) $x^2+y^2-6x-10y+9=0$
     (b) $x^2+y^2+6x-8y+24=0$
15. (a) $(0,0)$, 5   (b) $(-2,0)$, 5
     (c) $(2,5)$, 6   .(d) $(1,-1)$, 3
17. $(0,0)$, $(2,-1)$
19. 18/5, 16/5, 2
21. 1.2, 1.9, 20/13
23. 1, -19
25. $3x+4y=36$, $x+4=0$,
     $3x-4y+30=0$, $y+3=0$
27. (a) $\mathbf{r}=\begin{pmatrix}1\\5\end{pmatrix}+t\begin{pmatrix}-3\\1\end{pmatrix}$, $(-5,7)$
     (b) $\mathbf{r}=\begin{pmatrix}1\\5\end{pmatrix}+t\begin{pmatrix}1\\2\end{pmatrix}$, $(-3,-3)$
29. (a) $3y-4x=\pm25$
     (b) $4y+3x+19=\pm25$
     (c) $7y+24x+65=\pm625$
     (d) $y-5=\pm7$
31. $x+2y=4$
33. Circle, $(1,8)$, $\sqrt{20}$
35. $x^2+6xy+9y^2-20x-40y+50=0$
37. $2x-y+4=0$, $3x+6y-5=0$
39. (a) $\mathbf{r}=(3t+1)\mathbf{i}+t\mathbf{j}$
     (b) $\mathbf{r}=(1-2t)\mathbf{i}+(3t-1)\mathbf{j}$
41. (a) $2x-3y=4$
     (b) $10x+8y=31$
43. (a) $3x+y=5$
     (b) $2x-y+11=0$
45. $(5,0)$, $(-4,3)$
47. $(4,5)$
49. $(-8,15)$

EXERCISE 11S

1. (a) $2t+6$, 14
   (b) $5-3t^2$, -43
   (c) $12t^2-24t+9$, 105
   (d) $24-6t$, 0
3. (a) 7, 7
   (b) $8t-4$, 12
   (c) $4t^3-6t$, 20
   (d) $-10t$, -20
5. $\frac{4}{3}\pi(5-t)^3$, $4\pi(5-t)^2$, 100π
7. (a) $2t^2-5t+5$, 17
   (b) t^3+2t^2+9, 12
9. (a) t^2+5t+3, 153
   (b) $9.8t$, 49
11. 15
13. 42, 52, 126
15. 16, 9, 5/6
17. 4.5
19. 160/3
21. (a) x^4+c
    (b) $5x^2-x^3/3+c$
    (c) $x^2/2-1/x+c$
23. (a) $y=3x^2+5$
    (b) $y=(3x^4+5)/4$
    (c) $y=(3x^2-8x^{3/2}+6x-14)/6$
25. (a) $x^6/6+c$
    (b) $\frac{4}{3}x^3+6x^2+9x+c$
    (c) $\frac{2}{3}x^{3/2}+2x^{1/2}+c$
27. 1/2, 17/6, 19/12

EXERCISE 12S

1. -0.35
3. 3.162
5. 7/6
7. 1
9. 55/9
11. 0.45
13. 18.88
15. 7.023
17. 112.8
19. 18.88
21. 21.61 m
23. 1.767 s
25. 264.5 m, 14.69 s
27. 19.6 m/s, 19.6 m
29. After 1.910 s, 5.043 m up
31. 450 m from B
33. 0.48 m
35. 55 m
37. 0.0875 m/s², 171.4 s
39. (a) $v=2t+\frac{5}{2}t^2-3$,
        $x=t^2+\frac{5}{6}t^3-3t$

(b) $v=\frac{2}{3}t^3-\frac{3}{2}t^2-2t+2$,
    $x=\frac{1}{6}t^4-\frac{1}{2}t^3-t^2+2t$
41. 53.5 m/s
43. (a) $2\mathbf{i}-4\mathbf{j}$
    (b) $2t\mathbf{i}+2t\mathbf{j}$
    (c) $3t^2\mathbf{i}$
45. (a) $\mathbf{0}$
    (b) $2\mathbf{i}+2\mathbf{j}$
    (c) $6t\mathbf{i}$
47. $(t^2+1)\mathbf{i}+(3t+1)\mathbf{j}$
49. $(t-2)\mathbf{i}+(t^2-4)\mathbf{j}$
51. $2t\mathbf{i}-\mathbf{j}$, $6t\mathbf{i}-3\mathbf{j}$,
    $[5.660, -32.0°]$, $[7.8, -22.6°]$
53. (a) 1.276 m, 1.020 s, 10.20 m
    (b) 20.41 m, 4.082 s, 408.2 m
    (c) 127.6 m, 10.20 s, 10.20 m
55. (a) 2.462 m, 1.418 s, 55.84 m
    (b) 20.41 m, 4.082 s, 141.4 m
    (c) 61.22 m, 7.070 s, 141.4 m
    (d) 79.17 m, 8.039 s, 55.84 m
57. 2, -19.6, 1.429, 428.6
59. $12.5\mathbf{i}+19.6\mathbf{j}$, 23.25 m/s,
    17.4° above horizontal
61. Arctan (2), arctan (1/2)
63. 4000 m
65. 64.2°
67. 12 m/s²
69. 7 m/s
71. 24.5 N, 10.5 m/s
73. 11.18 km/h from 026.6°
75. 10.92 km/h from 301.2°,
    12.07 km/h from 062.0°
77. When $t=2$ at $(-3, -4)$
79. Upstream at 48.2° to current,
    13.42 s
81. 142.9 min
83. $+148.2°$, 0.8802
85. As in 83

EXERCISE 13S

1. 5/12
3. 1/6
5. 1/8
7. 365/372
9. 35/124
11. 61/62
13. 36/125
15. 51/125
17. 8/17
19. 0.44
21. 0.376
23. 3/5
25. 0.376

27. 42
29. 720
31. $n(n-1)$
33. 8
35. 21
37. 1
39. $n(n-1)/2$
41. 1
43. 9
47. 5005, 1200
49. 120, 907 200
51. 0.2620, 0.002 737
53. 1/2
55. 2/5, 1/4

EXERCISE 14S

1. 4.4, 5.9 N
3. $3.7\,\mathrm{m\,s^{-2}}$
5. 4.6, 2.3 kN
7. 1/3, $1.96\,\mathrm{m\,s^{-2}}$
9. 1.94, $0\,\mathrm{m\,s^{-2}}$
11. $\tan 30°$, 73.2 N
13. 80.4 N
15. 77.6 N at $15°$ above horizon
17. $5\,\mathrm{m\,s^{-1}}$
19. $-10.8\,\mathrm{N\,s}$
21. $-4\mathbf{i}+6\mathbf{j}\,\mathrm{m\,s^{-1}}$
23. 4 N s at $127°$

EXERCISE 15S

1. $(5,3)$ or $(-3,-5)$
3. $(3,-1/3)$
5. $(2,3)$ or $(3,2)$
7. $(2,-1)$ or $(-16/7,5/7)$
9. $(1/2,2)$
11. $210\,\mathrm{cm^2}$
17. $y=4x\pm9$
19. 1
21. 10
23. 16
25. $-2, -11$
27. $2, -5$
29. $(2x-3)(3x-4)(3x+2)$
31. (a) $3x(x+2y)(x-2y)$
(b) $(a-b+c-d)(a-b-c+d)$
33. $pq/(p+q)$
35. $-2, +2, +3$
37. $-1, +1, +1/2$
41. -1
43. $27+54x+36x^2+8x^3$
45. 2835
47. $928\sqrt{3}$

49. 15.682
51. (a) $1-x+x^2-x^3$
(b) $1-2x-2x^2-4x^3$
53. (a) 0.909
(b) 0.979 796
55. (a) 1.28
(b) 1.1
(c) 1.03
57. $-3-x+\frac{1}{2}x^3$
59. $1+2x+2x^2+2x^3$

EXERCISE 16S

1. $4\mathbf{i}$
3. $-4\mathbf{i}+3\mathbf{k}$
5. $-4\mathbf{i}+5\mathbf{j}$
7. $53.1°$
9. $90°$
11. $25.1°$
13. $31.0°$
15. $45°$
17. $36.9°$
19. e.g. $3\mathbf{i}+4\mathbf{k}$
21. $46.7°$
23. $25.6°$
25. $(\sqrt{3}-1)/(2\sqrt{2})$
31. $0°, 30°, 150°, 180°, 210°, 330°$
33. $r=13$, $\alpha=\arctan 2.4$
35. $127.6°, 356.2°$
37. $r=\sqrt{2}$, $\alpha=45°$

EXERCISE 17S

1. 1152π
3. 20π
5. 0.6599
7. $8\pi/15$
9. $8\pi/3$
11. $81\pi/2$
13. $\pi/30$
15. (a) 39.87
(b) 39.64
(c) 39.71
17. (a) 11.81
(b) 11.83
(c) 11.83
19. 62
21. 99.45
23. $16\pi\,\mathrm{m}$
25. $2x-2$
27. $6x^2-10x-7$
29. $4x/(1-x^2)^2$
31. $2/(x-1)^2$

33. $2\cos(2x+1)$
35. $-3\cos^2 x \sin x$
37. $\cos^2 x - \sin^2 x - \sin x$
39. $\sec x \tan x$
41. $3/(3x-1)$
43. $2/x$
45. $(1+x)e^x$
47. 1
49. $1/2$
51. 7
53. -0.9002
55. $\ln 3$
57. $\frac{1}{2}(e^2-1)$
59. $\frac{1}{2}(e^7-e^5)$

EXERCISE 18S

1. $200\,\text{J}$
3. $-200\,\text{J}$
5. $400, -144, 256\,\text{J}$
7. $157\,\text{kJ}$
9. $-126\,\text{kJ}$
11. $4.48\,\text{kJ}$
13. $3.73\,\text{kJ}$
15. $-12\,\text{J}$
17. $2\,\text{J}$
19. $-5\,\text{J}$
21. $50\,\text{J}$
23. $3920\,\text{J}$
25. $8.72\,\text{m s}^{-1}$
27. $110\,\text{J}, 6.63\,\text{m s}^{-1}$
29. $1.96\,\text{kJ}$
31. $9.72\,\text{m s}^{-1}$
33. $2.7 \times 10^{30}\,\text{kJ}$
37. $5400\,\text{J}$
39. $15\,\text{J}$
41. $1.85\,\text{m s}^{-1}, 75.9\,\text{m s}^{-1}$
43. $560\,\text{W}$
45. $180\,\text{W}$
47. $1.2\,\text{kN}, 12\,\text{kW}$

EXERCISE 19S

1. Yes
3. Yes
5. Yes
7. $\mathbb{R}$
9. $\{y: y \geqslant 1\}$
11. $\{y: y \geqslant 0\}$
13. $11-2x, 1-2x$
15. $4x^2+6x+4, 2x^2+6x+8$
17. $1-x$
19. $2/(x-4)$
21. 1.516

23. 2.506
25. $x = 2$ and $y = 2$ are asymptotes
27. $y = 0$ is an asymptote
29. $x = 2$ is an asymptote
31. $x = 6, 0 < x < 2$
33. $x = 1/2$ or $2, x < -2$ or $0 < x < 2$
35. $x = 1, 0 < x < 2$
37. $a = 300, b = -180$
39. $a = 17, b = -5$
47. $4, +\infty$
49. $5\frac{1}{4}$
53. A.P., $-1; 0, -1; -15, 5-n$
55. G.P., $2; 80, 160; 2\,621\,440, 5 \times 2^{n-1}$
57. $-110, n(9-n)/2$
59. $5\,242\,875, 5(2^n-1)$
61. $17, 28$
63. $36, 48$
65. 32
67. 11
69. (a) 54, (b) $1111\frac{1}{9}$
81. $9-4\text{i}, 41-23\text{i}$
83. $8, 15+29\text{i}$
85. $3+\text{i}$
87. $3\pm 2\text{i}$
89. $\text{i}, -2\text{i}$
91. $3\,\text{cis}\,0, 5\,\text{cis}\,(\pi/2), 4\,\text{cis}\,(-\pi/4)$
93. (a) -8, (b) 64

EXERCISE 20S

1. $P = 12, Q = 28$
3. $P = 5.8, Q = 6.2$
5. $R = 800, S = 900$
7. $W = 100, d = 6$
9. $Q = 5, c = 3$
11. $8\,\text{N}$, acting $2.5\,\text{m}$ from A
13. $20\,\text{N}$ at $(3,0)$
15. $240\,\text{N}, 2.5\,\text{m}$ from A
17. $50\,\text{cm}$ from the welding
19. $2.6\,\text{m}$ from OC, $1.8\,\text{m}$ from OA
21. $(3,2)$
23. $(2,5)$
25. $13\,\text{N}$, acting along $5y-12x = 3$
27. $2\sqrt{2}\,\text{N}$, acting along $x+y = 16$
29. $+15$
31. $10\sqrt{3}\,\text{N m}$
33. $29.4°$
35. $26.6°$
37. $750\sqrt{2}, 250\sqrt{10}\,\text{N}$
39. $500g\,\text{N}, 1800g\,\text{N m}$
41. $6.5\,\text{kN}, 10.3\,\text{kN}$
43. $80.0°$
45. $91.0\,\text{N}$
47. $70.9°$

INDEX